THE TRIALS OF

APOLLO

◄ 1 ►

THE HIDDEN ORACLE

RICK RIORDAN

THE TRIALS OF APOLLO

◄ 1 ►

THE HIDDEN ORACLE

SCHOLASTIC INC.

ISBN 978-1-338-24472-4

12 11 10 9 8   21 22

Printed in the U.S.A.   40

First Scholastic printing, September 2017

To the Muse Calliope
This is long overdue. Please don't hurt me.

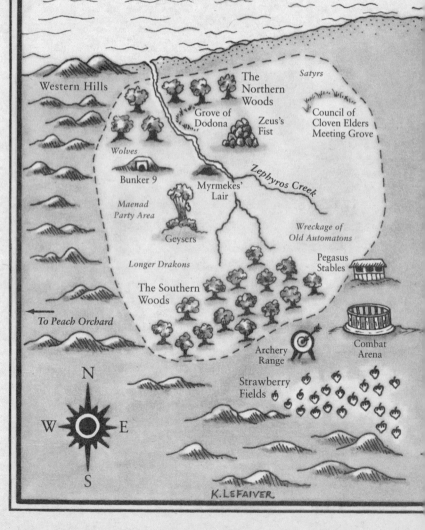

CAMP HALF-BLOOD

Western Hills

The Northern Woods

Satyrs

Grove of Dodona

Zeus's Fist

Council of Cloven Elders Meeting Grove

Wolves

Bunker 9

Myrmekes' Lair

Zephyros Creek

Maenad Party Area

Geysers

Wreckage of Old Automatons

Longer Drakons

Pegasus Stables

The Southern Woods

To Peach Orchard

Archery Range

Combat Arena

N
W · E
S

Strawberry Fields

K. LeFaiver

LONG ISLAND SOUND

The Beach

The Dunes

Eastern Hills

Euros Creek

Dining
Pavilion

Climbing
Wall

Canoe
Lake

Cabins

Green

Hestia's
Hearth

Armory

Forge

Arts &
Crafts

Amphitheater

Campfire

Athena
Parthenos

Thalia's Pine &
Golden Fleece

Half-Blood
Hill

Cave of
the Oracle

Volleyball Court

Big House

Strawberry Fields

Farm Road 3.141

To Montauk, etc.

THE TRIALS OF APOLLO

◄ 1 ►

THE HIDDEN ORACLE

1

Hoodlums punch my face
I would smite them if I could
Mortality blows

MY NAME IS APOLLO. I used to be a god.

In my four thousand six hundred and twelve years, I have done many things. I inflicted a plague on the Greeks who besieged Troy. I blessed Babe Ruth with three home runs in game four of the 1926 World Series. I visited my wrath upon Britney Spears at the 2007 MTV Video Music Awards.

But in all my immortal life, I never before crash-landed in a Dumpster.

I'm not even sure how it happened.

I simply woke up falling. Skyscrapers spiraled in and out of view. Flames streamed off my body. I tried to fly. I tried to change into a cloud or teleport across the world or do a hundred other things that should have been easy for me, but I just kept falling. I plunged into a narrow canyon between two buildings and *BAM!*

Is anything sadder than the sound of a god hitting a pile of garbage bags?

I lay groaning and aching in the open Dumpster. My nostrils burned with the stench of rancid bologna and used diapers. My ribs felt broken, though that shouldn't have been possible.

My mind stewed in confusion, but one memory floated to the surface—the voice of my father, Zeus: *YOUR FAULT. YOUR PUNISHMENT.*

I realized what had happened to me. And I sobbed in despair.

Even for a god of poetry such as myself, it is difficult to describe how I felt. How could you—a mere mortal—possibly understand? Imagine being stripped of your clothes, then blasted with a fire hose in front of a laughing crowd. Imagine the ice-cold water filling your mouth and lungs, the pressure bruising your skin, turning your joints to putty. Imagine feeling helpless, ashamed, completely vulnerable—publicly and brutally stripped of everything that makes you *you*. My humiliation was worse than that.

YOUR FAULT, Zeus's voice rang in my head.

"No!" I cried miserably. "No, it wasn't! Please!"

Nobody answered. On either side of me, rusty fire escapes zigzagged up brick walls. Above, the winter sky was gray and unforgiving.

I tried to remember the details of my sentencing. Had my father told me how long this punishment would last? What was I supposed to do to regain his favor?

My memory was too fuzzy. I could barely recall what Zeus looked like, much less why he'd decided to toss me to earth. There'd been a war with the giants, I thought. The gods had been caught off guard, embarrassed, almost defeated.

The only thing I knew for certain: my punishment was

unfair. Zeus needed someone to blame, so of course he'd picked the handsomest, most talented, most popular god in the pantheon: me.

I lay in the garbage, staring at the label inside the Dumpster lid: FOR PICK-UP, CALL 1-555-STENCHY.

Zeus will reconsider, I told myself. *He's just trying to scare me. Any moment, he will yank me back to Olympus and let me off with a warning.*

"Yes . . ." My voice sounded hollow and desperate. "Yes, that's it."

I tried to move. I wanted to be on my feet when Zeus came to apologize. My ribs throbbed. My stomach clenched. I clawed the rim of the Dumpster and managed to drag myself over the side. I toppled out and landed on my shoulder, which made a cracking sound against the asphalt.

"*Araggeeddeee*," I whimpered through the pain. "Stand up. Stand up."

Getting to my feet was not easy. My head spun. I almost passed out from the effort. I stood in a dead-end alley. About fifty feet away, the only exit opened onto a street with grimy storefronts for a bail bondsman's office and a pawnshop. I was somewhere on the west side of Manhattan, I guessed, or perhaps Crown Heights, in Brooklyn. Zeus must have been really angry with me.

I inspected my new body. I appeared to be a teenaged Caucasian male, clad in sneakers, blue jeans, and a green polo shirt. How utterly *drab*. I felt sick, weak, and so, so human.

I will never understand how you mortals tolerate it. You live your entire life trapped in a sack of meat, unable to enjoy simple pleasures like changing into a hummingbird or dissolving into pure light.

And now, heavens help me, I was one of you—just another meat sack.

I fumbled through my pants pockets, hoping I still had the keys to my sun chariot. No such luck. I found a cheap nylon wallet containing a hundred dollars in American currency— lunch money for my first day as a mortal, perhaps—along with a New York State junior driver's license featuring a photo of a dorky, curly-haired teen who could not possibly be me, with the name *Lester Papadopoulos*. The cruelty of Zeus knew no bounds!

I peered into the Dumpster, hoping my bow, quiver, and lyre might have fallen to earth with me. I would have settled for my harmonica. There was nothing.

I took a deep breath. *Cheer up*, I told myself. *I must have retained some of my godly abilities. Matters could be worse.*

A raspy voice called, "Hey, Cade, take a look at this loser."

Blocking the alley's exit were two young men: one squat and platinum blond, the other tall and redheaded. Both wore oversize hoodies and baggy pants. Serpentine tattoo designs covered their necks. All they were missing were the words I'M A THUG printed in large letters across their foreheads.

The redhead zeroed in on the wallet in my hand. "Now, be nice, Mikey. This guy looks friendly enough." He grinned and pulled a hunting knife from his belt. "In fact, I bet he wants to give us all his money."

———

I blame my disorientation for what happened next.

I knew my immortality had been stripped away, but I still considered myself the mighty Apollo! One cannot change one's way of thinking as easily as one might, say, turn into a snow leopard.

Also, on previous occasions when Zeus had punished me by making me mortal (yes, it had happened twice before), I had retained massive strength and at least some of my godly powers. I assumed the same would be true now.

I was *not* going to allow two young mortal ruffians to take Lester Papadopoulos's wallet.

I stood up straight, hoping Cade and Mikey would be intimidated by my regal bearing and divine beauty. (Surely those qualities could not be taken from me, no matter what my driver's license photo looked like.) I ignored the warm Dumpster juice trickling down my neck.

"I am Apollo," I announced. "You mortals have three choices: offer me tribute, flee, or be destroyed."

I wanted my words to echo through the alley, shake the towers of New York, and cause the skies to rain smoking ruin. None of that happened. On the word *destroyed*, my voice squeaked.

The redhead Cade grinned even wider. I thought how amusing it would be if I could make the snake tattoos around his neck come alive and strangle him to death.

"What do you think, Mikey?" he asked his friend. "Should we give this guy tribute?"

Mikey scowled. With his bristly blond hair, his cruel small eyes, and his thick frame, he reminded me of the monstrous sow that terrorized the village of Crommyon back in the good old days.

"Not feeling the tribute, Cade." His voice sounded like he'd been eating lit cigarettes. "What were the other options?"

"Fleeing?" said Cade.

"Nah," said Mikey.

"Being destroyed?"

Mikey snorted. "How about we destroy *him* instead?"

Cade flipped his knife and caught it by the handle. "I can live with that. After you."

I slipped the wallet into my back pocket. I raised my fists. I did not like the idea of flattening mortals into flesh waffles, but I was sure I could do it. Even in my weakened state, I would be far stronger than any human.

"I warned you," I said. "My powers are far beyond your comprehension."

Mikey cracked his knuckles. "Uh-huh."

He lumbered forward.

As soon as he was in range, I struck. I put all my wrath into that punch. It should have been enough to vaporize Mikey and leave a thug-shaped impression on the asphalt.

Instead he ducked, which I found quite annoying.

I stumbled forward. I have to say that when Prometheus fashioned you humans out of clay he did a shoddy job. Mortal legs are clumsy. I tried to compensate, drawing upon my boundless reserves of agility, but Mikey kicked me in the back. I fell on my divine face.

My nostrils inflated like air bags. My ears popped. The

taste of copper filled my mouth. I rolled over, groaning, and found the two blurry thugs staring down at me.

"Mikey," said Cade, "are you comprehending this guy's power?"

"Nah," said Mikey. "I'm not comprehending it."

"Fools!" I croaked. "I will destroy you!"

"Yeah, sure." Cade tossed away his knife. "But first I think we'll stomp you."

Cade raised his boot over my face, and the world went black.

2

A girl from nowhere
Completes my embarrassment
Stupid bananas

I HAD NOT BEEN STOMPED so badly since my guitar contest against Chuck Berry in 1957.

As Cade and Mikey kicked me, I curled into a ball, trying to protect my ribs and head. The pain was intolerable. I retched and shuddered. I blacked out and came to, my vision swimming with red splotches. When my attackers got tired of kicking me, they hit me over the head with a bag of garbage, which burst and covered me in coffee grounds and moldy fruit peels.

At last they stepped away, breathing heavily. Rough hands patted me down and took my wallet.

"Lookee here," said Cade. "Some cash and an ID for . . . Lester Papadopoulos."

Mikey laughed. "*Lester?* That's even worse than Apollo."

I touched my nose, which felt roughly the size and texture of a water-bed mattress. My fingers came away glistening red.

"Blood," I muttered. "That's not possible."

"It's very possible, Lester." Cade crouched next to me. "And there might be more blood in your near future. You want to explain why you don't have a credit card? Or a phone? I'd hate to think I did all that stomping for just a hundred bucks."

I stared at the blood on my fingertips. I was a god. I did not *have* blood. Even when I'd been turned mortal before, golden ichor still ran through my veins. I had never before been so . . . *converted*. It must be a mistake. A trick. Something.

I tried to sit up.

My hand hit a banana peel and I fell again. My attackers howled in delight.

"I love this guy!" Mikey said.

"Yeah, but the boss told us he'd be loaded," Cade complained.

"Boss . . ." I muttered. "Boss?"

"That's right, Lester." Cade flicked a finger against the side of my head. "'Go to that alley,' the boss told us. 'Easy score.' He said we should rough you up, take whatever you had. But this"—he waved the cash under my nose—"this isn't much of a payday."

Despite my predicament, I felt a surge of hopefulness. If these thugs had been sent here to find me, their "boss" must be a god. No mortal could have known I would fall to earth at this spot. Perhaps Cade and Mikey were not human either. Perhaps they were cleverly disguised monsters or spirits. At least that would explain why they had beaten me so easily.

"Who—who is your boss?" I struggled to my feet, coffee grounds dribbling from my shoulders. My dizziness made me feel as if I were flying too close to the fumes of primordial

Chaos, but I refused to be humbled. "Did Zeus send you? Or perhaps Ares? I demand an audience!"

Mikey and Cade looked at each other as if to say, *Can you believe this guy?*

Cade picked up his knife. "You don't take a hint, do you, Lester?"

Mikey pulled off his belt—a length of bike chain—and wrapped it around his fist.

I decided to sing them into submission. They may have resisted my fists, but no mortal could resist my golden voice. I was trying to decide between "You Send Me" and an original composition, "I'm Your Poetry God, Baby," when a voice yelled, "HEY!"

The hooligans turned. Above us, on the second-story fire escape landing, stood a girl of about twelve. "Leave him alone," she ordered.

My first thought was that Artemis had come to my aid. My sister often appeared as a twelve-year-old girl for reasons I'd never fully understood. But something told me this was not she.

The girl on the fire escape did not exactly inspire fear. She was small and pudgy, with dark hair chopped in a messy pageboy style and black cat-eye glasses with rhinestones glittering in the corners. Despite the cold, she wore no coat. Her outfit looked like it had been picked by a kindergartener—red sneakers, yellow tights, and a green tank dress. Perhaps she was on her way to a costume party dressed as a traffic light.

Still . . . there was something fierce in her expression.

She had the same obstinate scowl my old girlfriend Cyrene used to get whenever she wrestled lions.

Mikey and Cade did not seem impressed.

"Get lost, kid," Mikey told her.

The girl stamped her foot, causing the fire escape to shudder. "My alley. My rules!" Her bossy nasal voice made her sound like she was chiding a playmate in a game of make-believe. "Whatever that loser has is mine, including his money!"

"Why is everyone calling me a loser?" I asked weakly. The comment seemed unfair, even if I was beat-up and covered in garbage; but no one paid me any attention.

Cade glared at the girl. The red from his hair seemed to be seeping into his face. "You've got to be kidding me. Beat it, you brat!" He picked up a rotten apple and threw it.

The girl didn't flinch. The fruit landed at her feet and rolled harmlessly to a stop.

"You want to play with food?" The girl wiped her nose. "Okay."

I didn't see her kick the apple, but it came flying back with deadly accuracy and hit Cade in the nose. He collapsed on his rump.

Mikey snarled. He marched toward the fire escape ladder, but a banana peel seemed to slither directly into his path. He slipped and fell hard. "OWWW!"

I backed away from the fallen thugs. I wondered if I should make a run for it, but I could barely hobble. I also did not want to be assaulted with old fruit.

The girl climbed over the railing. She dropped to the

ground with surprising nimbleness and grabbed a sack of garbage from the Dumpster.

"Stop!" Cade did a sort of scuttling crab walk to get away from the girl. "Let's talk about this!"

Mikey groaned and rolled onto his back.

The girl pouted. Her lips were chapped. She had wispy black fuzz at the corners of her mouth.

"I don't like you guys," she said. "You should go."

"Yeah!" Cade said. "Sure! Just . . ."

He reached for the money scattered among the coffee grounds.

The girl swung her garbage bag. In mid arc the plastic exploded, disgorging an impossible number of rotten bananas. They knocked Cade flat. Mikey was plastered with so many peels he looked like he was being attacked by carnivorous starfish.

"Leave my alley," the girl said. "Now."

In the Dumpster, more trash bags burst like popcorn kernels, showering Cade and Mikey with radishes, potato peelings, and other compost material. Miraculously, none of it got on me. Despite their injuries, the two thugs scrambled to their feet and ran away, screaming.

I turned toward my pint-size savior. I was no stranger to dangerous women. My sister could rain down arrows of death. My stepmother, Hera, regularly drove mortals mad so that they would hack each other to pieces. But this garbage-wielding twelve-year-old made me nervous.

"Thank you," I ventured.

The girl crossed her arms. On her middle fingers she wore matching gold rings with crescent signets. Her eyes

THE HIDDEN ORACLE 15

glinted darkly like a crow's. (I can make that comparison because I invented crows.)

"Don't thank me," she said. "You're still in my alley."

She walked a full circle around me, scrutinizing my appearance as if I were a prize cow. (I can also make that comparison, because I used to collect prize cows.)

"You're the god Apollo?" She sounded less than awe-struck. She also didn't seem fazed by the idea of gods walking among mortals.

"You were listening, then?"

She nodded. "You don't look like a god."

"I'm not at my best," I admitted. "My father, Zeus, has exiled me from Olympus. And who are you?"

She smelled faintly of apple pie, which was surprising, since she looked so grubby. Part of me wanted to find a fresh towel, clean her face, and give her money for a hot meal. Part of me wanted to fend her off with a chair in case she decided to bite me. She reminded me of the strays my sister was always adopting: dogs, panthers, homeless maidens, small dragons.

"Name is Meg," she said.

"Short for Megara? Or Margaret?"

"Margaret. But don't ever call me Margaret."

"And are you a demigod, Meg?"

She pushed up her glasses. "Why would you think that?"

Again she didn't seem surprised by the question. I sensed she had heard the term *demigod* before.

"Well," I said, "you obviously have some power. You chased off those hooligans with rotten fruit. Perhaps you have banana-kinesis? Or you can control garbage? I once knew a Roman goddess, Cloacina, who presided over the city's sewer system. Perhaps you're related . . . ?"

Meg pouted. I got the impression I might have said something wrong, though I couldn't imagine what.

"I think I'll just take your money," Meg said. "Go on. Get out of here."

"No, wait!" Desperation crept into my voice. "Please, I—I may need a bit of assistance."

I felt ridiculous, of course. Me—the god of prophecy, plague, archery, healing, music, and several other things I couldn't remember at the moment—asking a colorfully dressed street urchin for help. But I had no one else. If this child chose to take my money and kick me into the cruel winter streets, I didn't think I could stop her.

"Say I believe you . . ." Meg's voice took on a singsong tone, as if she were about to announce the rules of the game: *I'll be the princess, and you'll be the scullery maid.* "Say I decide to help. What then?"

Good question, I thought. "We . . . we are in Manhattan?"

"Mm-hmm." She twirled and did a playful skip-kick. "Hell's Kitchen."

It seemed wrong for a child to say *Hell's Kitchen.* Then again, it seemed wrong for a child to live in an alley and have garbage fights with thugs.

I considered walking to the Empire State Building. That was the modern gateway to Mount Olympus, but I doubted the guards would let me up to the secret six hundredth floor. Zeus would not make it so easy.

Perhaps I could find my old friend Chiron the centaur. He had a training camp on Long Island. He could offer me shelter and guidance. But that would be a dangerous journey. A defenseless god makes for a juicy target. Any monster along the way would cheerfully disembowel me. Jealous spirits and minor gods might also welcome the opportunity. Then there was Cade and Mikey's mysterious "boss." I had no idea who he was, or whether he had other, worse minions to send against me.

Even if I made it to Long Island, my new mortal eyes might not be able to *find* Chiron's camp in its magically camouflaged valley. I needed a guide to get me there—someone experienced and close by. . . .

"I have an idea." I stood as straight as my injuries allowed. It wasn't easy to look confident with a bloody nose and coffee grounds dripping off my clothes. "I know someone who might help. He lives on the Upper East Side. Take me to him, and I shall reward you."

Meg made a sound between a sneeze and a laugh. "Reward me with what?" She danced around, plucking twenty-dollar bills from the trash. "I'm already taking all your money."

"Hey!"

She tossed me my wallet, now empty except for Lester Papadopoulos's junior driver's license.

Meg sang, "I've got your money, I've got your money."

I stifled a growl. "Listen, child, I won't be mortal forever. Someday I will become a god again. Then I will reward those who helped me—and punish those who didn't."

She put her hands on her hips. "How do *you* know what will happen? Have you ever been mortal before?"

"Yes, actually. Twice! Both times, my punishment only lasted a few years at most!"

"Oh, yeah? And how did you get back to being all goddy or whatever?"

"*Goddy* is not a word," I pointed out, though my poetic sensibilities were already thinking of ways I might use it. "Usually Zeus requires me to work as a slave for some important demigod. This fellow uptown I mentioned, for instance. He'd be perfect! I do whatever tasks my new master requires for a few years. As long as I behave, I am allowed back to Olympus. Right now I just have to recover my strength and figure out—"

"How do you know for sure which demigod?"

I blinked. "What?"

"Which demigod you're supposed to serve, dummy."

"I . . . uh. Well, it's usually obvious. I just sort of run into them. That's why I want to get to the Upper East Side. My new master will claim my service and—"

"I'm Meg McCaffrey!" Meg blew me a raspberry. "And I claim your service!"

Overhead, thunder rumbled in the gray sky. The sound echoed through the city canyons like divine laughter.

Whatever was left of my pride turned to ice water and trickled into my socks. "I walked right into that, didn't I?"

"Yep!" Meg bounced up and down in her red sneakers. "We're going to have fun!"

With great difficulty, I resisted the urge to weep. "Are you sure you're not Artemis in disguise?"

"I'm that other thing," Meg said, counting my money. "The thing you said before. A demigod."

"How do you know?"

"Just do." She gave me a smug smile. "And now I have a sidekick god named Lester!"

I raised my face to the heavens. "Please, Father, I get the point. Please, I can't do this!"

Zeus did not answer. He was probably too busy recording my humiliation to share on Snapchat.

"Cheer up," Meg told me. "Who's that guy you wanted to see—the guy on the Upper East Side?"

"Another demigod," I said. "He knows the way to a camp where I might find shelter, guidance, food—"

"Food?" Meg's ears perked up almost as much as the points on her glasses. "*Good* food?"

"Well, normally I just eat ambrosia, but, yes, I suppose."

"Then that's my first order! We're going to find this guy to take us to the camp place!"

I sighed miserably. It was going to be a very long servitude.

"As you wish," I said. "Let's find Percy Jackson."

3

Used to be goddy
Now uptown feeling shoddy
Bah, haiku don't rhyme

AS WE TRUDGED up Madison Avenue, my mind swirled with questions: Why hadn't Zeus given me a winter coat? Why did Percy Jackson live so far uptown? Why did pedestrians keep staring at me?

I wondered if my divine radiance was starting to return. Perhaps the New Yorkers were awed by my obvious power and unearthly good looks.

Meg McCaffrey set me straight.

"You smell," she said. "You look like you've just been mugged."

"I *have* just been mugged. Also enslaved by a small child."

"It's not slavery." She chewed off a piece of her thumb cuticle and spit it out. "It's more like mutual cooperation."

"Mutual in the sense that you give orders and I am forced to cooperate?"

"Yep." She stopped in front of a storefront window. "See? You look gross."

My reflection stared back at me, except it was *not* my

reflection. It couldn't be. The face was the same as on Lester Papadopoulos's ID.

I looked about sixteen. My medium-length hair was dark and curly—a style I had rocked in Athenian times, and again in the 1970s. My eyes were blue. My face was pleasing enough in a dorkish way, but it was marred by a swollen eggplant-colored nose, which had dripped a gruesome mustache of blood down my upper lip. Even worse, my cheeks were covered with some sort of rash that looked suspiciously like . . . My heart climbed into my throat.

"Horrors!" I cried. "Is that— Is that *acne*?"

Immortal gods do not *get* acne. It is one of our inalienable rights. Yet I leaned closer to the glass and saw that my skin was indeed a scarred landscape of whiteheads and pustules.

I balled my fists and wailed to the cruel sky, "Zeus, what have I done to deserve this?"

Meg tugged at my sleeve. "You're going to get yourself arrested."

"What does it matter? I have been made a teenager, and not even one with perfect skin! I bet I don't even have . . ." With a cold sense of dread, I lifted my shirt. My midriff was covered with a floral pattern of bruises from my fall into the Dumpster and my subsequent kicking. But even worse, I had *flab*.

"Oh, no, no, no." I staggered around the sidewalk, hoping the flab would not follow me. "Where are my eight-pack abs? I *always* have eight-pack abs. I *never* have love handles. Never in four thousand years!"

Meg made another snorting laugh. "Sheesh, crybaby, you're fine."

"I'm fat!"

"You're average. Average people don't have eight-pack abs. C'mon."

I wanted to protest that I was not average *nor* a person, but with growing despair, I realized the term now fit me perfectly.

On the other side of the storefront window, a security guard's face loomed, scowling at me. I allowed Meg to pull me farther down the street.

She skipped along, occasionally stopping to pick up a coin or swing herself around a streetlamp. The child seemed unfazed by the cold weather, the dangerous journey ahead, and the fact that I was suffering from acne.

"How are you so calm?" I demanded. "You are a demigod, walking with a god, on your way to a camp to meet others of your kind. Doesn't any of that surprise you?"

"Eh." She folded one of my twenty-dollar bills into a paper airplane. "I've seen a bunch of weird stuff."

I was tempted to ask what could be weirder than the morning we had just had. I decided I might not be able to stand the stress of knowing. "Where are you from?"

"I told you. The alley."

"No, but . . . your parents? Family? Friends?"

A ripple of discomfort passed over her face. She returned her attention to her twenty-dollar airplane. "Not important."

My highly advanced people-reading skills told me she was hiding something, but that was not unusual for demigods. For children blessed with an immortal parent, they were strangely sensitive about their backgrounds. "And you've never heard of Camp Half-Blood? Or Camp Jupiter?"

"Nuh-uh." She tested the airplane's point on her fingertip. "How much farther to Perry's house?"

"Percy's. I'm not sure. A few more blocks . . . I think."

That seemed to satisfy Meg. She hopscotched ahead, throwing the cash airplane and retrieving it. She cartwheeled through the intersection at East Seventy-Second Street—her clothes a flurry of traffic-light colors so bright I worried the drivers might get confused and run her down. Fortunately, New York drivers were used to swerving around oblivious pedestrians.

I decided Meg must be a feral demigod. They were rare but not unheard of. Without any support network, without being discovered by other demigods or taken in for proper training, she had still managed to survive. But her luck would not last. Monsters usually began hunting down and killing young heroes around the time they turned thirteen, when their true powers began to manifest. Meg did not have long. She needed to be brought to Camp Half-Blood as much as I did. She was fortunate to have met me.

(I know that last statement seems obvious. *Everyone* who meets me is fortunate, but you take my meaning.)

Had I been my usual omniscient self, I could have gleaned Meg's destiny. I could have looked into her soul and seen all I needed to know about her godly parentage, her powers, her motives and secrets.

Now I was blind to such things. I could only be sure she was a demigod because she had successfully claimed my service. Zeus had affirmed her right with a clap of thunder. I felt the binding upon me like a shroud of tightly wrapped banana peels. Whoever Meg McCaffrey was, however she had happened to find me, our fates were now intertwined.

It was almost as embarrassing as the acne.

We turned east on Eighty-Second Street.

By the time we reached Second Avenue, the neighborhood started to look familiar—rows of apartment buildings, hardware shops, convenience stores, and Indian restaurants. I knew that Percy Jackson lived around here somewhere, but my trips across the sky in the sun chariot had given me something of a Google Earth orientation. I wasn't used to traveling at street level.

Also, in this mortal form, my flawless memory had become . . . flawed. Mortal fears and needs clouded my thoughts. I wanted to eat. I wanted to use the restroom. My body hurt. My clothes stank. I felt as if my brain had been stuffed with wet cotton. Honestly, how do you humans stand it?

After a few more blocks, a mixture of sleet and rain began to fall. Meg tried to catch the precipitation on her tongue, which I thought a very ineffective way to get a drink—and of dirty water, no less. I shivered and concentrated on happy thoughts: the Bahamas, the Nine Muses in perfect harmony, the many horrible punishments I would visit on Cade and Mikey when I became a god again.

I still wondered about their boss, and how he had known where I would fall to earth. No mortal could've had that knowledge. In fact, the more I thought about it, I didn't see how even a god (other than myself) could have foreseen the future so accurately. After all, I had been the god of prophecy, master of the Oracle of Delphi, distributor of the highest quality sneak previews of destiny for millennia.

Of course, I had no shortage of enemies. One of the natural consequences of being so awesome is that I attracted envy from all quarters. But I could only think of one adversary who might be able to tell the future. And if *he* came looking for me in my weakened state . . .

I tamped down that thought. I had enough to worry about. No point scaring myself to death with what-ifs.

We began searching side streets, checking names on apartment mailboxes and intercom panels. The Upper East Side had a surprising number of Jacksons. I found that annoying.

After several failed attempts, we turned a corner and there—parked under a crape myrtle—sat an older model blue Prius. Its hood bore the unmistakable dents of pegasus hooves. (How was I sure? I know my hoof marks. Also, normal horses do not gallop over Toyotas. Pegasi often do.)

"Aha," I told Meg. "We're getting close."

Half a block down, I recognized the building: a five-story brick row house with rusty air conditioner units sagging from the windows. "*Voilà!*" I cried.

At the front steps, Meg stopped as if she'd run into an invisible barrier. She stared back toward Second Avenue, her dark eyes turbulent.

"What's wrong?" I asked.

"Thought I saw them again."

"Them?" I followed her gaze but saw nothing unusual. "The thugs from the alley?"

"No. Couple of . . ." She waggled her fingers. "Shiny blobs. Saw them back on Park Avenue."

My pulse increased from an andante tempo to a lively allegretto. "Shiny blobs? Why didn't you say anything?"

She tapped the temples of her glasses. "I've seen a lot of weird stuff. Told you that. Mostly, things don't bother me, but . . ."

"But if they are following us," I said, "that would be bad."

I scanned the street again. I saw nothing amiss, but I didn't doubt Meg had seen shiny blobs. Many spirits could appear that way. My own father, Zeus, once took the form of a shiny blob to woo a mortal woman. (Why the mortal woman found that attractive, I have no idea.)

"We should get inside," I said. "Percy Jackson will help us."

Still, Meg held back. She had shown no fear while pelting muggers with garbage in a blind alley, but now she seemed to be having second thoughts about ringing a doorbell. It occurred to me she might have met demigods before. Perhaps those meetings had not gone well.

"Meg," I said, "I realize some demigods are not good. I could tell you stories of all the ones I've had to kill or transform into herbs—"

"Herbs?"

"But Percy Jackson has always been reliable. You have nothing to fear. Besides, he likes me. I taught him everything he knows."

She frowned. "You did?"

I found her innocence somewhat charming. So many obvious things she did not know. "Of course. Now let's go up."

I rang the buzzer. A few moments later, the garbled voice of a woman answered, "Yes?"

"Hello," I said. "This is Apollo."

Static.

"The *god* Apollo," I said, thinking perhaps I should be more specific. "Is Percy home?"

More static, followed by two voices in muted conversation. The front door buzzed. I pushed it open. Just before I stepped inside, I caught a flash of movement in the corner of my eye. I peered down the sidewalk but again saw nothing.

Perhaps it had been a reflection. Or a whirl of sleet. Or perhaps it had been a shiny blob. My scalp tingled with apprehension.

"What?" Meg asked.

"Probably nothing." I forced a cheerful tone. I did not want Meg bolting off when we were so close to reaching safety. We were bound together now. I would have to follow her if she ordered me to, and I did not fancy living in the alley with her forever. "Let's go up. We can't keep our hosts waiting."

After all I had done for Percy Jackson, I expected delight upon my arrival. A tearful welcome, a few burnt offerings, and a small festival in my honor would not have been inappropriate.

Instead, the young man swung open the apartment door and said, "Why?"

As usual, I was struck by his resemblance to his father, Poseidon. He had the same sea-green eyes, the same dark tousled hair, the same handsome features that could shift from humor to anger so easily. However, Percy Jackson did not favor his father's chosen garb of beach shorts and Hawaiian shirts. He was dressed in ragged jeans and a blue hoodie with the words AHS SWIM TEAM stitched across the front.

Meg inched back into the hallway, hiding behind me.

I tried for a smile. "Percy Jackson, my blessings upon you! I am in need of assistance."

Percy's eyes darted from me to Meg. "Who's your friend?"

"This is Meg McCaffrey," I said, "a demigod who must be taken to Camp Half-Blood. She rescued me from street thugs."

"Rescued . . ." Percy scanned my battered face. "You mean the 'beat-up teenager' look isn't just a disguise? Dude, what happened to you?"

"I may have mentioned the street thugs."

"But you're a god."

"About that . . . I *was* a god."

Percy blinked. *"Was?"*

"Also," I said, "I'm fairly certain we're being followed by malicious spirits."

If I didn't know how much Percy Jackson adored me, I would have sworn he was about to punch me in my already-broken nose.

He sighed. "Maybe you two should come inside."

4

Casa de Jackson
No gold-plated throne for guests
Seriously, dude?

ANOTHER THING I have never understood: How can you mortals live in such tiny places? Where is your pride? Your sense of style?

The Jackson apartment had no grand throne room, no colonnades, no terraces or banquet halls or even a thermal bath. It had a tiny living room with an attached kitchen and a single hallway leading to what I assumed were the bedrooms. The place was on the fifth floor, and while I wasn't so picky as to expect an elevator, I did find it odd there was no landing deck for flying chariots. What did they do when guests from the sky wanted to visit?

Standing behind the kitchen counter, making a smoothie, was a strikingly attractive mortal woman of about forty. Her long brown hair had a few gray streaks, but her bright eyes, quick smile, and festive tie-dyed sundress made her look younger.

As we entered, she turned off the blender and stepped out from behind the counter.

"Sacred Sibyl!" I cried. "Madam, there is something wrong with your midsection!"

The woman stopped, mystified, and looked down at her hugely swollen belly. "Well, I'm seven months pregnant."

I wanted to cry for her. Carrying such a weight didn't seem natural. My sister, Artemis, had experience with mid-wifery, but I had always found it one area of the healing arts best left to others. "How can you bear it?" I asked. "My mother, Leto, suffered through a long pregnancy, but only because Hera cursed her. Are you cursed?"

Percy stepped to my side. "Um, Apollo? She's not cursed. And can you not mention Hera?"

"You poor woman." I shook my head. "A goddess would never allow herself to be so encumbered. She would give birth as soon as she felt like it."

"That must be nice," the woman agreed.

Percy Jackson coughed. "So anyway. Mom, this is Apollo and his friend Meg. Guys, this is my mom."

The Mother of Jackson smiled and shook our hands. "Call me Sally."

Her eyes narrowed as she studied my busted nose. "Dear, that looks painful. What happened?"

I attempted to explain, but I choked on my words. I, the silver-tongued god of poetry, could not bring myself to describe my fall from grace to this kind woman.

I understood why Poseidon had been so smitten with her. Sally Jackson possessed just the right combination of compassion, strength, and beauty. She was one of those rare mortal women who could connect spiritually with a god as an equal—to be neither terrified of us nor greedy for what we can offer, but to provide us with true companionship.

If I had still been an immortal, I might have flirted

with her myself. But I was now a sixteen-year-old boy. My mortal form was working its way upon my state of mind. I saw Sally Jackson as a mom—a fact that both consternated and embarrassed me. I thought about how long it had been since I had called my own mother. I should probably take her to lunch when I got back to Olympus.

"I tell you what." Sally patted my shoulder. "Percy can help you get bandaged and cleaned up."

"I can?" asked Percy.

Sally gave him the slightest motherly eyebrow raise. "There's a first-aid kit in your bathroom, sweetheart. Apollo can take a shower, then wear your extra clothes. You two are about the same size."

"That," Percy said, "is truly depressing."

Sally cupped her hand under Meg's chin. Thankfully, Meg did not bite her. Sally's expression remained gentle and reassuring, but I could see the worry in her eyes. No doubt she was thinking, *Who dressed this poor girl like a traffic light?*

"I have some clothes that might fit you, dear," Sally said. "Pre-pregnancy clothes, of course. Let's get you cleaned up. Then we'll get you something to eat."

"I like food," Meg muttered.

Sally laughed. "Well, we have that in common. Percy, you take Apollo. We'll meet you back here in a while."

In short order, I was showered, bandaged, and dressed in Jacksonesque hand-me-downs. Percy left me alone in the bathroom to take care of all this myself, for which I was grateful. He offered me some ambrosia and nectar—food and drink of the gods—to heal my wounds, but I was not sure it would be safe to consume in my mortal state. I didn't want to self-combust, so I stuck with mortal first-aid supplies.

When I was done, I stared at my battered face in the bathroom mirror. Perhaps teenage angst had permeated the clothes, because I felt more like a sulky high schooler than ever. I thought how unfair it was that I was being punished, how lame my father was, how no one else in the history of time had ever experienced problems like mine.

Of course, all that was empirically true. No exaggeration was required.

At least my wounds seemed to be healing at a faster rate than a normal mortal's. The swelling in my nose had subsided. My ribs still ached, but I no longer felt as if someone were knitting a sweater inside my chest with hot needles.

Accelerated healing was the *least* Zeus could do for me. I was a god of medicinal arts, after all. Zeus probably just wanted me to get well quickly so I could endure more pain, but I was grateful nonetheless.

I wondered if I should start a small fire in Percy Jackson's sink, perhaps burn some bandages in thanks, but I decided that might strain the Jacksons' hospitality.

I examined the black T-shirt Percy had given me. Emblazoned on the front was Led Zeppelin's logo for their record label: winged Icarus falling from the sky. I had no problem with Led Zeppelin. I had inspired all their best songs. But I had a sneaking suspicion that Percy had given me this shirt as a joke—the fall from the sky. Yes, ha-ha. I didn't need to be a god of poetry to spot the metaphor. I decided not to comment on it. I wouldn't give him the satisfaction.

I took a deep breath. Then I did my usual motivational speech in the mirror: "You are gorgeous and people love you!"

I went out to face the world.

Percy was sitting on his bed, staring at the trail of blood droplets I had made across his carpet.

"Sorry about that," I said.

Percy spread his hands. "Actually, I was thinking about the last time I had a nosebleed."

"Oh . . ."

The memory came back to me, though hazy and incomplete. Athens. The Acropolis. We gods had battled side by side with Percy Jackson and his comrades. We defeated an army of giants, but a drop of Percy's blood hit the earth and awakened the Earth Mother Gaea, who had not been in a good mood.

That's when Zeus turned on me. He'd accused me of starting the whole thing, just because Gaea had duped one of my progeny, a boy named Octavian, into plunging the Roman and Greek demigod camps into a civil war that almost destroyed human civilization. I ask you: How was that my fault?

Regardless, Zeus had held *me* responsible for Octavian's delusions of grandeur. Zeus seemed to consider egotism a trait the boy had inherited from me. Which is ridiculous. I am much too self-aware to be egotistical.

"What happened to you, man?" Percy's voice stirred me from my reverie. "The war ended in August. It's January."

"It is?" I suppose the wintry weather should have been a clue, but I hadn't given it much thought.

"Last I saw you," Percy said, "Zeus was chewing you out at the Acropolis. Then *bam*—he vaporized you. Nobody's seen or heard from you for six months."

I tried to recall, but my memories of godhood were getting fuzzier rather than clearer. What had happened in the last six months? Had I been in some kind of stasis? Had Zeus taken that long to decide what to do with me? Perhaps there was a reason he'd waited until this moment to hurl me to earth.

Father's voice still rang in my ears: *Your fault. Your punishment.* My shame felt fresh and raw, as if the conversation had just happened, but I could not be sure.

After being alive for so many millennia, I had trouble keeping track of time even in the best of circumstances. I would hear a song on Spotify and think, "Oh, that's new!" Then I'd realize it was Mozart's Piano Concerto no. 20 in D Minor from two hundred years ago. Or I'd wonder why Herodotus the historian wasn't in my contacts list. Then I'd remember Herodotus didn't have a smartphone, because he had been dead since the Iron Age.

It's very irritating how quickly you mortals die.

"I—I don't know where I've been," I admitted. "I have some memory gaps."

Percy winced. "I hate memory gaps. Last year I lost an entire semester thanks to Hera."

"Ah, yes." I couldn't quite remember what Percy Jackson was talking about. During the war with Gaea, I had been focused mostly on my own fabulous exploits. But I suppose he and his friends had undergone a few minor hardships.

"Well, never fear," I said. "There are always new opportunities to win fame! That's why I've come to you for help!"

He gave me that confusing expression again: as if he wanted to kick me, when I was sure he must be struggling to contain his gratitude.

"Look, man—"

"Would you please refrain from calling me *man*?" I asked. "It is a painful reminder that I am a man."

"Okay . . . Apollo, I'm fine with driving you and Meg to camp if that's what you want. I never turn away a demigod who needs help—"

"Wonderful! Do you have something besides the Prius? A Maserati, perhaps? I'd settle for a Lamborghini."

"*But*," Percy continued, "I can't get involved in another Big Prophecy or whatever. I've made promises."

I stared at him, not quite comprehending. "Promises?"

Percy laced his fingers. They were long and nimble. He would have made an excellent musician. "I lost most of my junior year because of the war with Gaea. I've spent this entire fall playing catch-up with my classes. If I want to go to college with Annabeth next fall, I have to stay out of trouble and get my diploma."

"Annabeth." I tried to place the name. "She's the blond scary one?"

"That's her. I promised her *specifically* that I wouldn't get myself killed while she's gone."

"Gone?"

Percy waved vaguely toward the north. "She's in Boston for a few weeks. Some family emergency. The point is—"

"You're saying you cannot offer me your undivided service to restore me to my throne?"

"Um . . . yeah." He pointed at the bedroom doorway. "Besides, my mom's pregnant. I'm going to have a baby sister. I'd like to be around to get to know her."

"Well, I understand that. I remember when Artemis was born—"

"Aren't you twins?"

"I've always regarded her as my little sister."

Percy's mouth twitched. "Anyway, my mom's got that going on, and her first novel is going to be published this spring as well, so I'd like to stay alive long enough to—"

"Wonderful!" I said. "Remind her to burn the proper sacrifices. Calliope is quite touchy when novelists forget to thank her."

"Okay. But what I'm saying . . . I can't go off on another world-stomping quest. I can't do that to my family."

Percy glanced toward his window. On the sill was a potted plant with delicate silver leaves—possibly moonlace. "I've already given my mom enough heart attacks for one lifetime. She's just about forgiven me for disappearing last year, but I swore to her and Paul that I wouldn't do anything like that again."

"Paul?"

"My stepdad. He's at a teacher in-service today. He's a good guy."

"I see." In truth, I didn't see. I wanted to get back to talking about my problems. I was impatient with Percy for turning the conversation to himself. Sadly, I have found this sort of self-centeredness common among demigods.

"You *do* understand that I must find a way to return to Olympus," I said. "This will probably involve many harrowing trials with a high chance of death. Can you turn down such glory?"

"Yeah, I'm pretty sure I can. Sorry."

I pursed my lips. It always disappointed me when mortals put themselves first and failed to see the big picture—the importance of putting *me* first—but I had to remind myself that this young man had helped me out on many previous occasions. He had earned my goodwill.

"I understand," I said with incredible generosity. "You will at least escort us to Camp Half-Blood?"

"That I can do." Percy reached into his hoodie pocket and pulled out a ballpoint pen. For a moment I thought he wanted my autograph. I can't tell you how often that happens. Then I remembered the pen was the disguised form of his sword, Riptide.

He smiled, and some of that old demigod mischief twinkled in his eyes. "Let's see if Meg's ready for a field trip."

5

Seven-layer dip
Chocolate chip cookies in blue
I love this woman

SALLY JACKSON was a witch to rival Circe. She had transformed Meg from a street urchin into a shockingly pretty young girl. Meg's dark pageboy hair was glossy and brushed. Her round face was scrubbed clean of grime. Her cat-eye glasses had been polished so the rhinestones sparkled. She had evidently insisted on keeping her old red sneakers, but she wore new black leggings and a knee-length frock of shifting green hues.

Mrs. Jackson had figured out how to keep Meg's old look but tweak it to be more complementary. Meg now had an elfish springtime aura that reminded me very much of a dryad. In fact . . .

A sudden wave of emotion overwhelmed me. I choked back a sob.

Meg pouted. "Do I look that bad?"

"No, no," I managed. "It's just . . ."

I wanted to say: *You remind me of someone*. But I didn't dare open that line of conversation. Only two mortals *ever* had broken my heart. Even after so many centuries, I couldn't think of her, couldn't say her name without falling into despair.

Don't misunderstand me. I felt no attraction to Meg. I was sixteen (or four thousand plus, depending on how you looked at it). She was a very young twelve. But the way she appeared now, Meg McCaffrey might have been the daughter of my former love . . . if my former love had lived long enough to have children.

It was too painful. I looked away.

"Well," Sally Jackson said with forced cheerfulness, "how about I make some lunch while you three . . . talk."

She gave Percy a worried glance, then headed to the kitchen, her hands protectively over her pregnant belly.

Meg sat on the edge of the sofa. "Percy, your mom is so normal."

"Thanks, I guess." He picked up a stack of test preparation manuals from the coffee table and chucked them aside.

"I see you like to study," I said. "Well done."

Percy snorted. "I *hate* to study. I've been guaranteed admission with a full scholarship to New Rome University, but they're still requiring me to pass all my high school courses and score well on the SAT. Can you believe that? Not to mention I have to pass the DSTOMP."

"The what?" Meg asked.

"An exam for Roman demigods," I told her. "The Demigod Standard Test of Mad Powers."

Percy frowned. "That's what it stands for?"

"I should know. I wrote the music and poetry analysis sections."

"I will never forgive you for that," Percy said.

Meg swung her feet. "So you're really a demigod? Like me?"

"Afraid so." Percy sank into the armchair, leaving me to take the sofa next to Meg. "My dad is the godly one—Poseidon. What about your parents?"

Meg's legs went still. She studied her chewed cuticles, the matching crescent rings glinting on her middle fingers. "Never knew them . . . much."

Percy hesitated. "Foster home? Stepparents?"

I thought of a certain plant, the *Mimosa pudica*, which the god Pan created. As soon as its leaves are touched, the plant closes up defensively. Meg seemed to be playing mimosa, folding inward under Percy's questions.

Percy raised his hands. "Sorry. Didn't mean to pry." He gave me an inquisitive look. "So how did you guys meet?"

I told him the story. I may have exaggerated my brave defense against Cade and Mikey—just for narrative effect, you understand.

As I finished, Sally Jackson returned. She set down a bowl of tortilla chips and a casserole dish filled with elaborate dip in multicolored strata, like sedimentary rock.

"I'll be back with the sandwiches," she said. "But I had some leftover seven-layer dip."

"Yum." Percy dug in with a tortilla chip. "She's kinda famous for this, guys."

Sally ruffled his hair. "There's guacamole, sour cream, refried beans, salsa—"

"Seven layers?" I looked up in wonder. "You knew seven is my sacred number? You invented this for *me*?"

Sally wiped her hands on her apron. "Well, actually, I can't take credit—"

"You are too modest!" I tried some of the dip. It tasted almost as good as ambrosia nachos. "You will have immortal fame for this, Sally Jackson!"

"That's sweet." She pointed to the kitchen. "I'll be right back."

Soon we were plowing through turkey sandwiches, chips and dip, and banana smoothies. Meg ate like a chipmunk, shoving more food in her mouth than she could possibly chew. My belly was full. I had never been so happy. I had a strange desire to fire up an Xbox and play *Call of Duty*.

"Percy," I said, "your mom is awesome."

"I know, right?" He finished his smoothie. "So back to your story . . . you have to be Meg's servant now? You guys barely know each other."

"*Barely* is generous," I said. "Nevertheless, yes. My fate is now linked with young McCaffrey."

"We are *cooperating*," Meg said. She seemed to savor that word.

From his pocket, Percy fished his ballpoint pen. He tapped it thoughtfully against his knee. "And this whole turning-into-a-mortal thing . . . you've done it twice before?"

"Not by choice," I assured him. "The first time, we had a little rebellion in Olympus. We tried to overthrow Zeus."

Percy winced. "I'm guessing that didn't go well."

"I got most of the blame, naturally. Oh, and your father, Poseidon. We were both cast down to earth as mortals, forced to serve Laomedon, the king of Troy. He was a harsh master. He even refused to pay us for our work!"

Meg nearly choked on her sandwich. "I have to pay you?"

I had a terrifying image of Meg McCaffrey trying to pay me in bottle caps, marbles, and pieces of colored string.

"Never fear," I told her. "I won't be presenting you with a bill. But as I was saying, the second time I became mortal, Zeus got mad because I killed some of his Cyclopes."

Percy frowned. "Dude, not cool. My brother is a Cyclops."

"These were wicked Cyclopes! They made the lightning bolt that killed one of my sons!"

Meg bounced on the arm of the sofa. "Percy's brother is a Cyclops? That's crazy!"

I took a deep breath, trying to find my happy place. "At any rate, I was bound to Admetus, the king of Thessaly. He was a kind master. I liked him so much, I made all his cows have twin calves."

"Can I have baby cows?" Meg asked.

"Well, Meg," I said, "first you would have to have some mommy cows. You see—"

"Guys," Percy interrupted. "So, just to recap, you have to be Meg's servant for . . . ?"

"Some unknown amount of time," I said. "Probably a year. Possibly more."

"And during that time—"

"I will undoubtedly face many trials and hardships."

"Like getting me my cows," Meg said.

I gritted my teeth. "What those trials will be, I do not yet know. But if I suffer through them and prove I am worthy, Zeus will forgive me and allow me to become a god again."

Percy did not look convinced—probably because I did not sound convincing. I *had* to believe my mortal punishment was temporary, as it had been the last two times. Yet Zeus had created a strict rule for baseball and prison sentences: *Three strikes, you're out.* I could only hope this would not apply to me.

"I need time to get my bearings," I said. "Once we get to Camp Half-Blood, I can consult with Chiron. I can figure out which of my godly powers remain with me in this mortal form."

"If any," Percy said.

"Let's think positive."

Percy sat back in his armchair. "Any idea what kind of spirits are following you?"

"Shiny blobs," Meg said. "They were shiny and sort of . . . blobby."

Percy nodded gravely. "Those are the worst kind."

"It hardly matters," I said. "Whatever they are, we have to flee. Once we reach camp, the magical borders will protect me."

"And me?" Meg asked.

"Oh, yes. You, too."

Percy frowned. "Apollo, if you're really mortal, like, one hundred percent mortal, can you even get *in* to Camp Half-Blood?"

The seven-layer dip began to churn in my stomach. "Please don't say that. Of course I'll get in. I *have* to."

"But you could get hurt in battle now . . ." Percy mused. "Then again, maybe monsters would ignore you because you're not important?"

"Stop!" My hands trembled. Being a mortal was traumatic enough. The thought of being barred from camp, of being *unimportant* . . . No. That simply could not be.

"I'm sure I've retained some powers," I said. "I'm still gorgeous, for instance, if I could just get rid of this acne and lose some flab. I must have other abilities!"

Percy turned to Meg. "What about you? I hear you throw a mean garbage bag. Any other skills we should know about? Summoning lightning? Making toilets explode?"

Meg smiled hesitantly. "That's not a power."

"Sure it is," Percy said. "Some of the best demigods have gotten their start by blowing up toilets."

Meg giggled.

I did not like the way she was grinning at Percy. I didn't want the girl to develop a crush. We might never get out of here. As much as I enjoyed Sally Jackson's cooking—the divine smell of baking cookies was even now wafting from the kitchen—I needed to make haste to camp.

"Ahem." I rubbed my hands. "How soon can we leave?"

Percy glanced at the wall clock. "Right now, I guess. If you're being followed, I'd rather have monsters on our trail than sniffing around the apartment."

"Good man," I said.

Percy gestured with distaste at his test manuals. "I just have to be back tonight. Got a lot of studying. The first two times I took the SAT—ugh. If it wasn't for Annabeth helping me out—"

"Who's that?" Meg asked.

"My girlfriend."

Meg frowned. I was glad there were no garbage bags nearby for her to throw.

"So take a break!" I urged. "Your brain will be refreshed after an easy drive to Long Island."

"Huh," Percy said. "There's a lazy kind of logic to that. Okay. Let's do it."

He rose just as Sally Jackson walked in with a plate of fresh-baked chocolate chip cookies. For some reason, the cookies were blue, but they smelled heavenly—and I should know. I'm from heaven.

"Mom, don't freak," Percy said.

Sally sighed. "I hate it when you say that."

"I'm just going to take these two to camp. That's all. I'll be right back."

"I think I've heard that before."

"I *promise*."

Sally looked at me, then Meg. Her expression softened, her innate kindness perhaps overweighing her concern. "All right. Be careful. It was lovely meeting you both. Please try not to die."

Percy kissed her on the cheek. He reached for the cookies, but she moved the plate away.

"Oh, no," she said. "Apollo and Meg can have one, but I'm keeping the rest hostage until you're back safely. And hurry, dear. It would be a shame if Paul ate them all when he gets home."

Percy's expression turned grim. He faced us. "You hear that, guys? A batch of cookies is depending on me. If you get me killed on the way to camp, I am going be ticked off."

6

Aquaman driving
Couldn't possibly be worse
Oh, wait, now it is

MUCH TO MY DISAPPOINTMENT, the Jacksons did not have a spare bow or quiver to lend me.

"I suck at archery," Percy explained.

"Yes, but *I* don't," I said. "This is why you should always plan for *my* needs."

Sally lent Meg and me some proper winter fleece jackets, however. Mine was blue, with the word BLOFIS written inside the neckline. Perhaps that was an arcane ward against evil spirits. Hecate would have known. Sorcery really wasn't my thing.

Once we reached the Prius, Meg called shotgun, which was yet another example of my unfair existence. Gods do not ride in the back. I again suggested following them in a Maserati or a Lamborghini, but Percy admitted he had neither. The Prius was the only car his family owned.

I mean . . . wow. Just *wow*.

Sitting in the backseat, I quickly became carsick. I was used to driving my sun chariot across the sky, where every lane was the fast lane. I was not used to the Long Island

Expressway. Believe me, even at midday in the middle of January, there is nothing *express* about your expressways.

Percy braked and lurched forward. I sorely wished I could launch a fireball in front of us and melt cars to make way for our clearly more important journey.

"Doesn't your Prius have flamethrowers?" I demanded. "Lasers? At least some Hephaestian bumper blades? What sort of cheap economy vehicle is this?"

Percy glanced in the rearview mirror. "You have rides like that on Mount Olympus?"

"We don't have traffic jams," I said. "That, I can promise you."

Meg tugged at her crescent moon rings. Again I wondered if she had some connection to Artemis. The moon was my sister's symbol. Perhaps Artemis had sent Meg to look after me?

Yet that didn't seem right. Artemis had trouble sharing anything with me—demigods, arrows, nations, birthday parties. It's a twin thing. Also, Meg McCaffrey did not strike me as one of my sister's followers. Meg had another sort of aura . . . one I would have been able to recognize easily if I were a god. But, no. I had to rely on mortal intuition, which was like trying to pick up sewing needles while wearing oven mitts.

Meg turned and gazed out the rear windshield, probably checking for any shiny blobs pursuing us. "At least we're not being—"

"Don't say it," Percy warned.

Meg huffed. "You don't know what I was going to—"

"You were going to say, 'At least we're not being followed,'" Percy said. "That'll jinx us. Immediately we'll notice that we *are* being followed. Then we'll end up in a big battle that totals my family car and probably destroys the whole freeway. Then we'll have to run all the way to camp."

Meg's eyes widened. "You can tell the future?"

"Don't need to." Percy changed lanes to one that was crawling slightly less slowly. "I've just done this a lot. Besides"—he shot me an accusing look—"nobody can tell the future anymore. The Oracle isn't working."

"What Oracle?" Meg asked.

Neither of us answered. For a moment, I was too stunned to speak. And believe me, I have to be *very* stunned for that to happen.

"It *still* isn't working?" I said in a small voice.

"You didn't know?" Percy asked. "I mean, sure, you've been out of it for six months, but this happened on your watch."

That was unjust. I had been busy hiding from Zeus's wrath at the time, which was a perfectly legitimate excuse. How was I to know that Gaea would take advantage of the chaos of war and raise my oldest, greatest enemy from the depths of Tartarus so he could take possession of his old lair in the cave of Delphi and cut off the source of my prophetic power?

Oh, yes, I hear you critics out there: *You're the god of prophecy, Apollo. How could you* not *know that would happen?*

The next sound you hear will be me blowing you a giant Meg-McCaffrey-quality raspberry.

I swallowed back the taste of fear and seven-layer dip. "I just . . . I assumed—I hoped this would be taken care of by now."

"You mean by demigods," Percy said, "going on a big quest to reclaim the Oracle of Delphi?"

"Exactly!" I knew Percy would understand. "I suppose Chiron just forgot. I'll remind him when we get to camp, and he can dispatch some of you talented fodder—I mean heroes—"

"Well, here's the thing," Percy said. "To go on a quest, we need a prophecy, right? Those are the rules. If there's no Oracle, there *are* no prophecies, so we're stuck in a—"

"A Catch-88." I sighed.

Meg threw a piece of lint at me. "It's a Catch-22."

"No," I explained patiently. "This is a Catch-88, which is four times as bad."

I felt as if I were floating in a warm bath and someone had pulled out the stopper. The water swirled around me, tugging me downward. Soon I would be left shivering and exposed, or else I would be sucked down the drain into the sewers of hopelessness. (Don't laugh. That's a perfectly fine metaphor. Also, when you're a god, you can get sucked down a drain quite easily—if you're caught off guard and relaxed, and you happen to change form at the wrong moment. Once I woke up in a sewage treatment facility in Biloxi, but that's another story.)

I was beginning to see what was in store for me during my mortal sojourn. The Oracle was held by hostile forces. My adversary lay coiled and waiting, growing stronger every day on the magical fumes of the Delphic caverns. And I was a weak mortal bound to an untrained demigod who threw garbage and chewed her cuticles.

No. Zeus could not *possibly* expect me to fix this. Not in my present condition.

And yet . . . *someone* had sent those thugs to intercept me in the alley. Someone had known where I would land.

Nobody can tell the future anymore, Percy had said.

But that wasn't quite true.

"Hey, you two." Meg hit us both with pieces of lint. Where was she finding this lint?

I realized I'd been ignoring her. It had felt good while it lasted.

"Yes, sorry, Meg," I said. "You see, the Oracle of Delphi is an ancient—"

"I don't care about that," she said. "There are three shiny blobs now."

"What?" Percy asked.

She pointed behind us. "Look."

Weaving through the traffic, closing in on us rapidly, were three glittery, vaguely humanoid apparitions—like billowing plumes from smoke grenades touched by King Midas.

"Just once I'd like an easy commute," Percy grumbled. "Everybody, hold on. We're going cross-country."

Percy's definition of *cross-country* was different from mine.

I envisioned crossing an actual countryside. Instead, Percy shot down the nearest exit ramp, wove across the parking lot of a shopping mall, then blasted through the drive-through of a Mexican restaurant without even ordering anything. We swerved into an industrial area of dilapidated warehouses, the smoking apparitions still closing in behind us.

My knuckles turned white on my seat belt's shoulder strap. "Is your plan to avoid a fight by dying in a traffic accident?" I demanded.

"Ha-ha." Percy yanked the wheel to the right. We sped north, the warehouses giving way to a hodgepodge of apartment buildings and abandoned strip malls. "I'm getting us to the beach. I fight better near water."

"Because Poseidon?" Meg asked, steadying herself against the door handle.

"Yep," Percy agreed. "That pretty much describes my entire life: *Because Poseidon*."

Meg bounced up and down with excitement, which seemed pointless to me, since we were already bouncing quite a lot.

"You're gonna be like Aquaman?" she asked. "Get the fish to fight for you?"

"Thanks," Percy said. "I haven't heard enough Aquaman jokes for one lifetime."

"I wasn't joking!" Meg protested.

I glanced out the rear window. The three glittering plumes were still gaining. One of them passed through a middle-aged man crossing the street. The mortal pedestrian instantly collapsed.

"Ah, I know these spirits!" I cried. "They are . . . um . . ." My brain clouded over.

"What?" Percy demanded. "They are what?"

"I've forgotten! I *hate* being mortal! Four thousand years

of knowledge, the secrets of the universe, a sea of wisdom—lost, because I can't contain it all in this teacup of a head!"

"Hold on!" Percy flew through a railroad crossing and the Prius went airborne. Meg yelped as her head hit the ceiling. Then she began giggling uncontrollably.

The landscape opened into actual countryside—fallow fields, dormant vineyards, orchards of bare fruit trees.

"Just another mile or so to the beach," Percy said. "Plus we're almost to the western edge of camp. We can do it. We can do it."

Actually, we couldn't. One of the shiny smoke clouds pulled a dirty trick, pluming from the pavement directly in front of us.

Instinctively, Percy swerved.

The Prius went off the road, straight through a barbed wire fence and into an orchard. Percy managed to avoid hitting any of the trees, but the car skidded in the icy mud and wedged itself between two trunks. Miraculously, the air bags did not deploy.

Percy popped his seat belt. "You guys okay?"

Meg shoved against her passenger-side door. "Won't open. Get me out of here!"

Percy tried his own door. It was firmly jammed against the side of a peach tree.

"Back here," I said. "Climb over!"

I kicked my door open and staggered out, my legs feeling like worn shock absorbers.

The three smoky figures had stopped at the edge of the orchard. Now they advanced slowly, taking on solid shapes.

They grew arms and legs. Their faces formed eyes and wide, hungry mouths.

I knew instinctively that I had dealt with these spirits before. I couldn't remember what they were, but I had dispelled them many times, swatting them into oblivion with no more effort than I would a swarm of gnats.

Unfortunately, I wasn't a god now. I was a panicky sixteen-year-old. My palms sweated. My teeth chattered. My only coherent thought was: *YIKES!*

Percy and Meg struggled to get out of the Prius. They needed time, which meant I had to run interference.

"STOP!" I bellowed at the spirits. "I am the god Apollo!"

To my pleasant surprise, the three spirits stopped. They hovered in place about forty feet away.

I heard Meg grunt as she tumbled out of the backseat. Percy scrambled after her.

I advanced toward the spirits, the frosty mud crunching under my shoes. My breath steamed in the cold air. I raised my hand in an ancient three-fingered gesture for warding off evil.

"Leave us or be destroyed!" I told the spirits. "BLOFIS!"

The smoky shapes trembled. My hopes lifted. I waited for them to dissipate or flee in terror.

Instead, they solidified into ghoulish corpses with yellow eyes. Their clothes were tattered rags, their limbs covered with gaping wounds and running sores.

"Oh, dear." My Adam's apple dropped into my chest like a billiard ball. "I remember now."

Percy and Meg stepped to either side of me. With a

metallic *shink*, Percy's pen grew into a blade of glowing Celestial bronze.

"Remember what?" he asked. "How to kill these things?"

"No," I said. "I remember what they are: *nosoi*, plague spirits. Also . . . they can't be killed."

7

Tag with plague spirits
You're it, and you're infectious
Have fun with that, LOL

"NOSOI?" PERCY PLANTED HIS FEET in a fighting stance. "You know, I keep thinking, *I have now killed every single thing in Greek mythology.* But the list never seems to end."

"You haven't killed me yet," I noted.

"Don't tempt me."

The three nosoi shuffled forward. Their cadaverous mouths gaped. Their tongues lolled. Their eyes glistened with a film of yellow mucus.

"These creatures are *not* myths," I said. "Of course, most things in those old myths are not myths. Except for that story about how I flayed the satyr Marsyas alive. That was a total lie."

Percy glanced at me. "You did *what?*"

"Guys." Meg picked up a dead tree branch. "Could we talk about that later?"

The middle plague spirit spoke. "Apollooooo . . ." His voice gurgled like a seal with bronchitis. "We have coooome to—"

"Let me stop you right there." I crossed my arms and feigned arrogant indifference. (Difficult for me, but I managed.) "You've come to take your revenge on me, eh?" I looked at my demigod friends. "You see, nosoi are the spirits of disease. Once *I* was born, spreading illnesses became part of *my* job. I use plague arrows to strike down naughty populations with smallpox, athlete's foot, that sort of thing."

"Gross," Meg said.

"Somebody's got to do it!" I said. "Better a god, regulated by the Council of Olympus and with the proper health permits, than a horde of uncontrolled spirits like *these*."

The spirit on the left gurgled. "We're trying to have a mooooment here. Stop interrupting! We wish to be free, uncontrooooolled—"

"Yes, I know. You'll destroy me. Then you'll spread every known malady across the world. You've been wanting to do that ever since Pandora let you out of that jar. But you can't. I will strike you down!"

Perhaps you are wondering how I could act so confident and calm. In fact, I was terrified. My sixteen-year-old mortal instincts were screaming, *RUN!* My knees were knocking together, and my right eye had developed a nasty twitch. But the secret to dealing with plague spirits was to keep talking so as to appear in charge and unafraid. I trusted that this would allow my demigod companions time to come up with a clever plan to save me. I certainly *hoped* Meg and Percy were working on such a plan.

The spirit on the right bared his rotten teeth. "What will you strike us down with? Where is your booow?"

"It appears to be missing," I agreed. "But is it really? What if it's cleverly hidden under this Led Zeppelin T-shirt, and I am about to whip it out and shoot you all?"

The nosoi shuffled nervously.

"Yooou lie," said the one in the middle.

Percy cleared his throat. "Um, hey, Apollo . . ."

Finally! I thought.

"I know what you're going to say," I told him. "You and Meg have come up with a clever plan to hold off these spirits while I run away to camp. I hate to see you sacrifice yourselves, but—"

"That's not what I was going to say." Percy raised his blade. "I was going to ask what happens if I just slice and dice these mouth-breathers with Celestial bronze."

The middle spirit chortled, his yellow eyes gleaming. "A sword is such a small weapon. It does not have the pooooetry of a good epidemic."

"Stop right there!" I said. "You can't claim both my plagues *and* my poetry!"

"You are right," said the spirit. "Enough wooooords."

The three corpses shambled forward. I thrust out my arms, hoping to blast them to dust. Nothing happened.

"This is insufferable!" I complained. "How do demigods do it without an auto-win power?"

Meg jabbed her tree branch into the nearest spirit's chest. The branch stuck. Glittering smoke began swirling down the length of the wood.

"Let go!" I warned. "Don't let the nosoi touch you!"

Meg released the branch and scampered away.

Meanwhile, Percy Jackson charged into battle. He swung his sword, dodging the spirits' attempts to snare him, but his efforts were futile. Whenever his blade connected with the nosoi, their bodies simply dissolved into glittery mist, then resolidified.

A spirit lunged to grab him. From the ground, Meg scooped up a frozen black peach and threw it with such force it embedded itself in the spirit's forehead, knocking him down.

"We gotta run," Meg decided.

"Yeah." Percy backtracked toward us. "I like that idea."

I knew running would not help. If it were possible to run from disease spirits, the medieval Europeans would've put on their track shoes and escaped the Black Death. (And FYI, the Black Death was *not* my fault. I took one century off to lie around the beach in Cabo, and came back and found that the nosoi had gotten loose and a third of the continent was dead. *Gods*, I was so irritated.)

But I was too terrified to argue. Meg and Percy sprinted off through the orchard, and I followed.

Percy pointed to a line of hills about a mile ahead. "That's the western border of camp. If we can just get there . . ."

We passed an irrigation tank on a tractor-trailer. With a casual flick of his hand, Percy caused the side of the tank to rupture. A wall of water crashed into the three nosoi behind us.

"That was good." Meg grinned, skipping along in her new green dress. "We're going to make it!"

No, I thought, we're not.

My chest ached. Each breath was a ragged wheeze. I resented that these two demigods could carry on a conversation while running for their lives while I, the immortal Apollo, was reduced to gasping like a catfish.

"We can't—" I gulped. "They'll just—"

Before I could finish, three glittering pillars of smoke plumed from the ground in front of us. Two of the nosoi solidified into cadavers—one with a peach for a third eye, the other with a tree branch sticking out of his chest.

The third spirit . . . Well, Percy didn't see it in time. He ran straight into the plume of smoke.

"Don't breathe!" I warned him.

Percy's eyes bugged out as if to say, *Seriously?* He fell to his knees, clawing at his throat. As a son of Poseidon, he could probably breathe underwater, but holding one's breath for an indeterminate amount of time was a different matter altogether.

Meg picked up another withered peach from the field, but it would offer her little defense against the forces of darkness.

I tried to figure out how to help Percy—because I am all about helping—but the branch-impaled nosos charged at me. I turned and fled, running face-first into a tree. I'd like to tell you that was part of my plan, but even I, with all my poetic skill, cannot put a positive spin on it.

I found myself flat on my back, spots dancing in my eyes, the cadaverous visage of the plague spirit looming over me.

"Which fatal illness shall I use to kill the great Apolloooo?" the spirit gurgled. "Anthrax? Perhaps eboooola . . ."

"Hangnails," I suggested, trying to squirm away from my tormentor. "I live in fear of hangnails."

"I have the answer!" the spirit cried, rudely ignoring me. "Let's try this!"

He dissolved into smoke and settled over me like a glittering blanket.

8

Peaches in combat
I am hanging it up now
My brain exploded

I WILL NOT SAY my life passed before my eyes.

I wish it had. That would've taken several months, giving me time to figure out an escape plan.

Instead, my regrets passed before my eyes. Despite being a gloriously perfect being, I do have a few regrets. I remembered that day at Abbey Road Studios, when my envy led me to set rancor in the hearts of John and Paul and break up the Beatles. I remembered Achilles falling on the plains of Troy, cut down by an unworthy archer because of my wrath.

I saw Hyacinthus, his bronze shoulders and dark ringlets gleaming in the sunlight. Standing on the sideline of the discus field, he gave me a brilliant smile. *Even you can't throw that far,* he teased.

Watch me, I said. I threw the discus, then stared in horror as a gust of wind made it veer, inexplicably, toward Hyacinthus's handsome face.

And of course I saw *her*—the other love of my life—her fair skin transforming into bark, her hair sprouting green leaves, her eyes hardening into rivulets of sap.

Those memories brought back so much pain, you might think I would welcome the glittering plague mist descending over me.

Yet my new mortal self rebelled. I was too young to die! I hadn't even had my first kiss! (Yes, my godly catalogue of exes was filled with more beautiful people than a Kardashian party guest list, but none of that seemed real to me.)

If I'm being totally honest, I have to confess something else: all gods fear death, even when we are *not* encased in mortal forms.

That may seem silly. We are immortal. But as you've seen, immortality can be taken away. (In my case, *three stinking times*.)

Gods know about fading. They know about being forgotten over the centuries. The idea of ceasing to exist altogether terrifies us. In fact—well, Zeus would not like me sharing this information, and if you tell anyone, I will deny I ever said it—but the truth is we gods are a little in awe of you mortals. You spend your whole lives knowing you will die. No matter how many friends and relatives you have, your puny existence will quickly be forgotten. How do you cope with it? Why are you not running around constantly screaming and pulling your hair out? Your bravery, I must admit, is quite admirable.

Now where was I?

Right. I was dying.

I rolled around in the mud, holding my breath. I tried to brush off the disease cloud, but it was not as easy as swatting a fly or an uppity mortal.

I caught a glimpse of Meg, playing a deadly game of tag

with the third nosos, trying to keep a peach tree between herself and the spirit. She yelled something to me, but her voice seemed tinny and far away.

Somewhere to my left, the ground shook. A miniature geyser erupted from the field. Percy crawled toward it desperately. He thrust his face in the water, washing away the smoke.

My eyesight began to dim.

Percy struggled to his feet. He ripped out the source of the geyser—an irrigation pipe—and turned the water on me.

Normally I do not like being doused. Every time I go camping with Artemis, she likes to wake me up with a bucket of ice-cold water. But in this case, I didn't mind.

The water disrupted the smoke, allowing me to roll away and gasp for air. Nearby, our two gaseous enemies re-formed as dripping wet corpses, their yellow eyes glowing with annoyance.

Meg yelled again. This time I understood her words. "GET DOWN!"

I found this inconsiderate, since I'd only just gotten up. All around the orchard, the frozen blackened remnants of the harvest were beginning to levitate.

Believe me, in four thousand years I have seen some strange things. I have seen the dreaming face of Ouranos etched in stars across the heavens, and the full fury of Typhon as he raged across the earth. I've seen men turn into snakes, ants turn into men, and otherwise rational people dance the macarena.

But never before had I seen an uprising of frozen fruit.

Percy and I hit the ground as peaches shot around

the orchard, ricocheting off trees like eight balls, ripping through the nosoi's cadaverous bodies. If I had been standing up, I would have been killed, but Meg simply stood there, unfazed and unhurt, as frozen dead fruit zinged around her.

All three nosoi collapsed, riddled with holes. Every piece of fruit dropped to the ground.

Percy looked up, his eyes red and puffy. "Whah jus happened?"

He sounded congested, which meant he hadn't completely escaped the effects of the plague cloud, but at least he wasn't dead. That was generally a good sign.

"I don't know," I admitted. "Meg, is it safe?"

She was staring in amazement at the carnage of fruit, mangled corpses, and broken tree limbs. "I—I'm not sure."

"How'd you do thah?" Percy snuffled.

Meg looked horrified. "I didn't! I just knew it would happen."

One of the cadavers began to stir. It got up, wobbling on its heavily perforated legs.

"But you *did* dooooo it," the spirit growled. "Yoooou are strong, child."

The other two corpses rose.

"Not strong enough," said the second nosos. "We will finish you now."

The third spirit bared his rotten teeth. "Your guardian would be sooooo disappointed."

Guardian? Perhaps the spirit meant me. When in doubt, I usually assumed the conversation was about me.

Meg looked as if she'd been punched in the gut. Her

face paled. Her arms trembled. She stamped her foot and yelled, "NO!"

More peaches swirled into the air. This time the fruit blurred together in a fructose dust devil, until standing in front of Meg was a creature like a pudgy human toddler wearing only a linen diaper. Protruding from his back were wings made of leafy branches. His babyish face might have been cute except for the glowing green eyes and pointy fangs. The creature snarled and snapped at the air.

"Oh, no." Percy shook his head. "I hate these things."

The three nosoi also did not look pleased. They edged away from the snarling baby.

"Wh-what is it?" Meg asked.

I stared at her in disbelief. She had to be the cause of this fruit-based strangeness, but she looked as shocked as we were. Unfortunately, if Meg didn't know how she had summoned this creature, she would not know how to make it go away, and like Percy Jackson, I was no fan of *karpoi*.

"It's a grain spirit," I said, trying to keep the panic out of my voice. "I've never seen a peach karpos before, but if it's as vicious as other types . . ."

I was about to say, *we're doomed*, but that seemed both obvious and depressing.

The peach baby turned toward the nosoi. For a moment, I feared he would make some hellish alliance—an axis of evil between illnesses and fruits.

The middle corpse, the one with the peach in his forehead, inched backward. "Do not interfere," he warned the karpos. "We will not allooow—"

The peach baby launched himself at the nosos and bit his head off.

That is not a figure of speech. The karpos's fanged mouth unhinged, expanding to an unbelievable circumference, then closed around the cadaver's head, and chomped it off in one bite.

Oh, dear . . . I hope you weren't eating dinner as you read that.

In a matter of seconds, the nosos had been torn to shreds and devoured.

Understandably, the other two nosoi retreated, but the karpos crouched and sprang. He landed on the second corpse and proceeded to rip it into plague-flavored Cream of Wheat.

The last spirit dissolved into glittering smoke and tried to fly away, but the peach baby spread his leafy wings and launched himself in pursuit. He opened his mouth and inhaled the sickness, snapping and swallowing until every wisp of smoke was gone.

He landed in front of Meg and belched. His green eyes gleamed. He did not appear even slightly sick, which I suppose wasn't surprising, since human diseases don't infect fruit trees. Instead, even after eating three whole nosoi, the little fellow looked hungry.

He howled and beat his small chest. "Peaches!"

Slowly, Percy raised his sword. His nose was still red and runny, and his face was puffy. "Meg, don move," he snuffled. "I'm gonna—"

"No!" she said. "Don't hurt him."

She put her hand tentatively on the creature's curly head. "You saved us," she told the karpos. "Thank you."

I started mentally preparing a list of herbal remedies for regenerating severed limbs, but to my surprise, the peach baby did not bite off Meg's hand. Instead he hugged Meg's leg and glared at us as if daring us to approach.

"Peaches," he growled.

"He likes you," Percy noted. "Um . . . why?"

"I don't know," Meg said. "Honestly, I didn't summon him!"

I was certain Meg *had* summoned him, intentionally or unintentionally. I also had some ideas now about her godly parentage, and some questions about this "guardian" that the spirits had mentioned, but I decided it would be better to interrogate her when she did not have a snarling carnivorous toddler wrapped around her leg.

"Well, whatever the case," I said, "we owe the karpos our lives. This brings to mind an expression I coined ages ago: A peach a day keeps the plague spirits away!"

Percy sneezed. "I thought it was apples and doctors."

The karpos hissed.

"Or peaches," Percy said. "Peaches work too."

"Peaches," agreed the karpos.

Percy wiped his nose. "Not criticizing, but why is he grooting?"

Meg frowned. "Grooting?"

"Yeah, like thah character in the movie . . . only saying one thing over and over."

"I'm afraid I haven't seen that movie," I said. "But this

karpos does seem to have a very . . . targeted vocabulary."

"Maybe Peaches is his name." Meg stroked the karpos's curly brown hair, which elicited a demonic purring from the creature's throat. "That's what I'll call him."

"Whoa, you are not adopting thah—" Percy sneezed with such force, another irrigation pipe exploded behind him, sending up a row of tiny geysers. "Ugh. Sick."

"You're lucky," I said. "Your trick with the water diluted the spirit's power. Instead of getting a deadly illness, you got a head cold."

"I hate head colds." His green irises looked like they were sinking in a sea of bloodshot. "Neither of you got sick?"

Meg shook her head.

"I have an excellent constitution," I said. "No doubt that's what saved me."

"And the fact thah I hosed the smoke off of you," Percy said.

"Well, yes."

Percy stared at me as if waiting for something. After an awkward moment, it occurred to me that if he was a god and I was a worshipper, he might expect gratitude.

"Ah . . . thank you," I said.

He nodded. "No problem."

I relaxed a little. If he had demanded a sacrifice, like a white bull or a fatted calf, I'm not sure what I would've done.

"Can we go now?" Meg asked.

"An excellent idea," I said. "Though I'm afraid Percy is in no condition—"

"I can drive you the rest of the way," he said. "If we can get my car out from between those trees. . . ." He glanced in that direction and his expression turned even more miserable. "Aw, Hades no. . . ."

A police cruiser was pulling over on the side of the road. I imagined the officers' eyes tracing the tire ruts in the mud, which led to the plowed-down fence and continued to the blue Toyota Prius wedged between two peach trees. The cruiser's roof lights flashed on.

"Great," Percy muttered. "If they tow the Prius, I'm dead. My mom and Paul *need* thah car."

"Go talk to the officers," I said. "You won't be any use to us anyway in your current state."

"Yeah, we'll be fine," Meg said. "You said the camp is right over those hills?"

"Right, but . . ." Percy scowled, probably trying to think straight through the effects of his cold. "Most people enter camp from the east, where Half-Blood Hill is. The western border is wilder—hills and woods, all heavily enchanted. If you're not careful, you can get lost. . . ." He sneezed again. "I'm still not even sure Apollo can get *in* if he's fully mortal."

"I'll get in." I tried to exude confidence. I had no alternative. If I was unable to enter Camp Half-Blood . . . No. I'd already been attacked twice on my first day as a mortal. There was no plan B that would keep me alive.

The police car's doors opened.

"Go," I urged Percy. "We'll find our way through the woods. You explain to the police that you're sick and you lost control of the car. They'll go easy on you."

Percy laughed. "Yeah. Cops love me almost as much as teachers do." He glanced at Meg. "You sure you're okay with the baby fruit demon?"

Peaches growled.

"All good," Meg promised. "Go home. Rest. Get lots of fluids."

Percy's mouth twitched. "You're telling a son of Poseidon to get lots of fluids? Okay, just try to survive until the weekend, will you? I'll come to camp and check on you guys if I can. Be careful and—CHOOOO!"

Muttering unhappily, he touched the cap of his pen to his sword, turning it back into a simple ballpoint. A wise precaution before approaching law enforcement. He trudged down the hill, sneezing and sniffling.

"Officer?" he called. "Sorry, I'm up here. Can you tell me where Manhattan is?"

Meg turned to me. "Ready?"

I was soaking wet and shivering. I was having the worst day in the history of days. I was stuck with a scary girl and an even scarier peach baby. I was by no means ready for anything. But I also desperately wanted to reach camp. I might find some friendly faces there—perhaps even jubilant worshippers who would bring me peeled grapes, Oreos, and other holy offerings.

"Sure," I said. "Let's go."

Peaches the karpos grunted. He gestured for us to follow, then scampered toward the hills. Maybe he knew the way. Maybe he just wanted to lead us to a grisly death.

Meg skipped after him, swinging from tree branches and cartwheeling through the mud as the mood took her.

You might've thought we'd just finished a nice picnic rather than a battle with plague-ridden cadavers.

I turned my face to the sky. "Are you sure, Zeus? It's not too late to tell me this was an elaborate prank and recall me to Olympus. I've learned my lesson. I promise."

The gray winter clouds did not respond. With a sigh, I jogged after Meg and her homicidal new minion.

9

A walk through the woods
Voices driving me bonkers
I hate spaghetti

I SIGHED WITH RELIEF. "This should be easy."

Granted, I'd said the same thing before I fought Poseidon in hand-to-hand combat, and that had *not* turned out to be easy. Nevertheless, our path into Camp Half-Blood looked straightforward enough. For starters, I was pleased I could *see* the camp, since it was normally shielded from mortal eyes. This boded well for me getting in.

From where we stood at the top of a hill, the entire valley spread out below us: roughly three square miles of woods, meadows, and strawberry fields bordered by Long Island Sound to the north and rolling hills on the other three sides. Just below us, a dense forest of evergreens covered the western third of the vale.

Beyond that, the buildings of Camp Half-Blood gleamed in the wintry light: the amphitheater, the sword-fighting stadium, the open-air dining pavilion with its white marble columns. A trireme floated in the canoe lake. Twenty cabins lined the central green where the communal hearth fire glowed cheerfully.

At the edge of the strawberry fields stood the Big House:

a four-story Victorian painted sky blue with white trim. My friend Chiron would be inside, probably having tea by the fireplace. I would find sanctuary at last.

My gaze rose to the far end of the valley. There, on the tallest hill, the Athena Parthenos shone in all its gold-and-alabaster glory. Once, the massive statue had graced the Parthenon in Greece. Now it presided over Camp Half-Blood, protecting the valley from intruders. Even from here I could feel its power, like the subsonic thrum of a mighty engine. Old Gray Eyes was on the lookout for threats, being her usual vigilant, no-fun, all-business self.

Personally, I would have installed a more interesting statue—of myself, for instance. Still, the panorama of Camp Half-Blood was an impressive sight. My mood always improved when I saw the place—a small reminder of the good old days when mortals knew how to build temples and do proper burnt sacrifices. Ah, everything was better in ancient Greece! Well, except for a few small improvements modern humans had made—the Internet, chocolate croissants, life expectancy.

Meg's mouth hung open. "How come I've never heard about this place? Do you need tickets?"

I chuckled. I always enjoyed the chance to enlighten a clueless mortal. "You see, Meg, magical borders camouflage the valley. From the outside, most humans would spy nothing here except boring farmland. If they approached, they would get turned around and find themselves wandering out again. Believe me, I tried to get a pizza delivered to camp once. It was quite annoying."

"You ordered a pizza?"

"Never mind," I said. "As for tickets . . . it's true the camp doesn't let in just anybody, but you're in luck. I know the management."

Peaches growled. He sniffed the ground, then chomped a mouthful of dirt and spit it out.

"He doesn't like the taste of this place," Meg said.

"Yes, well . . ." I frowned at the karpos. "Perhaps we can find him some potting soil or fertilizer when we arrive. I'll convince the demigods to let him in, but it would be helpful if he doesn't bite their heads off—at least not right away."

Peaches muttered something about peaches.

"Something doesn't feel right." Meg bit her nails. "Those woods . . . Percy said they were wild and enchanted and stuff."

I, too, felt as if something was amiss, but I chalked this up to my general dislike of forests. For reasons I'd rather not go into, I find them . . . uncomfortable places. Nevertheless, with our goal in sight, my usual optimism was returning.

"Don't worry," I assured Meg. "You're traveling with a god!"

"Ex-god."

"I wish you wouldn't keep harping on that. Anyway, the campers are very friendly. They'll welcome us with tears of joy. And wait until you see the orientation video!"

"The what?"

"I directed it myself! Now, come along. The woods can't be that bad."

———

The woods were that bad.

As soon as we entered their shadows, the trees seemed to crowd us. Trunks closed ranks, blocking old paths and opening new ones. Roots writhed across the forest floor, making an obstacle course of bumps, knots, and loops. It was like trying to walk across a giant bowl of spaghetti.

The thought of spaghetti made me hungry. It had only been a few hours since Sally Jackson's seven-layer dip and sandwiches, but my mortal stomach was already clenching and squelching for food. The sounds were quite annoying, especially while walking through dark scary woods. Even the karpos Peaches was starting to smell good to me, giving me visions of cobbler and ice cream.

As I said earlier, I was generally not a fan of the woods. I tried to convince myself that the trees were not watching me, scowling and whispering among themselves. They were just trees. Even if they had dryad spirits, those dryads couldn't possibly hold me responsible for what had happened thousands of years ago on a different continent.

Why not? I asked myself. *You still hold yourself responsible.*

I told myself to stuff a sock in it.

We hiked for hours . . . much longer than it should have taken to reach the Big House. Normally I could navigate by the sun—which shouldn't be a surprise, since I spent millennia driving it across the sky—but under the canopy of trees, the light was diffuse, the shadows confusing.

After we passed the same boulder for the third time, I stopped and admitted the obvious. "I have no idea where we are."

Meg plopped herself down onto a fallen log. In the green light, she looked more like a dryad than ever, though tree spirits do not often wear red sneakers and hand-me-down fleece jackets.

"Don't you have any wilderness skills?" she asked. "Reading moss on the sides of trees? Following tracks?"

"That's more my sister's thing," I said.

"Maybe Peaches can help." Meg turned to her karpos. "Hey, can you find us a way out of the woods?"

For the past few miles, the karpos had been muttering nervously, cutting his eyes from side to side. Now he sniffed the air, his nostrils quivering. He tilted his head.

His face flushed bright green. He emitted a distressed bark, then dissolved in a swirl of leaves.

Meg shot to her feet. "Where'd he go?"

I scanned the woods. I suspected Peaches had done the intelligent thing. He'd sensed danger approaching and abandoned us. I didn't want to suggest that to Meg, though. She'd already become quite fond of the karpos. (Ridiculous, getting attached to a small dangerous creature. Then again, we gods got attached to humans, so I had no room to criticize.)

"Perhaps he went scouting," I suggested. "Perhaps we should—"

APOLLO.

The voice reverberated in my head, as if someone had installed Bose speakers behind my eyes. It was not the voice of my conscience. My conscience was not female, and it was not that loud. Yet something about the woman's tone was eerily familiar.

"What's wrong?" Meg asked.

The air turned sickly sweet. The trees loomed over me like trigger hairs of a Venus flytrap.

A bead of sweat trickled down the side of my face.

"We can't stay here," I said. "Attend me, mortal."

"Excuse me?" Meg said.

"Uh, I mean come on!"

We ran, stumbling over tree roots, fleeing blindly through a maze of branches and boulders. We reached a clear stream over a bed of gravel. I barely slowed down. I waded in, sinking shin-deep into the ice-cold water.

The voice spoke again: *FIND ME*.

This time it was so loud, it stabbed through my forehead like a railroad spike. I stumbled, falling to my knees.

"Hey!" Meg gripped my arm. "Get up!"

"You didn't hear that?"

"Hear what?"

THE FALL OF THE SUN, the voice boomed. *THE FINAL VERSE*.

I collapsed face-first into the stream.

"Apollo!" Meg rolled me over, her voice tight with alarm. "Come on! I can't carry you!"

Yet she tried. She dragged me across the river, scolding me and cursing until, with her help, I managed to crawl to shore.

I lay on my back, staring wildly at the forest canopy. My soaked clothes were so cold they burned. My body trembled like an open E string on an electric bass.

Meg tugged off my wet winter coat. Her own coat was much too small for me, but she draped the warm dry fleece over my shoulders. "Keep yourself together," she ordered. "Don't go crazy on me."

My own laughter sounded brittle. "But I—I heard—"

THE FIRES WILL CONSUME ME. MAKE HASTE!

The voice splintered into a chorus of angry whispers. Shadows grew longer and darker. Steam rose from my clothes, smelling like the volcanic fumes of Delphi.

Part of me wanted to curl into a ball and die. Part of me wanted to get up and run wildly after the voices—to find their source—but I suspected that if I tried, my sanity would be lost forever.

Meg was saying something. She shook my shoulders. She put her face nose-to-nose with mine so my own derelict reflection stared back at me from the lenses of her cat-eye glasses. She slapped me, *hard*, and I managed to decipher her words: "GET UP!"

Somehow I did. Then I doubled over and retched.

I hadn't vomited in centuries. I'd forgotten how unpleasant it was.

The next thing I knew, we were staggering along, Meg bearing most of my weight. The voices whispered and argued, tearing off little pieces of my mind and carrying them away into the forest. Soon I wouldn't have much left.

There was no point. I might as well wander off into the forest and go insane. The idea struck me as funny. I began to giggle.

Meg forced me to keep walking. I couldn't understand her words, but her tone was insistent and stubborn, with just enough anger to outweigh her own terror.

In my fractured mental state, I thought the trees were

parting for us, grudgingly opening a path straight out of the woods. I saw a bonfire in the distance, and the open meadows of Camp Half-Blood.

It occurred to me that Meg was talking to the trees, telling them to get out of the way. The idea was ridiculous, and at the moment it seemed hilarious. Judging from the steam billowing from my clothes, I guessed I was running a fever of about a hundred and six.

I was laughing hysterically as we stumbled out of the forest, straight toward the campfire where a dozen teenagers sat making s'mores. When they saw us, they rose. In their jeans and winter coats, with assorted weapons at their sides, they were the dourest bunch of marshmallow roasters I had ever seen.

I grinned. "Oh, hi! I'm Apollo!"

My eyes rolled up in my head, and I passed out.

10

My bus is in flames
My son is older than me
Please, Zeus, make it stop

I DREAMED I WAS DRIVING the sun chariot across the sky. I had the top down in Maserati mode. I was cruising along, honking at jet planes to get out of my way, enjoying the smell of cold stratosphere, and bopping to my favorite jam: Alabama Shakes' "Rise to the Sun."

I was thinking about transforming the Spyder into a Google self-driving car. I wanted to get out my lute and play a scorching solo that would make Brittany Howard proud.

Then a woman appeared in my passenger seat. "You've got to hurry, man."

I almost jumped out of the sun.

My guest was dressed like a Libyan queen of old. (I should know. I dated a few of them.) Her gown swirled with red, black, and gold floral designs. Her long dark hair was crowned with a tiara that looked like a curved miniature ladder—two gold rails lined with rungs of silver. Her face was mature but stately, the way a benevolent queen should look.

So definitely not Hera, then. Besides, Hera would never smile at me so kindly. Also . . . this woman wore a large metal peace symbol around her neck, which did not seem like Hera's style.

Still, I felt I should know her. Despite the elder-hippie vibe, she was so attractive that I assumed we must be related.

"Who are you?" I asked.

Her eyes flashed a dangerous shade of gold, like a feline predator's. "Follow the voices."

A lump swelled in my throat. I tried to think straight, but my brain felt like it had been recently run through a Vitamix. "I heard you in the woods. . . . Were you—were you speaking a prophecy?"

"Find the gates." She grabbed my wrist. "You've gotta find them first, you dig?"

"But—"

The woman burst into flames. I pulled back my singed wrist and grabbed the wheel as the sun chariot plunged into a nosedive. The Maserati morphed into a school bus—a mode I only used when I had to transport a large number of people. Smoke filled the cabin.

Somewhere behind me, a nasal voice said, "By all means, find the gates."

I glanced in the rearview mirror. Through the smoke, I saw a portly man in a mauve suit. He lounged across the backseat, where the troublemakers normally sat. Hermes was fond of that seat—but this man was not Hermes.

He had a weak jawline, an overlarge nose, and a beard that wrapped around his double chin like a helmet strap. His hair was curly and dark like mine, except not as fashionably tousled or luxuriant. His lip curled as if he smelled something unpleasant. Perhaps it was the burning seats of the bus.

"Who are you?" I yelled, desperately trying to pull the chariot out of its dive. "Why are you on my bus?"

The man smiled, which made his face even uglier. "My own forefather does not recognize me? I'm hurt!"

I tried to place him. My cursed mortal brain was too small, too inflexible. It had jettisoned four thousand years of memories like so much ballast.

"I—I don't," I said. "I'm sorry."

The man laughed as flames licked at his purple sleeves. "You're not sorry yet, but you will be. Find me the gates. Lead me to the Oracle. I'll enjoy burning it down!"

Fire consumed me as the sun chariot careened toward the earth. I gripped the wheel and stared in horror as a massive bronze face loomed outside the windshield. It was the face of the man in purple, fashioned from an expanse of metal larger than my bus. As we hurtled toward it, the features shifted and became my own.

Then I woke, shivering and sweating.

"Easy." Someone's hand rested on my shoulder. "Don't try to sit up."

Naturally I tried to sit up.

My bedside attendant was a young man about my age—my mortal age—with shaggy blond hair and blue eyes. He wore doctor's scrubs with an open ski jacket, the words OKEMO MOUNTAIN stitched on the pocket. His face had a skier's tan. I felt I should know him. (I'd been having that sensation a lot since my fall from Olympus.)

I was lying in a cot in the middle of a cabin. On either

side, bunk beds lined the walls. Rough cedar beams ribbed the ceiling. The white plaster walls were bare except for a few hooks for coats and weapons.

It could have been a modest abode in almost any age—ancient Athens, medieval France, the farmlands of Iowa. It smelled of clean linen and dried sage. The only decorations were some flowerpots on the windowsill, where cheerful yellow blooms were thriving despite the cold weather outside.

"Those flowers . . ." My voice was hoarse, as if I'd inhaled the smoke from my dream. "Those are from Delos, my sacred island."

"Yep," said the young man. "They only grow in and around Cabin Seven—*your* cabin. Do you know who I am?"

I studied his face. The calmness of his eyes, the smile resting easily on his lips, the way his hair curled around his ears . . . I had a vague memory of a woman, an alt-country singer named Naomi Solace, whom I'd met in Austin. I blushed thinking about her even now. To my teenaged self, our romance felt like something that I'd watched in a movie a long ago time—a movie my parents wouldn't have allowed me to see.

But this boy was definitely Naomi's son.

Which meant he was *my* son too.

Which felt very, very strange.

"You're Will Solace," I said. "My, ah . . . erm—"

"Yeah," Will agreed. "It's awkward."

My frontal lobe did a one-eighty inside my skull. I listed sideways.

"Whoa, there." Will steadied me. "I tried to heal you, but honestly, I don't understand what's wrong. You've got blood, not ichor. You're recovering quickly from your injuries, but your vital signs are completely human."

"Don't remind me."

"Yeah, well . . ." He put his hand on my forehead and frowned in concentration. His fingers trembled slightly. "I didn't *know* any of that until I tried to give you nectar. Your lips started steaming. I almost killed you."

"Ah . . ." I ran my tongue across my bottom lip, which felt heavy and numb. I wondered if that explained my dream about smoke and fire. I hoped so. "I guess Meg forgot to tell you about my condition."

"I guess she did." Will took my wrist and checked my pulse. "You seem to be about my age, fifteen or so. Your heart rate is back to normal. Ribs are mending. Nose is swollen, but not broken."

"And I have acne," I lamented. "And flab."

Will tilted his head. "You're mortal, and *that's* what you're worried about?"

"You're right. I'm powerless. Weaker even than you puny demigods!"

"Gee, thanks. . . ."

I got the feeling that he almost said *Dad* but managed to stop himself.

It was difficult to think of this young man as my son. He was so poised, so unassuming, so free of acne. He also didn't appear to be awestruck in my presence. In fact, the corner of his mouth had started twitching.

"Are—are you amused?" I demanded.

Will shrugged. "Well, it's either find this funny or freak out. My dad, the god Apollo, is a fifteen-year-old—"

"*Sixteen*," I corrected. "Let's go with sixteen."

"A sixteen-year-old mortal, lying in a cot in my cabin, and with all my healing arts—which I got from *you*—I still can't figure out how to fix you."

"There is no fixing this," I said miserably. "I am cast out of Olympus. My fate is tied to a girl named Meg. It could not be worse!"

Will laughed, which I thought took a great deal of gall. "Meg seems cool. She's already poked Connor Stoll in the eyes and kicked Sherman Yang in the crotch."

"She did *what*?"

"She'll get along just fine here. She's waiting for you outside—along with most of the campers." Will's smile faded. "Just so you're prepared, they're asking a lot of questions. Everybody is wondering if your arrival, your *mortal* situation, has anything to do with what's been going on at camp."

I frowned. "What has been going on at camp?"

The cabin door opened. Two more demigods stepped inside. One was a tall boy of about thirteen, his skin burnished bronze and his cornrows woven like DNA helixes. In his black wool peacoat and black jeans, he looked as if he'd stepped from the deck of an eighteenth-century whaling vessel. The other newcomer was a younger girl in olive camouflage. She had a full quiver on her shoulder, and her short ginger hair was dyed with a shock of bright green, which seemed to defeat the point of wearing camouflage.

I smiled, delighted that I actually remembered their names.

"Austin," I said. "And Kayla, isn't it?"

Rather than falling to their knees and blubbering gratefully, they gave each other a nervous glance.

"So it's really you," Kayla said.

Austin frowned. "Meg told us you were beaten up by a couple of thugs. She said you had no powers and you went hysterical out in the woods."

My mouth tasted like burnt school bus upholstery. "Meg talks too much."

"But you're mortal?" Kayla asked. "As in completely mortal? Does that mean I'm going to lose my archery skills? I can't even qualify for the Olympics until I'm sixteen!"

"And if I lose my music . . ." Austin shook his head. "No, man, that's wrong. My last video got, like, five hundred thousand views in a week. What am I supposed to do?"

It warmed my heart that my children had the right priorities: their skills, their images, their views on YouTube. Say what you will about gods being absentee parents; our children inherit many of our finest personality traits.

"My problems should not affect you," I promised. "If Zeus went around retroactively yanking my divine power out of all my descendants, half the medical schools in the country would be empty. The Rock and Roll Hall of Fame would disappear. The Tarot-card reading industry would collapse overnight!"

Austin's shoulders relaxed. "That's a relief."

"So if you die while you're mortal," Kayla said, "we won't disappear?"

"Guys," Will interrupted, "why don't you run to the Big House and tell Chiron that our . . . our *patient* is conscious. I'll bring him along in a minute. And, uh, see if you can disperse the crowd outside, okay? I don't want everybody rushing Apollo at once."

Kayla and Austin nodded sagely. As my children, they no doubt understood the importance of controlling the paparazzi.

As soon as they were gone, Will gave me an apologetic smile. "They're in shock. We all are. It'll take some time to get used to . . . whatever this is."

"You do not seem shocked," I said.

Will laughed under his breath. "I'm terrified. But one thing you learn as head counselor: you have to keep it together for everyone else. Let's get you on your feet."

It was not easy. I fell twice. My head spun, and my eyes felt as if they were being microwaved in their sockets. Recent dreams continued to churn in my brain like river silt, muddying my thoughts—the woman with the crown and the peace symbol, the man in the purple suit. *Lead me to the Oracle. I'll enjoy burning it down!*

The cabin began to feel stifling. I was anxious to get some fresh air.

One thing my sister Artemis and I agree on: every worthwhile pursuit is better outdoors than indoors. Music is best played under the dome of heaven. Poetry should be shared in the *agora*. Archery is definitely easier outside, as I can attest after that one time I tried target practice in my father's throne room. And driving the sun . . . well, that's not really an indoor sport either.

Leaning on Will for support, I stepped outside. Kayla and Austin had succeeded in shooing the crowd away. The only one waiting for me—oh, joy and happiness—was my young overlord, Meg, who had apparently now gained fame at camp as Crotchkicker McCaffrey.

She still wore Sally Jackson's hand-me-down green dress, though it was a bit dirtier now. Her leggings were ripped and torn. On her bicep, a line of butterfly bandages closed a nasty cut she must have gotten in the woods.

She took one look at me, scrunched up her face, and stuck out her tongue. "You look *yuck.*"

"And you, Meg," I said, "are as charming as ever."

She adjusted her glasses until they were just crooked enough to be annoying. "Thought you were going to die."

"Glad to disappoint you."

"Nah." She shrugged. "You still owe me a year of service. We're bound, whether you like it or not!"

I sighed. It was ever so wonderful to be back in Meg's company.

"I suppose I should thank you. . . ." I had a hazy memory of my delirium in the forest, Meg carrying me along, the trees seeming to part before us. "How did you get us out of the woods?"

Her expression turned guarded. "Dunno. Luck." She jabbed a thumb at Will Solace. "From what he's been telling me, it's a good thing we got out before nightfall."

"Why?"

Will started to answer, then apparently thought better of it. "I should let Chiron explain. Come on."

I rarely visited Camp Half-Blood in winter. The last time had been three years ago, when a girl named Thalia Grace crash-landed my bus in the canoe lake.

I expected the camp to be sparsely populated. I knew

most demigods only came for the summer, leaving a small core of year-rounders during the school term—those who for various reasons found camp the only safe place they could live.

Still, I was struck by how few demigods I saw. If Cabin Seven was any indication, each god's cabin could hold beds for about twenty campers. That meant a maximum capacity of four hundred demigods—enough for several phalanxes or one really amazing yacht party.

Yet, as we walked across camp, I saw no more than a dozen people. In the fading light of sunset, a lone girl was scaling the climbing wall as lava flowed down either side. At the lake, a crew of three checked the rigging on the trireme.

Some campers had found reasons to be outside just so they could gawk at me. Over by the hearth, one young man sat polishing his shield, watching me in its reflective surface. Another fellow glared at me as he spliced barbed wire outside the Ares cabin. From the awkward way he walked, I assumed he was Sherman Yang of the recently kicked crotch.

In the doorway of the Hermes cabin, two girls giggled and whispered as I passed. Normally this sort of attention wouldn't have fazed me. My magnetism was understandably irresistible. But now my face burned. Me—the manly paragon of romance—reduced to a gawky, inexperienced boy!

I would have screamed at the heavens for this unfairness, but that would've been super-embarrassing.

We made our way through the fallow strawberry fields. Up on Half-Blood Hill, the Golden Fleece glinted in the lowest branch of a tall pine tree. Whiffs of steam rose from the head of Peleus, the guardian dragon coiled around the base of the trunk. Next to the tree, the Athena Parthenos looked angry red in the sunset. Or perhaps she just wasn't happy to see me. (Athena had never gotten over our little tiff during the Trojan War.)

Halfway down the hillside, I spotted the Oracle's cave, its entrance shrouded by thick burgundy curtains. The torches on either side stood unlit—usually a sign that my prophetess, Rachel Dare, was not in residence. I wasn't sure whether to be disappointed or relieved.

Even when she was not channeling prophecies, Rachel was a wise young lady. I had hoped to consult her about my problems. On the other hand, since her prophetic power had apparently stopped working (which I suppose in some *small* part was my fault), I wasn't sure Rachel would want to see me. She would expect explanations from her Main Man, and while I had invented *mansplaining* and was its foremost practitioner, I had no answers to give her.

The dream of the flaming bus stayed with me: the groovy crowned woman urging me to find the gates, the ugly mauve-suited man threatening to burn the Oracle.

Well . . . the cave was right there. I wasn't sure why the woman in the crown was having such trouble finding it, or why the ugly man would be so intent on burning its "gates," which amounted to nothing more than purple curtains.

Unless the dream was referring to something other than the Oracle of Delphi. . . .

I rubbed my throbbing temples. I kept reaching for memories that weren't there, trying to plunge into my vast lake of knowledge only to find it had been reduced to a kiddie pool. You simply can't do much with a kiddie pool brain.

On the porch of the Big House, a dark-haired young man was waiting for us. He wore faded black trousers, a Ramones T-shirt (bonus points for musical taste), and a black leather bomber jacket. At his side hung a Stygian iron sword.

"I remember you," I said. "Is it Nicholas, son of Hades?"

"Nico di Angelo." He studied me, his eyes sharp and colorless, like broken glass. "So it's true. You're completely mortal. There's an aura of death around you—a thick possibility of death."

Meg snorted. "Sounds like a weather forecast."

I did not find this amusing. Being face-to-face with a son of Hades, I recalled the many mortals I had sent to the Underworld with my plague arrows. It had always seemed like good clean fun—meting out richly deserved punishments for wicked deeds. Now, I began to understand the terror in my victims' eyes. I did not want an aura of death hanging over me. I definitely did not want to stand in judgment before Nico di Angelo's father.

Will put his hand on Nico's shoulder. "Nico, we need to have another talk about your people skills."

"Hey, I'm just stating the obvious. If this *is* Apollo, and he dies, we're all in trouble."

Will turned to me. "I apologize for my boyfriend."

Nico rolled his eyes. "Could you not—"

"Would you prefer *special guy?*" Will asked. "Or *significant other?*"

"Significant *annoyance,* in your case," Nico grumbled.

"Oh, I'll get you for that."

Meg wiped her dripping nose. "You guys fight a lot. I thought we were going to see a centaur."

"And here I am." The screen door opened. Chiron trotted out, ducking his head to avoid the doorframe.

From the waist up, he looked every bit the professor he often pretended to be in the mortal world. His brown wool jacket had patches on the elbows. His plaid dress shirt did not quite match his green tie. His beard was neatly trimmed, but his hair would have failed the tidiness inspection required for a proper rat's nest.

From the waist down, he was a white stallion.

My old friend smiled, though his eyes were stormy and distracted. "Apollo, it's good you are here. We need to talk about the disappearances."

11

Check your spam folder
The prophecies might be there
No? Well, I'm stumped. Bye

MEG GAWKED. "He—he really *is* a centaur."

"Well spotted," I said. "I suppose the lower body of a horse is what gave him away?"

She punched me in the arm.

"Chiron," I said, "this is Meg McCaffrey, my new master and wellspring of aggravation. You were saying something about disappearances?"

Chiron's tail flicked. His hooves clopped on the planks of the porch.

He was immortal, yet his visible age seemed to vary from century to century. I did not remember his whiskers ever being so gray, or the lines around his eyes so pronounced. Whatever was happening at camp must not have been helping his stress levels.

"Welcome, Meg." Chiron tried for a friendly tone, which I thought quite heroic, seeing as . . . well, *Meg*. "I understand you showed great bravery in the woods. You brought Apollo here despite many dangers. I'm glad to have you at Camp Half-Blood."

"Thanks," said Meg. "You're really tall. Don't you hit your head on light fixtures?"

Chiron chuckled. "Sometimes. If I want to be closer to human size, I have a magical wheelchair that allows me to compact my lower half into . . . Actually, that's not important now."

"Disappearances," I prompted. "What has disappeared?"

"Not *what*, but *who*," Chiron said. "Let's talk inside. Will, Nico, could you please tell the other campers we'll gather for dinner in one hour? I'll give everyone an update then. In the meantime, no one should roam the camp alone. Use the buddy system."

"Understood." Will looked at Nico. "Will you be my buddy?"

"You are a dork," Nico announced.

The two of them strolled off bickering.

At this point, you may be wondering how I felt seeing my son with Nico di Angelo. I'll admit I did not understand Will's attraction to a child of Hades, but if the dark foreboding type was what made Will happy . . .

Oh. Perhaps some of you are wondering how I felt seeing him with a boyfriend rather than a girlfriend. If that's the case, *please*. We gods are not hung up about such things. I myself have had . . . let's see, thirty-three mortal girlfriends and eleven mortal boyfriends? I've lost count. My two greatest loves were, of course, Daphne and Hyacinthus, but when you're a god as popular as I am—

Hold on. Did I just tell you who I liked? I did, didn't I? Gods of Olympus, forget I mentioned their names! I am so embarrassed. Please don't say anything. In this mortal life, I've never been in love with *anyone*!

I am so confused.

Chiron led us into the living room, where comfy leather couches made a V facing the stone fireplace. Above the mantel, a stuffed leopard head was snoring contentedly.

"Is it alive?" Meg asked.

"Quite." Chiron trotted over to his wheelchair. "That's Seymour. If we speak quietly, we should be able to avoid waking him."

Meg immediately began exploring the living room. Knowing her, she was searching for small objects to throw at the leopard to wake him up.

Chiron settled into his wheelchair. He placed his rear legs into the false compartment of the seat, then backed up, magically compacting his equine hindquarters until he looked like a man sitting down. To complete the illusion, hinged front panels swung closed, giving him fake human legs. Normally those legs were fitted with slacks and loafers to augment his "professor" disguise, but today it seemed Chiron was going for a different look.

"That's new," I said.

Chiron glanced down at his shapely female mannequin legs, dressed in fishnet stockings and red sequined high heels. He sighed heavily. "I see the Hermes cabin have been watching *Rocky Horror Picture Show* again. I will have to have a chat with them."

Rocky Horror Picture Show brought back fond memories. I used to cosplay as Rocky at the midnight showings, because, naturally, the character's perfect physique was based on my own.

"Let me guess," I said. "Connor and Travis Stoll are the pranksters?"

From a nearby basket, Chiron grabbed a flannel blanket and spread it over his fake legs, though the ruby shoes still peeked out at the bottom. "Actually, Travis went off to college last autumn, which has mellowed Connor quite a bit."

Meg looked over from the old *Pac-Man* arcade game. "I poked that guy Connor in the eyes."

Chiron winced. "That's nice, dear. . . . At any rate, we have Julia Feingold and Alice Miyazawa now. They have taken up pranking duty. You'll meet them soon enough."

I recalled the girls who had been giggling at me from the Hermes cabin doorway. I felt myself blushing all over again.

Chiron gestured toward the couches. "Please sit."

Meg moved on from *Pac-Man* (having given the game twenty seconds of her time) and began literally climbing the wall. Dormant grapevines festooned the dining area—no doubt the work of my old friend Dionysus. Meg scaled one of the thicker trunks, trying to reach the Gorgon-hair chandelier.

"Ah, Meg," I said, "perhaps you should watch the orientation film while Chiron and I talk?"

"I know plenty," she said. "I talked to the campers while you were passed out. 'Safe place for modern demigods.' Blah, blah, blah."

"Oh, but the film is very good," I urged. "I shot it on a

tight budget in the 1950s, but some of the camera work was revolutionary. You should really—"

The grapevine peeled away from the wall. Meg crashed to the floor. She popped up completely unscathed, then spotted a platter of cookies on the sideboard. "Are those free?"

"Yes, child," Chiron said. "Bring the tea as well, would you?"

So we were stuck with Meg, who draped her legs over the couch's armrest, chomped on cookies, and threw crumbs at Seymour's snoring head whenever Chiron wasn't looking.

Chiron poured me a cup of Darjeeling. "I'm sorry Mr. D is not here to welcome you."

"Mr. Dee?" Meg asked.

"Dionysus," I explained. "The god of wine. Also the director of this camp."

Chiron handed me my tea. "After the battle with Gaea, I thought Mr. D might return to camp, but he never did. I hope he's all right."

The old centaur looked at me expectantly, but I had nothing to share. The last six months were a complete void; I had no idea what the other Olympians might be up to.

"I don't know anything," I admitted. I hadn't said those words very often in the last four millennia. They tasted bad. I sipped my tea, but that was no less bitter. "I'm a bit behind on the news. I was hoping you could fill me in."

Chiron did a poor job hiding his disappointment. "I see. . . ."

I realized he had been hoping for help and guidance—the

exact same things I needed from *him*. As a god, I was used to lesser beings relying on me—praying for this and pleading for that. But now that I was mortal, being relied upon was a little terrifying.

"So what is your crisis?" I asked. "You have the same look Cassandra had in Troy, or Jim Bowie at the Alamo—as if you're under siege."

Chiron did not dispute the comparison. He cupped his hands around his tea.

"You know that during the war with Gaea, the Oracle of Delphi stopped receiving prophecies. In fact, all known methods of divining the future suddenly failed."

"Because the original cave of Delphi was retaken," I said with a sigh, trying not to feel picked on.

Meg bounced a chocolate chip off Seymour the leopard's nose. "Oracle of Delphi. Percy mentioned that."

"Percy Jackson?" Chiron sat up. "Percy was with you?"

"For a time." I recounted our battle in the peach orchard and Percy's return to New York. "He said he would drive out this weekend if he could."

Chiron looked disheartened, as if my company alone wasn't good enough. Can you imagine?

"At any rate," he continued, "we hoped that once the war was over, the Oracle might start working again. When it did not . . . Rachel became concerned."

"Who's Rachel?" Meg asked.

"Rachel Dare," I said. "The Oracle."

"Thought the Oracle was a place."

"It is."

"Then Rachel is a place, and she stopped working?"

Had I still been a god, I would have turned her into a blue-belly lizard and released her into the wilderness never to be seen again. The thought soothed me.

"The original Delphi was a place in Greece," I told her. "A cavern filled with volcanic fumes, where people would come to receive guidance from my priestess, the Pythia."

"*Pythia.*" Meg giggled. "That's a funny word."

"Yes. Ha-ha. So the Oracle is both a place and a person. When the Greek gods relocated to America back in . . . what was it, Chiron, 1860?"

Chiron seesawed his hand. "More or less."

"I brought the Oracle here to continue speaking prophecies on my behalf. The power has passed down from priestess to priestess over the years. Rachel Dare is the present Oracle."

From the cookie platter, Meg plucked the only Oreo, which I had been hoping to have myself. "Mm-kay. Is it too late to watch that movie?"

"Yes," I snapped. "Now, the way I gained possession of the Oracle of Delphi in the first place was by killing this monster called Python who lived in the depths of the cavern."

"A python like the snake," Meg said.

"Yes and no. The snake species is named after Python the monster, who is also rather snaky, but who is much bigger and scarier and devours small girls who talk too much. At any rate, last August, while I was . . . indisposed, my ancient foe Python was released from Tartarus. He reclaimed the cave of Delphi. That's why the Oracle stopped working."

"But if the Oracle is in America now, why does it matter if some snake monster takes over its old cave?"

That was about the longest sentence I had yet heard her speak. She'd probably done it just to spite me.

"It's too much to explain," I said. "You'll just have to—"

"Meg." Chiron gave her one of his heroically tolerant smiles. "The original site of the Oracle is like the deepest taproot of a tree. The branches and leaves of prophecy may extend across the world, and Rachel Dare may be our loftiest branch, but if the taproot is strangled, the whole tree is endangered. With Python back in residence at his old lair, the spirit of the Oracle has been completely blocked."

"Oh." Meg made a face at me. "Why didn't you just say so?"

Before I could strangle her like the annoying taproot she was, Chiron refilled my teacup.

"The larger problem," he said, "is that we have no other source of prophecies."

"Who cares?" Meg asked. "So you don't know the future. Nobody knows the future."

"*Who cares?!*" I shouted. "Meg McCaffrey, prophecies are the catalysts for every important event—every quest or battle, disaster or miracle, birth or death. Prophecies don't simply foretell the future. They shape it! They *allow* the future to happen."

"I don't get it."

Chiron cleared his throat. "Imagine prophecies are flower seeds. With the right seeds, you can grow any garden you desire. Without seeds, no growth is possible."

"Oh." Meg nodded. "That would suck."

I found it strange that Meg, a street urchin and Dumpster warrior, would relate so well to garden metaphors, but Chiron was an excellent teacher. He had picked up on something about the girl . . . an impression that had been lurking in the back of my mind as well. I hoped I was wrong about what it meant, but with my luck, I would be right. I usually was.

"So where is Rachel Dare?" I asked. "Perhaps if I spoke with her . . . ?"

Chiron set down his tea. "Rachel planned to visit us during her winter vacation, but she never did. It might not mean anything. . . ."

I leaned forward. It was not unheard of for Rachel Dare to be late. She was artistic, unpredictable, impulsive, and rule-averse—all qualities I dearly admired. But it wasn't like her not to show up at all.

"Or?" I asked.

"Or it might be part of the larger problem," Chiron said. "Prophecies are not the only things that have failed. Travel and communication have become difficult in the last few months. We haven't heard from our friends at Camp Jupiter in weeks. No new demigods have arrived. Satyrs aren't reporting from the field. Iris messages no longer work."

"Iris what?" Meg asked.

"Two-way visions," I said. "A form of communication overseen by the rainbow goddess. Iris has always been flighty. . . ."

"Except that normal human communications are also on the fritz," Chiron said. "Of course, phones have always been dangerous for demigods—"

"Yeah, they attract monsters," Meg agreed. "I haven't used a phone in *forever*."

"A wise move," Chiron said. "But recently our phones have stopped working altogether. Mobile, landline, Internet . . . it doesn't seem to matter. Even the archaic form of communication known as *e-mail* is strangely unreliable. The messages simply don't arrive."

"Did you look in the junk folder?" I offered.

"I fear the problem is more complicated," Chiron said. "We have no communication with the outside world. We are alone and understaffed. You are the first newcomers in almost two months."

I frowned. "Percy Jackson mentioned nothing of this."

"I doubt Percy is even aware," Chiron said. "He's been busy with school. Winter is normally our quietest time. For a while, I was able to convince myself that the communication failures were nothing but an inconvenient happenstance. Then the disappearances started."

In the fireplace, a log slipped from the andiron. I may or may not have jumped in my seat.

"The disappearances, yes." I wiped drops of tea from my pants and tried to ignore Meg's snickering. "Tell me about those."

"Three in the last month," Chiron said. "First it was Cecil Markowitz from the Hermes cabin. One morning his bunk was simply empty. He didn't say anything about wanting to leave. No one saw him go. And in the past few weeks, no one has seen or heard from him."

"Children of Hermes do tend to sneak around," I offered.

"At first, that's what we thought," said Chiron. "But a

week later, Ellis Wakefield disappeared from the Ares cabin. Same story: empty bunk, no signs that he had either left on his own *or* was . . . ah, taken. Ellis was an impetuous young man. It was conceivable he might have charged off on some ill-advised adventure, but it made me uneasy. Then this morning we realized a third camper had vanished: Miranda Gardiner, head of the Demeter cabin. That was the worst news of all."

Meg swung her feet off the armrest. "Why is that the worst?"

"Miranda is one of our senior counselors," Chiron said. "She would never leave on her own without notice. She is too smart to be tricked away from camp, and too powerful to be forced. Yet something happened to her . . . something I can't explain."

The old centaur faced me. "Something is very wrong, Apollo. These problems may not be as alarming as the rise of Kronos or the awakening of Gaea, but in a way I find them even more unsettling, because I have never seen anything like this before."

I recalled my dream of the burning sun bus. I thought of the voices I'd heard in the woods, urging me to wander off and find their source.

"These demigods . . ." I said. "Before they disappeared, did they act unusual in any way? Did they report . . . hearing things?"

Chiron raised an eyebrow. "Not that I am aware of. Why?"

I was reluctant to say more. I didn't want to cause a panic without knowing what we were facing. When mortals panic, it can be an ugly scene, especially if they expect *me* to fix the problem.

Also, I will admit I felt a bit impatient. We had not yet addressed the most important issues—*mine*.

"It seems to me," I said, "that our first priority is to bend all the camp's resources to helping me regain my divine state. Then I can assist you with these other problems."

Chiron stroked his beard. "But what if the problems are connected, my friend? What if the only way to restore you to Olympus is by reclaiming the Oracle of Delphi, thus freeing the power of prophecy? What if Delphi is the key to it all?"

I had forgotten about Chiron's tendency to lay out obvious and logical conclusions that I tried to avoid thinking about. It was an infuriating habit.

"In my present state, that's impossible." I pointed at Meg. "Right now, my job is to serve this demigod, probably for a year. After I've done whatever tasks she assigns me, Zeus will judge that my sentence has been served, and I can once again become a god."

Meg pulled apart a Fig Newton. "I could order you to go to this Delphi place."

"No!" My voice cracked in midshriek. "You should assign me *easy* tasks—like starting a rock band, or just hanging out. Yes, hanging out is good."

Meg looked unconvinced. "Hanging out isn't a task."

"It is if you do it right. Camp Half-Blood can protect me while I hang out. After my year of servitude is up, I'll become a god. *Then* we can talk about how to restore Delphi."

Preferably, I thought, by ordering some demigods to undertake the quest for me.

"Apollo," Chiron said, "if demigods keep disappearing, we may not have a year. We may not have the strength to protect you. And, forgive me, but Delphi *is* your responsibility."

I tossed up my hands. "*I* wasn't the one who opened the Doors of Death and let Python out! Blame Gaea! Blame Zeus for his bad judgment! When the giants started to wake, I drew up a very clear *Twenty-Point Plan of Action to Protect Apollo and Also You Other Gods*, but he didn't even read it!"

Meg tossed half of her cookie at Seymour's head. "I still think it's your fault. Hey, look! He's awake!"

She said this as if the leopard had decided to wake up on his own rather than being beaned in the eye with a Fig Newton.

"*RARR,*" Seymour complained.

Chiron wheeled his chair back from the table. "My dear, in that jar on the mantel, you'll find some Snausages. Why don't you feed him dinner? Apollo and I will wait on the porch."

We left Meg happily making three-point shots into Seymour's mouth with the treats.

Once Chiron and I reached the porch, he turned his wheelchair to face me. "She's an interesting demigod."

"*Interesting* is such a nonjudgmental term."

"She really summoned a karpos?"

"Well . . . the spirit appeared when she was in trouble. Whether she consciously summoned it, I don't know. She named him Peaches."

Chiron scratched his beard. "I have not seen a demigod with the power to summon grain spirits in a very long time. You know what it means?"

My feet began to quake. "I have my suspicions. I'm trying to stay positive."

"She guided you out of the woods," Chiron noted. "Without her—"

"Yes," I said. "Don't remind me."

It occurred to me that I'd seen that keen look in Chiron's eyes before—when he'd assessed Achilles's sword technique and Ajax's skill with a spear. It was the look of a seasoned coach scouting new talent. I'd never dreamed the centaur would look at *me* that way, as if I had something to prove to him, as if my mettle were untested. I felt so . . . so *objectified*.

"Tell me," Chiron said, "what did you hear in the woods?"

I silently cursed my big mouth. I should not have asked whether the missing demigods had heard anything strange.

I decided it was fruitless to hold back now. Chiron was more perceptive than your average horse-man. I told him what I'd experienced in the forest, and afterward in my dream.

His hands curled into his lap blanket. The bottom of it rose higher above his red sequined pumps. He looked about as worried as it is possible for a man to look while wearing fishnet stockings.

"We will have to warn the campers to stay away from the forest," he decided. "I do not understand what is happening, but I still maintain it *must* be connected to Delphi, and your present . . . ah, situation. The Oracle must be liberated from the monster Python. We must find a way."

I translated that easily enough: I must find a way.

Chiron must have read my desolate expression.

"Come, come, old friend," he said. "You have done it before. Perhaps you are not a god now, but the first time you killed Python it was no challenge at all! Hundreds of storybooks have praised the way you easily slew your enemy."

"Yes," I muttered. "Hundreds of storybooks."

I recalled some of those stories: I had killed Python without breaking a sweat. I flew to the mouth of the cave, called him out, unleashed an arrow, and *BOOM!*—one dead giant snake monster. I became Lord of Delphi, and we all lived happily ever after.

How did storytellers get the idea that I vanquished Python so quickly?

All right . . . possibly it's because I told them so. Still, the truth was rather different. For centuries after our battle, I had bad dreams about my old foe.

Now I was almost grateful for my imperfect memory. I could not recollect all of the nightmarish details of my fight with Python, but I *did* know he had been no pushover. I had needed all my godly strength, my divine powers, and the world's most deadly bow.

What chance would I have as a sixteen-year-old mortal with acne, hand-me-down clothes, and the nom de guerre Lester Papadopoulos? I was not going to charge off to Greece and get myself killed, thank you very much, especially not without my sun chariot or the ability to teleport. I'm sorry; gods do *not* fly commercial.

I tried to figure out how to explain this to Chiron in a calm, diplomatic way that did not involve stomping my feet or screaming. I was saved from the effort by the sound of a conch horn in the distance.

"That means dinner." The centaur forced a smile. "We will talk more later, eh? For now, let's celebrate your arrival."

12

Ode to a hot dog
With bug juice and tater chips
I got nothing, man

I WAS NOT IN THE MOOD TO CELEBRATE.

Especially sitting at a picnic table eating mortal food. With mortals.

The dining pavilion was pleasant enough. Even in winter, the camp's magical borders shielded us from the worst of the elements. Sitting outdoors in the warmth of the torches and braziers, I felt only slightly chilly. Long Island Sound glittered in the light of the moon. (Hello, Artemis. Don't bother to say hi.) On Half-Blood Hill, the Athena Parthenos glowed like the world's largest nightlight. Even the woods did not seem so creepy with the pine trees blanketed in soft silvery fog.

My dinner, however, was less than poetic. It consisted of hot dogs, potato chips, and a red liquid I was told was bug juice. I did not know why humans consumed bug juice, or from which type of bug it had been extracted, but it was the tastiest part of the meal, which was disconcerting.

I sat at the Apollo table with my children Austin, Kayla, and Will, plus Nico di Angelo. I could see no difference between my table and any of the other gods' tables. Mine should have been shinier and more elegant. It should have played music or recited poetry upon command. Instead it was just a slab of stone with benches on either side. I found the seating uncomfortable, though my offspring didn't seem to mind.

Austin and Kayla peppered me with questions about Olympus, the war with Gaea, and what it felt like to be a god and then a human. I knew they did not mean to be rude. As my children, they were inherently inclined to the utmost grace. However, their questions were painful reminders of my fallen status.

Besides, as the hours passed, I remembered less and less about my divine life. It was alarming how fast my cosmically perfect neurons had deteriorated. Once, each memory had been like a high-definition audio file. Now those recordings were on wax cylinders. And believe me, I remember wax cylinders. They did not last long in the sun chariot.

Will and Nico sat shoulder to shoulder, bantering good-naturedly. They were so cute together it made me feel desolate. It jogged my memories of those few short golden months I'd shared with Hyacinthus before the jealousy, before the horrible accident . . .

"Nico," I said at last, "shouldn't you be sitting at the Hades table?"

He shrugged. "Technically, yes. But if I sit alone at my table, strange things happen. Cracks open in the floor. Zombies crawl out and start roaming around. It's a mood disorder. I can't control it. That's what I told Chiron."

"And is it true?" I asked.

Nico smiled thinly. "I have a note from my doctor."

Will raised his hand. "I'm his doctor."

"Chiron decided it wasn't worth arguing about," Nico said. "As long as I sit at a table with other people, like . . . oh, these guys for instance . . . the zombies stay away. Everybody's happier."

Will nodded serenely. "It's the strangest thing. Not that Nico would ever misuse his powers to get what he wants."

"Of course not," Nico agreed.

I glanced across the dining pavilion. As per camp tradition, Meg had been placed with the children of Hermes, since her godly parentage had not yet been determined. Meg didn't seem to mind. She was busy re-creating the Coney Island Hot Dog Eating Contest all by herself. The other two girls, Julia and Alice, watched her with a mixture of fascination and horror.

Across the table from her sat an older skinny boy with curly brown hair—Connor Stoll, I deduced, though I'd never been able to tell him apart from his older brother, Travis. Despite the darkness, Connor wore sunglasses, no doubt to protect his eyes from a repeat poking. I also noted that he wisely kept his hands away from Meg's mouth.

In the entire pavilion, I counted nineteen campers. Most sat alone at their respective tables—Sherman Yang for Ares; a girl I did not know for Aphrodite; another girl for Demeter. At the Nike table, two dark-haired young ladies who were obviously twins conversed over a war map. Chiron himself, again in full centaur form, stood at the head table, sipping his bug juice as he chatted with two satyrs, but their mood was subdued. The goat-men kept glancing at me, then eating their silverware, as satyrs tend to do when nervous. Half a dozen gorgeous dryads moved between the tables, offering food and drink, but I was so preoccupied I couldn't fully appreciate their beauty. Even more tragic: I felt too embarrassed to flirt with them. What was *wrong* with me?

I studied the campers, hoping to spot some potential servants . . . I mean new friends. Gods always like to keep a few strong veteran demigods handy to throw into battle, send on dangerous quests, or pick the lint off our togas. Unfortunately, no one at dinner jumped out at me as a likely minion. I longed for a bigger pool of talent.

"Where are the . . . others?" I asked Will.

I wanted to say *the A-List*, but I thought that might be taken the wrong way.

Will took a bite of his pizza. "Were you looking for somebody in particular?"

"What about the ones who went on that quest with the boat?"

Will and Nico exchanged a look that might have meant, *Here we go*. I suppose they got asked a lot about the seven legendary demigods who had fought side by side with the gods against Gaea's giants. It pained me that I had not gotten to see those heroes again. After any major battle, I liked to get a group photo—along with exclusive rights to compose epic ballads about their exploits.

"Well," Nico started, "you saw Percy. He and Annabeth

are spending their senior year in New York. Hazel and Frank are at Camp Jupiter doing the Twelfth Legion thing."

"Ah, yes." I tried to bring up a clear mental picture of Camp Jupiter, the Roman enclave near Berkeley, California, but the details were hazy. I could only remember my conversations with Octavian, the way he'd turned my head with his flattery and promises. That stupid boy . . . it was his fault I was here.

A voice whispered in the back of my mind. This time I thought it might be my conscience: *Who was the stupid boy? It wasn't Octavian.*

"Shut up," I murmured.

"What?" Nico asked.

"Nothing. Continue."

"Jason and Piper are spending the school year in Los Angeles with Piper's dad. They took Coach Hedge, Mellie, and Little Chuck with them."

"Uh-huh." I did not know those last three names, so I decided they probably weren't important. "And the seventh hero . . . Leo Valdez?"

Nico raised his eyebrows. "You remember his name?"

"Of course! He invented the Valdezinator. Oh, what a musical instrument! I barely had time to master its major scales before Zeus zapped me at the Parthenon. If anyone could help me, it would be Leo Valdez."

Nico's expression tightened with annoyance. "Well, Leo isn't here. He died. Then he came back to life. And if I see him again, I'll kill him."

Will elbowed him. "No, you won't." He turned to me.

"During the fight with Gaea, Leo and his bronze dragon, Festus, disappeared in a midair fiery explosion."

I shivered. After so many centuries driving the sun chariot, the term *midair fiery explosion* did not sit well with me.

I tried to remember the last time I'd seen Leo Valdez on Delos, when he'd traded the Valdezinator for information. . . .

"He was looking for the physician's cure," I recalled, "the way to bring someone back from the dead. I suppose he planned all along to sacrifice himself?"

"Yep," Will said. "He got rid of Gaea in the explosion, but we all assumed he died too."

"Because he *did*," Nico said.

"Then, a few days later," Will continued, "this scroll came fluttering into camp on the wind. . . ."

"I still have it." Nico rummaged through the pockets of his bomber jacket. "I look at it whenever I want to get angry."

He produced a thick parchment scroll. As soon as he spread it on the table, a flickering hologram appeared above the surface: Leo Valdez, looking impish as usual with his dark wispy hair, his mischievous grin, and his diminutive stature. (Of course, the hologram was only three inches tall, but even in real life Leo was not much more imposing.) His jeans, blue work shirt, and tool belt were speckled with machine oil.

"Hey, guys!" Leo spread his arms for a hug. "Sorry to leave you like that. Bad news: I died. Good news: I got better! I had to go rescue Calypso. We're both fine now. We're taking Festus to—" The image guttered like a flame in a strong breeze, disrupting Leo's voice. "Back as soon as—" Static. "Cook tacos when—" More static. "*¡Vaya con queso! Love ya!*" The image winked out.

"That's all we got," Nico complained. "And that was in August. We have no idea what he was planning, where he is now, or whether he's still safe. Jason and Piper spent most of September looking for him until Chiron finally insisted they go start their school year."

"Well," I said, "it sounds like Leo was planning to cook tacos. Perhaps that took longer than he anticipated. And *vaya con queso* . . . I believe he is admonishing us to *go with cheese*, which is always sound advice."

This did not seem to reassure Nico.

"I don't like being in the dark," he muttered.

An odd complaint for a child of Hades, but I understood what he meant. I, too, was curious to know the fate of Leo Valdez. Once upon a time, I could have divined his whereabouts as easily as you might check a Facebook timeline, but now I could only stare at the sky and wonder when a small impish demigod might appear with a bronze dragon and a plate of tacos.

And if Calypso was involved . . . that complicated things. The sorceress and I had a rocky history, but even I had to admit she was beguiling. If she'd captured Leo's heart, it was entirely possible he had gotten sidetracked. Odysseus spent seven years with her before returning home.

Whatever the case, it seemed unlikely that Valdez would be back in time to help me. My quest to master the Valdezinator's arpeggios would have to wait.

Kayla and Austin had been very quiet, following our

conversation with wonder and amazement. (My words have that effect on people.)

Now Kayla scooted toward me. "What did you guys talk about in the Big House? Chiron told you about the disappearances . . . ?"

"Yes." I tried to avoid looking in the direction of the woods. "We discussed the situation."

"And?" Austin spread his fingers on the table. "What's going on?"

I didn't want to talk about it. I didn't want them to see my fear.

I wished my head would stop pounding. On Olympus, headaches were so much easier to cure. Hephaestus simply split one's skull open and extracted whatever newborn god or goddess happened to be banging around in there. In the mortal world, my options were more limited.

"I need time to think about it," I said. "Perhaps in the morning I'll have some of my godly powers back."

Austin leaned forward. In the torchlight, his cornrows seemed to twist into new DNA patterns. "Is that how it works? Your strength comes back over time?"

"I—I think so." I tried to remember my years of servitude with Admetus and Laomedon, but I could barely conjure their names and faces. My contracting memory terrified me. It made each moment of the present balloon in size and importance, reminding me that time for mortals was limited.

"I have to get stronger," I decided. "I *must*."

Kayla squeezed my hand. Her archer's fingers were rough

and calloused. "It's okay, Apollo . . . Dad. We'll help you."

Austin nodded. "Kayla's right. We're in this together. If anybody gives you trouble, Kayla will shoot them. Then I'll curse them so bad they'll be speaking in rhyming couplets for weeks."

My eyes watered. Not so long ago—like this morning, for instance—the idea of these young demigods being able to help me would have struck me as ridiculous. Now their kindness moved me more than a hundred sacrificial bulls. I couldn't recall the last time someone had cared about me enough to curse my enemies with rhyming couplets.

"Thank you," I managed.

I could not add *my children*. It didn't seem right. These demigods were my protectors and my family, but for the present I could not think of myself as their father. A father should do more—a father should give more to his children than he takes. I have to admit that this was a novel idea for me. It made me feel even worse than before.

"Hey . . ." Will patted my shoulder. "It's not so bad. At least with everybody being on high alert, we might not have to do Harley's obstacle course tomorrow."

Kayla muttered an ancient Greek curse. If I had been a *proper* godly father, I would have washed her mouth out with olive oil.

"I forgot all about that," she said. "They'll *have* to cancel it, won't they?"

I frowned. "What obstacle course? Chiron mentioned nothing about this."

I wanted to object that my entire day had been an

obstacle course. Surely they couldn't expect me to do their camp activities as well. Before I could say as much, one of the satyrs blew a conch horn at the head table.

Chiron raised his arms for attention.

"Campers!" His voice filled the pavilion. He could be quite impressive when he wanted to be. "I have a few announcements, including news about tomorrow's three-legged death race!"

13

Three-legged death race
Five terrible syllables
Oh, gods. Please not Meg

IT WAS ALL HARLEY'S FAULT.

After addressing the disappearance of Miranda Gardiner—"As a precautionary measure, please stay away from the woods until we know more"—Chiron called forward the young son of Hephaestus to explain how the three-legged death race would work. It quickly became apparent that Harley had masterminded the whole project. And, really, the idea was so horrifying, it could only have sprung from the mind of an eight-year-old boy.

I confess I lost track of the specifics after he explained the exploding chain-saw Frisbees.

"And they'll be like, ZOOM!" He bounced up and down with excitement. "And then BUZZ! And POW!" He pantomimed all sorts of chaos with his hands. "You have to be really quick or you'll die, and it's awesome!"

The other campers grumbled and shifted on their benches.

Chiron raised his hand for silence. "Now, I know there were problems last time," he said, "but fortunately our healers in the Apollo cabin were able to reattach Paolo's arms."

At a table in back, a muscular teen boy rose and began ranting in what I thought was Portuguese. He wore a white tank top over his dark chest, and I could see faint white scars around the tops of his biceps. Cursing rapidly, he pointed at Harley, the Apollo cabin, and pretty much everyone else.

"Ah, thank you, Paolo," Chiron said, clearly baffled. "I'm glad you are feeling better."

Austin leaned toward me and whispered, "Paolo understands English okay, but he only speaks Portuguese. At least, that's what he claims. None of us can understand a word he says."

I didn't understand Portuguese either. Athena had been lecturing us for years about how Mount Olympus might migrate to Brazil someday, and we should all be prepared for the possibility. She'd even bought the gods Berlitz Portuguese DVDs for Saturnalia presents, but what does Athena know?

"Paolo seems agitated," I noted.

Will shrugged. "He's lucky he's a fast healer—son of Hebe, goddess of youth, and all that."

"You're staring," Nico noted.

"I am not," Will said. "I am merely assessing how well Paolo's arms are functioning after surgery."

"Hmph."

Paolo finally sat down. Chiron went through a long list of other injuries they had experienced during the first three-legged death race, all of which he hoped to avoid this time: second-degree burns, burst eardrums, a pulled groin, and two cases of chronic Irish step dancing.

The lone demigod at the Athena table raised his hand.

"Chiron, just going to throw this out there. . . . We've had three campers disappear. Is it really wise to be running a dangerous obstacle course?"

Chiron gave him a pained smile. "An excellent question, Malcolm, but this course will not take you into the woods, which we believe is the most hazardous area. The satyrs, dryads, and I will continue to investigate the disappearances. We will not rest until our missing campers are found. In the meantime, however, this three-legged race can foster important team-building skills. It also expands our understanding of the Labyrinth."

The word smacked me in the face like Ares's body odor. I turned to Austin. "The Labyrinth? As in *Daedalus's* Labyrinth?"

Austin nodded, his fingers worrying the ceramic camp beads around his neck. I had a sudden memory of his mother, Latricia—the way she used to fiddle with her cowry necklace when she lectured at Oberlin. Even *I* learned things from Latricia Lake's music theory class, though I had found her distractingly beautiful.

"During the war with Gaea," Austin said, "the maze reopened. We've been trying to map it ever since."

"That's impossible," I said. "Also insane. The Labyrinth is a malevolent sentient creation! It can't be mapped or trusted."

As usual, I could only draw on random bits and pieces of my memories, but I was fairly certain I spoke the truth. I remembered Daedalus. Back in the old days, the king of Crete had ordered him to build a maze to contain the monstrous Minotaur. But, oh no, a simple maze wasn't *good* enough for a brilliant inventor like Daedalus. He had to make his Labyrinth self-aware and self-expanding. Over the centuries, it had honeycombed under the planet's surface like an invasive root system.

Stupid brilliant inventors.

"It's different now," Austin told me. "Since Daedalus died . . . I don't know. It's hard to describe. Doesn't feel so evil. Not quite as deadly."

"Oh, that's hugely reassuring. So of course you decided to do three-legged races through it."

Will coughed. "The other thing, Dad . . . Nobody wants to disappoint Harley."

I glanced at the head table. Chiron was still holding forth about the virtues of team building while Harley bounced up and down. I could see why the other campers might adopt the boy as their unofficial mascot. He was a cute little pip-squeak, even if he was scarily buff for an eight-year-old. His grin was infectious. His enthusiasm seemed to lift the mood of the entire group. Still, I recognized the mad gleam in his eyes. It was the same look his father, Hephaestus, got whenever he invented some automaton that would later go berserk and start destroying cities.

"Also keep in mind," Chiron was saying, "that none of the unfortunate disappearances has been linked to the Labyrinth. Remain with your partner and you should be safe . . . at least, as safe as one can be in a three-legged death race."

"Yeah," Harley said. "Nobody has even *died* yet." He sounded disappointed, as if he wanted us to try harder.

"In the face of a crisis," Chiron said, "it's important to

stick to our regular activities. We must stay alert and in top condition. Our missing campers would expect no less from us. Now, as to the teams for the race, you will be allowed to choose your partner—"

There followed a sort of piranha attack of campers lunging toward each other to grab their preferred teammate. Before I could contemplate my options, Meg McCaffrey pointed at me from across the pavilion, her expression exactly like Uncle Sam's in the recruitment poster.

Of course, I thought. Why should my luck improve now?

Chiron struck his hoof against the floor. "All right, everyone, settle down! The race will be tomorrow afternoon. Thank you, Harley, for your hard work on the . . . um, various lethal surprises in store."

"BLAM!" Harley ran back to the Hephaestus table to join his older sister, Nyssa.

"This brings us to our other news," Chiron said. "As you may have heard, two special newcomers joined us today. First, please welcome the god Apollo!"

Normally this was my cue to stand up, spread my arms, and grin as radiant light shone around me. The adoring crowd would applaud and toss flowers and chocolate bonbons at my feet.

This time I received no applause—just nervous looks. I had a strange, uncharacteristic impulse to slide lower in my seat and pull my coat over my head. I restrained myself through heroic effort.

Chiron struggled to maintain his smile. "Now, I know this is unusual," he said, "but gods *do* become mortal from time to time. You should not be overly alarmed. Apollo's presence among us could be a good omen, a chance for us to . . ." He seemed to lose track of his own argument. "Ah . . . do something good. I'm sure the best course of action will become clear in time. For now, please make Apollo feel at home. Treat him as you would any other new camper."

At the Hermes table, Connor Stoll raised his hand. "Does that mean the Ares cabin should stick Apollo's head in a toilet?"

At the Ares table, Sherman Yang snorted. "We don't do that to everyone, Connor. Just the newbies who deserve it."

Sherman glanced at Meg, who was obliviously finishing her last hot dog. The wispy black whiskers at the sides of her mouth were now frosted with mustard.

Connor Stoll grinned back at Sherman—a conspiratorial look if ever I saw one. That's when I noticed the open backpack at Connor's feet. Peeking from the top was something that looked like a net.

The implication sank in: two boys whom Meg had humiliated, preparing for payback. I didn't have to be Nemesis to understand the allure of revenge. Still . . . I felt an odd desire to warn Meg.

I tried to catch her eye, but she remained focused on her dinner.

"Thank you, Sherman," Chiron continued. "It's good to know you won't be giving the god of archery a swirly. As for the rest of you, we will keep you posted on our guest's situation. I'm sending two of our finest satyrs, Millard and Herbert"—he gestured to the satyrs on his left—"to hand-deliver a message to Rachel Dare in New York. With any luck, she will be able to join us soon and help determine how we can best assist Apollo."

There was some grumbling about this. I caught the words *Oracle* and *prophecies*. At a nearby table, a girl muttered to herself in Italian: *The blind leading the blind.*

I glared at her, but the young lady was quite beautiful. She was perhaps two years older than I (mortally speaking), with dark pixie hair and devastatingly fierce almond eyes. I may have blushed.

I turned back to my tablemates. "Um . . . yes, satyrs. Why not send that other satyr, the friend of Percy's?"

"Grover?" Nico asked. "He's in California. The whole Council of Cloven Elders is out there, meeting about the drought."

"Oh." My spirits fell. I remembered Grover as being quite resourceful, but if he was dealing with California's natural disasters, he was unlikely to be back anytime in the next decade.

"Finally," Chiron said, "we welcome a new demigod to camp—Meg McCaffrey!"

She wiped her mouth and stood.

Next to her, Alice Miyazawa said, "Stand up, Meg."

Julia Feingold laughed.

At the Ares table, Sherman Yang rose. "Now *this* one—this one deserves a special welcome. What do you think, Connor?"

Connor reached into his backpack. "I think maybe the canoe lake."

I started to say, "Meg—"

Then all Hades broke loose.

Sherman Yang strode toward Meg. Connor Stoll pulled out a golden net and threw it over her head. Meg yelped and tried to squirm free, while some of the campers chanted, "Dunk—her! Dunk—her!" Chiron did his best to shout them down: "Now, demigods, wait a moment!"

A guttural howl interrupted the proceedings. From the top of the colonnade, a blur of chubby flesh, leafy wings, and linen diaper hurtled downward and landed on Sherman Yang's back, knocking him face-first into the stone floor. Peaches the karpos stood and wailed, beating his chest. His eyes glowed green with anger. He launched himself at Connor Stoll, locked his plump legs around the demigod's neck, and began pulling out Connor's hair with his claws.

"Get it off!" Connor wailed, thrashing blindly around the pavilion. "Get it off!"

Slowly the other demigods overcame their shock. Several drew swords.

"*C'è un karpos!*" yelled the Italian girl.

"Kill it!" said Alice Miyazawa.

"No!" I cried.

Normally such a command from me would've initiated a prison lockdown situation, with all the mortals dropping to their bellies to await my further orders. Alas, now I was a mere mortal with a squeaky adolescent voice.

I watched in horror as my own daughter Kayla nocked an arrow in her bow.

"Peaches, get off him!" Meg screamed. She untangled herself from the net, threw it down, then ran toward Connor.

The karpos hopped off Connor's neck. He landed at

Meg's feet, baring his fangs and hissing at the other campers who had formed a loose semicircle with weapons drawn.

"Meg, get out of the way," said Nico di Angelo. "That thing is dangerous."

"No!" Meg's voice was shrill. "Don't kill him!"

Sherman Yang rolled over, groaning. His face looked worse than it probably was—a gash on the forehead can produce a shocking amount of blood—but the sight steeled the resolve of the other campers. Kayla drew her bow. Julia Feingold unsheathed a dagger.

"Wait!" I pleaded.

What happened next, a lesser mind could never have processed.

Julia charged. Kayla shot her arrow.

Meg thrust out her hands and faint gold light flashed between her fingers. Suddenly young McCaffrey was holding two swords—each a curved blade in the old Thracian style, *siccae* made from Imperial gold. I had not seen such weapons since the fall of the Rome. They seemed to have appeared from nowhere, but my long experience with magic items told me they must have been summoned from the crescent rings Meg always wore.

Both her blades whirled. Meg simultaneously sliced Kayla's arrow out of the air and disarmed Julia, sending her dagger skittering across the floor.

"What the Hades?" Connor demanded. His hair had been pulled out in chunks so he looked like an abused doll. "Who *is* this kid?"

Peaches crouched at Meg's side, snarling, as Meg fended off the confused and enraged demigods with her two swords.

My vision must have been better than the average mortal's, because I saw the glowing sign first—a light shining above Meg's head.

When I recognized the symbol, my heart turned to lead. I hated what I saw, but I thought I should point it out. "Look."

The others seemed confused. Then the glow became brighter: a holographic golden sickle with a few sheaves of wheat, rotating just above Meg McCaffrey.

A boy in the crowd gasped. "She's a communist!"

A girl who'd been sitting at Cabin Four's table gave him a disgusted sneer. "No, Damien, that's my *mom's* symbol." Her face went slack as the truth sank in. "Uh, which means . . . it's *her* mom's symbol."

My head spun. I did not want this knowledge. I did not want to serve a demigod with Meg's parentage. But now I understood the crescents on Meg's rings. They were not moons; they were sickle blades. As the only Olympian present, I felt I should make her title official.

"My friend is no longer unclaimed," I announced.

The other demigods knelt in respect, some more reluctantly than others.

"Ladies and gentlemen," I said, my voice as bitter as Chiron's tea, "please give it up for Meg McCaffrey, daughter of Demeter."

14

You've got to be kid—
Well, crud, what just happened there?
I ran out of syl—

NO ONE KNEW WHAT TO MAKE OF MEG.

I couldn't blame them.

The girl made even less sense to me now that I knew who her mother was.

I'd had my suspicions, yes, but I'd hoped to be proven wrong. Being right so much of the time was a terrible burden.

Why would I dread a child of Demeter?

Good question.

Over the past day, I had been doing my best to piece together my remembrances of the goddess. Once Demeter had been my favorite aunt. That first generation of gods could be a stuffy bunch (I'm looking at you, Hera, Hades, Dad), but Demeter had always been a kind and loving presence—except when she was destroying mankind through pestilence and famine, but everyone has their bad days.

Then I made the mistake of dating one of her daughters. I think her name was Chrysothemis, but you'll have to excuse me if I'm wrong. Even when I was a god, I had trouble remembering the names of all my exes. The young woman sang a harvest song at one of my Delphic festivals. Her voice was so beautiful, I fell in love. True, I fell in love with each year's winner and the runners-up, but what can I say? I'm a sucker for a melodious voice.

Demeter did not approve. Ever since her daughter Persephone was kidnapped by Hades, she'd been a little touchy about her children dating gods.

At any rate, she and I had words. We reduced a few mountains to rubble. We laid waste to a few city-states. You know how family arguments can get. Finally we settled into an uneasy truce, but ever since then I'd made a point to steer clear of Demeter's children.

Now here I was—a servant to Meg McCaffrey, the most ragamuffin daughter of Demeter ever to swing a sickle.

I wondered who Meg's father had been to attract the attention of the goddess. Demeter rarely fell in love with mortals. Meg was unusually powerful, too. Most children of Demeter could do little more than make crops grow and keep bacterial fungi at bay. Dual-wielding golden blades and summoning karpoi—that was top-shelf stuff.

All of this went through my mind as Chiron dispersed the crowd, urging everyone to put away their weapons. Since head counselor Miranda Gardiner was missing, Chiron asked Billie Ng, the only other camper from Demeter, to escort Meg to Cabin Four. The two girls made a quick retreat, Peaches bouncing along excitedly behind them. Meg shot me a worried look.

Not sure what else to do, I gave her two thumbs-up. "See you tomorrow!"

She seemed less than encouraged as she disappeared in the darkness.

Will Solace tended to Sherman Yang's head injuries. Kayla and Austin stood over Connor, debating the need for a hair graft. This left me alone to make my way back to the Me cabin.

I lay on my sick cot in the middle of the room and stared at the ceiling beams. I thought again about what a depressingly simple, utterly mortal place this was. How did my children stand it? Why did they not keep a blazing altar, and decorate the walls with hammered gold reliefs celebrating my glory?

When I heard Will and the others coming back, I closed my eyes and pretended to be asleep. I could not face their questions or kindnesses, their attempts to make me feel at home when I clearly did not belong.

As they came in the door, they got quiet.

"Is he okay?" whispered Kayla.

Austin said, "Would you be, if you were him?"

A moment of silence.

"Try to get some sleep, guys," Will advised.

"This is crazy weird," Kayla said. "He looks so . . . human."

"We'll watch out for him," Austin said. "We're all he's got now."

I held back a sob. I couldn't bear their concern. Not being able to reassure them, or even disagree with them, made me feel very small.

A blanket was draped over me.

Will said, "Sleep well, Apollo."

Perhaps it was his persuasive voice, or the fact that I was more exhausted than I had been in centuries. Immediately, I drifted into unconsciousness.

Thank the remaining eleven Olympians, I had no dreams.

I woke in the morning feeling strangely refreshed. My chest no longer hurt. My nose no longer felt like a water balloon attached to my face. With the help of my offspring (*cabin mates*—I will call them cabin mates), I managed to master the arcane mysteries of the shower, the toilet, and the sink. The toothbrush was a shock. The last time I was mortal, there had been no such thing. And underarm deodorant—what a ghastly idea that I should need enchanted salve to keep my armpits from producing stench!

When I was done with my morning ablutions and dressed in clean clothes from the camp store—sneakers, jeans, an orange Camp Half-Blood T-shirt, and a comfy winter coat of flannel wool—I felt almost optimistic. Perhaps I could survive this human experience.

I perked up even more when I discovered bacon.

Oh, gods—bacon! I promised myself that once I achieved immortality again, I would assemble the Nine Muses and together we would create an ode, a hymnal to the power of bacon, which would move the heavens to tears and cause rapture across the universe.

Bacon is good.

Yes—that may be the title of the song: "Bacon Is Good."

Seating for breakfast was less formal than dinner. We filled our trays at a buffet line and were allowed to sit wherever we wished. I found this delightful. (Oh, what a sad commentary on my new mortal mind that I, who once dictated the course of nations, should get excited about open seating.) I took my tray and found Meg, who was sitting by herself on the edge of the pavilion's retaining wall, dangling her feet over the side and watching the waves at the beach.

"How are you?" I asked.

Meg nibbled on a waffle. "Yeah. Great."

"You are a powerful demigod, daughter of Demeter."

"Mm-hm."

If I could trust my understanding of human responses, Meg did not seem thrilled.

"Your cabin mate, Billie . . . Is she nice?"

"Sure. All good."

"And Peaches?"

She looked at me sideways. "Disappeared overnight. Guess he only shows up when I'm in danger."

"Well, that's an appropriate time for him to show up."

"Ap-pro-pri-ate." Meg touched a waffle square for each syllable. "Sherman Yang had to get seven stitches."

I glanced over at Sherman, who sat at a safe distance across the pavilion, glaring daggers at Meg. A nasty red zigzag ran down the side of his face.

"I wouldn't worry," I told Meg. "Ares's children like scars. Besides, Sherman wears the Frankenstein look rather well."

The corner of her mouth twitched, but her gaze remained far away. "Our cabin has a grass floor—like, *green* grass. There's a huge oak tree in the middle, holding up the ceiling."

"Is that bad?"

"I have allergies."

"Ah . . ." I tried to imagine the tree in her cabin. Once upon a time, Demeter had had a sacred grove of oaks. I remembered she'd gotten quite angry when a mortal prince tried to cut it down.

A sacred grove . . .

Suddenly the bacon in my stomach expanded, wrapping around my organs.

Meg gripped my arm. Her voice was a distant buzz. I only heard the last, most important word: "—Apollo?"

I stirred. "What?"

"You blanked out." She scowled. "I said your name six times."

"You did?"

"Yeah. Where did you go?"

I could not explain. I felt as if I'd been standing on the deck of a ship when an enormous, dark, and dangerous shape passed beneath the hull—a shape almost discernible, then simply gone.

"I—I don't know. Something about trees. . . ."

"Trees," Meg said.

"It's probably nothing."

It *wasn't* nothing. I couldn't shake the image from my dreams: the crowned woman urging me to find the gates. That woman wasn't Demeter—at least, I didn't think so. But the idea of sacred trees stirred a memory within me . . . something very old, even by *my* standards.

I didn't want to talk about this with Meg, not until I'd had time to reflect. She had enough to worry about. Besides, after last night, my new young master made me more apprehensive than ever.

I glanced at the rings on her middle fingers. "So yesterday . . . those swords. And don't do that thing."

Meg's eyebrows furrowed. "What thing?"

"That thing where you shut down and refuse to talk. Your face turns to cement."

She gave me a furious pout. "It does not. I've got swords. I fight with them. So what?"

"So it might have been nice to know that earlier, when we were in combat with plague spirits."

"You said it yourself: those spirits couldn't be killed."

"You're sidestepping." I knew this because it was a tactic I had mastered centuries ago. "The style you fight in, with two curved blades, is the style of a *dimachaerus*, a gladiator from the late Roman Empire. Even back then, it was rare— possibly the most difficult fighting style to master, and one of the most deadly."

Meg shrugged. It was an eloquent shrug, but it did not offer much in the way of explanation.

"Your swords are Imperial gold," I said. "That would indicate *Roman* training, and mark you as a good prospect for Camp Jupiter. Yet your mother is Demeter, the goddess in her Greek form, not Ceres."

"How do you know?"

"Aside from the fact that I was a god? Demeter claimed you here at Camp Half-Blood. That was no accident. Also, her older Greek form is much more powerful. You, Meg, are powerful."

Her expression turned so guarded I expected Peaches to hurtle from the sky and start pulling out chunks of my hair.

"I never met my mom," she said. "I didn't know who she was."

"Then where did you get the swords? Your father?"

Meg tore her waffle into tiny pieces. "No. . . . My step-dad raised me. He gave me these rings."

"Your stepfather. Your stepfather gave you rings that turn into Imperial golden swords. What sort of man—"

"A good man," she snapped.

I noted the steel in Meg's voice and let the subject rest. I sensed a great tragedy in her past. Also, I feared that if I pressed my questions, I might find those golden blades at my neck.

"I'm sorry," I said.

"Mm-hm." Meg tossed a piece of waffle into the air. Out of nowhere, one of the camp's cleaning harpies swooped down like a two-hundred-pound kamikaze chicken, snatched up the food, and flew away.

Meg continued as if nothing had happened. "Let's just get through today. We've got the race after lunch."

A shiver ran down my neck. The last thing I wanted was to be strapped to Meg McCaffrey in the Labyrinth, but I managed to avoid screaming.

"Don't worry about the race," I said. "I have a plan for how to win it."

She raised an eyebrow. "Yeah?"

"Or rather, I *will* have a plan by this afternoon. All I need is a little time—"

Behind us, the conch horn blew.

"Morning boot camp!" Sherman Yang bellowed. "Let's go, you special snowflakes! I want you all in tears by lunchtime!"

15

Practice makes perfect
Ha, ha, ha, I don't think so
Ignore my sobbing

I WISHED I HAD A DOCTOR'S NOTE. I wanted to be excused from PE.

Honestly, I will never understand you mortals. You try to maintain good physical shape with push-ups, sit-ups, five-mile runs, obstacle courses, and other hard work that involves sweating. All the while, you know it is a losing battle. Eventually your weak, limited-use bodies will deteriorate and fail, giving you wrinkles, sagging parts, and old-person breath.

It's horrific! If I want to change shape, or age, or gender, or species, I simply wish it to happen and—*ka-bam!*—I am a young, large, female three-toed sloth. No amount of push-ups will accomplish that. I simply don't see the logic in your constant struggles. Exercise is nothing more than a depressing reminder that one is not a god.

By the end of Sherman Yang's boot camp, I was gasping and drenched in sweat. My muscles felt like quivering columns of gelatinous dessert.

I did *not* feel like a special snowflake (though my

mother, Leto, always assured me I was one), and I was sorely tempted to accuse Sherman of not treating me as such.

I grumbled about this to Will. I asked where the old head counselor of Ares had gone. Clarisse La Rue I could at least charm with my dazzling smile. Alas, Will reported she was attending the University of Arizona. Oh, why does college have to happen to perfectly good people?

After the torture, I staggered back to my cabin and took another shower.

Showers are good. Perhaps not as good as bacon, but good.

My second morning session was painful for a different reason. I was assigned to music lessons in the amphitheater with a satyr named Woodrow.

Woodrow seemed nervous to have me join his little class. Perhaps he had heard the legend about my skinning the satyr Marsyas alive after he challenged me to a music contest. (As I said, the flaying part was *totally* untrue, but rumors do have amazing staying power, especially when I may have been guilty of spreading them.)

Using his panpipe, Woodrow reviewed the minor scales. Austin had no problem with these, even though he was challenging himself by playing the violin, which was not his instrument. Valentina Diaz, a daughter of Aphrodite, did her best to throttle a clarinet, producing sounds like a basset hound whimpering in a thunderstorm. Damien White, son of Nemesis, lived up to his namesake by wreaking vengeance on an acoustic guitar. He played with such force that he broke the D string.

"You killed it!" said Chiara Benvenuti. She was the pretty Italian girl I'd noticed the night before—a child of Tyche, goddess of good fortune. "I needed to use that guitar!"

"Shut up, Lucky," Damien muttered. "In the *real* world, accidents happen. Strings snap sometimes."

Chiara unleashed some rapid-fire Italian that I decided not to translate.

"May I?" I reached for the guitar.

Damien reluctantly handed it over. I leaned toward the guitar case by Woodrow's feet. The satyr leaped several inches into the air.

Austin laughed. "Relax, Woodrow. He's just getting another string."

I'll admit I found the satyr's reaction gratifying. If I could still scare satyrs, perhaps there was hope for me reclaiming some of my former glory. From here I could work my way up to scaring farm animals, then demigods, monsters, and minor deities.

In a matter of seconds, I had replaced the string. It felt good to do something so familiar and simple. I adjusted the pitch, but stopped when I realized Valentina was sobbing.

"That was so beautiful!" She wiped a tear from her cheek. "What was that song?"

I blinked. "It's called tuning."

"Yeah, Valentina, control yourself," Damien chided, though his eyes were red. "It wasn't *that* beautiful."

"No." Chiara sniffled. "It wasn't."

Only Austin seemed unaffected. His eyes shone with what looked like pride, though I didn't understand why he would feel that way.

I played a C minor scale. The B string was flat. It's *always* the B string. Three thousand years since I invented the guitar (during a wild party with the Hittites—long story), and I still couldn't figure out how to make a B string that stays in tune.

I ran through the other scales, delighted that I still remembered them.

"Now this is a Lydian progression," I said. "It starts on the fourth of the major scale. They say it's called Lydian after the old kingdom of Lydia, but actually, I named it for an old girlfriend of mine, Lydia. She was the fourth woman I dated that year, so . . ."

I looked up mid-arpeggio. Damien and Chiara were weeping in each other's arms, hitting each other weakly and cursing, "I hate you. I hate you."

Valentina lay on the amphitheater bench, silently shaking. Woodrow was pulling apart his panpipes.

"I'm worthless!" he sobbed. "Worthless!"

Even Austin had a tear in his eye. He gave me a thumbs-up.

I was thrilled that some of my old skill remained intact, but I imagined Chiron would be annoyed if I drove the entire music class into major depression.

I pulled the D string slightly sharp—a trick I used to use to keep my adoring fans from exploding in rapture at my concerts. (And I mean literally exploding. Some of those gigs at the Fillmore in the 1960s . . . well, I'll spare you the gruesome details.)

I strummed a chord that was intentionally out of tune. To me it sounded awful, but the campers stirred from their misery. They sat up, wiped their tears, and watched in fascination as I played a simple one-four-five progression.

"Yeah, man." Austin brought his violin to his chin and began to improvise. His resin bow danced across the strings. He and I locked eyes, and for a moment we were more than family. We became part of the music, communicating on a level only gods and musicians will ever understand.

Woodrow broke the spell.

"That's amazing," the satyr sobbed. "You two should be teaching the class. What was I thinking? Please don't flay me!"

"My dear satyr," I said, "I would never—"

Suddenly, my fingers spasmed. I dropped the guitar in surprise. The instrument tumbled down the stone steps of the amphitheater, clanging and *sproinging*.

Austin lowered his bow. "You okay?"

"I . . . yes, of course."

But I was not okay. For a few moments, I had experienced the bliss of my formerly easy talent. Yet, clearly, my new mortal fingers were not up to the task. My hand muscles were sore. Red lines dug into my finger pads where I had touched the fret board. I had overextended myself in other ways, too. My lungs felt shriveled, drained of oxygen, even though I had done no singing.

"I'm . . . tired," I said, dismayed.

"Well, yeah." Valentina nodded. "The way you were playing was *unreal*!"

"It's okay, Apollo," Austin said. "You'll get stronger. When demigods use their powers, especially at first, they get tired quickly."

"But I'm not . . ."

I couldn't finish the sentence. I wasn't a demigod. I wasn't a god. I wasn't even myself. How could I ever play music again, knowing that I was a flawed instrument? Each note would bring me nothing but pain and exhaustion. My B string would *never* be in tune.

My misery must have shown on my face.

Damien White balled his fists. "Don't you worry, Apollo. It's not your fault. I'll make that stupid guitar pay for this!"

I didn't try to stop him as he marched down the stairs. Part of me took perverse satisfaction in the way he stomped the guitar until it was reduced to kindling and wires.

Chiara huffed. "*Idiota!* Now I'll never get my turn!"

Woodrow winced. "Well, um . . . thanks, everyone! Good class!"

Archery was an even bigger travesty.

If I ever become a god again (no, not if; *when, when*), my first act will be to wipe the memories of everyone who saw me embarrass myself in that class. I hit one bull's-eye. *One*. The grouping on my other shots was abysmal. Two arrows actually hit *outside* the black ring at a mere one hundred meters. I threw down my bow and wept with shame.

Kayla was our class instructor, but her patience and kindness only made me feel worse. She scooped up my bow and offered it back to me.

"Apollo," she said, "those shots were fantastic. A little more practice and—"

"I'm the god of archery!" I wailed. "I don't practice!"

Next to me, the daughters of Nike snickered.

They had the insufferably appropriate names Holly and Laurel Victor. They reminded me of the gorgeous, ferociously athletic African nymphs Athena used to hang out with at Lake Tritonis.

"Hey, ex-god," Holly said, nocking an arrow, "practice is the only way to improve." She scored a seven on the red ring, but she did not seem at all discouraged.

"For *you*, maybe," I said. "You're a mortal!"

Her sister, Laurel, snorted. "So are you now. Suck it up. Winners don't complain." She shot her arrow, which landed next to her sister's but just inside the red ring. "That's why I'm better than Holly. She's always complaining."

"Yeah, right," Holly growled. "The only thing I complain about is how lame *you* are."

"Oh, yeah?" said Laurel. "Let's go. Right now. Best two out of three shots. The loser scrubs the toilets for a month."

"You're on!"

Just like that, they forgot about me. They definitely would've made excellent Tritonian nymphs.

Kayla took me by the arm and led me downrange. "Those two, I swear. We made them Nike co-counselors so they'd compete with each other. If we hadn't, they would've taken over the camp by now and proclaimed a dictatorship."

I suppose she was trying to cheer me up, but I was not consoled.

I stared at my fingers, now blistered from archery as well as sore from guitar. Impossible. Agonizing.

"I can't do this, Kayla," I muttered. "I'm too old to be sixteen again!"

Kayla cupped her hand over mine. Beneath the green

shock of her hair, she had a ginger complexion—like cream painted over copper, the auburn sheen peeking through in the freckles of her face and arms. She reminded me very much of her father, the Canadian archery coach Darren Knowles.

I mean her *other* father. And, yes, of course it's possible for a demigod child to spring from such a relationship. Why not? Zeus gave birth to Dionysus out of his own thigh. Athena once had a child who was created from a handkerchief. Why should such things surprise you? We gods are capable of infinite marvels.

Kayla took a deep breath, as if preparing for an important shot. "You can do it, Dad. You're already good. *Very* good. You've just got to adjust your expectations. Be patient; be brave. You'll get better."

I was tempted to laugh. How could I get used to being merely *good*? Why would I strain myself to get better when before I had been *divine*?

"No," I said bitterly. "No, it is too painful. I swear upon the River Styx—until I am a god again, I will not use a bow or a musical instrument!"

Go ahead and chide me. I know it was a foolish oath, spoken in a moment of misery and self-pity. And it was binding. An oath sworn on the River Styx can have terrible consequences if broken.

But I didn't care. Zeus had cursed me with mortality. I was not going to pretend that everything was normal. I would not be Apollo until I was *really* Apollo. For now, I was just a stupid young man named Lester Papadopoulos. Maybe I would waste my time on skills I didn't care about—like sword fighting or badminton—but I would *not* sully the memory of my once-perfect music and archery.

Kayla stared at me in horror. "Dad, you don't mean it."

"I do!"

"Take it back! You can't . . ." She glanced over my shoulder. "What is he doing?"

I followed her gaze.

Sherman Yang was walking slowly, trancelike, into the woods.

It would have been foolhardy to run after him, straight into the most dangerous part of camp.

So that's exactly what Kayla and I did.

We almost didn't make it. As soon as we reached the tree line, the forest darkened. The temperature dropped. The horizon stretched out as if bent through a magnifying glass.

A woman whispered in my ear. This time I knew the voice well. It had never stopped haunting me. *You did this to me. Come. Chase me again.*

Fear rolled through my stomach.

I imagined the branches turning to arms; the leaves undulated like green hands.

Daphne, I thought.

Even after so many centuries, the guilt was overwhelming. I could not look at a tree without thinking of her. Forests made me nervous. The life force of each tree seemed to bear down on me with righteous hatred, accusing me of so many crimes. . . . I wanted to fall to my knees. I wanted to beg forgiveness. But this was not the time.

I couldn't allow the woods to confuse me again. I would not let anyone else fall into its trap.

Kayla didn't seem affected. I grabbed her hand to make sure we stayed together. We only had to go a few steps, but it felt like a boot camp run before we reached Sherman Yang.

"Sherman." I grabbed his arm.

He tried to shake me off. Fortunately, he was sluggish and dazed, or I would have ended up with scars of my own. Kayla helped me turn him around.

His eyes twitched as if he were in some sort of half-conscious REM sleep. "No. Ellis. Got to find him. Miranda. My girl."

I glanced at Kayla for explanation.

"Ellis is from the Ares cabin," she said. "He's one of the missing."

"Yes, but Miranda, his girl?"

"Sherman and she started dating about a week ago."

"Ah."

Sherman struggled to free himself. "Find her."

"Miranda is right over here, my friend," I lied. "We'll take you there."

He stopped fighting. His eyes rolled until only the whites were visible. "Over . . . here?"

"Yes."

"Ellis?"

"Yes, it's me," I said. "I'm Ellis."

"I love you, man," Sherman sobbed.

Still, it took all our strength to lead him out of the trees. I was reminded of the time Hephaestus and I had to wrestle the god Hypnos back to bed after he sleepwalked into Artemis's private chambers on Mount Olympus. It's a wonder any of us escaped without silver arrows pincushioning our posteriors.

We led Sherman to the archery range. Between one step and the next, he blinked his eyes and became his normal self. He noticed our hands on his arms and shook us off.

"What is this?" he demanded.

"You were walking into the woods," I said.

He gave us his drill sergeant glower. "No, I wasn't."

Kayla reached for him, then obviously thought better about it. Archery would be difficult with broken fingers. "Sherman, you were in some kind of trance. You were muttering about Ellis and Miranda."

Along Sherman's cheek, his zigzag scar darkened to bronze. "I don't remember that."

"Although you didn't mention the other missing camper," I added helpfully. "Cecil?"

"Why would I mention Cecil?" Sherman growled. "I can't stand the guy. And why should I believe you?"

"The woods had you," I said. "The trees were pulling you in."

Sherman studied the forest, but the trees looked normal again. The lengthening shadows and swaying green hands were gone.

"Look," Sherman said, "I have a head injury, thanks to your annoying friend Meg. If I was acting strange, *that's* why."

Kayla frowned. "But—"

"Enough!" Sherman snapped. "If either of you mention this, I'll make you eat your quivers. I don't need people questioning my self-control. Besides, I've got the race to think about."

He brushed past us.

"Sherman," I called.

He turned, his fists clenched.

"The last thing you remember," I said, "before you found yourself with us . . . what were you thinking about?"

For a microsecond, the dazed look passed across his face again. "About Miranda and Ellis . . . like you said. I was thinking . . . I wanted to know where they were."

"You were asking a question, then." A blanket of dread settled over me. "You wanted information."

"I . . ."

At the dining pavilion, the conch horn blew.

Sherman's expression hardened. "Doesn't matter. Drop it. We've got lunch now. Then I'm going to destroy you all in the three-legged death race."

As threats went, I had heard worse, but Sherman made it sound intimidating enough. He marched off toward the pavilion.

Kayla turned to me. "What just happened?"

"I think I understand now," I said. "I know why those campers went missing."

16

Tied to McCaffrey

We might end up in Lima

Harley is evil

NOTE TO SELF: trying to reveal important information just before a three-legged death race is not a good idea.

No one would listen to me.

Despite last night's grumbling and complaining, the campers were now buzzing with excitement. They spent their lunch hour frantically cleaning weapons, lacing armor straps, and whispering among one another to form secret alliances. Many tried to convince Harley, the course architect, to share hints about the best strategies.

Harley loved the attention. By the end of lunch, his table was piled high with offerings (read: bribes)—chocolate bars, peanut butter cups, gummy bears, and Hot Wheels. Harley would have made an excellent god. He took the gifts, mumbled a few pleasantries, but told his worshippers nothing helpful.

I tried to speak with Chiron about the dangers of the woods, but he was so frantic with last-minute race preparations that I almost got trampled just standing near him. He trotted nervously around the pavilion with a team of satyr and dryad referees in tow, comparing maps and issuing orders.

"The teams will be almost impossible to track," he murmured, his face buried in a Labyrinth schematic. "And we don't have any coverage in grid D."

"But, Chiron," I said, "if I could just—"

"The test group this morning ended up in Peru," he told the satyrs. "We can't have that happen again."

"About the woods," I said.

"Yes, I'm sorry, Apollo. I understand you are concerned—"

"The woods are actually speaking," I said. "You remember the old—"

A dryad ran up to Chiron with her dress billowing smoke. "The flares are exploding!"

"Ye gods!" Chiron said. "Those were for emergencies!"

He galloped over my feet, followed by his mob of assistants.

And so it went. When one is a god, the world hangs on your every word. When one is sixteen . . . not so much.

I tried to talk to Harley, hoping he might postpone the race, but the boy brushed me off with a simple "Nah."

As was so often the case with Hephaestus's children, Harley was tinkering with some mechanical device, moving the springs and gears around. I didn't really care what it was, but I asked Harley about it, hoping to win the boy's goodwill.

"It's a beacon," he said, adjusting a knob. "For lost people."

"You mean the teams in the Labyrinth?"

"No. You guys are on your own. This is for Leo."

"Leo Valdez."

Harley squinted at the device. "Sometimes, if you can't find your way back, a beacon can help. Just got to find the right frequency."

"And . . . how long have you been working on this?"

"Since he disappeared. Now I gotta concentrate. Can't stop the race." He turned his back on me and walked off.

I stared after him in amazement. For six months, the boy had been working on a beacon to help his missing brother Leo. I wondered if anyone would work so hard to bring me back home to Olympus. I very much doubted it.

I stood forlornly in a corner of the pavilion and ate a sandwich. I watched the sun wane in the winter sky and I thought about my chariot, my poor horses stuck in their stables with no one to take them out for a ride.

Of course, even without my help, other forces would keep the cosmos chugging along. Many different belief systems powered the revolution of the planets and stars. Wolves would still chase Sol across the sky. Ra would continue his daily journey in his sun barque. Tonatiuh would keep running on his surplus blood from human sacrifices back in the Aztec days. And that other thing—science—would still generate gravity and quantum physics and whatever.

Nevertheless, I felt like I wasn't doing my part, standing around waiting for a three-legged race.

Even Kayla and Austin were too distracted to talk with me. Kayla had told Austin about our experience rescuing

Sherman Yang from the woods, but Austin was more interested in swabbing out his saxophone.

"We can tell Chiron at dinner," he mumbled with a reed in his mouth. "Nobody's going to listen until the race is over, and we'll be staying out of the woods anyway. Besides, if I can play the right tune in the Labyrinth . . ." He got a gleam in his eyes. "Ooh. Come here, Kayla. I have an idea."

He steered her away and left me alone again.

I understood Austin's enthusiasm, of course. His saxophone skills were so formidable, I was certain he would become the foremost jazz instrumentalist of his generation, and if you think it's easy to get half a million views on YouTube playing jazz saxophone, think again. Still, his musical career was not going to happen if the force in the woods destroyed us all.

As a last resort (a *very* last resort), I sought out Meg McCaffrey.

I spotted her at one of the braziers, talking with Julia Feingold and Alice Miyazawa. Or rather, the Hermes girls were talking while Meg devoured a cheeseburger. I marveled that Demeter—the queen of grains, fruits, and vegetables—could have a daughter who was such an unrepentant carnivore.

Then again, Persephone was the same way. You'll hear stories about the goddess of springtime being all sweetness and daffodils and nibbling on pomegranate seeds, but I'm telling you, that girl was frightening when she attacked a mound of pork spareribs.

I strode over to Meg's side. The Hermes girls stepped

back as if I were a snake handler. I found this reaction pleasing.

"Hello," I said. "What are we talking about?"

Meg wiped her mouth on the back of her hand. "These two wanna know our plans for the race."

"I'm sure they do." I plucked a small magnetic listening device from Meg's coat sleeve and tossed it back to Alice.

Alice smiled sheepishly. "Can't blame us for trying."

"No, of course not," I said. "In the same spirit, I hope you won't mind what I did to your shoes. Have a good race!"

The girls shuffled off nervously, checking the soles of their sneakers.

Meg looked at me with something resembling respect. "What did you do to them?"

"Nothing," I said. "Half the trick to being a god is knowing how to bluff."

She snorted. "So what's our top secret plan? Wait. Let me guess. You don't have one."

"You're learning. Honestly, I meant to come up with one, but I got sidetracked. We have a problem."

"Sure do." From her coat pocket, she pulled two loops of bronze, like resistance bands of braided metal. "You've seen these? They wrap around our legs. Once they're on, they *stay* on until the race is over. No way to get them off. I *hate* restraints."

"I agree." I was tempted to add *especially when I am tied to a small child named Meg*, but my natural diplomacy won out. "However, I was referring to a different problem."

I told her about the incident during archery, when Sherman had almost been lured into the forest.

Meg removed her cat-eye glasses. Without the lenses, her dark irises looked softer and warmer, like tiny plots of planting soil. "You think something in the woods is calling to people?"

"I think something in the woods is *answering* people. In ancient times, there was an Oracle—"

"Yeah, you told me. Delphi."

"No. Another Oracle, even older than Delphi. It involved trees. An entire grove of talking trees."

"Talking trees." Meg's mouth twitched. "What was that Oracle called?"

"I—I can't remember." I ground my teeth. "I *should* know. I should be able to tell you instantly! But the information . . . It's almost as if it is eluding me on purpose."

"That happens sometimes," Meg said. "You'll think of it."

"But it *never* happens to me! Stupid human brain! At any rate, I believe this grove is somewhere in those woods. I don't know how or why. But the whispering voices . . . they are from this hidden Oracle. The sacred trees are trying to speak prophecies, reaching out to those with burning questions, luring them in."

Meg put her glasses back on. "You know that sounds crazy, right?"

I steadied my breathing. I had to remind myself that I was no longer a god. I had to put up with insults from mortals without being able to blast them to ashes.

"Just be on guard," I said.

"But the race doesn't even go through the woods."

"Nevertheless . . . we are not safe. If you can summon your friend Peaches, I would welcome his company."

"I told you, he sort of pops up when he feels like it. I can't—"

Chiron blew a hunting horn so loudly my vision doubled. Another pledge to myself: once I became a god again, I would descend upon this camp and take away all their horns.

"Demigods!" said the centaur. "Tie your legs together and follow me to your starting positions!"

We gathered in a meadow about a hundred yards from the Big House. Making it *that* far without a single life-threatening incident was a minor miracle. With my left leg bound to Meg's right, I felt the way I used to in Leto's womb just before my sister and I were born. And, yes, I remember that quite well. Artemis was always shoving me aside, elbowing me in the ribs and generally being a womb hog.

I said a silent prayer that if I got through this race alive, I would sacrifice a bull to myself and possibly even build myself a new temple. I am a sucker for bulls and temples.

The satyrs directed us to spread out across the meadow.

"Where is the starting line?" Holly Victor demanded, shoving her shoulder ahead of her sister's. "I want to be the closest."

"*I* want to be closest," Laurel corrected. "You can be *second* closest."

"Not to worry!" Woodrow the satyr sounded very worried. "We'll explain everything in a moment. As soon as I, um, know what to explain."

Will Solace sighed. He was, of course, tied to Nico. He

propped his elbow on Nico's shoulder as if the son of Hades were a convenient shelf. "I miss Grover. He used to organize things like this so well."

"I'd settle for Coach Hedge." Nico pushed Will's arm off. "Besides, don't talk about Grover too loudly. Juniper's right over there."

He pointed to one of the dryads—a pretty girl dressed in pale green.

"Grover's girlfriend," Will explained to me. "She misses him. A lot."

"Okay, everybody!" Woodrow shouted. "Spread out a little bit more, please! We want you to have plenty of room so, you know, if you die, you won't take down all the other teams too!"

Will sighed. "I am *so* excited."

He and Nico loped off. Julia and Alice from the Hermes cabin checked their shoes one more time, then glared at me. Connor Stoll was paired with Paolo Montes, the Brazilian son of Hebe, and neither of them seemed happy about it.

Perhaps Connor looked glum because his mangled scalp was covered in so much medicinal salve his head looked like it had been coughed up by a cat. Or perhaps he just missed his brother Travis.

As soon as Artemis and I were born, we couldn't *wait* to get some distance between us. We staked out our own territories and that was that. But I would've given anything to see her just then. I was sure Zeus had threatened her with severe punishment if she tried to help me during my time as a mortal, but she could have at least sent me a care package from Olympus—a decent toga, some magical acne cream, and maybe a dozen cranberry ambrosia scones from the Scylla Cafe. They made *excellent* scones.

I scanned the other teams. Kayla and Austin were bound together, looking like a deadly pair of street performers with her bow and his saxophone. Chiara, the cute girl from Tyche, was stuck with her nemesis, Damien White, son of . . . well, Nemesis. Billie Ng from Demeter was leg-tied with Valentina Diaz, who was hastily checking her makeup in the reflective surface of Billie's silver coat. Valentina didn't seem to notice that two twigs were sprouting from her hair like tiny deer antlers.

I decided the biggest threat would be Malcolm Pace. You can never be too careful with children of Athena. Surprisingly, though, he'd paired himself with Sherman Yang. That didn't seem like a natural partnership, unless Malcolm had some sort of plan. Those Athena children *always* had a plan. It rarely included letting me win.

The only demigods not participating were Harley and Nyssa, who had set up the course.

Once the satyrs judged we had all spread out sufficiently and our leg bindings had been double-checked, Harley clapped for our attention.

"Okay!" He bounced up and down eagerly, reminding me of the Roman children who used to cheer for executions at the Colosseum. "Here's the deal. Each team has to find three golden apples, then get back to this meadow alive."

Grumbling broke out among the demigods.

"Golden apples," I said. "I *hate* golden apples. They bring nothing but trouble."

Meg shrugged. "I like apples."

I remembered the rotten one she'd used to break Cade's nose in the alley. I wondered if perhaps she could use golden apples with the same deadly skill. Perhaps we stood a chance after all.

Laurel Victor raised her hand. "You mean the first team back wins?"

"*Any* team that gets back alive wins!" Harley said.

"That's ridiculous!" Holly said. "There can only be one winner. First team back wins!"

Harley shrugged. "Have it your way. My only rules are stay alive, and don't kill each other."

"*O quê?*" Paolo started complaining so loudly in Portuguese that Connor had to cover his left ear.

"Now, now!" Chiron called. His saddlebags were overflowing with extra first-aid kits and emergency flares. "We won't need any *help* making this a dangerous challenge. Let's have a good clean three-legged death race. And another thing, campers, given the problems our test group had this morning, please repeat after me: *Do not end up in Peru.*"

"Do not end up in Peru," everyone chanted.

Sherman Yang cracked his knuckles. "So where *is* the starting line?"

"There is no starting line," Harley said with glee. "You're all starting from right where you are."

The campers looked around in confusion. Suddenly the

meadow shook. Dark lines etched across the grass, forming a giant green checkerboard.

"Have fun!" Harley squealed.

The ground opened beneath our feet, and we fell into the Labyrinth.

17

Bowling balls of death
Rolling toward my enemies
I'll trade you problems

AT LEAST WE DID NOT LAND IN PERU.

My feet hit stone, jarring my ankles. We stumbled against a wall, but Meg provided me with a convenient cushion.

We found ourselves in a dark tunnel braced with oaken beams. The hole we'd fallen through was gone, replaced by an earthen ceiling. I saw no sign of the other teams, but from somewhere above I could vaguely hear Harley chanting, "Go! Go! Go!"

"When I get my powers back," I said, "I will turn Harley into a constellation called the Ankle Biter. At least constellations are silent."

Meg pointed down the corridor. "Look."

As my eyes adjusted, I realized the tunnel's dim light emanated from a glowing piece of fruit about thirty meters away.

"A golden apple," I said.

Meg lurched forward, pulling me with her.

"Wait!" I said. "There might be traps!"

As if to illustrate my point, Connor and Paolo emerged

from the darkness at the other end of the corridor. Paolo scooped up the golden apple and shouted, *"BRASIL!"*

Connor grinned at us. "Too slow, suckers!"

The ceiling opened above them, showering them with iron orbs the size of cantaloupes.

Connor yelped, "Run!"

He and Paolo executed an awkward one-eighty and hobbled away, hotly pursued by a rolling herd of cannon-balls with sparking fuses.

The sounds quickly faded. Without the glowing apple, we were left in total darkness.

"Great." Meg's voice echoed. "Now what?"

"I suggest we go the other direction."

That was easier said than done. Being blind seemed to bother Meg more than it did me. Thanks to my mortal body, I already felt crippled and deprived of my senses. Besides, I often relied on more than sight. Music required keen hearing. Archery required a sensitive touch and the ability to feel the direction of the wind. (Okay, sight was also helpful, but you get the idea.)

We shuffled ahead, our arms extended in front of us. I listened for suspicious clicks, snaps, or creaks that might indicate an incoming flock of explosions, but I suspected that if I *did* hear any warning signs, it would be too late.

Eventually Meg and I learned to walk with our bound legs in synchronicity. It wasn't easy. I had a flawless sense of rhythm. Meg was always a quarter beat slow or fast, which kept us veering left or right and running into walls.

We lumbered along for what might have been minutes or days. In the Labyrinth, time was deceptive.

I remembered what Austin had told me about the Labyrinth feeling different since the death of its creator. I was beginning to understand what he meant. The air seemed fresher, as if the maze hadn't been chewing up quite so many bodies. The walls didn't radiate the same malignant heat. As far as I could tell, they weren't oozing blood or slime, either, which was a definite improvement. In the old days, you couldn't take a step inside Daedalus's Labyrinth without sensing its all-consuming desire: *I will destroy your mind and your body.* Now the atmosphere was sleepier, the message not quite as virulent: *Hey, if you die in here, that's cool.*

"I never liked Daedalus," I muttered. "That old rascal didn't know when to stop. He always had to have the latest tech, the most recent updates. I *told* him not to make his maze self-aware. 'A.I. will destroy us, man,' I said. But noooo. He *had* to give the Labyrinth a malevolent consciousness."

"I don't know what you're talking about," Meg said. "But maybe you shouldn't bad-mouth the maze while we're inside it."

Once, I stopped when I heard the sound of Austin's saxophone. It was faint, echoing through so many corridors I couldn't pinpoint where it was coming from. Then it was gone. I hoped he and Kayla had found their three apples and escaped safely.

Finally, Meg and I reached a Y in the corridor. I could tell this from the flow of the air and the temperature differential against my face.

"Why'd we stop?" Meg asked.

"Shh." I listened intently.

From the right-hand corridor came a faint whining sound like a table saw. The left-hand corridor was quiet, but it exuded a faint odor that was unpleasantly familiar . . . not sulfur, exactly, but a vaporous mix of minerals from deep in the earth.

"I don't hear anything," Meg complained.

"A sawing noise to the right," I told her. "To the left, a bad smell."

"I choose the bad smell."

"Of course you do."

Meg blew me one of her trademark raspberries, then hobbled to the left, pulling me along with her.

The bronze bands around my leg began to chafe. I could feel Meg's pulse through her femoral artery, messing up my rhythm. Whenever I get nervous (which doesn't happen often), I like to hum a song to calm myself—usually Ravel's *Boléro* or the ancient Greek "Song of Seikilos." But with Meg's pulse throwing me off, the only tune I could conjure was the "Chicken Dance." That was not soothing.

We edged forward. The smell of volcanic fumes intensified. My pulse lost its perfect rhythm. My heart knocked against my chest with every *cluck, cluck, cluck, cluck* of the "Chicken Dance." I feared I knew where we were. I told myself it wasn't possible. We couldn't have walked halfway around the world. But this was the Labyrinth. Down here, distance was meaningless. The maze knew how to exploit its victims' weaknesses. Worse: it had a vicious sense of humor.

"I see light!" Meg said.

She was right. The absolute darkness had changed to

murky gray. Up ahead, the tunnel ended, joining with a narrow, lengthwise cavern like a volcanic vent. It looked as if a colossal claw had slashed across the corridor and left a wound in the earth. I had seen creatures with claws that big down in Tartarus. I did not fancy seeing them again.

"We should turn around," I said.

"That's stupid," Meg said. "Don't you see the golden glow? There's an apple in there."

All I saw were swirling plumes of ash and gas. "The glow could be lava," I said. "Or radiation. Or eyes. Glowing eyes are *never* good."

"It's an apple," Meg insisted. "I can smell apple."

"Oh, *now* you develop keen senses?"

Meg forged onward, giving me little choice but to go with. For a small girl, she was quite good at throwing her weight around. At the end of the tunnel, we found ourselves on a narrow ledge. The cliff wall opposite was only ten feet away, but the crevasse seemed to plunge downward forever. Perhaps a hundred feet above us, the jagged vent opened into a bigger chamber.

A painfully large ice cube seemed to be working its way down my throat. I had never seen this place from below, but I knew exactly where we were. We stood at the *omphalus*—the navel of the ancient world.

"You're shaking," Meg said.

I tried to cover her mouth with my hand, but she promptly bit it.

"Don't touch me," she snarled.

"*Please* be quiet."

"Why?"

"Because right above us—" My voice cracked. "Delphi. The chamber of the Oracle."

Meg's nose quivered like a rabbit's. "That's impossible."

"No, it's not," I whispered. "And if this is Delphi, that means . . ."

From overhead came a hiss so loud, it sounded as if the entire ocean had hit a frying pan and evaporated into a massive steam cloud. The ledge shook. Pebbles rained down. Above, a monstrous body slid across the crevasse, completely covering the opening. The smell of molting snakeskin seared my nostrils.

"Python." My voice was now an octave higher than Meg's. "He is here."

18

The Beast is calling
Tell him I'm not here. Let's hide
Where? In garbage. Natch

HAD I EVER BEEN SO TERRIFIED?

Perhaps when Typhon raged across the earth, scattering the gods before him. Perhaps when Gaea unleashed her giants to tear down Olympus. Or perhaps when I accidentally saw Ares naked in the gymnasium. That had been enough to turn my hair white for a century.

But I had been a god all of those times. Now I was a weak, tiny mortal cowering in the darkness. I could only pray my old enemy would not sense my presence. For once in my long glorious life, I wanted to be invisible.

Oh, why had the Labyrinth brought me here?

As soon as I thought this, I chided myself: Of *course* it would bring me where I least wanted to be. Austin had been wrong about the maze. It was still evil, designed to kill. It was just a little subtler about its homicides now.

Meg seemed oblivious to our danger. Even with an immortal monster a hundred feet above us, she had the nerve to stay on task. She elbowed me and pointed to a tiny ledge on the opposite wall, where a golden apple glowed cheerfully.

Had Harley *placed* it there? I couldn't imagine. More likely the boy had simply rolled golden apples down various corridors, trusting that they would find the most dangerous spots to roost. I was really starting to dislike that boy.

Meg whispered, "Easy jump."

I gave her a look that under different circumstances would've incinerated her. "Too dangerous."

"Apple," she hissed.

"Monster!" I hissed back.

"One."

"No!"

"Two."

"No!"

"Three." She jumped.

Which meant that I also jumped. We made the ledge, though our heels sent a spray of rubble into the chasm. Only my natural coordination and grace saved us from toppling backward to our deaths. Meg snatched up the apple.

Above us, the monster rumbled, "Who approaches?"

His voice . . . Gods above, I remembered that voice— deep and gruff, as if he breathed xenon rather than air. For all I knew, he did. Python could certainly *produce* his share of unhealthy gasses.

The monster shifted his weight. More gravel spilled into the crevasse.

I stood absolutely still, pressed against the cold face of the rock. My eardrums pulsed with every beat of my heart. I wished I could stop Meg from breathing. I wished I could stop the rhinestones on her eyeglasses from glittering.

Python had heard us. I prayed to all the gods that the monster would decide the noise was nothing. All he had to do was breathe down into the crevasse and he would kill us. There was no escaping his poisonous belch—not from this distance, not for a mortal.

Then, from the cavern above, came another voice, smaller and much closer to human. "Hello, my reptilian friend."

I nearly wept with relief. I had no idea who this newcomer was, or why he had been so foolish as to announce his presence to Python, but I always appreciated it when humans sacrificed themselves to save me. Common courtesy was not dead after all!

Python's harsh laugh shook my teeth. "Well, I was wondering if you would make the trip, Monsieur Beast."

"Don't call me that," the man snapped. "And the commute was quite easy now that the Labyrinth is back in service."

"I'm so pleased." Python's tone was dry as basalt.

I couldn't tell much about the man's voice, muffled as it was by several tons of reptile flesh, but he sounded calmer and more in control than I would have been talking to Python. I had heard the term *Beast* used to describe someone before, but as usual, my mortal brainpower failed me.

If only I'd been able to retain just the *important* information! Instead, I could tell you what I had for dessert the first time I dined with King Minos. (Spice cake.) I could tell you what color *chitons* the sons of Niobe were wearing when I slew them. (A very unflattering shade of orange.)

But I couldn't remember something as basic as whether this Beast was a wrestler, a movie star, or a politician. Possibly all three?

Next to me, in the glow of the apple, Meg seemed to have turned to bronze. Her eyes were wide with fear. A little late for that, but at least she was quiet. If I didn't know better, I might have thought the man's voice terrified her more than the monster's.

"So, Python," the man continued, "any prophetic words to share with me?"

"In time . . . my lord."

The last words were spoken with amusement, but I'm not sure anyone else would've recognized it. Aside from myself, few had been on the receiving end of Python's sarcasm and lived to tell the tale.

"I need more than your assurances," the man said. "Before we proceed, we must have *all* the Oracles under our control."

All the Oracles. Those words almost sent me off the cliff, but somehow I retained my balance.

"In time," Python said, "as we agreed. We have come this far by biding our time, yes? You did not reveal your hand when the Titans stormed New York. I did not march to war with Gaea's giants. We both realized the time for victory was not yet right. You must remain patient for a while longer."

"Don't lecture me, snake. While you slumbered, I built an empire. I have spent centuries—"

"Yes, yes." The monster exhaled, causing a tremor along

the cliff face. "And if you ever want your empire to come out of the shadows, you need to deliver on *your* side of the bargain first. When will you destroy Apollo?"

I stifled a yelp. I should not have been surprised that they were talking about me. For millennia, I had assumed that *everyone* talked about me all the time. I was so interesting they simply couldn't help it. But this business about destroying me—I didn't like that.

Meg looked more terrified than I'd ever seen her. I wanted to think she was worried for my sake, but I had a feeling she was equally concerned about herself. Again, those mixed-up demigod priorities.

The man stepped closer to the chasm. His voice became clearer and louder. "Don't worry about Apollo. He is exactly where I need him to be. He will serve our purpose, and once he is no longer useful . . ."

He did not bother finishing the statement. I was afraid it did not end with *we will give him a nice present and send him on his way.* With a chill, I recognized the voice from my dream. It was the nasal sneer of the man in the purple suit. I also had a feeling I'd heard him sing before, years and years ago, but that didn't make sense. . . . Why would I suffer through a concert given by an ugly purple-suited man who called himself the Beast? I was not even a *fan* of death metal polka!

Python shifted his bulk, showering us with more rubble. "And how exactly will you convince him to serve our purpose?"

The Beast chuckled. "I have well-placed help within

the camp who will steer Apollo toward us. Also, I have upped the stakes. Apollo will have no choice. He and the girl will open the gates."

A whiff of Python vapor floated across my nose— enough to make me dizzy, hopefully not enough to kill me.

"I trust you are right," said the monster. "Your judgment in the past has been . . . questionable. I wonder if you have chosen the right tools for this job. Have you learned from your past mistakes?"

The man snarled so deeply I could almost believe he was turning into a beast. I'd seen that happen enough times. Next to me, Meg whimpered.

"Listen here, you overgrown reptile," the man said, "my only mistake was not burning my enemies fast enough, often enough. I assure you, I am stronger than ever. My organization is everywhere. My colleagues stand ready. When we control all four Oracles, we will control fate itself!"

"And what a glorious day that will be." Python's voice was jagged with contempt. "But beforehand, you must destroy the *fifth* Oracle, yes? That is the only one I *cannot* control. You must set flame to the grove of—"

"Dodona," I said.

The word leaped unbidden from my mouth and echoed through the chasm. Of all the stupid times to retrieve a piece of information, of all the stupid times to say it aloud . . . oh, the body of Lester Papadopoulos was a terrible place to live.

Above us, the conversation stopped.

Meg hissed at me, "You idiot."

The Beast said, "What was that sound?"

Rather than answer, *Oh, that's just us,* we did something

even more foolish. One of us, Meg or me—personally, I blame her—must have slipped on a pebble. We toppled off the ledge and fell into the sulfurous clouds below.

SQUISH.

The Labyrinth most definitely had a sense of humor. Instead of allowing us to smash into a rock floor and die, the maze dropped us into a mound of wet, full garbage bags.

If you're keeping score, that was the *second* time since becoming mortal that I had crash-landed in garbage, which was two times more than any god should endure.

We tumbled down the pile in a frenzy of three-legged flailing. We landed at the bottom, covered with muck, but, miraculously, still alive.

Meg sat up, glazed in a layer of coffee grounds.

I pulled a banana peel off my head and flicked it aside. "Is there some reason you keep landing us in trash heaps?"

"Me? You're the one who lost his balance!" Meg wiped her face without much luck. In her other hand, she clutched the golden apple with trembling fingers.

"Are you all right?" I asked.

"Fine," she snapped.

Clearly that was not true. She looked as if she'd just gone through Hades's haunted house. (Pro tip: DO NOT.) Her face was pallid. She had bit her lip so hard, her teeth were pink with blood. I also detected the faint smell of urine, meaning one of us had gotten scared enough to lose bladder control, and I was seventy-five percent sure it wasn't me.

"That man upstairs," I said. "You recognized his voice?"

"Shut up. That's an order!"

I attempted to reply. To my consternation, I found that I couldn't. My voice had heeded Meg's command all on its own, which did not bode well. I decided to file away my questions about the Beast for later.

I scanned our surroundings. Garbage chutes lined the walls on all four sides of the dismal little basement. As I watched, another bag of refuse slid down the right-hand chute and hit the pile. The smell was so strong, it could have burned paint off the walls, if the gray cinder blocks had been painted. Still, it was better than smelling the fumes of Python. The only visible exit was a metal door marked with a biohazard sign.

"Where are we?" Meg asked.

I glared at her, waiting.

"You can talk now," she added.

"This is going to shock you," I said, "but it appears we are in a garbage room."

"But where?"

"Could be anywhere. The Labyrinth intersects with subterranean places all around the world."

"Like Delphi." Meg glowered at me as if our little Greek excursion had been my fault and not . . . well, only indirectly my fault.

"That was unexpected," I agreed. "We need to speak with Chiron."

"What is Dodona?"

"I—I'll explain it all later." I didn't want Meg to shut me up again. I also didn't want to talk about Dodona while trapped in the Labyrinth. My skin was crawling, and I didn't think it was just because I was covered in sticky soda syrup. "First, we need to get out of here."

Meg glanced behind me. "Well, it wasn't a total waste." She reached into the garbage and pulled out a second piece of glowing fruit. "Only one more apple to go."

"Perfect." The last thing I cared about was finishing Harley's ridiculous race, but at least it would get Meg moving. "Now, why don't we see what fabulous biohazards await us behind that door?"

19

They have gone missing?

No, no, no, no, no, no, no

No, et cetera

THE ONLY BIOHAZARDS we encountered were vegan cupcakes.

After navigating several torchlit corridors, we burst into a crowded modern bakery that, according to the menu board, had the dubious name THE LEVEL TEN VEGAN. Our garbage/volcanic gas stench quickly dispersed the customers, driving most toward the exit, and causing many non-dairy gluten-free baked goods to be trampled. We ducked behind the counter, charged through the kitchen doors, and found ourselves in a subterranean amphitheater that looked centuries old.

Tiers of stone seats ringed a sandy pit about the right size for a gladiator fight. Hanging from the ceiling were dozens of thick iron chains. I wondered what ghastly spectacles might have been staged here, but we didn't stay very long.

We limped out the opposite side, back into the Labyrinth's twisting corridors.

By this point, we had perfected the art of three-legged

running. Whenever I started to tire, I imagined Python behind us, spewing poisonous gas.

At last we turned a corner, and Meg shouted, "There!"

In the middle of the corridor sat a third golden apple.

This time I was too exhausted to care about traps. We loped forward until Meg scooped up the fruit.

In front of us, the ceiling lowered, forming a ramp. Fresh air filled my lungs. We climbed to the top, but instead of feeling elated, my insides turned as cold as the garbage juice on my skin. We were back in the woods.

"Not here," I muttered. "Gods, no."

Meg hopped us in a full circle. "Maybe it's a different forest."

But it wasn't. I could feel the resentful stare of the trees, the horizon stretching out in all directions. Voices began to whisper, waking to our presence.

"Hurry," I said.

As if on cue, the bands around our legs sprang loose. We ran.

Even with her arms full of apples, Meg was faster. She veered between trees, zigzagging left and right as if following a course only she could see. My legs ached and my chest burned, but I didn't dare fall behind.

Up ahead, flickering points of light resolved into torches. At last we burst out of the woods, right into a crowd of campers and satyrs.

Chiron galloped over. "Thank the gods!"

"You're welcome," I gasped, mostly out of habit. "Chiron . . . we have to talk."

In the torchlight, the centaur's face seemed carved from shadow. "Yes, we do, my friend. But first, I fear one more team is still missing . . . your children, Kayla and Austin."

Chiron forced us to take showers and change clothes. Otherwise I would have plunged straight back into the woods.

By the time I was done, Kayla and Austin still had not returned.

Chiron had sent search parties of dryads into the forest, on the assumption that they would be safe in their home territory, but he adamantly refused to let demigods join the hunt.

"We cannot risk anyone else," he said. "Kayla, Austin, and—and the other missing . . . They would not want that."

Five campers had now disappeared. I harbored no illusions that Kayla and Austin would return on their own. The Beast's words still echoed in my ears: *I have upped the stakes. Apollo will have no choice.*

Somehow he had targeted my children. He was inviting me to look for them, and to find the gates of this hidden Oracle. There was still so much I did not understand—how the ancient grove of Dodona had relocated here, what sort of "gates" it might have, why the Beast thought I could open them, and how he'd snared Austin and Kayla. But there was one thing I did know: the Beast was right. I had no choice. I had to find my children . . . my *friends.*

I would have ignored Chiron's warning and run into the forest except for Will's panicked shout, "Apollo, I need you!"

At the far end of the field, he had set up an impromptu hospital where half a dozen campers lay injured on stretchers. He was frantically tending to Paolo Montes while Nico held down the screaming patient.

I ran to Will's side and winced at what I saw.

Paolo had managed to get one of his legs sawed off.

"I got it reattached," Will told me, his voice shaky with exhaustion. His scrubs were speckled with blood. "I need somebody to keep him stable."

I pointed to the woods. "But—"

"I know!" Will snapped. "Don't you think I want to be out there searching too? We're shorthanded for healers. There's some salve and nectar in that pack. Go!"

I was stunned by his tone. I realized he was just as concerned about Kayla and Austin as I was. The only difference: Will knew his duty. He had to heal the injured first. And he needed my help.

"Y-yes," I said. "Yes, of course."

I grabbed the supply pack and took charge of Paolo, who had conveniently passed out from the pain.

Will changed his surgical gloves and glared at the woods. "We *will* find them. We *have* to."

Nico di Angelo gave him a canteen. "Drink. Right now, this is where you need to be."

I could tell the son of Hades was angry too. Around his feet, the grass steamed and withered.

Will sighed. "You're right. But that doesn't make me feel better. I have to set Valentina's broken arm now. You want to assist?"

"Sounds gruesome," Nico said. "Let's go."

I tended to Paolo Montes until I was sure he was out of danger, then asked two satyrs to carry his stretcher to the Hebe cabin.

I did what I could to nurse the others. Chiara had a mild concussion. Billie Ng had come down with a case of Irish step dancing. Holly and Laurel needed pieces of shrapnel removed from their backs, thanks to a close encounter with an exploding chain-saw Frisbee.

The Victor twins had placed in first, predictably, but they also demanded to know which of them had the *most* pieces of shrapnel extracted, so they could have bragging rights. I told them to be quiet or I would never allow them to wear laurel wreaths again. (As the guy who held the patent on laurel wreaths, that was my prerogative.)

I found my mortal healing skills were passable. Will Solace far outshone me, but that didn't bother me as much as my failures with archery and music had. I suppose I was used to being second in healing. My son Asclepius had become the god of medicine by the time he was fifteen, and I couldn't have been happier for him. It left me time for my other interests. Besides, it's every god's dream to have a child who grows up to be a doctor.

As I was washing up from the shrapnel extraction, Harley shuffled over, fiddling with his beacon device. His eyes were puffy from crying.

"It's my fault," he muttered. "I got them lost. I . . . I'm sorry."

He was shaking. I realized the little boy was terrified of what I might do.

For the past two days, I had yearned to cause fear in mortals again. My stomach had boiled with resentment and bitterness. I wanted someone to blame for my predicament, for the disappearances, for my own powerlessness to fix things.

Looking at Harley, my anger evaporated. I felt hollow, silly, ashamed of myself. Yes, me, Apollo . . . ashamed. Truly, it was an event so unprecedented, it should have ripped apart the cosmos.

"It's all right," I told him.

He sniffled. "The racecourse went into the woods. It shouldn't have done that. They got lost and . . . and—"

"Harley"—I placed my hands over his—"may I see your beacon?"

He blinked the tears away. I guess he was afraid I might smash his gadget, but he let me take it.

"I'm not an inventor," I said, turning the gears as gently as possible. "I don't have your father's skills. But I *do* know music. I believe automatons prefer a frequency of E at 329.6 hertz. It resonates best with Celestial bronze. If you adjust your signal—"

"Festus might hear it?" Harley's eyes widened. "Really?"

"I don't know," I admitted. "Just as you could not have known what the Labyrinth would do today. But that doesn't mean we should stop trying. Never stop inventing, son of Hephaestus."

I gave him back his beacon. For a count of three, Harley stared at me in disbelief. Then he hugged me so hard he nearly rebroke my ribs, and he dashed away.

I tended to the last of the injured while the harpies

cleaned the area, picking up bandages, torn clothing, and damaged weapons. They gathered the golden apples in a basket and promised to bake us some lovely glowing apple turnovers for breakfast.

At Chiron's urging, the remaining campers dispersed back to their cabins. He promised them we would determine what to do in the morning, but I had no intention of waiting.

As soon as we were alone, I turned to Chiron and Meg.

"I'm going after Kayla and Austin," I told them. "You can join me or not."

Chiron's expression tightened. "My friend, you're exhausted and unprepared. Go back to your cabin. It will serve no purpose—"

"No." I waved him off, as I once might have done when I was a god. The gesture probably looked petulant coming from a sixteen-year-old nobody, but I didn't care. "I have to do this."

The centaur lowered his head. "I should have listened to you before the race. You tried to warn me. What—what did you discover?"

The question stopped my momentum like a seat belt.

After rescuing Sherman Yang, after listening to Python in the Labyrinth, I had felt certain I knew the answers. I had remembered the name *Dodona*, the stories about talking trees . . .

Now my mind was once again a bowl of fuzzy mortal soup. I couldn't recall what I'd been so excited about, or what I had intended to do about it.

Perhaps exhaustion and stress had taken their toll. Or

maybe Zeus was manipulating my brain—allowing me tantalizing glimpses of the truth, then snatching them away, turning my aha! moments into huh? moments.

I howled in frustration. "I don't remember!"

Meg and Chiron exchanged nervous glances.

"You're not going," Meg told me firmly.

"*What?* You can't—"

"That's an order," she said. "No going into the woods until I say so."

The command sent a shudder from the base of my skull to my heels.

I dug my fingernails into my palms. "Meg McCaffrey, if my children die because you wouldn't let me—"

"Like Chiron said, you'd just get yourself killed. We'll wait for daylight."

I thought how satisfying it would be to drop Meg from the sun chariot at high noon. Then again, some small rational part of me realized she might be right. I was in no condition to launch a one-man rescue operation. That just made me angrier.

Chiron's tail swished from side to side. "Well, then . . . I will see you both in the morning. We *will* find a solution. I promise you that."

He gave me one last look, as if worried I might start running in circles and baying at the moon. Then he trotted back toward the Big House.

I scowled at Meg. "I'm staying out here tonight, in case Kayla and Austin come back. Unless you want to forbid me from doing that, *too*."

She only shrugged. Even her *shrugs* were annoying.

I stormed off to the Me cabin and grabbed a few supplies: a flashlight, two blankets, a canteen of water. As an afterthought, I took a few books from Will Solace's bookshelf. No surprise, he kept reference materials about me to share with new campers. I thought perhaps the books might help jog my memories. Failing that, they'd make good tinder for a fire.

When I returned to the edge of the woods, Meg was still there.

I hadn't expected her to keep vigil with me. Being Meg, she had apparently decided it would be the best way to irritate me.

She sat next to me on my blanket and began eating a golden apple, which she had hidden in her coat. Winter mist drifted through the trees. The night breeze rippled through the grass, making patterns like waves.

Under different circumstances, I might have written a poem about it. In my present state of mind, I could only have managed a funeral dirge, and I did not want to think about death.

I tried to stay mad at Meg, but I couldn't manage it. I supposed she'd had my best interests at heart . . . or at least, she wasn't ready to see her new godly servant get himself killed.

She didn't try to console me. She asked me no questions. She amused herself by picking up small rocks and tossing them into the woods. That, I didn't mind. I happily would've given her a catapult if I had one.

As the night wore on, I read about myself in Will's books.

Normally this would have been a happy task. I am, after all, a fascinating subject. This time, however, I gained no satisfaction from my glorious exploits. They all seemed like exaggerations, lies, and . . . well, myths. Unfortunately, I found a chapter about Oracles. Those few pages stirred my memory, confirming my worst suspicions.

I was too angry to be terrified. I stared at the woods and dared the whispering voices to disturb me. I thought, *Come on, then. Take me, too.* The trees remained silent. Kayla and Austin did not return.

Toward dawn, it started to snow. Only then did Meg speak. "We should go inside."

"And abandon them?"

"Don't be stupid." Snow salted the hood of her winter coat. Her face was hidden except for the tip of her nose and the glint of rhinestones on her glasses. "You'll freeze out here."

I noticed she didn't complain about the cold herself. I wondered if she even felt uncomfortable, or if the power of Demeter kept her safe through the winter like a leafless tree or a dormant seed in the earth.

"They were my children." It hurt me to use the past tense, but Kayla and Austin felt irretrievably lost. "I should've done more to protect them. I should have antici-pated that my enemies would target them to hurt me."

Meg chucked another rock at the trees. "You've had a lot of children. You take the blame every time one of them gets in trouble?"

The answer was no. Over the millennia, I had barely managed to remember my children's names. If I sent them an occasional birthday card or a magic flute, I felt really good about myself. Sometimes I wouldn't realize one of them had died until decades later. During the French Revolution, I got worried about my boy Louis XIV, the Sun King, then went down to check on him and found out he had died seventy-five years earlier.

Now, though, I had a mortal conscience. My sense of guilt seemed to have expanded as my life span contracted. I couldn't explain that to Meg. She would never understand. She'd probably just throw a rock at me.

"It's my fault Python retook Delphi," I said. "If I had killed him the moment he reappeared, while I was still a god, he would never have become so powerful. He would never have made an alliance with this . . . this *Beast*."

Meg lowered her face.

"You know him," I guessed. "In the Labyrinth, when you heard the Beast's voice, you were terrified."

I was worried she might order me to shut up again. Instead, she silently traced the crescents on her gold rings.

"Meg, he wants to *destroy* me," I said. "Somehow, he's behind these disappearances. The more we understand about this man—"

"He lives in New York."

I waited. It was difficult to glean much information from the top of Meg's hood.

"All right," I said. "That narrows it down to eight and a half million people. What else?"

Meg picked at the calluses on her fingers. "If you're a demigod on the streets, you hear about the Beast. He takes people like me."

A snowflake melted on the back of my neck. "Takes people . . . why?"

"To train," Meg said. "To use like . . . servants, soldiers. I don't know."

"And you've met him."

"Please don't ask me—"

"Meg."

"He killed my dad."

Her words were quiet, but they hit me harder than a rock in the face. "Meg, I—I'm sorry. How . . . ?"

"I refused to work for him," she said. "My dad tried to . . ." She closed her fists. "I was really small. I hardly remember it. I got away. Otherwise, the Beast would've killed me, too. My stepdad took me in. He was good to me. You asked why he trained me to fight? Why he gave me the rings? He wanted me to be safe, to be able to protect myself."

"From the Beast."

Her hood dipped. "Being a good demigod, training hard . . . that's the only way to keep the Beast away. Now you know."

In fact, I had more questions than ever, but I sensed that Meg was in no mood for further sharing. I remembered her expression as we stood on that ledge under the chamber of Delphi—her look of absolute terror when she recognized the Beast's voice. Not all monsters were three-ton reptiles with poisonous breath. Many wore human faces.

I peered into the woods. Somewhere in there, five demigods were being used as bait, including two of my children. The Beast wanted me to search for them, and I would. But I would *not* let him use me.

I have well-placed help within the camp, the Beast had said.

That bothered me.

I knew from experience that any demigod could be turned against Olympus. I had been at the banquet table when Tantalus tried to poison the gods by feeding us his chopped-up son in a stew. I'd watched as King Mithridates sided with the Persians and massacred every Roman in Anatolia. I'd witnessed Queen Clytemnestra turn homicidal, killing her husband Agamemnon just because he made one little human sacrifice to me. Demigods are an unpredictable bunch.

I glanced at Meg. I wondered if she could be lying to me—if she was some sort of spy. It seemed unlikely. She was too contrary, impetuous, and annoying to be an effective mole. Besides, she was technically my master. She could order me to do almost any task and I would have to obey. If she was out to destroy me, I was already as good as dead.

Perhaps Damien White . . . a son of Nemesis was a natural choice for backstabbing duty. Or Connor Stoll, Alice, or Julia . . . a child of Hermes had recently betrayed the gods by working for Kronos. They might do so again. Maybe that pretty Chiara, daughter of Tyche, was in league with the Beast. Children of luck were natural gamblers. The truth was, I had no idea.

The sky turned from black to gray. I became aware of a distant *thump, thump, thump*—a quick, relentless pulse that got louder and louder. At first, I feared it might be the blood in my head. Could human brains explode from too many worrisome thoughts? Then I realized the noise was mechanical, coming from the west. It was the distinctly modern sound of rotor blades cutting the air.

Meg lifted her head. "Is that a helicopter?"

I got to my feet.

The machine appeared—a dark red Bell 412 cutting north along the coastline. (Riding the skies as often as I do, I know my flying machines.) Painted on the helicopter's side was a bright green logo with the letters D.E.

Despite my misery, a small bit of hope kindled inside me. The satyrs Millard and Herbert must have succeeded in delivering their message.

"That," I told Meg, "is Rachel Elizabeth Dare. Let's go see what the Oracle of Delphi has to say."

20

Don't paint over gods
If you're redecorating
That's, like, common sense

RACHEL ELIZABETH DARE was one of my favorite mortals. As soon as she'd become the Oracle two summers ago, she'd brought new vigor and excitement to the job.

Of course, the previous Oracle had been a withered corpse, so perhaps the bar was low. Regardless, I was elated as the Dare Enterprises helicopter descended just beyond the eastern hills, outside the camp's boundary. I wondered what Rachel had told her father—a fabulously wealthy real estate magnate—to convince him she needed to borrow a helicopter. I knew Rachel could be quite convincing.

I jogged across the valley with Meg in tow. I could already imagine the way Rachel would look as she came over the summit: her frizzy red hair, her vivacious smile, her paint-spattered blouse, and jeans covered with doodles. I needed her humor, wisdom, and resilience. The Oracle would cheer us all up. Most importantly, she would cheer *me* up.

I was not prepared for the reality. (Which again, was a stunning surprise. Normally, reality prepares itself for *me*.)

Rachel met us on the hill near the entrance to her cave. Only later would I realize Chiron's two satyr messengers were not with her, and I would wonder what had happened to them.

Miss Dare looked thinner and older—less like a high school girl and more like a young farmer's wife from ancient times, weathered from hard work and gaunt from shortage of food. Her red hair had lost its vibrancy. It framed her face in a curtain of dark copper. Her freckles had faded to watermarks. Her green eyes did not sparkle. And she was wearing a dress—a white cotton frock with a white shawl, and a patina-green jacket. Rachel *never* wore dresses.

"Rachel?" I didn't trust myself to say any more. She was not the same person.

Then I remembered that I wasn't either.

She studied my new mortal form. Her shoulders slumped. "So it's true."

From below us came the voices of other campers. No doubt woken by the sound of the helicopter, they were emerging from their cabins and gathering at the base of the hill. None tried to climb toward us, though. Perhaps they sensed that all was not right.

The helicopter rose from behind Half-Blood Hill. It veered toward Long Island Sound, passing so close to the Athena Parthenos that I thought its landing skids might clip the goddess's winged helmet.

I turned to Meg. "Would you tell the others that Rachel needs some space? Fetch Chiron. He should come up. The rest should wait."

It wasn't like Meg to take orders from me. I half expected her to kick me. Instead, she glanced nervously at Rachel, turned, and trudged down the hill.

"A friend of yours?" Rachel asked.

"Long story."

"Yes," she said. "I have a story like that, too."

"Shall we talk in your cave?"

Rachel pursed her lips. "You won't like it. But yes, that's probably the safest place."

The cave was not as cozy as I remembered.

The sofas were overturned. The coffee table had a broken leg. The floor was strewn with easels and canvases. Even Rachel's tripod stool, the throne of prophecy itself, lay on its side on a pile of paint-splattered drop cloths.

Most disturbing was the state of the walls. Ever since taking up residence, Rachel had been painting them, like her cave-dwelling ancestors of old. She had spent hours on elaborate murals of events from the past, images from the future she'd seen in prophecies, favorite quotes from books and music, and abstract designs so good they would have given M. C. Escher vertigo. The art made the cave feel like a mixture of art studio, psychedelic hangout, and graffiti-covered highway underpass. I loved it.

But most of the images had been blotted out with a sloppy coat of white paint. Nearby, a roller was stuck in an encrusted tray. Clearly Rachel had defaced her own work months ago and hadn't been back since.

She waved listlessly at the wreckage. "I got frustrated."

"Your art . . ." I gaped at the field of white. "There was a lovely portrait of me—right there."

I get offended whenever art is damaged, especially if that art features me.

Rachel looked ashamed. "I—I thought a blank canvas might help me think." Her tone made it obvious that the whitewashing had accomplished nothing. I could have told her as much.

The two of us did our best to clean up. We hauled the sofas back into place to form a sitting area. Rachel left the tripod stool where it lay.

A few minutes later, Meg returned. Chiron followed in full centaur form, ducking his head to fit through the entrance. They found us sitting at the wobbly coffee table like civilized cave people, sharing lukewarm Arizona tea and stale crackers from the Oracle's larder.

"Rachel." Chiron sighed with relief. "Where are Millard and Herbert?"

She bowed her head. "They arrived at my house badly wounded. They . . . they didn't make it."

Perhaps it was the morning light behind him, but I fancied I could see new gray whiskers growing in Chiron's beard. The centaur trotted over and lowered himself to the ground, folding his legs underneath himself. Meg joined me on the couch.

Rachel leaned forward and steepled her fingers, as she did when she spoke a prophecy. I half hoped the spirit of Delphi would possess her, but there was no smoke, no hissing, no raspy voice of divine possession. It was a bit disappointing.

"You first," she told us. "Tell me what's been going on here."

We brought her up to speed on the disappearances and my misadventures with Meg. I explained about the three-legged race and our side trip to Delphi.

Chiron blanched. "I did not know this. You went to Delphi?"

Rachel stared at me in disbelief. "*The* Delphi. You saw Python and you . . ."

I got the feeling she wanted to say *and you didn't kill him?* But she restrained herself.

I felt like standing with my face against the wall. Perhaps Rachel could blot me out with white paint. Disappearing would've been less painful than facing my failures.

"At present," I said, "I cannot defeat Python. I am much too weak. And . . . well, the Catch-88."

Chiron sipped his Arizona tea. "Apollo means that we cannot send a quest without a prophecy, and we cannot get a prophecy without an Oracle."

Rachel stared at her overturned tripod stool. "And this man . . . the Beast. What do you know about him?"

"Not much." I explained what I had seen in my dream, and what Meg and I had overheard in the Labyrinth. "The Beast apparently has a reputation for snatching up young demigods in New York. Meg says . . ." I faltered when I saw her expression, clearly cautioning me to stay away from her personal history. "Um, she's had some experience with the Beast."

Chiron raised his brows. "Can you tell us anything that might help, dear?"

Meg sank into the sofa's cushions. "I've crossed paths with him. He's—he's scary. The memory is blurry."

"Blurry," Chiron repeated.

Meg became very interested in the cracker crumbs on her dress.

Rachel gave me a quizzical look. I shook my head, trying my best to impart a warning: *Trauma. Don't ask. Might get attacked by a peach baby.*

Rachel seemed to get the message. "That's all right, Meg," she said. "I have some information that may help."

She fished her phone from her coat pocket. "Don't touch this. You guys have probably figured it out, but phones are going even more haywire than usual around demigods. I'm not technically one of you, and even *I* can't place calls. I was able to take a couple of pictures, though." She turned the screen toward us. "Chiron, you recognize this place?"

The nighttime shot showed the upper floors of a glass residential tower. Judging from the background, it was somewhere in downtown Manhattan.

"That is the building you described last summer," Chiron said, "where you parleyed with the Romans."

"Yeah," Rachel said. "Something didn't feel right about that place. I got to thinking . . . how did the Romans take over such prime Manhattan real estate on such short notice? Who owns it? I tried to contact Reyna, to see if she could tell me anything, but—"

"Communications problems?" Chiron guessed.

"Exactly. I even sent physical mail to Camp Jupiter's drop box in Berkeley. No response. So I asked my dad's real estate lawyers to do some digging."

Meg peeked over the top of her glasses. "Your dad has lawyers? And a helicopter?"

"Several helicopters." Rachel sighed. "He's annoying. Anyway, that building is owned by a shell corporation, which is owned by another shell corporation, blah, blah, blah. The mother company is something called Triumvirate Holdings."

I felt a trickle like white paint rolling down my back. "*Triumvirate* . . ."

Meg made a sour face. "What does that mean?"

"A triumvirate is a ruling council of three," I said. "At least, that's what it meant in ancient Rome."

"Which is interesting," Rachel said, "because of this next shot." She tapped her screen. The new photo zoomed in on the building's penthouse terrace, where three shadowy figures stood talking together—men in business suits, illuminated only by the light from inside the apartment. I couldn't see their faces.

"These are the owners of Triumvirate Holdings," Rachel said. "Just getting this *one* picture wasn't easy." She blew a frizzy strand of hair out of her face. "I've spent the last two months investigating them, and I don't even know their names. I don't know where they live or where they came from. But I can tell you they own so much property and have so much money, they make my dad's company look like a kid's lemonade stand."

I stared at the picture of the three shadowy figures. I could almost imagine that the one on the left was the Beast. His slouching posture and the over-large shape of his head reminded me of the man in purple from my dream.

"The Beast said that his organization was everywhere," I recalled. "He mentioned he had colleagues."

Chiron's tail flicked, sending a paintbrush skidding across the cave floor. "Adult demigods? I can't imagine they would be Greek, but perhaps Roman? If they helped Octavian with his war—"

"Oh, they helped," Rachel said. "I found a paper trail—not much, but you remember those siege weapons Octavian built to destroy Camp Half-Blood?"

"No," said Meg.

I would have ignored her, but Rachel was a more generous soul.

She smiled patiently. "Sorry, Meg. You seem so at home here, I forgot you were new. Basically, the Roman demigods attacked this camp with giant catapulty things called onagers. It was all a big misunderstanding. Anyway, the weapons were paid for by Triumvirate Holdings."

Chiron frowned. "That is not good."

"I found something even more disturbing," Rachel continued. "You remember before that, during the Titan War, Luke Castellan mentioned he had backers in the mortal world? They had enough money to buy a cruise ship, helicopters, weapons. They even hired mortal mercenaries."

"Don't remember that, either," Meg said.

I rolled my eyes. "Meg, we can't stop and explain every major war to you! Luke Castellan was a child of Hermes. He betrayed this camp and allied himself with the Titans. They attacked New York. Big battle. I saved the day. Et cetera."

Chiron coughed. "At any rate, I do remember Luke

claiming that he had lots of supporters. We never found out exactly who they were."

"Now we know," Rachel said. "That cruise ship, the *Princess Andromeda*, was property of Triumvirate Holdings."

A cold sense of unease gripped me. I felt I should know something about this, but my mortal brain was betraying me again. I was more certain than ever that Zeus was toying with me, keeping my vision and memory limited. I remembered some assurances Octavian had given me, though—how easy it would be to win his little war, to raise new temples to me, how much support he had.

Rachel's phone screen went dark—much like my brain—but the grainy photo remained burned into my retinas.

"These men . . ." I picked up an empty tube of burnt sienna paint. "I'm afraid they are not modern demigods."

Rachel frowned. "You think they're ancient demigods who came through the Doors of Death—like Medea, or Midas? The thing is, Triumvirate Holdings has been around since way before Gaea started to wake. Decades, at least."

"Centuries," I said. "The Beast said that he'd been building his empire for centuries."

The cave became so silent, I imagined the hiss of Python, the soft exhale of fumes from deep in the earth. I wished we had some background music to drown it out . . . jazz or classical. I would have settled for death metal polka.

Rachel shook her head. "Then who—?"

"I don't know," I admitted. "But the Beast . . . in my dream, he called me his forefather. He assumed I would recognize him. And if my godly memory was intact, I think

I would. His demeanor, his accent, his facial structure—I have met him before, just not in modern times."

Meg had grown very quiet. I got the distinct impression she was trying to disappear into the couch cushions. Normally, this would not have bothered me, but after our experience in the Labyrinth, I felt guilty every time I mentioned the Beast. My pesky mortal conscience must have been acting up.

"The name Triumvirate . . ." I tapped my forehead, trying to shake loose information that was no longer there. "The last triumvirate I dealt with included Lepidus, Marc Antony, and my son, the *original* Octavian. A triumvirate is a very Roman concept . . . like patriotism, skullduggery, and assassination."

Chiron stroked his beard. "You think these men are ancient Romans? How is that possible? Hades is quite good at tracking down escaped spirits from the Underworld. He would not allow three men from ancient times to run amok in the modern world for centuries."

"Again, I do not know." Saying this so often offended my divine sensibilities. I decided that when I returned to Olympus, I would have to gargle the bad taste out of my mouth with Tabasco-flavored nectar. "But it seems these men have been plotting against us for a very long time. They funded Luke Castellan's war. They supplied aid to Camp Jupiter when the Romans attacked Camp Half-Blood. And despite those two wars, the Triumvirate is still out there— still plotting. What if this company is the root cause of . . . well, everything?"

Chiron looked at me as if I were digging his grave. "That is a very troubling thought. Could three men be so powerful?"

I spread my hands. "You've lived long enough to know, my friend. Gods, monsters, Titans . . . these are always dangerous. But the greatest threat to demigods has always been other demigods. Whoever this Triumvirate is, we must stop them before they take control of the Oracles."

Rachel sat up straight. "Excuse me? Oracles plural?"

"Ah . . . didn't I tell you about them when I was a god?"

Her eyes regained some of their dark green intensity. I feared she was envisioning ways she might inflict pain upon me with her art supplies.

"No," she said levelly, "you did not tell me about them."

"Oh . . . well, my mortal memory has been faulty, you see. I had to read some books in order to—"

"Oracles," she repeated. "Plural."

I took a deep breath. I wanted to assure her that those other Oracles didn't mean a thing to me! Rachel was special! Unfortunately, I doubted she was in a place where she could hear that right now. I decided it was best to speak plainly.

"In ancient times," I said, "there were many Oracles. Of course Delphi was the most famous, but there were four others of comparable power."

Chiron shook his head. "But those were destroyed ages ago."

"So I thought," I agreed. "Now I am not so sure. I believe Triumvirate Holdings wants to control *all* the ancient Oracles. And I believe the most ancient Oracle of all, the Grove of Dodona, is right here at Camp Half-Blood."

21

Up in my business
Always burning Oracles
Romans gonna hate

I WAS A DRAMATIC GOD.

I thought my last statement was a great line. I expected gasps, perhaps some organ music in the background. Maybe the lights would go out just before I could say more. Moments later, I would be found dead with a knife in my back. That would be exciting!

Wait. I'm mortal. Murder would kill me. Never mind.

At any rate, none of that happened. My three companions just stared at me.

"Four other Oracles," Rachel said. "You mean you have four other Pythias—"

"No, my dear. There is only one Pythia—*you*. Delphi is absolutely unique."

Rachel still looked like she wanted to jam a number ten bristle paintbrush up my nose. "So these other four *non-unique* Oracles . . ."

"Well, one was the Sybil of Cumae." I wiped the sweat off my palms. (Why did mortal palms sweat?) "You know, she wrote the Sibylline Books—those prophecies that Ella the harpy memorized."

Meg looked back and forth between us. "A harpy . . . like those chicken ladies who clean up after lunch?"

Chiron smiled. "Ella is a very special harpy, Meg. Years ago, she somehow came across a copy of the prophetic books, which we thought were burned before the Fall of Rome. Right now, our friends at Camp Jupiter are trying to reconstruct them based on Ella's recollections."

Rachel crossed her arms. "And the other three Oracles? I'm sure none of them was a beautiful young priestess whom you praised for her . . . what was it? . . . 'scintillating conversation'?"

"Ah . . ." I wasn't sure why, but it felt like my acne was turning into live insects and crawling across my face. "Well, according to my extensive research—"

"Some books he flipped through last night," Meg clarified.

"Ahem! There was an Oracle at Erythaea, and another at the Cave of Trophonius."

"Goodness," Chiron said. "I'd forgotten about those two."

I shrugged. I remembered almost nothing about them either. They had been some of my less successful prophetic franchises.

"And the fifth," I said, "was the Grove of Dodona."

"A grove," Meg said. "Like trees."

"Yes, Meg, like trees. Groves are typically composed of trees, rather than, say, Fudgsicles. Dodona was a stand of sacred oaks planted by the Mother Goddess in the first days of the world. They were ancient even when the Olympians were born."

"The Mother Goddess?" Rachel shivered in her patina jacket. "Please tell me you don't mean Gaea."

"No, thankfully. I mean Rhea, Queen of the Titans, the mother of the first generation of Olympian gods. Her sacred trees could actually speak. Sometimes they issued prophecies."

"The voices in the woods," Meg guessed.

"Exactly. I believe the Grove of Dodona has regrown itself here in the woods at camp. In my dreams, I saw a crowned woman imploring me to find her Oracle. I believe it was Rhea, though I still don't understand why she was wearing a peace symbol or using the term *dig it*."

"A peace symbol?" Chiron asked.

"A large brass one," I confirmed.

Rachel drummed her fingers on the couch's armrest. "If Rhea is a Titan, isn't she evil?"

"Not all Titans were bad," I said. "Rhea was a gentle soul. She sided with the gods in their first great war. I think she wants us to succeed. She doesn't want her grove in the hands of our enemies."

Chiron's tail twitched. "My friend, Rhea has not been seen for millennia. Her grove was burned in the ancient times. Emperor Theodosius ordered the last oak cut down in—"

"I know." I got a stabbing pain right between my eyes, as I always did when someone mentioned Theodosius. I now recalled that the bully had closed all the ancient temples across the empire, basically evicting us Olympian gods. I used to have an archery target with his face on it. "Nevertheless, many things from the old days have survived or regenerated.

The Labyrinth has rebuilt itself. Why couldn't a grove of sacred trees spring up again right here in this valley?"

Meg pushed herself deeper into the cushions. "This is all weird." Leave it to the young McCaffrey to summarize our conversation so effectively. "So if the tree voices are sacred and stuff, why are they making people get lost?"

"For once, you ask a good question." I hoped such praise wouldn't go to Meg's head. "In the old days, the priests of Dodona would take care of the trees, pruning them, watering them, and channeling their voices by hanging wind chimes in their branches."

"How would that help?" Meg asked.

"I don't know. I'm not a tree priest. But with proper care, these trees could divine the future."

Rachel smoothed her skirt. "And without proper care?"

"The voices were unfocused," I said. "A wild choir of disharmony." I paused, quite pleased with that line. I was hoping someone might write it down for posterity, but no one did. "Untended, the grove could most definitely drive mortals to madness."

Chiron furrowed his brow. "So our missing campers are wandering in the trees, perhaps already insane from the voices."

"Or they're dead," Meg added.

"No." I could not abide that thought. "No, they are still alive. The Beast is using them, trying to bait me."

"How can you be sure?" Rachel asked. "And why? If Python already controls Delphi, why are these other Oracles so important?"

I gazed at the wall formerly graced by my picture. Alas,

no answers magically appeared in the whitewashed space. "I'm not sure. I believe our enemies want to cut us off from every possible source of prophecy. Without a way to see and direct our fates, we will wither and die—gods and mortals alike, anyone who opposes the Triumvirate."

Meg turned upside down on the sofa and kicked off her red shoes. "They're strangling our taproots." She wriggled her toes to demonstrate.

I looked back at Rachel, hoping she would excuse my street urchin overlord's bad manners. "As for why the Grove of Dodona is so important, Python mentioned that it was the one Oracle he could not control. I don't understand exactly why—perhaps because Dodona is the only Oracle that has no connection with me. Its power comes from Rhea. So if the grove is working, and it is free of Python's influence, and it is here at Camp Half-Blood—"

"It could provide us with prophecies." Chiron's eyes gleamed. "It could give us a chance against our enemies."

I gave Rachel an apologetic smile. "Of course, we'd rather have our beloved Oracle of Delphi working again. And we will, eventually. But for now, the Grove of Dodona could be our best hope."

Meg's hair swept the floor. Her face was now the color of one of my sacred cattle. "Aren't prophecies all twisted and mysterious and murky, and people die trying to escape them?"

"Meg," I said, "you can't trust those reviews on RateMyOracle.com. The hotness factor for the Sibyl of Cumae, for instance, is *completely* off. I remember *that* quite clearly."

Rachel put her chin on her fist. "Really? Do tell."

"Uh, what I meant to say: the Grove of Dodona is a benevolent force. It has helped heroes before. The masthead of the original *Argo*, for instance, was carved from a branch of the sacred trees. It could speak to the Argonauts and give them guidance."

"Mm." Chiron nodded. "And that's why our mysterious Beast wants the grove burned."

"Apparently," I said. "And that's why we have to save it."

Meg rolled backward off the couch. Her legs knocked over the three-legged coffee table, spilling our Arizona tea and crackers. "Oops."

I ground my mortal teeth, which would not last a year if I kept hanging around Meg. Rachel and Chiron wisely ignored my young friend's display of Megness.

"Apollo . . ." The old centaur watched a waterfall of tea trickling from the edge of the table. "If you are right about Dodona, how do we proceed? We are already shorthanded. If we send search teams into the woods, we have no guarantee they'll come back."

Meg brushed the hair out of her eyes. "We'll go. Just Apollo and me."

My tongue attempted to hide in the depths of my throat. "We—we will?"

"You said you gotta do a bunch of trials or whatever to prove you're worthy, right? This'll be the first one."

Part of me knew she was right, but the remnants of my godly self rebelled at the idea. I never did my own dirty work. I would rather have picked a nice group of heroes and sent them to their deaths—or, you know, glorious success.

Yet Rhea had been clear in my dream: finding the Oracle was my job. And thanks to the cruelty of Zeus, where I went, Meg went. For all I knew, Zeus was aware of the Beast and his plans, and he had sent me here specifically to deal with the situation . . . a thought that did not make me any more likely to get him a nice tie for Father's Day.

I also remembered the other part of my dream: the Beast in his mauve suit, encouraging me to find the Oracle so he could burn it down. There was still too much I didn't understand, but I had to act. Austin and Kayla were depending on me.

Rachel put her hand on my knee, which made me flinch. Surprisingly, she did not inflict any pain. Her gaze was more earnest than angry. "Apollo, you have to try. If we can get a glimpse of the future . . . well, it may be the only way to get things back to normal." She looked longingly at the blank walls of her cave. "I'd like to have a future again."

Chiron shifted his forelegs. "What do you need from us, old friend? How can we help?"

I glanced at Meg. Sadly, I could tell that we were in agreement. We were stuck with each other. We couldn't risk anyone else.

"Meg is right," I said. "We have to do this ourselves. We should leave immediately, but—"

"We've been up all night," Meg said. "We need some sleep."

Wonderful, I thought. Now Meg is finishing my sentences.

This time I could not argue with her logic. Despite my fervor to rush into the woods and save my children, I had to proceed cautiously. I could not mess up this rescue. And I was increasingly certain that the Beast would keep his captives alive for now. He needed them to lure me into his trap.

Chiron rose on his front hooves. "This evening, then. Rest and prepare, my heroes. I fear you will need all your strength and wits for what comes next."

22

Armed to the eyeballs:
A combat ukulele
Magic Brazil scarf

SUN GODS ARE NOT GOOD at sleeping during the day, but somehow I managed a fitful nap.

When I woke in the late afternoon, I found the camp in a state of agitation.

Kayla and Austin's disappearance had been the tipping point. The other campers were now so rattled, no one could maintain a normal schedule. I suppose a single demigod disappearing every few weeks felt like a normal casualty rate. But a pair of demigods disappearing in the middle of a camp-sanctioned activity—that meant no one was safe.

Word must have spread of our conference in the cave. The Victor twins had stuffed wads of cotton in their ears to foil the oracular voices. Julia and Alice had climbed to the top of the lava wall and were using binoculars to scan the woods, no doubt hoping to spot the Grove of Dodona, but I doubted they could see the trees for the forest.

Everywhere I went, people were unhappy to see me. Damien and Chiara sat together at the canoe dock, glowering in my direction. Sherman Yang waved me away when

I tried to talk with him. He was busy decorating the Ares cabin with frag grenades and brightly decorated claymores. If it had been Saturnalia, he definitely would have won the prize for most violent holiday decorations.

Even the Athena Parthenos stared down at me accusingly from the top of the hill as if to say, *This is all your fault*.

She was right. If I hadn't let Python take over Delphi, if I'd paid more attention to the other ancient Oracles, if I hadn't lost my divinity—

Stop it, Apollo, I scolded myself. *You're beautiful and everyone loves you.*

But it was becoming increasingly difficult to believe that. My father, Zeus, did not love me. The demigods at Camp Half-Blood did not love me. Python and the Beast and his comrades at Triumvirate Holdings did not love me. It was almost enough to make me question my self-worth.

No, no. That was crazy talk.

Chiron and Rachel were nowhere to be seen. Nyssa Barrera informed me that they were hoping against hope to use the camp's sole Internet connection, in Chiron's office, to access more information about Triumvirate Holdings. Harley was with them for tech support. They were presently on hold with Comcast customer service and might not emerge for hours, if indeed they survived the ordeal at all.

I found Meg at the armory, browsing for battle supplies. She had strapped a leather cuirass over her green dress and greaves over orange leggings, so she looked like a kindergartener reluctantly stuffed into combat gear by her parents.

"Perhaps a shield?" I suggested.

"Nuh-uh." She showed me her rings. "I always use two

swords. Plus I need a free hand for slapping when you act stupid."

I had the uncomfortable sense she was serious.

From the weapon rack, she pulled out a long bow and offered it to me.

I recoiled. "No."

"It's your best weapon. You're Apollo."

I swallowed back the tang of mortal bile. "I swore an oath. I'm not the god of archery or music anymore. I won't use a bow or a musical instrument until I can use them *properly*."

"Stupid oath." She didn't slap me, but she looked like she wanted to. "What will you do, just stand around and cheer while I fight?"

That had indeed been my plan, but now I felt silly admitting it. I scanned the weapon display and grabbed a sword. Even without drawing it, I could tell it would be too heavy and awkward for me to use, but I strapped the scabbard around my waist.

"There," I said. "Happy?"

Meg did not appear happy. Nevertheless, she returned the bow to its place.

"Fine," she said. "But you'd better have my back."

I had never understood that expression. It made me think of the KICK ME signs Artemis used to tape to my toga during festival days. Still, I nodded. "Your back shall be had."

We reached the edge of the woods and found a small going-away party waiting for us: Will and Nico, Paolo Montes, Malcolm Pace, and Billie Ng, all with grim faces.

"Be careful," Will told me. "And here."

Before I could object, he placed a ukulele in my hands.
I tried to give it back. "I can't. I made an oath—"

"Yeah, I know. That was stupid of you. But it's a combat ukulele. You can fight with it if you need to."

I looked more closely at the instrument. It was made from Celestial bronze—thin sheets of metal acid-etched to resemble the grain of blond oak wood. The instrument weighed next to nothing, yet I imagined it was almost indestructible.

"The work of Hephaestus?" I asked.

Will shook his head. "The work of Harley. He wanted you to have it. Just sling it over your back. For me and Harley. It'll make us both feel better."

I decided I was obliged to honor the request, though my possession of a ukulele had rarely made anyone feel better. Don't ask me why. When I was a god, I used to do an absolutely blistering ukulele version of "Satisfaction."

Nico handed me some ambrosia wrapped in a napkin.

"I can't eat this," I reminded him.

"It's not for you." He glanced at Meg, his eyes full of misgiving. I remembered that the son of Hades had his own ways of sensing the future—futures that involved the possibility of death. I shivered and tucked the ambrosia into my coat pocket. As aggravating as Meg could be, I was deeply unsettled by the idea that she might come to harm. I decided that I could not allow that to happen.

Malcolm was showing Meg a parchment map, pointing out various places in the woods that we should avoid. Paolo—looking completely healed from his leg surgery—stood next to him, carefully and earnestly providing Portuguese commentary that no one could understand.

When they were finished with the map, Billie Ng approached Meg.

Billie was a wisp of a girl. She compensated for her diminutive stature with the fashion sense of a K-Pop idol. Her winter coat was the color of aluminum foil. Her bobbed hair was aquamarine and her makeup gold. I completely approved. In fact, I thought I could rock that look myself if I could just get my acne under control.

Billie gave Meg a flashlight and a small packet of flower seeds.

"Just in case," Billie said.

Meg seemed quite overwhelmed. She gave Billie a fierce hug.

I didn't understand the purpose of the seeds, but it was comforting to know that in a dire emergency I could hit people with my ukulele while Meg planted geraniums.

Malcolm Pace gave me his parchment map. "When in doubt, veer to the right. That usually works in the woods, though I don't know why."

Paolo offered me a green-and-gold scarf—a bandana version of the Brazilian flag. He said something that, of course, I could not understand.

Nico smirked. "That's Paolo's good-luck bandana. I think he wants you to wear it. He believes it will make you invincible."

I found this dubious, since Paolo was prone to serious injury, but as a god, I had learned never to turn down offerings. "Thank you."

Paolo gripped my shoulders and kissed my cheeks. I may have blushed. He was quite handsome when he wasn't bleeding out from dismemberment.

I rested my hand on Will's shoulder. "Don't worry. We'll be back by dawn."

His mouth trembled ever so slightly. "How can you be sure?"

"I'm the sun god," I said, trying to muster more confidence than I felt. "I *always* return at dawn."

Of course it rained. Why would it not?

Up in Mount Olympus, Zeus must have been having a good laugh at my expense. Camp Half-Blood was supposed to be protected from severe weather, but no doubt my father had told Aeolus to pull out all the stops on his winds. My jilted ex-girlfriends among the air nymphs were probably enjoying their moment of payback.

The rain was just on the edge of sleet—liquid enough to soak my clothes, icy enough to slam against my exposed face like glass shards.

We stumbled along, lurching from tree to tree to find any shelter we could. Patches of old snow crunched under my feet. My ukulele got heavier as its sound hole filled with rain. Meg's flashlight beam cut across the storm like a cone of yellow static.

I led the way, not because I had any destination in mind, but because I was angry. I was tired of being cold and soaked. I was tired of being picked on. Mortals often talk about the whole world being against them, but that is ridiculous. Mortals aren't that important. In my case, the whole world really *was* against me. I refused to surrender to such abuse. I would do something about it! I just wasn't quite sure what.

From time to time we heard monsters in the distance—the roar of a drakon, the harmonized howl of a two-headed wolf—but nothing showed itself. On a night like this, any self-respecting monster would've remained in its lair, warm and cozy.

After what seemed like hours, Meg stifled a scream. I heroically leaped to her side, my hand on my sword. (I would have drawn it, but it was really heavy and got stuck in the scabbard.) At Meg's feet, wedged in the mud, was a glistening black shell the size of a boulder. It was cracked down the middle, the edges splattered with a foul gooey substance.

"I almost stepped on that." Meg covered her mouth as if she might be sick.

I inched closer. The shell was the crushed carapace of a giant insect. Nearby, camouflaged among the tree roots, lay one of the beast's dismembered legs.

"It's a *myrmeke*," I said. "Or it was."

Behind her rain-splattered glasses, Meg's eyes were impossible to read. "A *murr-murr-key?*"

"A giant ant. There must be a colony somewhere in the woods."

Meg gagged. "I hate bugs."

That made sense for a daughter of the agriculture goddess, but to me the dead ant didn't seem any grosser than the piles of garbage in which we often swam.

"Well, don't worry," I said. "This one is dead. Whatever killed it must've had powerful jaws to crack that shell."

"Not comforting. Are—are these things dangerous?"

I laughed. "Oh, yes. They range in size from as small as dogs to larger than grizzly bears. One time I watched a colony of myrmekes attack a Greek army in India. It was hilarious. They spit acid that can melt through bronze armor and—"

"Apollo."

My smile faded. I reminded myself I was no longer a spectator. These ants could kill us. Easily. And Meg was scared.

"Right," I said. "Well, the rain should keep the myrmekes in their tunnels. Just don't make yourself an attractive target. They like bright, shiny things."

"Like flashlights?"

"Um . . ."

Meg handed me the flashlight. "Lead on, Apollo."

I thought that was unfair, but we forged ahead.

After another hour or so (surely the woods weren't this big), the rain tapered off, leaving the ground steaming.

The air got warmer. The humidity approached bathhouse levels. Thick white vapor curled off the tree branches.

"What's going on?" Meg wiped her face. "Feels like a tropical rain forest now."

I had no answer. Then, up ahead, I heard a massive flushing sound—like water being forced through pipes . . . or fissures.

I couldn't help but smile. "A geyser."

"A geyser," Meg repeated. "Like Old Faithful?"

"This is excellent news. Perhaps we can get directions. Our lost demigods might have even found sanctuary there!"

"With the geysers," Meg said.

"No, my ridiculous girl," I said. "With the geyser *gods*. Assuming they're in a good mood, this could be great."

"And if they're in a bad mood?"

"Then we'll cheer them up before they can boil us. Follow me!"

23

Scale of one to ten
How would you rate your demise?
Thanks for your input

WAS I RECKLESS to rush toward such volatile nature gods?

Please. Second-guessing myself is not in my nature. It's a trait I've never needed.

True, my memories about the *palikoi* were a little hazy. As I recalled, the geyser gods in ancient Sicily used to give refuge to runaway slaves, so they must be kindly spirits. Perhaps they would also give refuge to lost demigods, or at least notice when five of them wandered through their territory, muttering incoherently. Besides, I was Apollo! The palikoi would be honored to meet a major Olympian such as myself! The fact that geysers often blew their tops, spewing columns of scalding hot water hundreds of feet in the air, wasn't going to stop me from making some new fans . . . I mean *friends*.

The clearing opened before us like an oven door. A wall of heat billowed through the trees and washed over my face. I could feel my pores opening to drink in the moisture, which would hopefully help my spotty complexion.

The scene before us had no business being in a Long

Island winter. Glistening vines wreathed the tree branches. Tropical flowers bloomed from the forest floor. A red parrot sat on a banana tree heavy with green bunches.

In the midst of the glade stood two geysers—twin holes in the ground, ringed with a figure eight of gray mud pots. The craters bubbled and hissed, but they were not spewing at the moment. I decided to take that as a good omen.

Meg's boots squished in the mud. "Is it safe?"

"Definitely not," I said. "We'll need an offering. Perhaps your packet of seeds?"

Meg punched my arm. "Those are magic. For life-and-death emergencies. What about your ukulele? You're not going to play it anyway."

"A man of honor *never* surrenders his ukulele." I perked up. "But wait. You've given me an idea. I will offer the geyser gods a poem! I can still do that. It doesn't count as music."

Meg frowned. "Uh, I don't know if—"

"Don't be envious, Meg. I will make up a poem for you later. This will surely please the geyser gods!" I walked forward, spread my arms, and began to improvise:

> "Oh, geyser, my geyser,
> Let us spew then, you and I,
> Upon this midnight dreary, while we ponder
> Whose woods are these?
> For we have not gone gentle into this good night,
> But have wandered lonely as clouds.
> We seek to know for whom the bell tolls,
> So I hope, springs eternal,
> That the time has come to talk of many things!"

I don't wish to brag, but I thought it was rather good, even if I did recycle a few bits from my earlier works. Unlike my music and archery, my godly skills with poetry seemed to be completely intact.

I glanced at Meg, hoping to see shining admiration on her face. It was high time the girl started to appreciate me. Instead, her mouth hung open, aghast.

"What?" I demanded. "Did you fail poetry appreciation in school? That was first-rate stuff!"

Meg pointed toward the geysers. I realized she was not looking at me at all.

"Well," said a raspy voice, "you got my attention."

One of the palikoi hovered over his geyser. His lower half was nothing but steam. From the waist up, he was perhaps twice the size of a human, with muscular arms the color of caldera mud, chalk-white eyes, and hair like cappuccino foam, as if he had shampooed vigorously and left it sudsy. His massive chest was stuffed into a baby-blue polo shirt with a logo of trees embroidered on the chest pocket.

"O, Great Palikos!" I said. "We beseech you—"

"What was that?" the spirit interrupted. "That stuff you were saying?"

"Poetry!" I said. "For you!"

He tapped his mud-gray chin. "No. That wasn't poetry."

I couldn't believe it. Did *no one* appreciate the beauty of language anymore? "My good spirit," I said. "Poetry doesn't have to rhyme, you know."

"I'm not talking about rhyming. I'm talking about getting your message across. We do a lot of market research, and that would *not* fly for our campaign. Now, the Oscar

Meyer Weiner song—*that* is poetry. The ad is fifty years old and people are still singing it. Do you think you could give us some poetry like that?"

I glanced at Meg to be sure I was not imagining this conversation.

"Listen here," I told the geyser god, "I've been the lord of poetry for four thousand years. I ought to know good poetry—"

The palikos waved his hands. "Let's start over. I'll run through our spiel, and maybe you can advise me. Hi, I'm Pete. Welcome to the Woods at Camp Half-Blood! Would you be willing to take a short customer satisfaction survey after this encounter? Your feedback is important."

"Um—"

"Great. Thanks."

Pete fished around in his vaporous region where his pockets would be. He produced a glossy brochure and began to read. "The Woods are your one-stop destination for . . . Hmm, it says *fun*. I thought we changed that to *exhilaration*. See, you've got to choose your words with care. If Paulie were here . . ." Pete sighed. "Well, he's better with the showmanship. Anyway, welcome to the Woods at Camp Half-Blood!"

"You already said that," I noted.

"Oh, right." Pete produced a red pen and began to edit.

"Hey." Meg shouldered past me. She had been speech-less with awe for about twelve seconds, which must've been a new record. "Mr. Steamy Mud, have you seen any lost demigods?"

"Mr. Steamy Mud!" Pete slapped his brochure. "*That* is

effective branding! And great point about lost demigods. We can't have our guests wandering around aimlessly. We should be handing out maps at the entrance to the woods. So many wonderful things to see in here, and no one even knows about them. I'll talk to Paulie when he gets back."

Meg took off her fogged-up glasses. "Who's Paulie?"

Pete gestured at the second geyser. "My partner. Maybe we could add a map to this brochure if—"

"So *have* you seen any lost demigods?" I asked.

"What?" Pete tried to mark his brochure, but the steam had made it so soggy, his red pen went right through the paper. "Oh, no. Not recently. But we should have better signage. For instance, did you even know these geysers were here?"

"No," I admitted.

"Well, there you go! Double geysers—the only ones on Long Island!—and no one even knows about us. No outreach. No word-of-mouth. This is why we convinced the board of directors to hire us!"

Meg and I looked at each other. I could tell that for once we were on the same wavelength: utter confusion.

"Sorry," I said. "Are you telling me the forest has a board of directors?"

"Well, of course," Pete said. "The dryads, the other nature spirits, the sentient monsters . . . I mean, *somebody* has to think about property values and services and public relations. It wasn't easy getting the board to hire us for marketing, either. If we mess up this job . . . oh, man."

Meg squished her shoes in the mud. "Can we go? I don't understand what this guy's talking about."

"And that's the problem!" Pete moaned. "How do we write clear ad copy that conveys the right image of the Woods? For instance, palikoi like Paulie and me used to be famous! Major tourist destinations! People would come to us to make binding oaths. Runaway slaves would seek us out for shelter. We'd get sacrifices, offerings, prayers . . . it was great. Now, nothing."

I heaved a sigh. "I know how you feel."

"Guys," Meg said, "we're looking for missing demigods."

"Right," I agreed. "O, Great . . . Pete, do you have any idea where our lost friends might have gone? Perhaps you know of some secret locations within the woods?"

Pete's chalk-white eyes brightened. "Did you know the children of Hephaestus have a hidden workshop to the north called Bunker Nine?"

"I did, actually," I said.

"Oh." A puff of steam escaped Pete's left nostril. "Well, did you know the Labyrinth has rebuilt itself? There is an entrance right here in the woods—"

"We know," Meg said.

Pete looked crestfallen.

"But perhaps," I said, "that's because your marketing campaign is working."

"Do you think so?" Pete's foamy hair began to swirl. "Yes. Yes, that may be true! Did you happen to see our spotlights, too? Those were my idea."

"Spotlights?" Meg asked.

Twin beams of red light blasted from the geysers and swept across the sky. Lit from beneath, Pete looked like the world's scariest teller of ghost stories.

"Unfortunately, they attracted the wrong kind of attention." Pete sighed. "Paulie doesn't let me use them often. He suggested advertising on a blimp instead, or perhaps a giant inflatable King Kong—"

"That's cool," Meg interrupted. "But can you tell us anything about a secret grove with whispering trees?"

I had to admit, Meg was good at getting us back on topic. As a poet, I did not cultivate directness. But as an archer, I could appreciate the value of a straight shot.

"Oh." Pete floated lower in his cloud of steam, the spotlight turning him the color of cherry soda. "I'm not supposed to talk about the grove."

My once-godly ears tingled. I resisted the urge to scream, *AHA!* "Why can't you talk about the grove, Pete?"

The spirit fiddled with his soggy brochure. "Paulie said it would scare away tourists. 'Talk about the dragons,' he told me. 'Talk about the wolves and serpents and ancient killing machines. But don't mention the grove.'"

"Ancient killing machines?" Meg asked.

"Yeah," Pete said halfheartedly. "We're marketing them as fun family entertainment. But the grove . . . Paulie said that was our worst problem. The neighborhood isn't even *zoned* for an Oracle. Paulie went there to see if maybe we could relocate it, but—"

"He didn't come back," I guessed.

Pete nodded miserably. "How am I supposed to run the marketing campaign all by myself? Sure, I can use robo-calls for the phone surveys, but a lot of networking has to be done face-to-face, and Paulie was always better with that stuff." Pete's voice broke into a sad hiss. "I miss him."

"Maybe we could find him," Meg suggested, "and bring him back."

Pete shook his head. "Paulie made me promise not to follow him and not to tell anybody else where the grove is. He's pretty good at resisting those weird voices, but you guys wouldn't stand a chance."

I was tempted to agree. Finding ancient killing machines sounded much more reasonable. Then I pictured Kayla and Austin wandering through the ancient grove, slowly going mad. They needed me, which meant I needed their location.

"Sorry, Pete." I gave him my most critical stare—the one I used to crush aspiring singers during Broadway auditions. "I'm just not buying it."

Mud bubbled around Pete's caldera. "Wh-what do you mean?"

"I don't think this grove exists," I said. "And if it does, I don't think you know its location."

Pete's geyser rumbled. Steam swirled in his spotlight beam. "I—I *do* know! Of course it exists!"

"Oh, really? Then why aren't there billboards about it all over the place? And a dedicated Web site? Why haven't I seen a groveofdodona hashtag on social media?"

Pete glowered. "I suggested all that! Paulie shot me down!"

"So do some outreach!" I demanded. "Sell us on your product! Show us where this grove is!"

"I can't. The only entrance . . ." He glanced over my shoulder and his face went slack. "Ah, spew." His spotlights shut off.

I turned. Meg made a squelching sound even louder than her shoes in the mud.

It took a moment for my vision to adjust, but at the edge of the clearing stood three black ants the size of Sherman tanks.

"Pete," I said, trying to remain calm, "when you said your spotlights attracted the wrong kind of attention—"

"I meant the myrmekes," he said. "I hope this won't affect your online review of the Woods at Camp Half-Blood."

24

Breaking my promise
Spectacularly failing
I blame Neil Diamond

MYRMEKES SHOULD BE high on your list of monsters not to fight.

They attack in groups. They spit acid. Their pincers can snap through Celestial bronze.

Also, they are ugly.

The three soldier ants advanced, their ten-foot-long antennae waving and bobbing in a mesmerizing way, trying to distract me from the true danger of their mandibles.

Their beaked heads reminded me of chickens—chickens with dark flat eyes and black armored faces. Each of their six legs would have made a fine construction winch. Their oversize abdomens throbbed and pulsed like noses sniffing for food.

I silently cursed Zeus for inventing ants. The way I heard it, he got upset with some greedy man who was always stealing from his neighbors' crops, so Zeus turned him into the first ant—a species that does nothing but scavenge, steal, and breed. Ares liked to joke that if Zeus wanted such a species, he could've just left humans the way they were. I used to laugh. Now that I am one of you, I no longer find it funny.

The ants stepped toward us, their antennae twitching. I imagined their train of thought was something like *Shiny? Tasty? Defenseless?*

"No sudden movements," I told Meg, who did not seem inclined to move at all. In fact, she looked petrified.

"Oh, Pete?" I called. "How do you deal with myrmekes invading your territory?"

"By hiding," he said, and disappeared into the geyser.

"Not helpful," I grumbled.

"Can we dive in?" Meg asked.

"Only if you fancy boiling to death in a pit of scalding water."

The tank bugs clacked their mandibles and edged closer.

"I have an idea." I unslung my ukulele.

"I thought you swore not to play," Meg said.

"I did. But if I throw this shiny object to one side, the ants might—"

I was about to say *the ants might follow it and leave us alone.*

I neglected to consider that, in my hands, the ukulele made me look shinier and tastier. Before I could throw the instrument, the soldier ants surged toward us. I stumbled back, only remembering the geyser behind me when my shoulder blades began to blister, filling the air with Apollo-scented steam.

"Hey, bugs!" Meg's scimitars flashed in her hands, making her the new shiniest thing in the clearing.

Can we take a moment to appreciate that Meg did this

on purpose? Terrified of insects, she could have fled and left me to be devoured. Instead, she chose to risk her life by distracting three tank-size ants. Throwing garbage at street thugs was one thing. But this . . . this was an entirely new level of foolishness. If I lived, I might have to nominate Meg McCaffrey for Best Sacrifice at the next Demi Awards.

Two of the ants charged at Meg. The third stayed on me, though he turned his head long enough for me to sprint to one side.

Meg ran between her opponents, her golden blades severing a leg from each. Their mandibles snapped at empty air. The soldier bugs wobbled on their five remaining legs, tried to turn, and bonked heads.

Meanwhile, the third ant charged me. In a panic, I threw my combat ukulele. It bounced off the ant's forehead with a dissonant *twang.*

I tugged my sword free of its scabbard. I've always hated swords. Such inelegant weapons, and they require you to be in close combat. How unwise, when you can shoot your enemies with an arrow from across the world!

The ant spit acid, and I tried to swat away the goop.

Perhaps that wasn't the brightest idea. I often got sword fighting and tennis confused. At least some of the acid splattered the ant's eyes, which bought me a few seconds. I valiantly retreated, raising my sword only to find that the blade had been eaten away, leaving me nothing but a steaming hilt.

"Oh, Meg?" I called helplessly.

She was otherwise occupied. Her swords whirled in golden arcs of destruction, lopping off leg segments, slicing antennae. I had never seen a dimachaerus fight with such skill, and I had seen all the best gladiators in combat. Unfortunately, her blades only sparked off the ants' thick main carapaces. Glancing blows and dismemberment did not faze them at all. As good as Meg was, the ants had more legs, more weight, more ferocity, and slightly more acid-spitting ability.

My own opponent snapped at me. I managed to avoid its mandibles, but its armored face bashed the side of my head. I staggered and fell. One ear canal seemed to fill with molten iron.

My vision clouded. Across the clearing, the other ants flanked Meg, using their acid to herd her toward the woods. She dove behind a tree and came up with only one of her blades. She tried to stab the closest ant but was driven back by acid cross fire. Her leggings were smoking, peppered with holes. Her face was tight with pain.

"Peaches," I muttered to myself. "Where is that stupid diaper demon when we need him?"

The karpos did not appear. Perhaps the presence of the geyser gods or some other force in the woods kept him away. Perhaps the board of directors had a rule against pets.

The third ant loomed over me, its mandibles foaming with green saliva. Its breath smelled worse than Hephaestus's work shirts.

My next decision I could blame on my head injury. I could tell you I wasn't thinking clearly, but that isn't true. I was desperate. I was terrified. I wanted to help Meg. Mostly I wanted to save myself. I saw no other option, so I dove for my ukulele.

I know. I promised on the River Styx not to play music until I was a god once more. But even such a dire oath can seem unimportant when a giant ant is about to melt your face off.

I grabbed the instrument, rolled onto my back, and belted out "Sweet Caroline."

Even without my oath, I would only have done something like that in the most extreme emergency. When I sing that song, the chances of mutually assured destruction are too great. But I saw no other choice. I gave it my utmost effort, channeling all the saccharine schmaltz I could muster from the 1970s.

The giant ant shook its head. Its antennae quivered. I got to my feet as the monster crawled drunkenly toward me. I put my back to the geyser and launched into the chorus.

The *Dah! Dah! Dah!* did the trick. Blinded by disgust and rage, the ant charged. I rolled aside as the monster's momentum carried it forward, straight into the muddy cauldron.

Believe me, the only thing that smells *worse* than Hephaestus's work shirts is a myrmeke boiling in its own shell.

Somewhere behind me, Meg screamed. I turned in time to see her second sword fly from her hand. She collapsed as one of the myrmekes caught her in its mandibles.

"NO!" I shrieked.

The ant did not snap her in half. It simply held her— limp and unconscious.

"Meg!" I yelled again. I strummed the ukulele desperately. "Sweet Caroline!"

But my voice was gone. Defeating one ant had taken all my energy. (I don't think I have ever written a sadder sentence than that.) I tried to run to Meg's aid, but I stumbled and fell. The world turned pale yellow. I hunched on all fours and vomited.

I have a concussion, I thought, but I had no idea what to do about it. It seemed like ages since I had been a god of healing.

I may have lay in the mud for minutes or hours while my brain slowly gyrated inside my skull. By the time I managed to stand, the two ants were gone.

There was no sign of Meg McCaffrey.

25

I'm on a roll now
Boiling, burning, throwing up
Lions? Hey, why not?

I STUMBLED THROUGH the glade, shouting Meg's name. I knew it was pointless, but yelling felt good. I looked for signs of broken branches or trampled ground. Surely two tank-size ants would leave a trail I could follow. But I was not Artemis; I did not have my sister's skill with tracking. I had no idea which direction they'd taken my friend.

I retrieved Meg's swords from the mud. Instantly, they changed into gold rings—so small, so easily lost, like a mortal life. I may have cried. I tried to break my ridiculous combat ukulele, but the Celestial bronze instrument defied my attempts. Finally, I yanked off the A string, threaded it through Meg's rings, and tied them around my neck.

"Meg, I will find you," I muttered.

Her abduction was my fault. I was sure of this. By playing music and saving myself, I had broken my oath on the River Styx. Instead of punishing me directly, Zeus or the Fates or all the gods together had visited their wrath upon Meg McCaffrey.

How could I have been so foolish? Whenever I angered

the other gods, those closest to me were struck down. I'd lost Daphne because of one careless comment to Eros. I'd lost the beautiful Hyacinthus because of a quarrel with Zephyros. Now my broken oath would cost Meg her life.

No, I told myself. *I won't allow it.*

I was so nauseous, I could barely walk. Someone seemed to be inflating a balloon inside my brain. Yet I managed to stumble to the rim of Pete's geyser.

"Pete!" I shouted. "Show yourself, you cowardly tele-marketer!"

Water shot skyward with a sound like the blast of an organ's lowest pipe. In the swirling steam, the palikos appeared, his mud-gray face hardening with anger.

"You call me a TELEMARKETER?" he demanded. "We run a full-service PR firm!"

I doubled over and vomited in his crater, which I thought an appropriate response.

"Stop that!" Pete complained.

"I need to find Meg." I wiped my mouth with a shaky hand. "What would the myrmekes do with her?"

"I don't know!"

"Tell me or I will *not* complete your customer service survey."

Pete gasped. "That's terrible! Your feedback is import-ant!" He floated down to my side. "Oh, dear . . . your head doesn't look good. You've got a big gash on your scalp, and there's blood. That must be why you're not thinking clearly."

"I don't care!" I yelled, which only made the pounding in my head worse. "Where is the myrmekes' nest?"

Pete wrung his steamy hands. "Well, that's what we were talking about earlier. That's where Paulie went. The nest is the only entrance."

"To what?"

"To the Grove of Dodona."

My stomach solidified into a pack of ice, which was unfair, because I needed one for my head. "The ant nest . . . is the way to the grove?"

"Look, you need medical attention. I *told* Paulie we should have a first-aid station for visitors." He fished around in his nonexistent pockets. "Let me just mark the location of the Apollo cabin—"

"If you pull out a brochure," I warned, "I will make you eat it. Now, explain how the nest leads to the grove."

Pete's face turned yellow, or perhaps that was just my vision getting worse. "Paulie didn't tell me everything. There's this thicket of woods that's grown so dense, nobody can get in. I mean, even from above, the branches are like . . ." He laced his muddy fingers, then caused them to liquefy and melt into one another, which made his point quite well.

"Anyway"—he pulled his hands apart—"the grove is in there. It could have been slumbering for centuries. Nobody on the board of directors even knew about it. Then, all of a sudden, the trees started whispering. Paulie figured those darned ants must have burrowed into the grove from underneath, and that's what woke it up."

I tried to make sense of that. It was difficult with a swollen brain. "Which way is the nest?"

"North of here," Pete said. "Half a mile. But, man, you are in no shape—"

"I must! Meg needs me!"

Pete grabbed my arm. His grip was like a warm wet tourniquet. "She's got time. If they carried her off in one piece, that means she's not dead yet."

"She will be soon enough!"

"Nah. Before Paulie . . . before he disappeared, he went into that nest a few times looking for the tunnel to the grove. He told me those myrmekes like to goop up their victims and let them, um, ripen until they're soft enough for the hatchlings to eat."

I made an un-godlike squeak. If there had been anything left in my stomach, I would have lost it. "How long does she have?"

"Twenty-four hours, give or take. Then she'll start to . . . um, soften."

It was difficult to imagine Meg McCaffrey softening under any circumstances, but I pictured her alone and scared, encased in insect goop, tucked in some larder of carcasses in the ants' nest. For a girl who hated bugs— Oh, Demeter had been right to hate me and keep her children away from me. I was a terrible god!

"Go get some help," Pete urged. "The Apollo cabin can heal that head wound. You're not doing your friend any favors by charging after her and getting yourself killed."

"Why do you care what happens to us?"

The geyser god looked offended. "Visitor satisfaction is always our top priority! Besides, if you find Paulie while you're in there . . ."

I tried to stay angry at the palikos, but the loneliness and worry on his face mirrored my own feelings. "Did Paulie explain how to navigate the ants' nest?"

Pete shook his head. "Like I said, he didn't want me to follow him. The myrmekes are dangerous enough. And if those other guys are still wandering around—"

"Other guys?"

Pete frowned. "Didn't I mention that? Yeah. Paulie saw three humans, heavily armed. They were looking for the grove too."

My left leg started thumping nervously, as if it missed its three-legged race partner. "How did Paulie know what they were looking for?"

"He heard them talking in Latin."

"*Latin?* Were they campers?"

Pete spread his hands. "I—I don't think so. Paulie described them like they were adults. He said one of them was the leader. The other two addressed him as *imperator.*"

The entire planet seemed to tilt. "Imperator."

"Yeah, you know, like in Rome—"

"Yes, I know." Suddenly, too many things made sense. Pieces of the puzzle flew together, forming one huge picture that smacked me in the face. The Beast . . . Triumvirate Holdings . . . adult demigods completely off the radar.

It was all I could do to avoid pitching forward into the geyser. Meg needed me more than ever. But I would have to do this right. I would have to be careful—even more careful than when I gave the fiery horses of the sun their yearly vaccinations.

"Pete," I said, "do you still oversee sacred oaths?"

"Well, yes, but—"

"Then hear my solemn oath!"

"Uh, the thing is, you've got this aura around you like you just *broke* a sacred oath, maybe one you swore on the River Styx? And if you break *another* oath with me—"

"I swear that I will save Meg McCaffrey. I will use every means at my disposal to bring her safely from the ants' lair, and this oath supersedes any previous oath I have made. This I swear upon your sacred and extremely hot waters!"

Pete winced. "Well, okay. It's done now. But keep in mind that if you don't keep that oath, if Meg dies, even if it's not your fault . . . you'll face the consequences."

"I am already cursed for breaking my earlier oath! What does it matter?"

"Yeah, but see, those River Styx oaths can take *years* to destroy you. They're like cancer. My oaths . . ." Pete shrugged. "If you break it, there's nothing I can do to stop your punishment. Wherever you are, a geyser will instantly blast through the ground at your feet and boil you alive."

"Ah . . ." I tried to stop my knees from knocking. "Yes, of course I knew that. I stand by my oath."

"You've got no choice now."

"Right. I think I'll—I'll go get healed."

I staggered off.

"Camp is the other direction," Pete said.

I changed course.

"Remember to complete our survey online!" Pete called after me. "Just curious, on a scale of one to ten, how would you rate your overall satisfaction with the Woods at Camp Half-Blood?"

I didn't reply. As I stumbled into the darkness, I was too busy contemplating, on a scale of one to ten, the pain I might have to endure in the near future.

I didn't have the strength to make it back to camp. The farther I walked, the clearer that became. My joints were pudding. I felt like a marionette, and as much as I'd enjoyed controlling mortals from above in the past, I did not relish being on the other end of the strings.

My defenses were at level zero. The smallest hellhound or dragon could have easily made a meal of the great Apollo. If an irritated badger had taken issue with me, I would have been doomed.

I leaned against a tree to catch my breath. The tree seemed to push me away, whispering in a voice I remembered so well: *Keep moving, Apollo. You can't rest here.*

"I loved you," I muttered.

Part of me knew I was delirious—imagining things only because of my concussion—but I swore I could see the face of my beloved Daphne rising from each tree trunk I passed, her features floating under the bark like a mirage of wood— her slightly crooked nose, her offset green eyes, those lips I had never kissed but never stopped dreaming of.

You loved every pretty girl, she scolded. *And every pretty boy, for that matter.*

"Not like you," I cried. "You were my first true love. Oh, Daphne!"

Wear my crown, she said. *And repent.*

I remembered chasing her—her lilac scent on the breeze, her lithe form flitting through the dappled light of the forest.

I pursued her for what seemed like years. Perhaps it was.

For centuries afterward, I blamed Eros.

In a moment of recklessness, I had ridiculed Eros's archery skills. Out of spite, he struck me with a golden arrow. He bent all my love toward the beautiful Daphne, but that was not the worst of it. He also struck Daphne's heart with a lead arrow, leeching all possible affection she might have had for me.

What people do not understand: Eros's arrows can't summon emotion from nothing. They can only cultivate potential that is already there. Daphne and I could have been a perfect pair. She was my true love. She could have loved me back. Yet thanks to Eros, my love-o-meter was cranked to one hundred percent, while Daphne's feelings turned to pure hate (which is, of course, only the flip side of love). Nothing is more tragic than loving someone to the depths of your soul and knowing they cannot and will not ever love you back.

The stories say I chased her on a whim, that she was just another pretty dress. The stories are wrong. When she begged Gaea to turn her into a laurel tree in order to escape me, part of my heart hardened into bark as well. I invented the laurel wreath to commemorate my failure—to punish myself for the fate of my greatest love. Every time some hero wins the laurels, I am reminded of the girl I can never win.

After Daphne, I swore I would never marry. Sometimes I claimed that was because I couldn't decide between the Nine Muses. A convenient story. The Nine Muses were my constant companions, all of them beautiful in their own way. But they never possessed my heart like Daphne did.

Only one other person ever affected me so deeply—the perfect Hyacinthus—and he, too, was taken from me.

All these thoughts rambled through my bruised brain. I staggered from tree to tree, leaning against them, grabbing their lowest branches like handrails.

You cannot die here, Daphne whispered. *You have work to do. You made an oath.*

Yes, my oath. Meg needed me. I had to . . .

I fell face forward in the icy mulch.

How long I lay there, I'm not sure.

A warm snout breathed in my ear. A rough tongue lapped my face. I thought I was dead and Cerberus had found me at the gates of the Underworld.

Then the beast pushed me over onto my back. Dark tree branches laced the sky. I was still in the forest. The golden visage of a lion appeared above me, his amber eyes beautiful and deadly. He licked my face, perhaps trying to decide if I would make a good supper.

"*Ptfh.*" I spit mane fur out of my mouth.

"Wake up," said a woman's voice, somewhere to my right. It wasn't Daphne, but it was vaguely familiar.

I managed to raise my head. Nearby, a second lion sat at the feet of a woman with tinted glasses and a silver-and-gold tiara in her braided hair. Her batik dress swirled with images of fern fronds. Her arms and hands were covered in henna tattoos. She looked different than she had in my dream, but I recognized her.

"Rhea," I croaked.

She inclined her head. "Peace, Apollo. I don't want to bum you out, but we need to talk."

26

Imperators here?

Gag me with a peace symbol

Not groovy, Mama

MY HEAD WOUND MUST have tasted like Wagyu beef.

The lion kept licking the side of my face, making my hair stickier and wetter. Strangely, this seemed to clear my thoughts. Perhaps lion saliva had curative properties. I guess I should have known that, being a god of healing, but you'll have to excuse me if I haven't done trial-and-error experiments with the drool of every single animal.

With difficulty, I sat up and faced the Titan queen.

Rhea leaned against the side of a VW safari van painted with swirling black frond designs like those on her dress. I seemed to recall that the black fern was one of Rhea's symbols, but I couldn't remember why. Among the gods, Rhea had always been something of a mystery. Even Zeus, who knew her best, did not often speak of her.

Her turret crown circled her brow like a glittering railroad track. When she looked down at me, her tinted glasses changed from orange to purple. A macramé belt cinched her waist, and on a chain around her neck hung her brass peace symbol.

She smiled. "Glad you're awake. I was worried, man."

I really wished people would stop calling me *man*. "Why are you . . . Where have you been all these centuries?"

"Upstate." She scratched her lion's ears. "After Woodstock, I stuck around, started a pottery studio."

"You . . . what?"

She tilted her head. "Was that last week or last millennium? I've lost track."

"I—I believe you're describing the 1960s. That was last century."

"Oh, bummer." Rhea sighed. "I get mixed up after so many years."

"I sympathize."

"After I left Kronos . . . well, that man was so square, you could cut yourself on his corners, you know what I mean? He was the ultimate 1950s dad—wanted us to be Ozzie and Harriet or Lucy and Ricky or something."

"He—he swallowed his children alive."

"Yeah." Rhea brushed her hair from her face. "That was some bad karma. Anyway, I left him. Back then divorce wasn't cool. You just didn't do it. But me, I burned my *apodesmos* and got liberated. I raised Zeus in a commune with a bunch of naiads and *kouretes*. Lots of wheat germ and nectar. The kid grew up with a strong Aquarian vibe."

I was fairly sure Rhea was misremembering her centuries, but I thought it would be impolite to keep pointing that out.

"You remind me of Iris," I said. "She went organic vegan several decades ago."

Rhea made a face—just a ripple of disapproval before

regaining her karmic balance. "Iris is a good soul. I dig her. But you know, these younger goddesses, they weren't around to fight the revolution. They don't get what it was like when your old man was eating your children and you couldn't get a real job and the Titan chauvinists just wanted you to stay home and cook and clean and have more Olympian babies. And speaking of Iris . . ."

Rhea touched her forehead. "Wait, *were* we speaking of Iris? Or did I just have a flashback?"

"I honestly don't know."

"Oh, I remember now. She's a messenger of the gods, right? Along with Hermes and that other groovy liberated chick . . . Joan of Arc?"

"Er, I'm not sure about that last one."

"Well, anyway, the communication lines are down, man. Nothing works. Rainbow messages, flying scrolls, Hermes Express . . . it's all going haywire."

"We know this. But we don't know why."

"It's *them*. They're doing it."

"Who?"

She glanced to either side. "The Man, man. Big Brother. The suits. The imperators."

I had been hoping she would say something else: giants, Titans, ancient killing machines, aliens. I would've rather tangled with Tartarus or Ouranos or Primordial Chaos itself. I had hoped Pete the geyser misunderstood what his brother told him about the imperator in the ants' nest.

Now that I had confirmation, I wanted to steal Rhea's safari van and drive to some commune far, far upstate.

"Triumvirate Holdings," I said.

"Yeah," Rhea agreed. "That's their new military-industrial complex. It's bumming me out in a big way."

The lion stopped licking my face, probably because my blood had turned bitter. "How is this possible? How have they come back?"

"They never went away," Rhea said. "They did it to themselves, you know. Wanted to make themselves gods. That never works out well. Ever since the old days they've been hiding out, influencing history from behind the curtains. They're stuck in a kind of twilight life. They can't die; they can't really live."

"But how could we not *know* about this?" I demanded. "We are gods!"

Rhea's laugh reminded me of a piglet with asthma. "Apollo, Grandson, beautiful child . . . Has being a god ever stopped someone from being stupid?"

She had a point. Not about me personally, of course, but the stories I could tell you about the *other* Olympians . . .

"The emperors of Rome." I tried to come to terms with the idea. "They can't *all* be immortal."

"No," Rhea said. "Just the worst of them, the most notorious. They live in human memory, man. That's what keeps them alive. Same as us, really. They're tied to the course of Western civilization, even though that whole concept is imperialist Eurocentric propaganda, man. Like my guru would tell you—"

"Rhea"—I put my hands against my throbbing temples—"can we stick to one problem at a time?"

"Yeah, okay. I didn't mean to blow your mind."

"But how can they affect our lines of communication? How can they be so powerful?"

"They've had centuries, Apollo. *Centuries*. All that time, plotting and making war, building up their capitalist empire, waiting for this moment when you are mortal, when the Oracles are vulnerable for a hostile takeover. It's just evil. They have no chill whatsoever."

"I thought that was a more modern term."

"Evil?"

"No. *Chill*. Never mind. The Beast . . . he is the leader?"

"Afraid so. He's as twisted as the others, but he's the smartest and the most stable—in a sociopathic homicidal way. You know who he is—who he was, right?"

Unfortunately, I did. I remembered where I had seen his smirking ugly face. I could hear his nasal voice echoing through the arena, ordering the execution of hundreds while the crowds cheered. I wanted to ask Rhea who his two compatriots were in the Triumvirate, but I decided I could not bear the information at present. None of the options were good, and knowing their names might bring me more despair than I could handle.

"It's true, then," I said. "The other Oracles still exist. The emperors hold them all?"

"They're working on it. Python has Delphi—that's the biggest problem. But you won't have the strength to take him head-on. You've got to pry their fingers off the minor Oracles first, loosen their power. To do that, you need a new source of prophecy for this camp—an Oracle that is older and independent."

"Dodona," I said. "Your whispering grove."

"Right on," Rhea said. "I thought the grove was gone forever. But then—I don't know how—the oak trees regrew themselves in the heart of these woods. You have to find the grove and protect it."

"I'm working on that." I touched the sticky wound on the side of my face. "But my friend Meg—"

"Yeah. You had some setbacks. But there are always setbacks, Apollo. When Lizzy Stanton and I hosted the first women's rights convention in Woodstock—"

"I think you mean Seneca Falls?"

Rhea frowned. "Wasn't that in the '60s?"

"The '40s," I said. "The 1840s, if memory serves."

"So . . . Jimi Hendrix wasn't there?"

"Doubtful."

Rhea fiddled with her peace symbol. "Then who set that guitar on fire? Ah, never mind. The point is, you have to persevere. Sometimes change takes centuries."

"Except that I'm mortal now," I said. "I don't *have* centuries."

"But you have willpower," Rhea said. "You have mortal drive and urgency. Those are things the gods often lack."

At her side, her lion roared.

"I've gotta split," Rhea said. "If the imperators track me down—bad scene, man. I've been off the grid too long. I'm not going to get sucked into that patriarchal institutional oppression again. Just find Dodona. That's your first trial."

"And if the Beast finds the grove first?"

"Oh, he's already found the gates, but he'll never get through them without you and the girl."

"I—I don't understand."

"That's cool. Just breathe. Find your center. Enlightenment has to come from *within*."

It was very much like a line I would've given *my* worshippers. I was tempted to choke Rhea with her macramé belt, but I doubted I would have the strength. Also, she had two lions. "But what do I do? How do I save Meg?"

"First, get healed. Rest up. Then . . . well, how you save Meg is up to you. The journey is greater than the destination, you know?"

She held out her hand. Draped on her fingers was a set of wind chimes—a collection of hollow brass tubes and medallions engraved with ancient Greek and Cretan symbols. "Hang these in the largest ancient oak. That will help you focus the voices of the Oracle. If you get a prophecy, groovy. It'll only be the beginning, but without Dodona, nothing else will be possible. The emperors will suffocate our future and divide up the world. Only when you have defeated Python can you reclaim your rightful place on Olympus. My kid, Zeus . . . he's got this whole 'tough love' disciplinarian hang-up, you dig? Taking back Delphi is the only way you're going to get on his good side."

"I—I was afraid you would say that."

"There's one other thing," she warned. "The Beast is planning some kind of attack on your camp. I don't know what it is, but it's going to be big. Like, even worse than napalm. You have to warn your friends."

The nearest lion nudged me. I wrapped my arms around his neck and allowed him to pull me to my feet. I managed to remain standing, but only because my legs locked up in complete fright. For the first time, I understood the trials that awaited me. I knew the enemies I must face. I would need more than wind chimes and enlightenment. I'd need a miracle. And as a god, I can tell you that those are never distributed lightly.

"Good luck, Apollo." The Titan queen placed the wind chimes in my hands. "I've got to check my kiln before my pots crack. Keep on trucking, and save those trees!"

The woods dissolved. I found myself standing in the central green at Camp Half-Blood, face-to-face with Chiara Benvenuti, who jumped back in alarm. "Apollo?"

I smiled. "Hey, girl." My eyes rolled up in my head and, for the second time that week, I charmingly passed out in front of her.

27

I apologize
For pretty much everything
Wow, I'm a good guy

"WAKE," SAID A VOICE.

I opened my eyes and saw a ghost—his face just as precious to me as Daphne's. I knew his copper skin, his kind smile, the dark curls of his hair, and those eyes as purple as senatorial robes.

"Hyacinthus," I sobbed. "I'm so sorry . . ."

He turned his face toward the sunlight, revealing the ugly dent above his left ear where the discus had struck him. My own wounded face throbbed in sympathy.

"Seek the caverns," he said. "Near the springs of blue. Oh, Apollo . . . your sanity will be taken away, but do not . . ."

His image faded and began to retreat. I rose from my sickbed. I rushed after him and grabbed his shoulders. "Do not *what*? Please don't leave me again!"

My vision cleared. I found myself by the window in Cabin Seven, holding a ceramic pot of purple and red hyacinths. Nearby, looking very concerned, Will and Nico stood as if ready to catch me.

"He's talking to the flowers," Nico noted. "Is that normal?"

"Apollo," Will said, "you had a concussion. I healed you, but—"

"These hyacinths," I demanded. "Have they always been here?"

Will frowned. "Honestly, I don't know where they came from, but . . ." He took the flowerpot from my hands and set it back on the windowsill. "Let's worry about you, okay?"

Usually that would've been excellent advice, but now I could only stare at the hyacinths and wonder if they were some sort of message. How cruel to see them—the flowers that I had created to honor my fallen love, with their plumes stained red like his blood or hued violet like his eyes. They bloomed so cheerfully in the window, reminding me of the joy I had lost.

Nico rested his hand on Will's shoulder. "Apollo, we were worried. Will was especially."

Seeing them together, supporting each other, made my heart feel even heavier. During my delirium, both of my great loves had visited me. Now, once again, I was devastatingly alone.

Still, I had a task to complete. A friend needed my help.

"Meg is in trouble," I said. "How long was I unconscious?"

Will and Nico glanced at each other.

"It's about noon now," Will said. "You showed up on the green around six this morning. When Meg didn't return with you, we wanted to search the woods for her, but Chiron wouldn't let us."

"Chiron was absolutely correct," I said. "I won't allow any others to put themselves at risk. But I must hurry. Meg has until tonight at the latest."

"Then what happens?" Nico asked.

I couldn't say it. I couldn't even *think* about it without losing my nerve. I looked down. Aside from Paolo's Brazilian-flag bandana and my ukulele-string necklace, I was wearing only my boxer shorts. My offensive flabbiness was on display for everyone to see, but I no longer cared about that. (Well, not much, anyway.) "I have to get dressed."

I staggered back to my cot. I fumbled through my meager supplies and found Percy Jackson's Led Zeppelin T-shirt. I tugged it on. It seemed more appropriate than ever.

Will hovered nearby. "Look, Apollo, I don't think you're back to a hundred percent."

"I'll be fine." I pulled on my jeans. "I have to save Meg."

"Let us help you," Nico said. "Tell us where she is and I can shadow-travel—"

"No!" I snapped. "No, you have to stay here and protect the camp."

Will's expression reminded me very much of his mother, Naomi—that look of trepidation she got just before she went onstage. "Protect the camp from what?"

"I—I'm not sure. You must tell Chiron the emperors have returned. Or rather, they never went away. They've been plotting, building their resources for centuries."

Nico's eyes glinted warily. "When you say emperors—"

"I mean the Roman ones."

Will stepped back. "You're saying the emperors of ancient Rome are alive? *How?* The Doors of Death?"

"No." I could barely speak through the taste of bile. "The emperors made themselves gods. They had their own temples and altars. They encouraged the people to worship them."

"But that was just propaganda," Nico said. "They weren't really divine."

I laughed mirthlessly. "Gods are sustained by worship, son of Hades. They continue to exist because of the collective memories of a culture. It's true for the Olympians; it's also true for the emperors. Somehow, the most powerful of them have survived. All these centuries, they have clung to half-life, hiding, waiting to reclaim their power."

Will shook his head. "That's impossible. How—?"

"I don't know!" I tried to steady my breathing. "Tell Rachel the men behind Triumvirate Holdings are former emperors of Rome. They've been plotting against us all this time, and we gods have been blind. *Blind.*"

I pulled on my coat. The ambrosia Nico had given me yesterday was still in the left pocket. In the right pocket, Rhea's wind chimes clanked, though I had no idea how they'd gotten there.

"The Beast is planning some sort of attack on the camp," I said. "I don't know what, and I don't know when, but tell Chiron you must be prepared. I have to go."

"Wait!" Will said as I reached the door. "Who is the Beast? Which emperor are we dealing with?"

"The worst of my descendants." My fingers dug into the doorframe. "The Christians called him the Beast because he burned them alive. Our enemy is Emperor Nero."

———

They must have been too stunned to follow me.

I ran toward the armory. Several campers gave me strange looks. Some called after me, offering help, but I ignored them. I could only think about Meg alone in the myrmekes' lair, and the visions I'd had of Daphne, Rhea, and Hyacinthus—all of them urging me onward, telling me to do the impossible in this inadequate mortal form.

When I reached the armory, I scanned the rack of bows. My hand trembling, I picked out the weapon Meg had tried to give me the day before. It was carved from mountain laurel wood. The bitter irony appealed to me.

I had sworn not to use a bow until I was a god again. But I had also sworn not to play music, and I had already broken that part of the oath in the most egregious, Neil-Diamondy way possible.

The curse of the River Styx could kill me in its slow cancerous way, or Zeus could strike me down. But my oath to save Meg McCaffrey had to come first.

I turned my face to the sky. "If you want to punish me, Father, be my guest, but have the courage to hurt *me* directly, not my mortal companion. BE A MAN!"

To my surprise, the skies remained silent. Lightning did not vaporize me. Perhaps Zeus was too taken aback to react, but I knew he would never overlook such an insult.

To Tartarus with him. I had work to do.

I grabbed a quiver and stuffed it with all the extra arrows I could find. Then I ran for the woods, Meg's two rings jangling on my makeshift necklace. Too late, I realized I had forgotten my combat ukulele, but I had no time to turn back. My singing voice would have to be enough.

I'm not sure how I found the nest.

Perhaps the forest simply allowed me to reach it, knowing that I was marching to my death. I've found that when one is searching for danger, it's never hard to find.

Soon I was crouched behind a fallen tree, studying the myrmekes' lair in the clearing ahead. To call the place an anthill would be like calling Versailles Palace a single-family home. Earthen ramparts rose almost to the tops of the surrounding trees—a hundred feet at least. The circumference could have accommodated a Roman hippodrome. A steady stream of soldiers and drones swarmed in and out of the mound. Some carried fallen trees. One, inexplicably, was dragging a 1967 Chevy Impala.

How many ants would I be facing? I had no idea. After you reach the number *impossible*, there's no point in counting.

I nocked an arrow and stepped into the clearing.

When the nearest myrmeke spotted me, he dropped his Chevy. He watched me approach, his antennae bobbing. I ignored him and strolled past, heading for the nearest tunnel entrance. That confused him even more.

Several other ants gathered to watch.

I've learned that if you act like you are supposed to be somewhere, most people (or ants) will not confront you. Normally, acting confident isn't a problem for me. Gods are allowed to be anywhere. It was a bit tougher for Lester Papadopoulos, dork teen extraordinaire, but I made it all the way to the nest without being challenged.

I plunged inside and began to sing.

This time I needed no ukulele. I needed no muse for

my inspiration. I remembered Daphne's face in the trees. I remembered Hyacinthus turning away, his death wound glistening on his scalp. My voice filled with anguish. I sang of heartbreak. Rather than collapsing under my own despair, I projected it outward.

The tunnels amplified my voice, carrying it through the nest, making the entire hill my musical instrument.

Each time I passed an ant, it curled its legs and touched its forehead to the floor, its antennae quivering from the vibrations of my voice.

Had I been a god, the song would have been stronger, but this was enough. I was impressed by how much sorrow a human voice could convey.

I wandered deeper into the hill. I had no idea where I was going until I spotted a geranium blooming from the tunnel floor.

My song faltered.

Meg. She must have regained consciousness. She had dropped one of her emergency seeds to leave me a trail. The geranium's purple flowers all faced a smaller tunnel leading off to the left.

"Clever girl," I said, choosing that tunnel.

A clattering sound alerted me to the approaching myrmeke.

I turned and raised my bow. Freed from the enchantment of my voice, the insect charged, its mouth foaming with acid. I drew and fired. The arrow embedded itself up to the fletching in the ant's forehead.

The creature dropped, its back legs twitching in death throes. I tried to retrieve my arrow, but the shaft snapped in my hand, the broken end covered in steaming corrosive goo. So much for reusing ammunition.

I called, "MEG!"

The only answer was the clattering of more giant ants moving in my direction. I began to sing again. Now, though, I had higher hopes of finding Meg, which made it difficult to summon the proper amount of melancholy. The ants I encountered were no longer catatonic. They moved slowly and unsteadily, but they still attacked. I was forced to shoot one after another.

I passed a cave filled with glittering treasure, but I was not interested in shiny things at the moment. I kept moving.

At the next intersection, another geranium sprouted from the floor, all its flowers facing right. I turned that direction, calling Meg's name again, then returning to my song.

As my spirits lifted, my song became less effective and the ants more aggressive. After a dozen kills, my quiver was growing dangerously light.

I had to reach deeper into my feelings of despair. I had to get the blues, good and proper.

For the first time in four thousand years, I sang of my own faults.

I poured out my guilt about Daphne's death. My boastfulness, envy, and desire had caused her destruction. When she ran from me, I should have let her go. Instead, I chased her relentlessly. I wanted her, and I intended to have her. Because of that, I had left Daphne no choice. To escape me, she sacrificed her life and turned into a tree, leaving my heart scarred forever. . . . But it was *my* fault. I apologized in song. I begged Daphne's forgiveness.

I sang of Hyacinthus, the most handsome of men. The West Wind Zephyros had also loved him, but I refused to share even a moment of Hyacinthus's time. In my jealousy, I threatened Zephyros. I dared him, *dared* him to interfere.

I sang of the day Hyacinthus and I played discus in the fields, and how the West Wind blew my disc off course— right into the side of Hyacinthus's head.

To keep Hyacinthus in the sunlight where he belonged, I created hyacinth flowers from his blood. I held Zephyros accountable, but my own petty greed had caused Hyacinthus's death. I poured out my sorrow. I took all the blame.

I sang of my failures, my eternal heartbreak and loneliness. I was the worst of the gods, the most guilt-ridden and unfocused. I couldn't commit myself to one lover. I couldn't even choose what to be the god of. I kept shifting from one skill to another—distracted and dissatisfied.

My golden life was a sham. My coolness was pretense. My heart was a lump of petrified wood.

All around me, myrmekes collapsed. The nest itself trembled with grief.

I found a third geranium, then a fourth.

Finally, pausing between verses, I heard a small voice up ahead: the sound of a girl crying.

"Meg!" I gave up on my song and ran.

She lay in the middle of a cavernous food larder, just as I had imagined. Around her were stacked the carcasses of animals—cows, deer, horses—all sheathed in hardened goop and slowly decaying. The smell hit my nasal passages like an avalanche.

Meg was also enveloped, but she was fighting back with the power of geraniums. Patches of leaves sprouted from the thinnest parts of her cocoon. A frilly collar of flowers kept the goo away from her face. She had even managed to free one of her arms, thanks to an explosion of pink geraniums at her left armpit.

Her eyes were puffy from crying. I assumed she was frightened, possibly in pain, but when I knelt next to her, her first words were, "I'm so sorry."

I brushed a tear from the tip of her nose. "Why, dear Meg? You did nothing wrong. I failed *you*."

A sob caught in her throat. "You don't understand. That song you were singing. Oh, gods . . . Apollo, if I'd known—"

"Hush, now." My throat was so raw I could barely talk. The song had almost destroyed my voice. "You're just reacting to the grief in the music. Let's get you free."

I was considering how to do that when Meg's eyes widened. She made a whimpering sound.

The hairs on the nape of my neck came to attention. "There are ants behind me, aren't there?" I asked.

Meg nodded.

I turned as four of them entered the cavern. I reached for my quiver. I had one arrow left.

28

Parenting advice:
Mamas, don't let your larvae
Grow up to be ants

MEG THRASHED IN HER GOO CASE. "Get me out of here!"

"I don't have a blade!" My fingers crept to the ukulele string around my neck. "Actually I have *your* blades, I mean your rings—"

"You don't need to cut me out. When the ant dumped me here, I dropped the packet of seeds. It should be close."

She was right. I spotted the crumpled pouch near her feet.

I inched toward it, keeping one eye on the ants. They stood together at the entrance as if hesitant to come closer. Perhaps the trail of dead ants leading to this room had given them pause.

"Nice ants," I said. "Excellent calm ants."

I crouched and scooped up the packet. A quick glance inside told me half a dozen seeds remained. "Now what, Meg?"

"Throw them on the goo," Meg said.

I gestured to the geraniums bursting from her neck and armpit. "How many seeds did that?"

"One."

"Then this many will choke you to death. I've turned too many people I cared about into flowers, Meg. I won't—"

"JUST DO IT!"

The ants did not like her tone. They advanced, snapping their mandibles. I shook the geranium seeds over Meg's cocoon, then nocked my arrow. Killing one ant would do no good if the other three tore us apart, so I chose a different target. I shot the roof of the cavern, just above the ants' heads.

It was a desperate idea, but I'd had success bringing down buildings with arrows before. In 464 BCE, I caused an earthquake that wiped out most of Sparta by hitting a fault line at the right angle. (I never liked the Spartans much.)

This time, I had less luck. The arrow embedded itself in the packed earth with a dull *thunk*. The ants took another step forward, acid dripping from their mouths. Behind me, Meg struggled to free herself from her cocoon, which was now covered in a shag carpet of purple flowers.

She needed more time.

Out of ideas, I tugged my Brazilian-flag handkerchief from my neck and waved it like a maniac, trying to channel my inner Paolo.

"BACK, FOUL ANTS!" I yelled. *"BRASIL!"*

The ants wavered—perhaps because of the bright colors, or my voice, or my sudden insane confidence. While they hesitated, cracks spread across the roof from my arrow's impact site, and then thousands of tons of earth collapsed on top of the myrmekes.

When the dust cleared, half the room was gone, along with the ants.

I looked at my handkerchief. "I'll be Styxed. It *does* have magic power. I can never tell Paolo about this or he'll be insufferable."

"Over here!" Meg yelled.

I turned. Another myrmeke was crawling over a pile of carcasses—apparently from a second exit I had failed to notice behind the disgusting food stores.

Before I could think what to do, Meg roared and burst from her cage, spraying geraniums in every direction. She shouted, "My rings!"

I yanked them from my neck and tossed them through the air. As soon as Meg caught them, two golden scimitars flashed into her hands.

The myrmeke barely had time to think *Uh-oh* before Meg charged. She sliced off his armored head. His body collapsed in a steaming heap.

Meg turned to me. Her face was a tempest of guilt, misery, and bitterness. I was afraid she might use her swords on me.

"Apollo, I . . ." Her voice broke.

I supposed she was still suffering from the effects of my song. She was shaken to her core. I made a mental note never again to sing so honestly when a mortal might be listening.

"It's all right, Meg," I said. "I should be apologizing to you. I got you into this mess."

Meg shook her head. "You don't understand. I—"

An enraged shriek echoed through the chamber, shaking the compromised ceiling and raining clods of dirt on our heads. The tone of the scream reminded me of Hera whenever she stormed through the hallways of Olympus, yelling at me for leaving the godly toilet seat up.

"That's the queen ant," I guessed. "We need to leave."

Meg pointed her sword toward the room's only remaining exit. "But the sound came from there. We'll be walking in her direction."

"Exactly. So perhaps we should hold off on making amends with each other, eh? We might still get each other killed."

We found the queen ant.

Hooray.

All corridors must have led to the queen. They radiated from her chamber like spikes on a morning star. Her Majesty was three times the size of her largest soldiers—a towering mass of black chitin and barbed appendages, with diaphanous oval wings folded against her back. Her eyes were glassy swimming pools of onyx. Her abdomen was a pulsing translucent sac filled with glowing eggs. The sight of it made me regret ever inventing gel capsule medications.

Her swollen abdomen might slow her down in a fight, but she was so large, she could intercept us before we reached the nearest exit. Those mandibles would snap us in half like dried twigs.

"Meg," I said, "how do you feel about dual-wielding scimitars against this lady?"

Meg looked appalled. "She's a mother giving birth."

"Yes . . . and she's an insect, which you hate. And her children were ripening you up for dinner."

Meg frowned. "Still . . . I don't feel right about it."

The queen hissed—a dry spraying noise. I imagined she would have already hosed us down with acid if she weren't worried about the long-term effects of corrosives on her larvae. Queen ants can't be too careful these days.

"You have another idea?" I asked Meg. "Preferably one that does not involve dying?"

She pointed to a tunnel directly behind the queen's clutch of eggs. "We need to go that way. It leads to the grove."

"How can you be sure?"

Meg tilted her head. "Trees. It's like . . . I can hear them growing."

That reminded me of something the Muses once told me—how they could actually hear the ink drying on new pages of poetry. I suppose it made sense that a daughter of Demeter could hear the growth of plants. Also, it didn't surprise me that the tunnel we needed was the most dangerous one to reach.

"Sing," Meg told me. "Sing like you did before."

"I—I can't. My voice is almost gone."

Besides, I thought, I don't want to risk losing you again.

I had freed Meg, so perhaps I'd fulfilled my oath to Pete the geyser god. Still, by singing and practicing archery, I had broken my oath upon the River Styx not once but twice. More singing would only make me *more* of a scofflaw.

Whatever cosmic punishments awaited me, I did not want them to fall on Meg.

Her Majesty snapped at us—a warning shot, telling us to back off. A few feet closer and my head would have rolled in the dirt.

I burst into song—or rather, I did the best I could with the raspy voice that remained. I began to rap. I started with the rhythm *boom chicka chicka*. I busted out some footwork the Nine Muses and I had been working on just before the war with Gaea.

The queen arched her back. I don't think she had expected to be rapped to today.

I gave Meg a look that clearly meant *Help me out!*

She shook her head. Give the girl two swords and she was a maniac. Ask her to lay down a simple beat and she suddenly got stage fright.

Fine, I thought. I'll do it by myself.

I launched into "Dance" by Nas, which I have to say was one of the most moving odes to mothers that I ever inspired an artist to write. (You're welcome, Nas.) I took some liberties with the lyrics. I may have changed *angel* to *brood mother* and *woman* to *insect*. But the sentiment remained. I serenaded the pregnant queen, channeling my love for my own dear mother, Leto. When I sang that I could only wish to marry a woman (or insect) so fine someday, my heartbreak was real. I would never have such a partner. It was not in my destiny.

The queen's antennae quivered. Her head seesawed back and forth. Eggs kept extruding from her abdomen, which made it difficult for me to concentrate, but I persevered.

When I was done, I dropped to one knee and held up my arms in tribute, waiting for the queen's verdict. Either she would kill me or she would not. I was spent. I had poured everything into that song and could not rap another line.

Next to me, Meg stood very still, gripping her swords.

Her Majesty shuddered. She threw back her head and wailed—a sound more brokenhearted than angry.

She leaned down and gently nudged my chest, pushing me in the direction of the tunnel we needed.

"Thank you," I croaked. "I—I'm sorry about the ants I killed."

The queen purred and clicked, extruding a few more eggs as if to say, *Don't worry; I can always make more.*

I stroked the queen ant's forehead. "May I call you Mama?"

Her mouth frothed in a pleased sort of way.

"Apollo," Meg urged, "let's go before she changes her mind."

I was not sure Mama *would* change her mind. I got the feeling she had accepted my fealty and adopted us into her brood. But Meg was right; we needed to hurry. Mama watched as we edged around her clutch of eggs.

We plunged into the tunnel and saw the glow of daylight above us.

29

Nightmares of torches
And a man in purple clothes
But that's not the worst

I HAD NEVER BEEN SO HAPPY to see a killing field.

We emerged into a glade littered with bones. Most were from forest animals. A few appeared human. I guessed we had found the myrmekes' dumping site, and they apparently didn't get regular garbage pickup.

The clearing was hemmed with trees so thick and tangled that traveling through them would've been impossible. Over our heads, the branches wove together in a leafy dome that let in sunlight but not much else. Anyone flying above the forest would never have realized this open space existed under the canopy.

At the far end of the glade stood a row of objects like football tackle dummies—six white cocoons staked on tall wooden poles, flanking a pair of enormous oaks. Each tree was at least eighty feet tall. They had grown so close together that their massive trunks appeared to have fused. I had the distinct impression I was looking at a set of living doors.

"It's a gateway," I said. "To the Grove of Dodona."

Meg's blades retracted, once again becoming gold rings on her middle fingers. "Aren't we *in* the grove?"

"No . . ." I stared across the clearing at the white cocoon Popsicles. They were too far away to make out clearly, but something about them seemed familiar in an evil, unwelcome sort of way. I wanted to get closer. I also wanted to keep my distance.

"I think this is more of an antechamber," I said. "The grove itself is behind those trees."

Meg gazed warily across the field. "I don't hear any voices."

It was true. The forest was absolutely quiet. The trees seemed to be holding their breath.

"The grove knows we are here," I guessed. "It's waiting to see what we'll do."

"We'd better do something, then." Meg didn't sound any more excited than I was, but she marched forward, bones crunching under her feet.

I wished I had more than a bow, an empty quiver, and a hoarse voice to defend myself with, but I followed, trying not to trip over rib cages and deer antlers. About halfway across the glade, Meg let out a sharp exhale.

She was staring at the posts on either side of the tree gates.

At first I couldn't process what I was seeing. Each stake was about the height of a crucifix—the kind Romans used to set up along the roadside to advertise the fates of criminals. (Personally, I find modern billboards much more tasteful.) The upper half of each post was wrapped in thick lumpy wads of white cloth, and sticking from the top of each cocoon was something that looked like a human head.

My stomach somersaulted. They *were* human heads. Arrayed in front of us were the missing demigods, all tightly bound. I watched, petrified, until I discerned the slightest expansions and contractions in the wrappings around their chests. They were still breathing. Unconscious, not dead. Thank the gods.

On the left were three teenagers I didn't know, though I assumed they must be Cecil, Ellis, and Miranda. On the right side was an emaciated man with gray skin and white hair—no doubt the geyser god Paulie. Next to him hung my children . . . Austin and Kayla.

I shook so violently, the bones around my feet clattered. I recognized the smell coming from the prisoners' wrappings—sulfur, oil, powdered lime, and liquid Greek fire, the most dangerous substance ever created. Rage and disgust fought in my throat, vying for the right to make me throw up.

"Oh, monstrous," I said. "We need to free them immediately."

"Wh-what's wrong with them?" Meg stammered.

I dared not put it into words. I had seen this form of execution once before, at the hands of the Beast, and I never wished to see it again.

I ran to Austin's stake. With all my strength I tried to push it over, but it wouldn't budge. The base was sunk too deep in the earth. I tore at the cloth bindings but only managed to coat my hands in sulfurous resin. The wadding was stickier and harder than myrmekes' goo.

"Meg, your swords!" I wasn't sure they would do any good either, but I could think of nothing else to try.

Then from above us came a familiar snarl.

The branches rustled. Peaches the karpos dropped from the canopy, landing with a somersault at Meg's feet. He looked like he'd been through quite an ordeal to get here. His arms were sliced up and dripping peach nectar. His legs were dotted with bruises. His diaper sagged dangerously.

"Thank the gods!" I said. That was not my usual reaction when I saw the grain spirit, but his teeth and claws might be just the things to free the demigods. "Meg, hurry! Order your friend to—"

"Apollo." Her voice was heavy. She pointed to the tunnel from which we'd come.

Emerging from the ants' nest were two of the largest humans I had ever seen. Each was seven feet tall and perhaps three hundred pounds of pure muscle stuffed into horsehide armor. Their blond hair glinted like silver floss. Jeweled rings glittered in their beards. Each man carried an oval shield and a spear, though I doubted they needed weapons to kill. They looked like they could crack open cannonballs with their bare hands.

I recognized them from their tattoos and the circular designs on their shields. Such warriors weren't easy to forget.

"Germani." Instinctively, I moved in front of Meg. The elite imperial bodyguards had been cold-blooded death reapers in ancient Rome. I doubted they'd gotten any sweeter over the centuries.

The two men glared at me. They had serpent tattoos curling around their necks, just like the ruffians who had jumped me in New York. The Germani parted, and their master climbed from the tunnel.

Nero hadn't changed much in one thousand nine hundred and some-odd years. He appeared to be no more than thirty, but it was a *hard* thirty, his face haggard and his belly distended from too much partying. His mouth was fixed in a permanent sneer. His curly hair extended into a wraparound neck beard. His chin was so weak, I was tempted to create a GoFundMe campaign to buy him a better jaw.

He tried to compensate for his ugliness with an expensive Italian suit of purple wool, his gray shirt open to display gold chains. His shoes were hand-tooled leather, not the sort of thing to wear while stomping around in an ant pile. Then again, Nero had always had expensive, impractical tastes. That was perhaps the only thing I admired about him.

"Emperor Nero," I said. "The Beast."

He curled his lip. "Nero will do. It's good to see you, my honored ancestor. I'm sorry I've been so lax about my offerings during the past few millennia, but"—he shrugged—"I haven't needed you. I've done rather well on my own."

My fists clenched. I wanted to strike down this pot-bellied emperor with a bolt of white-hot power, except that I had no bolts of white-hot power. I had no arrows. I had no singing voice left. Against Nero and his seven-foot-tall bodyguards, I had a Brazilian handkerchief, a packet of ambrosia, and some brass wind chimes.

"It's me you want," I said. "Cut these demigods down from their stakes. Let them leave with Meg. They've done nothing to you."

Nero chuckled. "I'll be happy to let them go once we've

come to an agreement. As for Meg . . ." He smiled at her. "How are you, my dear?"

Meg said nothing. Her face was as hard and gray as a geyser god's. At her feet, Peaches snarled and rustled his leafy wings.

One of Nero's guards said something in his ear.

The Emperor nodded. "Soon."

He turned his attention back to me. "But where are my manners? Allow me to introduce my right hand, Vincius, and my left hand, Garius."

The bodyguards pointed across to each other.

"Ah, sorry," Nero corrected. "My right hand, Garius, and my left hand, Vincius. Those are the Romanized versions of their Batavi names, which I can't pronounce. Usually I just call them Vince and Gary. Say hello, boys."

Vince and Gary glowered at me.

"They have serpent tattoos," I noted, "like those street thugs you sent to attack me."

Nero shrugged. "I have many servants. Cade and Mikey are quite low on the pay scale. Their only job was to rattle you a bit, welcome you to my city."

"*Your* city." I found it just like Nero to go claiming major metropolitan areas that clearly belonged to me. "And these two gentlemen . . . they are actually Germani from the ancient times? How?"

Nero made a snide little barking sound in the back of his nose. I'd forgotten how much I hated his laugh.

"Lord Apollo, please," he said. "Even before Gaea commandeered the Doors of Death, souls escaped from Erebos all the time. It was quite easy for a god-emperor such as myself to call back my followers."

"A god-emperor?" I growled. "You mean a delusional ex-emperor."

Nero arched his eyebrows. "What made *you* a god, Apollo . . . back when you were one? Wasn't it the power of your name, your sway over those who believed in you? I am no different." He glanced to his left. "Vince, fall on your spear, please."

Without hesitation, Vince planted the butt of his spear against the ground. He braced the point under his rib cage.

"Stop," Nero said. "I changed my mind."

Vince betrayed no relief. In fact, his eyes tightened with faint disappointment. He brought his spear back to his side.

Nero grinned at me. "You see? I hold the power of life and death over my worshippers, like any proper god should."

I felt like I'd swallowed some gel capsule larvae. "The Germani were always crazy, much like you."

Nero put his hand to his chest. "I'm hurt! My barbarian friends are loyal subjects of the Julian dynasty! And, of course, we are all descended from you, Lord Apollo."

I didn't need the reminder. I'd been so proud of my son, the original Octavian, later Caesar Augustus. After his death, his descendants became increasingly arrogant and unstable (which I blamed on their mortal DNA; they certainly didn't get those qualities from me). Nero had been the last of the Julian line. I had not wept when he died. Now here he was, as grotesque and chinless as ever.

Meg stood at my shoulder. "Wh-what do you want, Nero?"

Considering she was facing the man who killed her father, she sounded remarkably calm. I was grateful for her strength. It gave me hope to have a skilled dimachaerus and a ravenous peach baby at my side. Still, I did not like our odds against two Germani.

Nero's eyes gleamed. "Straight to the point. I've always admired that about you, Meg. Really, it's simple. You and Apollo will open the gates of Dodona for me. Then these six"—he gestured to the staked prisoners—"will be released."

I shook my head. "You'll destroy the grove. Then you'll kill us."

The emperor made that horrible bark again. "Not unless you force me to. I'm a reasonable god-emperor, Apollo! I'd much rather have the Grove of Dodona under my control if it can be managed, but I certainly can't allow *you* to use it. You had your chance at being the guardian of the Oracles. You failed miserably. Now it's my responsibility. Mine . . . and my partners'."

"The two other emperors," I said. "Who are they?"

Nero shrugged. "Good Romans—men who, like me, have the willpower to do what is needed."

"Triumvirates have never worked. They always lead to civil war."

He smiled as if that idea did not bother him. "The three of us have come to an agreement. We have divided up the new empire . . . by which I mean North America. Once we have the Oracles, we'll expand and do what Romans have always done best—conquer the world."

I could only stare at him. "You truly learned nothing from your previous reign."

"Oh, but I did! I've had centuries to reflect, plan, and prepare. Do you have any idea how annoying it is to be a god-emperor, unable to die but unable to fully live? There was a period of about three hundred years during the Middle Ages when my name was almost forgotten. I was little more than a mirage! Thank goodness for the Renaissance, when our Classical greatness was remembered. And then came the Internet. Oh, gods, I *love* the Internet! It is impossible for me to fade completely now. I am immortal on Wikipedia!"

I winced. I was now fully convinced of Nero's insanity. Wikipedia was always getting stuff wrong about me.

He rolled his hand. "Yes, yes. You think I am crazy. I could explain my plans and prove otherwise, but I have a lot on my plate today. I need you and Meg to open those gates. They've resisted my best efforts, but together you two can do it. Apollo, you have an affinity with Oracles. Meg has a way with trees. Get to it. Please and thank you."

"We would rather die," I said. "Wouldn't we, Meg?"

No response.

I glanced over. A silvery streak glistened on Meg's cheek. At first I thought one of her rhinestones had melted. Then I realized she was crying.

"Meg?"

Nero clasped his hands as if in prayer. "Oh, my. It seems we've had a slight miscommunication. You see, Apollo, Meg brought you here, just as I asked her to. Well done, my sweet."

Meg wiped her face. "I—I didn't mean . . ."

My heart compressed to the size of a pebble. "Meg, no. I can't believe—"

I reached for her. Peaches snarled and inserted himself between us. I realized the karpos was not here to protect us from Nero. He was defending Meg from *me*.

"Meg?" I said. "This man killed your father! He's a murderer!"

She stared at the ground. When she spoke, her voice was even more tortured than mine was when I sang in the anthill. "The *Beast* killed my father. This is Nero. He's— he's my stepfather."

I could not fully grasp this before Nero spread his arms.

"That's right, my darling," he said. "And you've done a wonderful job. Come to Papa."

30

I school McCaffrey
Yo, girl, your stepdad is wack
Why won't she listen?

I HAD BEEN BETRAYED BEFORE.

The memories came flooding back to me in a painful tide. Once, my former girlfriend Cyrene took up with Ares just to get back at me. Another time, Artemis shot me in the groin because I was flirting with her Hunters. In 1928, Alexander Fleming failed to give me credit for inspiring his discovery of penicillin. I mean, *ouch.* That stung.

But I couldn't remember *ever* being so wrong about someone as I had been about Meg. Well . . . at least not since Irving Berlin. *"Alexander's Ragtime Band"?* I remember telling him. *You'll never make it big with a corny song like that!*

"Meg, we are friends." My voice sounded petulant even to myself. "How could you do this to me?"

Meg looked down at her red sneakers—the primary-colored shoes of a traitor. "I tried to tell you, to warn you."

"She has a good heart." Nero smiled. "But, Apollo, you and Meg have been friends for just a few days—and only because I *asked* Meg to befriend you. I have been Meg's stepfather, protector, and caretaker for years. She is a member of the Imperial Household."

I stared at my beloved Dumpster waif. Yes, somehow over the past week she had become beloved to me. I could not imagine her as Imperial *anything*—definitely not as a part of Nero's entourage.

"I risked my life for you," I said in amazement. "And that actually *means* something, because I can die!"

Nero clapped politely. "We're all impressed, Apollo. Now, if you'd open the gates. They've defied me for too long."

I tried to glare at Meg, but my heart wasn't in it. I felt too hurt and vulnerable. We gods do not like feeling vulnerable. Besides, Meg wasn't even looking at me.

In a daze, I turned to the oak tree gates. I saw now that their fused trunks were marred from Nero's previous efforts—chain-saw scars, burn marks, bites from ax blades, even some bullet holes. All these had barely chipped the outer bark. The most damaged area was an inch-deep impression in the shape of a human hand, where the wood had bubbled and peeled away. I glanced at the unconscious face of Paulie the geyser god, strung up and bound with the five demigods.

"Nero, what have you done?"

"Oh, a number of things! We found a way into this antechamber weeks ago. The Labyrinth has a convenient opening in the myrmekes' nest. But getting through these gates—"

"You forced the palikos to help you?" I had to restrain myself from throwing my wind chimes at the emperor. "You used a nature spirit to destroy nature? Meg, how can you tolerate this?"

Peaches growled. For once I had the feeling that the grain spirit might be in agreement with me. Meg's expression was as closed up as the gates. She stared intently at the bones littering the field.

"Come now," Nero said. "Meg knows there are good nature spirits, and bad ones. This geyser god was annoying. He kept asking us to fill out surveys. Besides, he shouldn't have ventured so far from his source of power. He was quite easy to capture. His steam, as you can see, didn't do us much good anyway."

"And the five demigods?" I demanded. "Did you 'use' them, too?"

"Of course. I didn't plan on luring them here, but every time we attacked the gates, the grove started wailing. I suppose it was calling for help, and the demigods couldn't resist. The first to wander in was this one." He pointed to Cecil Markowitz. "The last two were your own children—Austin and Kayla, yes? They showed up after we forced Paulie to steam-broil the trees. I guess the grove was quite nervous about that attempt. We got two demigods for the price of one!"

I lost control. I let out a guttural howl and charged the emperor, intending to wring his hairy excuse for a neck. The Germani would have killed me before I ever got that far, but I was saved the indignity. I tripped over a human pelvis and belly-surfed through the bones.

"Apollo!" Meg ran toward me.

I rolled over and kicked at her like a fussy child. "I don't need *your* help! Don't you understand who your protector is? He's a monster! He's the emperor who—"

"Don't say it," Nero warned. "If you say 'who fiddled while Rome burned,' I will have Vince and Gary flay you for a set of hide armor. You know as well as I do, Apollo, we didn't *have* fiddles back then. And I did *not* start the Great Fire of Rome."

I struggled to my feet. "But you profited from it."

Facing Nero, I remembered all the tawdry details of his rule—the extravagance and cruelty that had made him so embarrassing to me, his forefather. Nero was that relative you never wanted to invite to Lupercalia dinner.

"Meg," I said, "your stepfather watched as seventy percent of Rome was destroyed. Tens of thousands died."

"I was thirty miles away in Antium!" Nero snarled. "I rushed back to the city and personally led the fire brigades!"

"Only when the fire threatened your palace."

Nero rolled his eyes. "I can't help it if I arrived just in time to save the most important building!"

Meg cupped her hands over her ears. "Stop arguing. Please."

I didn't stop. Talking seemed better than my other options, like helping Nero or dying.

"After the Great Fire," I told her, "instead of rebuilding the houses on Palatine Hill, Nero leveled the neighborhood and built a new palace—the Domus Aurea."

Nero got a dreamy look on his face. "Ah, yes . . . the House of Gold. It was beautiful, Meg! I had my own lake, three hundred rooms, frescoes of gold, mosaics done in pearls and diamonds—I could finally live like a human being!"

"You had the nerve to put a hundred-foot-tall bronze statue in your front lawn!" I said. "A statue of yourself as

Sol-Apollo, the sun god. In other words, you claimed to be *me*."

"Indeed," Nero agreed. "Even after I died, that statue lived on. I understand it became famous as the Colossus of Nero! They moved it to the gladiators' amphitheater and everyone began calling the theater after the statue—*the Colosseum*." Nero puffed up his chest. "Yes . . . the statue was the perfect choice."

His tone sounded even more sinister than usual.

"What are you talking about?" I demanded.

"Hmm? Oh, nothing." He checked his watch . . . a mauve-and-gold Rolex. "The point is, I had style! The people loved me!"

I shook my head. "They turned against you. The people of Rome were sure you'd started the Great Fire, so you scapegoated the Christians."

I was aware that this arguing was pointless. If Meg had hidden her true identity all this time, I doubted I could change her mind now. But perhaps I could stall long enough for the cavalry to arrive. If only I *had* a cavalry.

Nero waved dismissively. "But the Christians were terrorists, you see. Perhaps they didn't start the fire, but they were causing all sorts of other trouble. I recognized that before anyone else!"

"He fed them to the lions," I told Meg. "He burned them as human torches, the way he will burn these six."

Meg's face turned green. She gazed at the unconscious prisoners on the stakes. "Nero, you wouldn't—"

"They will be released," Nero promised, "as long as Apollo cooperates."

"Meg, you can't trust him," I said. "The last time he did this, he strung up Christians all over his backyard and burned them to illuminate his garden party. I was there. I remember the screaming."

Meg clutched her stomach.

"My dear, don't believe his stories!" Nero said. "That was just propaganda invented by my enemies."

Meg studied the face of Paulie the geyser god. "Nero . . . you didn't say anything about making them into torches."

"They won't burn," he said, straining to soften his voice. "It won't come to that. The Beast will not have to act."

"You see, Meg?" I wagged a finger at the emperor. "It's never a good sign when someone starts referring to himself in the third person. Zeus used to scold me about that constantly!"

Vince and Gary stepped forward, their knuckles whitening on their spears.

"I would be careful," Nero warned. "My Germani are sensitive about insults to the Imperial person. Now, as much as I love talking about myself, we're on a schedule." He checked his watch again. "You'll open the gates. Then Meg will see if she can use the trees to interpret the future. If so, wonderful! If not . . . well, we'll burn that bridge when we come to it."

"Meg," I said, "he's a madman."

At her feet, Peaches hissed protectively.

Meg's chin quivered. "Nero cared about me, Apollo. He gave me a home. He taught me to fight."

"You said he killed your father!"

"No!" She shook her head adamantly, a look of panic in her eyes. "No, that's not what I said. The *Beast* killed him."

"But—"

Nero snorted. "Oh, Apollo . . . you understand so little. Meg's father was weak. She doesn't even remember him. He couldn't protect her. *I* raised her. I kept her alive."

My heart sank even further. I did not understand everything Meg had been through, or what she was feeling now, but I knew Nero. I saw how easily he could have twisted a scared child's understanding of the world—a little girl all alone, yearning for safety and acceptance after her father's murder, even if that acceptance came from her father's killer. "Meg . . . I am so sorry."

Another tear traced her cheek.

"She doesn't NEED sympathy." Nero's voice turned as hard as bronze. "Now, my dear, if you would be so kind, open the gates. If Apollo objects, remind him that he is bound to follow your orders."

Meg swallowed. "Apollo, don't make it harder. Please . . . help me open the gates."

I shook my head. "Not by choice."

"Then I—I command you. Help me. Now."

31

Listen to the trees
The trees know what is up, yo
They know all the things

MEG'S RESOLVE may have been wavering, but Peaches's was not.

When I hesitated to follow Meg's orders, the grain spirit bared his fangs and hissed, "Peaches," as if that was a new torture technique.

"Fine," I told Meg, my voice turning bitter. The truth was, I had no choice. I could feel Meg's command sinking into my muscles, compelling me to obey.

I faced the fused oaks and put my hands against their trunks. I felt no oracular power within. I heard no voices—just heavy stubborn silence. The only message the trees seemed to be sending was: *GO AWAY.*

"If we do this," I told Meg, "Nero will destroy the grove."

"He won't."

"He has to. He can't control Dodona. Its power is too ancient. He can't let anyone else use it."

Meg placed her hands against the trees, just below mine. "Concentrate. Open them. Please. You don't want to anger the Beast."

She said this in a low voice—again speaking as if the

Beast was someone I had not yet met . . . a boogeyman lurking under the bed, not a man in a purple suit standing a few feet away.

I could not refuse Meg's orders, but perhaps I should have protested more vigorously. Meg might have backed down if I called her bluff. But then Nero or Peaches or the Germani would have just killed me. I will confess to you: I was afraid of dying. Courageously, nobly, handsomely afraid, true. But afraid nonetheless.

I closed my eyes. I sensed the trees' implacable resistance, their mistrust of outsiders. I knew that if I forced open these gates, the grove would be destroyed. Yet I reached out with all my willpower and sought the voice of prophecy, drawing it to me.

I thought of Rhea, Queen of the Titans, who had first planted this grove. Despite being a child of Gaea and Ouranos, despite being married to the cannibal king Kronos, Rhea had managed to cultivate wisdom and kindness. She had given birth to a new, better breed of immortals. (If I do say so myself.) She represented the best of the ancient times.

True, she had withdrawn from the world and started a pottery studio in Woodstock, but she still cared about Dodona. She had sent me here to open the grove, to share its power. She was not the kind of goddess who believed in closed gates or NO TRESPASSING signs. I began to hum softly "This Land Is Your Land."

The bark grew warm under my fingertips. The tree roots trembled.

I glanced at Meg. She was deep in concentration, leaning against the trunks as if trying to push them over.

Everything about her was familiar: her ratty pageboy hair, her glittering cat-eye glasses, her runny nose and chewed cuticles and faint scent of apple pie.

But she was someone I didn't know at all: stepdaughter to the immortal crazy Nero. A member of the Imperial Household. What did that even *mean*? I pictured the Brady Bunch in purple togas, lined up on the family staircase with Nero at the bottom in Alice's maid uniform. Having a vivid imagination is a terrible curse.

Unfortunately for the grove, Meg was also the daughter of Demeter. The trees responded to her power. The twin oaks rumbled. Their trunks began to move.

I wanted to stop, but I was caught up in the momentum. The grove seemed to be drawing on my power now. My hands stuck to the trees. The gates opened wider, forcibly spreading my arms. For a terrifying moment, I thought the trees might keep moving and rip me limb from limb. Then they stopped. The roots settled. The bark cooled and released me.

I stumbled back, exhausted. Meg remained, transfixed, in the newly opened gateway.

On the other side were . . . well, more trees. Despite the winter cold, the young oaks rose tall and green, growing in concentric circles around a slightly larger specimen in the center. Littering the ground were acorns glowing with a faint amber light. Around the grove stood a protective wall of trees even more formidable than the ones in the antechamber. Above, another tightly woven dome of branches guarded the place from aerial intruders.

Before I could warn her, Meg stepped across the

threshold. The voices exploded. Imagine forty nail guns firing into your brain from all directions at once. The words were babble, but they tore at my sanity, demanding my attention. I covered my ears. The noise just got louder and more persistent.

Peaches clawed frantically at the dirt, trying to bury his head. Vince and Gary writhed on the ground. Even the unconscious demigods thrashed and moaned on their stakes.

Nero reeled, his hand raised as if to block an intense light. "Meg, control the voices! Do it now!"

Meg didn't appear hurt by the noise, but she looked bewildered. "They're saying something . . ." She swept her hands through the air, pulling at invisible threads to untangle the pandemonium. "They're agitated. I can't— Wait . . ."

Suddenly the voices shut off, as if they'd made their point.

Meg turned toward Nero, her eyes wide. "It's true. The trees told me you mean to burn them."

The Germani groaned, half-conscious on the ground. Nero recovered more quickly. He raised a finger, admonishing, guiding. "Listen to me, Meg. I'd hoped the grove could be useful, but obviously it is fractured and confused. You can't believe what it says. It's the mouthpiece of a senile Titan queen. The grove must be razed. It's the only way, Meg. You understand that, don't you?"

He kicked Gary over onto his back and rifled through the bodyguard's pouches. Then Nero stood, triumphantly holding a box of matches.

"After the fire, we'll rebuild," he said. "It will be glorious!"

Meg stared at him as if noticing his horrendous neck beard for the first time. "Wh-what are you talking about?"

"He's going to burn and level Long Island," I said. "Then he'll make it his private domain, just like he did with Rome."

Nero laughed in exasperation. "Long Island is a mess anyway! No one will miss it. My new imperial complex will extend from Manhattan to Montauk—the greatest palace ever built! We'll have private rivers and lakes, one hundred miles of beachfront property, gardens big enough for their own zip codes. I'll build each member of my household a private skyscraper. Oh, Meg, imagine the parties we will have in our new Domus Aurea!"

The truth was a heavy thing. Meg's knees buckled under its weight.

"You can't." Her voice shook. "The woods— I'm the daughter of Demeter."

"You're *my* daughter," Nero corrected. "And I care for you deeply. Which is why you need to move aside. Quickly."

He set a match to the striking surface of the box. "As soon as I light these stakes, our human torches will send a wave of fire straight through that gateway. Nothing will be able to stop it. The entire forest will burn."

"Please!" Meg cried.

"Come along, dearest." Nero's frown hardened. "Apollo is of no use to us anymore. You don't want to wake the Beast, do you?"

He lit his match and stepped toward the nearest stake, where my son Austin was bound.

32

It takes a Village

People to protect your mind

"Y.M.C.A." Yeah

OH, THIS PART IS DIFFICULT TO TELL.

I am a natural storyteller. I have an infallible instinct for drama. I want to relate what *should* have happened: how I leaped forward shouting, "Nooooo!" and spun like an acrobat, knocking aside the lit match, then twisted in a series of blazing-fast Shaolin moves, cracking Nero's head and taking out his bodyguards before they could recover.

Ah, yes. That would have been perfect.

Alas, the truth constrains me.

Curse you, truth!

In fact, I spluttered something like, "Nuh-uh, dundoot!" I may have waved my Brazilian handkerchief with the hope that its magic would destroy my enemies.

The real hero was Peaches. The karpos must have sensed Meg's true feelings, or perhaps he just didn't like the idea of burning forests. He hurtled through the air, screaming his war cry (you guessed it), "Peaches!" He landed on Nero's arm, chomped the lit match from the emperor's hand, then landed a few feet away, wiping his tongue and crying, "Hat!

Hat!" (Which I assumed meant *hot* in the dialect of deciduous fruit.)

The scene might have been funny except that the Germani were now back on their feet, five demigods and a geyser spirit were still tied to highly flammable posts, and Nero still had a box of matches.

The emperor stared at his empty hand. "Meg . . . ?" His voice was as cold as an icicle. "What is the meaning of this?"

"P-Peaches, come here!" Meg's voice had turned brittle with fear.

The karpos bounded to her side. He hissed at me, Nero, and the Germani.

Meg took a shaky breath, clearly gathering her nerve. "Nero . . . Peaches is right. You—you can't burn these people alive."

Nero sighed. He looked at his bodyguards for moral support, but the Germani still appeared woozy. They were hitting the sides of their heads as if trying to clear water from their ears.

"Meg," said the emperor, "I am trying so hard to keep the Beast at bay. Why won't you help me? I know you are a good girl. I wouldn't have allowed you to roam around Manhattan so much on your own, playing the street waif, if I didn't know you could take care of yourself. But softness toward your enemies is not a virtue. You are my stepdaughter. Any of these demigods would kill you without hesitation given the chance."

"Meg, that's not true!" I said. "You've seen what Camp Half-Blood is like."

She studied me uneasily. "Even . . . even if it was true . . ." She turned to Nero. "You told me never to lower myself to my enemies' level."

"No, indeed." Nero's tone had frayed like a weathered rope. "We are better. We are stronger. We will build a glorious new world. But these nonsense-spewing trees stand in our way, Meg. Like any invasive weeds, they must be burned. And the only way to do that is with a true conflagration—flames stoked by blood. Let us do this together, and not involve the Beast, shall we?"

Finally, in my mind, something clicked. I remembered how my father used to punish me centuries ago, when I was a young god learning the ways of Olympus. Zeus used to say, *Don't get on the wrong side of my lightning bolts, boy.*

As if the lightning bolt had a mind of its own—as if Zeus had nothing to do with the punishments he meted out upon me.

Don't blame me, his tone implied. *It's the lightning bolt that seared every molecule in your body.* Many years later, when I killed the Cyclopes who made Zeus's lightning, it was no rash decision. I'd always *hated* those lightning bolts. It was easier than hating my father.

Nero took the same tone when he referred to himself as the Beast. He spoke of his anger and cruelty as if they were forces outside his control. If he flew into a rage . . . well then, he would hold Meg responsible.

The realization sickened me. Meg had been trained to regard her kindly stepfather Nero and the terrifying Beast as two separate people. I understood now why she preferred to spend her time in the alleys of New York. I understood why she had such quick mood changes, going from cartwheels to full shutdown in a matter of seconds. She never knew what might unleash the Beast.

She fixed her eyes on me. Her lips quivered. I could tell she wanted a way out—some eloquent argument that would mollify her stepfather and allow her to follow her conscience. But I was no longer a silver-tongued god. I could not outtalk an orator like Nero. And I would not play the Beast's blame game.

Instead, I took a page from Meg's book, which was always short and to the point.

"He's evil," I said. "You're good. You must make your own choice."

I could tell that this was not the news Meg wanted. Her mouth tightened. She drew back her shoulder blades as if preparing for a measles shot—something painful but necessary. She placed her hand on the karpos's curly scalp. "Peaches," she said in a small but firm voice, "get the matchbox."

The karpos sprang into action. Nero barely had time to blink before Peaches ripped the box from his hand and jumped back to Meg's side.

The Germani readied their spears. Nero raised his hand for restraint. He gave Meg a look that might have been heartbreak—if he had possessed a heart.

"I see you weren't ready for this assignment, my dear," he said. "It's my fault. Vince, Gary, detain Meg but don't hurt her. When we get home . . ." He shrugged, his expression full of regret. "As for Apollo and the little fruit demon, they will have to burn."

"No," Meg croaked. Then, at full volume, she shouted, "NO!" And the Grove of Dodona shouted with her.

The blast was so powerful, it knocked Nero and his guards off their feet. Peaches screamed and beat his head against the dirt.

This time, however, I was more prepared. As the trees' ear-splitting chorus reached its crescendo, I anchored my mind with the catchiest tune I could imagine. I hummed "Y.M.C.A.," which I used to perform with the Village People in my construction worker costume until the Indian chief and I got in a fight over— Never mind. That's not important.

"Meg!" I pulled the brass wind chimes from my pocket and tossed them to her. "Put these on the center tree! Y.M.C.A. Focus the grove's energy! Y.M.C.A."

I wasn't sure she could hear me. She raised the chimes and watched as they swayed and clanked, turning the noise from the trees into snatches of coherent speech: *Happiness approaches. The fall of the sun; the final verse. Would you like to hear our specials today?*

Meg's face went slack with surprise. She turned toward the grove and sprinted through the gateway. Peaches crawled after her, shaking his head.

I wanted to follow, but I couldn't leave Nero and his guards alone with six hostages. Still humming "Y.M.C.A.," I marched toward them.

The trees screamed louder than ever, but Nero rose to his knees. He pulled something from his coat pocket—a vial of liquid—and splashed it on the ground in front of him. I doubted that was a good thing, but I had more immediate concerns. Vince and Gary were getting up. Vince thrust his spear in my direction.

I was angry enough to be reckless. I grabbed the point of his weapon and yanked the spear up, smacking Vince under his chin. He fell, stunned, and I grabbed fistfuls of his hide armor.

He was easily twice my size. I didn't care. I lifted him off his feet. My arms sizzled with power. I felt invincibly strong—the way a god *should* feel. I had no idea why my strength had returned, but I decided this was not the moment to question my good luck. I spun Vince like a discus, tossing him skyward with such force that he punched a Germanus-shaped hole in the tree canopy and sailed out of sight.

Kudos to the Imperial Guard for having stupid amounts of courage. Despite my show of force, Gary charged me. With one hand, I snapped his spear. With the other, I punched a fist straight through his shield and hit his chest with enough might to fell a rhinoceros.

He collapsed in a heap.

I faced Nero. I could already feel my strength ebbing. My muscles were returning to their pathetic mortal flabbiness. I just hoped I'd have enough time to rip off Nero's head and stuff it down his mauve suit.

The emperor snarled. "You're a fool, Apollo. You *always* focus on the wrong thing." He glanced at his Rolex. "My wrecking crew will be here any minute. Once Camp Half-Blood is destroyed, I'll make it my new front lawn! Meanwhile, you'll be here . . . putting out fires."

From his vest pocket, he produced a silver cigarette lighter. Typical of Nero to keep several forms of fire-making close at hand. I looked at the glistening streaks of oil he had splashed on the ground. . . . Greek fire, of course.

"Don't," I said.

Nero grinned. "Good-bye, Apollo. Only eleven more Olympians to go."

He dropped the lighter.

I did not have the pleasure of tearing Nero's head off.

Could I have stopped him from fleeing? Possibly. But the flames were roaring between us, burning grass and bones, tree roots, and the earth itself. The blaze was too strong to stamp out, if Greek fire even *could* be stamped out, and it was rolling hungrily toward the six bound hostages.

I let Nero go. Somehow he hauled Gary to his feet and lugged the punch-drunk Germanus toward the ants' nest. Meanwhile, I ran to the stakes.

The closest was Austin's. I wrapped my arms around the base and pulled, completely disregarding proper heavy-lifting techniques. My muscles strained. My eyes swam with the effort. I managed to raise the stake enough to topple it backward. Austin stirred and groaned.

I dragged him, cocoon and all, to the other side of the clearing, as far from the fire as possible. I would have brought him into the Grove of Dodona, but I had a feeling I wouldn't be doing him any favors by putting him in a dead-end clearing full of insane voices, in the direct path of approaching flames.

I ran back to the stakes. I repeated the process—uprooting Kayla, then Paulie the geyser god, then the others. By the time I pulled Miranda Gardiner to safety, the fire was a raging red tidal wave, only inches from the gates of the grove.

My divine strength was gone. Meg and Peaches were nowhere to be seen. I had bought a few minutes for the hostages, but the fire would eventually consume us all. I fell to my knees and sobbed.

"Help." I scanned the dark trees, tangled and foreboding. I did not expect any help. I was not even used to *asking* for help. I was Apollo. Mortals called to *me*! (Yes, occasionally I might have ordered demigods to run trivial errands for me, like starting wars or retrieving magic items from monsters' lairs, but those requests didn't count.)

"I can't do this alone." I imagined Daphne's face floating beneath the trunk of one tree, then another. Soon the woods would burn. I couldn't save them any more than I could save Meg or the lost demigods or myself. "I'm so sorry. Please . . . forgive me."

My head must have been spinning from smoke inhalation. I began to hallucinate. The shimmering forms of dryads emerged from their trees—a legion of Daphnes in green gossamer dresses. Their expressions were melancholy, as if they knew they were going to their deaths, yet they circled the fire. They raised their arms, and the earth erupted at their feet. A torrent of mud churned over the flames. The dryads drew the fire's heat into their bodies. Their skin charred black. Their faces hardened and cracked.

As soon as the last flames were snuffed out, the dryads crumbled to ash. I wished I could crumble with them. I wanted to cry, but the fire had seared all the moisture from my tear ducts. I had not asked for so many sacrifices. I had not expected it! I felt hollow, guilty, and ashamed.

Then it occurred to me how many times I *had* asked for sacrifices, how many heroes I had sent to their deaths. Had they been any less noble and courageous than these dryads? Yet I had felt no remorse when I sent them off on deadly tasks. I had used them and discarded them, laid waste to their lives to build my own glory. I was no less of a monster than Nero.

Wind blew through the clearing—an unseasonably warm gust that swirled up the ashes and carried them through the forest canopy into the sky. Only after the breeze calmed did I realize it must have been the West Wind, my old rival, offering me consolation. He had swept up the remains and taken them off to their next beautiful reincarnation. After all these centuries, Zephyros had accepted my apology.

I discovered I had some tears left after all.

Behind me, someone groaned. "Where am I?"

Austin was awake.

I crawled to his side, now weeping with relief, and kissed his face. "My beautiful son!"

He blinked at me in confusion. His cornrows were sprinkled with ashes like frost on a field. I suppose it took a moment for him to process why he was being fawned over by a grungy, half-deranged boy with acne.

"Ah, right . . . Apollo." He tried to move. "What the—?

Why am I wrapped in smelly bandages? Could you free me, maybe?"

I laughed hysterically, which I doubt helped Austin's peace of mind. I clawed at his bindings but made no progress. Then I remembered Gary's snapped spear. I retrieved the point and spent several minutes sawing Austin free.

Once pulled from the stake, he stumbled around, trying to shake the circulation back into his limbs. He took in the scene—the smoldering forest, the other prisoners. The Grove of Dodona had stopped its wild chorus of screaming. (When had that happened?) A radiant amber light now glowed from the gateway.

"What's going on?" Austin asked. "Also, where is my saxophone?"

Sensible questions. I wished I had sensible answers. All I knew was that Meg McCaffrey was still wandering in the grove, and I did not like the fact that the trees had gone silent.

I stared at my weak mortal arms. I wondered why I'd experienced a sudden surge of divine strength when facing the Germani. Had my emotions triggered it? Was it the first sign of my godly vigor returning for good? Or perhaps Zeus was just messing with me again—giving me a taste of my old power before yanking it away once more. *Remember this, kid? WELL, YOU CAN'T HAVE IT!*

I wished I could summon that strength again, but I would have to make do.

I handed Austin the broken spear. "Free the others. I'll be back."

Austin stared at me incredulously. "You're going in *there*? Is it safe?"

"I doubt it," I said.

Then I ran toward the Oracle.

33

Parting is sorrow
Nothing about it is sweet
Don't step on my face

THE TREES WERE using their inside voices.

As I stepped through the gateway, I realized they were still talking in conversational tones, babbling nonsensically like sleepwalkers at a cocktail party.

I scanned the grove. No sign of Meg. I called her name. The trees responded by raising their voices, driving me cross-eyed with dizziness.

I steadied myself on the nearest oak.

"Watch it, man," the tree said.

I lurched forward, the trees trading bits of verse as if playing a game of rhymes:

> *Caves of blue.*
> *Strike the hue.*
> *Westward, burning.*
> *Pages turning.*
> *Indiana.*
> *Ripe banana.*
> *Happiness approaches.*
> *Serpents and roaches.*

None of it made sense, but each line carried the weight of prophecy. I felt as if dozens of important statements, each vital to my survival, were being blended together, loaded in a shotgun, and fired at my face.

(Oh, that's a rather good image. I'll have to use it in a haiku.)

"Meg!" I called again.

Still no reply. The grove did not seem so large. How could she not hear me? How could I not see her?

I slogged along, humming a perfect A 440 hertz tone to keep myself focused. When I reached the second ring of trees, the oaks became more conversational.

"Hey, buddy, got a quarter?" one asked.

Another tried to tell me a joke about a penguin and a nun walking into a Shake Shack.

A third oak was giving its neighbor an infomercial sales pitch about a food processor. "And you won't believe what it does with pasta!"

"Wow!" said the other tree. "It makes pasta, too?"

"Fresh linguine in minutes!" the sales oak enthused.

I did not understand why an oak tree would want linguine, but I kept moving. I was afraid that if I listened too long, I would order the food processor for three easy installments of $39.99, and my sanity would be lost forever.

Finally, I reached the center of the grove. On the far side of the largest oak tree, Meg stood with her back to the trunk, her eyes closed tight. The wind chimes were still in her hand, but they hung forgotten at her side. The brass cylinders clanked, muted against her dress.

At her feet, Peaches rocked back and forth, giggling. "Apples? Peaches! Mangoes? Peaches!"

"Meg." I touched her shoulder.

She flinched. She focused on me as if I were a clever optical illusion. Her eyes simmered with fear. "It's too much," she said. "Too much."

The voices had her in their grip. It was bad enough for me to endure—like a hundred radio stations playing at once, forcibly splitting my brain into different channels. But I was used to prophecies. Meg, on the other hand, was a daughter of Demeter. The trees liked her. They were all trying to share with her, to get her attention at the same time. Soon they would permanently fracture her mind.

"The wind chimes," I said. "Hang them in the tree!"

I pointed to the lowest branch, well above our heads. Alone, neither of us could reach it, but if I gave Meg a boost . . .

Meg backed away, shaking her head. The voices of Dodona were so chaotic I wasn't sure she had heard me. If she had, she either didn't understand or didn't trust me.

I had to tamp down my feelings of betrayal. Meg was Nero's stepdaughter. She had been sent to lure me here, and our whole friendship was a lie. She had no right to mistrust *me*.

But I could not stay bitter. If I blamed her for the way Nero had twisted her emotions, I was no better than the Beast. Also, just because she had lied about being my friend did not mean I wasn't hers. She was in danger. I was not going to leave her to the madness of the grove's penguin jokes.

I crouched and laced my fingers to make a foothold. "Please."

To my left, Peaches rolled onto his back and wailed, "Linguine? Peaches!"

Meg grimaced. I could see from her eyes that she was deciding to cooperate with me—not because she trusted me, but because Peaches was suffering.

Just when I thought my feelings could not be hurt any worse. It was one thing to be betrayed. It was another thing to be considered less important than a diapered fruit spirit.

Nevertheless, I remained steady as Meg placed her left foot in my hands. With all my remaining strength, I hoisted her up. She stepped onto my shoulders, then planted one red sneaker on top of my head. I made a mental note to put a safety label on my scalp: WARNING, TOP STEP IS NOT FOR STANDING.

With my back against the oak, I could feel the voices of the grove coursing up its trunk and drumming through its bark. The central tree seemed to be one giant antenna for crazy talk.

My knees were about to buckle. Meg's treads were grinding into my forehead. The A 440 I had been humming rapidly deflated to a G sharp.

Finally, Meg tied the wind chimes to the branch. She jumped down as my legs collapsed, and we both ended up sprawled in the dirt.

The brass chimes swayed and clanged, picking notes out of the wind and making chords from the dissonance.

The grove hushed, as if the trees were listening and thinking, *Oooh, pretty.*

Then the ground trembled. The central oak shook with such energy, it rained acorns.

Meg got to her feet. She approached the tree and touched its trunk.

"Speak," she commanded.

A single voice boomed forth from the wind chimes, like a cheerleader screaming through a megaphone:

> *There once was a god named Apollo*
> *Who plunged in a cave blue and hollow*
> *Upon a three-seater*
> *The bronze fire-eater*
> *Was forced death and madness to swallow*

The wind chimes stilled. The grove settled into tranquility, as if satisfied with the death sentence it had given me.

Oh, the horror!

A sonnet I could have handled. A quatrain would have been cause for celebration. But only the deadliest prophecies are couched in the form of a limerick.

I stared at the wind chimes, hoping they would speak again and correct themselves. *Oops, our mistake! That prophecy was for a different Apollo!*

But my luck was not that good. I had been handed an edict worse than a thousand advertisements for pasta makers.

Peaches rose. He shook his head and hissed at the oak tree, which expressed my own sentiments perfectly. He hugged Meg's calf as if she were the only thing keeping him from falling off the world. The scene was almost sweet, except for the karpos's fangs and glowing eyes.

Meg regarded me warily. The lenses of her glasses were spiderwebbed with cracks.

"That prophecy," she said. "Did you understand it?"

I swallowed a mouthful of soot. "Perhaps. Some of it. We'll need to talk to Rachel—"

"There's no more *we*." Meg's tone was as acrid as the volcanic gas of Delphi. "Do what you need to do. That's my final order."

This hit me like a spear shaft to the chin, despite the fact that she had lied to me and betrayed me.

"Meg, you can't." I couldn't keep the shakiness out of my voice. "You claimed my service. Until my trials are over—"

"I release you."

"No!" I could not stand the idea of being abandoned. Not again. Not by this ragamuffin Dumpster queen whom I'd learned to care about so much. "You can't *possibly* believe in Nero now. You heard him explain his plans. He means to level this entire island! You saw what he tried to do to his hostages."

"He—he wouldn't have let them burn. He promised. He held back. You saw it. That wasn't the Beast."

My rib cage felt like an over-tightened harp. "Meg . . . Nero *is* the Beast. He killed your father."

"No! Nero is my stepfather. My dad . . . my dad unleashed the Beast. He made it angry."

"Meg—"

"Stop!" She covered her ears. "You don't know him. Nero is good to me. I can talk to him. I can make it okay."

Her denial was so complete, so irrational, I realized there was no way I could argue with her. She reminded me painfully of myself when I fell to earth—how I had refused to accept my new reality. Without Meg's help, I would've gotten myself killed. Now our roles were reversed.

I edged toward her, but Peaches's snarl stopped me in my tracks.

Meg backed away. "We're done."

"We can't be," I said. "We're bound, whether you like it or not."

It occurred to me that she'd said the exact same thing to me only a few days before.

She gave me one last look through her cracked lenses. I would have given anything for her to blow a raspberry. I wanted to walk the streets of Manhattan with her doing cartwheels in the intersections. I missed hobbling with her through the Labyrinth, our legs tied together. I would've settled for a good garbage fight in an alley. Instead, she turned and fled, with Peaches at her heels. It seemed to me that they dissolved into the trees, just the way Daphne had done long ago.

Above my head, a breeze made the wind chimes jingle. This time, no voices came from the trees. I didn't know how long Dodona would remain silent, but I didn't want to be here if the oaks decided to start telling jokes again.

I turned and saw something strange at my feet: an arrow with an oak shaft and green fletching.

There shouldn't have been an arrow. I hadn't brought any into the grove. But in my dazed state, I didn't question this. I did what any archer would do: I retrieved it, and returned it to my quiver.

34

Uber's got nothing

Lyft is weak. And taxis? Nah

My ride is da mom

AUSTIN HAD FREED THE OTHER PRISONERS.
They looked like they had been dipped in a vat of glue and cotton swabs, but otherwise they seemed remarkably undamaged. Ellis Wakefield staggered around with his fists clenched, looking for something to punch. Cecil Markowitz, son of Hermes, sat on the ground trying to clean his sneakers with a deer's thighbone. Austin—resourceful boy!—had produced a canteen of water and was washing the Greek fire off of Kayla's face. Miranda Gardiner, the head counselor of Demeter, knelt by the place where the dryads had sacrificed themselves. She wept silently.

Paulie the palikos floated toward me. Like his partner, Pete, his lower half was all steam. From the waist up he looked like a slimmer, more abused version of his geyser buddy. His mud skin was cracked like a parched riverbed. His face was withered, as if every bit of moisture had been squeezed out of him. Looking at the damage Nero had done to him, I added a few more items to a mental list I was preparing: *Ways to Torture an Emperor in the Fields of Punishment.*

"You saved me," Paulie said with amazement. "Bring it in!"

He threw his arms around me. His power was so diminished that his body heat did not kill me, but it did open up my sinuses quite well.

"You should get home," I said. "Pete is worried, and you need to regain your strength."

"Ah, man . . ." Paulie wiped a steaming tear from his face. "Yeah, I'm gone. But anything you ever need—a free steam cleaning, some PR work, a mud scrub, you name it."

As he dissolved into mist, I called after him. "And Paulie? I'd give the Woods at Camp Half-Blood a ten for customer satisfaction."

Paulie beamed with gratitude. He tried to hug me again, but he was already ninety percent steam. All I got was a humid waft of mud-scented air. Then he was gone.

The five demigods gathered around me.

Miranda looked past me at the grove of Dodona. Her eyes were still puffy from crying, but she had beautiful irises the color of new foliage. "So, the voices I heard from that grove . . . It's really an oracle? Those trees can give us prophecies?"

I shivered, thinking of the oak trees' limerick. "Perhaps."

"Can I see—?"

"No," I said. "Not until we understand the place better."

I had already lost one daughter of Demeter today. I didn't intend to lose another.

"I don't get it," Ellis grumbled. "You're Apollo? Like, *the* Apollo."

"I'm afraid so. It's a long story."

"Oh, gods . . ." Kayla scanned the clearing. "I thought I heard Meg's voice earlier. Did I dream that? Was she with you? Is she okay?"

The others looked at me for an explanation. Their expressions were so fragile and tentative, I decided I couldn't break down in front of them.

"She's . . . alive," I managed. "She had to leave."

"*What?*" Kayla asked. "Why?"

"Nero," I said. "She . . . she went after Nero."

"Hold up." Austin raised his fingers like goalposts. "When you say Nero . . ."

I did my best to explain how the mad emperor had captured them. They deserved to know. As I recounted the story, Nero's words kept replaying in my mind: *My wrecking crew will be here any minute. Once Camp Half-Blood is destroyed, I'll make it my new front lawn!*

I wanted to think this was just bluster. Nero had always loved threats and grandiose statements. Unlike me, he was a terrible poet. He used flowery language like . . . well, like every sentence was a pungent bouquet of metaphors. (Oh, that's another good one. Jotting that down.)

Why had he kept checking his watch? And what wrecking crew could he have been talking about? I had a flashback to my dream of the sun bus careening toward a giant bronze face.

I felt like I was free-falling again. Nero's plan became horribly clear. After dividing the few demigods defending the camp, he had meant to burn this grove. But that was only part of his attack. . . .

"Oh, gods," I said. "The Colossus."

The five demigods shifted uneasily.

"What Colossus?" Kayla asked. "You mean the Colossus of Rhodes?"

"No," I said. "The Colossus Neronis."

Cecil scratched his head. "The Colossus Neurotic?"

Ellis Wakefield snorted. "*You're* a Colossus Neurotic, Markowitz. Apollo's talking about the big replica of Nero that stood outside the amphitheater in Rome, right?"

"I'm afraid so," I said. "While we're standing here, Nero is going to try to destroy Camp Half-Blood. And the Colossus will be his wrecking crew."

Miranda flinched. "You mean a giant statue is about to stomp on *camp*? I thought the Colossus was destroyed centuries ago."

Ellis frowned. "Supposedly, so was the Athena Parthenos. Now it's sitting on top of Half-Blood Hill."

The others' expressions turned grim. When a child of Ares makes a valid point, you know the situation is serious.

"Speaking of Athena . . ." Austin picked some incendiary fluff off his shoulder. "Won't the statue protect us? I mean, that's what she's there for, right?"

"She will try," I guessed. "But you must understand, the Athena Parthenos draws her power from her followers. The more demigods under her care, the more formidable her magic. And right now—"

"The camp is practically empty," Miranda finished.

"Not only that," I said, "but the Athena Parthenos is roughly forty feet tall. If memory serves, Nero's Colossus was more than twice that."

Ellis grunted. "So they're not in the same weight class. It's an uneven match."

Cecil Markowitz stood a little straighter. "Guys . . . did you feel that?"

I thought he might be playing one of his Hermes pranks. Then the ground shook again, ever so slightly. From somewhere in the distance came a rumbling sound like a battleship scraping over a sandbar.

"Please tell me that was thunder," Kayla said.

Ellis cocked his head, listening. "It's a war machine. A big automaton wading ashore about half a klick from here. We need to get to camp right now."

No one argued with Ellis's assessment. I supposed he could distinguish between the sounds of war machines the same way I could pick out an off-tune violin in a Rachmaninoff symphony.

To their credit, the demigods rose to the challenge. Despite the fact that they'd been recently bound, doused in flammable substances, and staked like human tiki torches, they closed ranks and faced me with determination in their eyes.

"How do we get out of here?" Austin asked. "The myrmekes' lair?"

I felt suddenly suffocated, partly because I had five people looking at me as if I knew what to do. I didn't. In fact, if you want to know a secret, we gods usually don't. When confronted for answers, we usually say something Rhea-like: *You will have to find out for yourself!* Or *True wisdom must be earned!* But I didn't think that would fly in this situation.

Also, I had no desire to plunge back into the ants' nest.

Even if we made it through alive, it would take much too long. Then we would have to run perhaps half the length of the forest.

I stared at the Vince-shaped hole in the canopy. "I don't suppose any of you can fly?"

They shook their heads.

"I can cook," Cecil offered.

Ellis smacked him on the shoulder.

I looked back at the myrmekes' tunnel. The solution came to me like a voice whispering in my ear: *You know someone who can fly, stupid.*

It was a risky idea. Then again, rushing off to fight a giant automaton was also not the safest plan of action.

"I think there's a way," I said. "But I'll need your help."

Austin balled his fists. "Anything you need. We're ready to fight."

"Actually . . . I don't need you to fight. I need you to lay down a beat."

My next important discovery: Children of Hermes cannot rap. At all.

Bless his conniving little heart, Cecil Markowitz tried his best, but he kept throwing off my rhythm section with his spastic clapping and terrible air mic noises. After a few trial runs, I demoted him to dancer. His job would be to shimmy back and forth and wave his hands, which he did with the enthusiasm of a tent-revival preacher.

The others managed to keep up. They still looked like half-plucked, highly combustible chickens, but they bopped with the proper amount of soul.

I launched into "Mama," my throat reinforced with water and cough drops from Kayla's belt pack. (Ingenious girl! Who brings cough drops on a three-legged death race?)

I sang directly into the mouth of the myrmekes' tunnel, trusting the acoustics to carry my message. We did not have to wait long. The earth began to rumble beneath our feet. I kept singing. I had warned my comrades not to stop laying down the righteous beat until the song was over.

Still, I almost lost it when the ground exploded. I had been watching the tunnel, but Mama did not use tunnels. She exited wherever she wanted—in this case, straight out of the earth twenty yards away, spraying dirt, grass, and small boulders in all directions. She scuttled forward, mandibles clacking, wings buzzing, dark Teflon eyes focused on me. Her abdomen was no longer swollen, so I assumed she had finished depositing her most recent batch of killer-ant larvae. I hoped this meant she would be in a good mood, not a hungry mood.

Behind her, two winged soldiers clambered out of the earth. I had not been expecting bonus ants. (Really, *bonus ants* is not a term most people would like to hear.) They flanked the queen, their antennae quivering.

I finished my ode, then dropped to one knee, spreading my arms as I had before.

"Mama," I said, "we need a ride."

My logic was this: Mothers were used to giving rides. With thousands upon thousands of offspring, I assumed the queen ant would be the ultimate soccer mom. And indeed, Mama grabbed me with her mandibles and tossed me over her head.

Despite what the demigods may tell you, I did not flail, scream, or land in a way that damaged my sensitive parts. I landed heroically, straddling the queen's neck, which was no larger than the back of an average warhorse. I shouted to my comrades, "Join me! It's perfectly safe!"

For some reason, they hesitated. The ants did not. The queen tossed Kayla just behind me. The soldier ants followed Mama's lead—snapping up two demigods each and throwing them aboard.

The three myrmekes revved their wings with a noise like radiator fan blades. Kayla grabbed my waist.

"Is this *really* safe?" she yelled.

"Perfectly!" I hoped I was right. "Perhaps even safer than the sun chariot!"

"Didn't the sun chariot almost destroy the world once?"

"Well, twice," I said. "Three times, if you count the day I let Thalia Grace drive, but—"

"Forget I asked!"

Mama launched herself into the sky. The canopy of twisted branches blocked our path, but Mama didn't pay any more attention to them than she had to the ton of solid earth she'd plowed through.

I yelled, "Duck!"

We flattened ourselves against Mama's armored head as she smashed through the trees, leaving a thousand wooden splinters embedded in my back. It felt so good to fly again, I didn't care. We soared above the woods and banked to the east.

For two or three seconds, I was exhilarated.

Then I heard the screaming from Camp Half-Blood.

35

Buck-naked statue
A Neurotic Colossus
Where art thy undies?

EVEN MY SUPERNATURAL POWERS of description fail me.

Imagine seeing yourself as a hundred-foot-tall bronze statue—a replica of your own magnificence, gleaming in the late afternoon light.

Now imagine that this ridiculously handsome statue is wading out of Long Island Sound onto the North Shore. In his hand is a ship's rudder—a blade the size of a stealth bomber, fixed to a fifty-foot-long pole—and Mr. Gorgeous is raising said rudder to smash the crud out of Camp Half-Blood.

This was the sight that greeted us as we flew in from the woods.

"How is that thing *alive*?" Kayla demanded. "What did Nero do—order it online?"

"The Triumvirate has vast resources," I told her. "They've had centuries to prepare. Once they reconstructed the statue, all they had to do was fill it with some animating magic—usually the harnessed life forces of wind or water spirits. I'm not sure. That's really more of Hephaestus's specialty."

"So how do we kill it?"

"I'm . . . I'm working on that."

All across the valley, campers screamed and ran for their weapons. Nico and Will were floundering in the lake, apparently having been capsized in the middle of a canoe ride. Chiron galloped through the dunes, harrying the Colossus with his arrows. Even by my standards, Chiron was a very fine archer. He targeted the statue's joints and seams, yet his shots did not seem to bother the automaton at all. Already dozens of missiles stuck from the Colossus's armpits and neck like unruly hair.

"More quivers!" Chiron shouted. "Quickly!"

Rachel Dare stumbled from the armory carrying half a dozen, and she ran to resupply him.

The Colossus brought down his rudder to smash the dining pavilion, but his blade bounced off the camp's magical barrier, sparking as if it had hit solid metal. Mr. Gorgeous took another step inland, but the barrier resisted him, pushing him back with the force of a wind tunnel.

On Half-Blood Hill, a silver aura surrounded the Athena Parthenos. I wasn't sure the demigods could see it, but every so often a beam of ultraviolet light shot from Athena's helmet like a search lamp, hitting the Colossus's chest and pushing back the invader. Next to her, in the tall pine tree, the Golden Fleece blazed with fiery energy. The dragon Peleus hissed and paced around the trunk, ready to defend his turf.

These were powerful forces, but I did not need godly sight to tell me that they would soon fail. The camp's defensive barriers were designed to turn away the occasional stray monster, to confuse mortals and prevent them from detecting the valley, and to provide a first line of defense against invading forces. A criminally beautiful hundred-foot-tall Celestial bronze giant was another thing entirely. Soon the Colossus would break through and destroy everything in its path.

"Apollo!" Kayla nudged me in the ribs. "What do we do?"

I stirred, again with the unpleasant realization that I was expected to have answers. My first instinct was to order a seasoned demigod to take charge. Wasn't it the weekend yet? Where was Percy Jackson? Or those Roman praetors Frank Zhang and Reyna Ramírez-Arellano? Yes, they would have done nicely.

My second instinct was to turn to Meg McCaffrey. How quickly I had grown used to her annoying yet strangely endearing presence! Alas, she was gone. Her absence felt like a Colossus stomping upon my heart. (This was an easy metaphor to summon, since the Colossus was presently stomping on a great many things.)

Flanking us on either side, the soldier ants flew in formation, awaiting the queen's orders. The demigods watched me anxiously, random bits of bandage fluff swirling from their bodies as we sped through the air.

I leaned forward and spoke to Mama in a soothing tone, "I know I cannot ask you to risk your life for us."

Mama hummed as if to say, *You're darn right!*

"Just give us one pass around that statue's head?" I asked. "Enough to distract it. Then set us down on the beach?"

She clicked her mandibles doubtfully.

"You're the best mama in the whole world," I added, "and you look lovely today."

That line always worked with Leto. It did the trick with Mama Ant, too. She twitched her antennae, perhaps sending a high-frequency signal to her soldiers, and all three ants banked hard to the right.

Below us, more campers joined the battle. Sherman Yang had harnessed two pegasi to a chariot and was now circling the statue's legs, while Julia and Alice threw electric javelins at the Colossus's knees. The missiles stuck in his joints, discharging tendrils of blue lightning, but the statue barely seemed to notice. Meanwhile, at his feet, Connor Stoll and Harley used twin flamethrowers to give the Colossus a molten pedicure, while the Nike twins manned a catapult, lobbing boulders at the Colossus's Celestial bronze crotch.

Malcolm Pace, a true child of Athena, was coordinating the attacks from a hastily organized command post on the green. He and Nyssa had spread war maps across a card table and were shouting targeting coordinates, while Chiara, Damien, Paolo, and Billie rushed to set up ballistae around the communal hearth.

Malcolm looked like the perfect battlefield commander, except for the fact that he'd forgotten his pants. His red briefs made quite a statement with his sword and leather cuirass.

Mama dove toward the Colossus, leaving my stomach at a higher altitude.

I had a moment to appreciate the statue's regal features, its metal brow rimmed with a spiky crown meant to represent the beams of the sun. The Colossus was supposed to be Nero as the sun god, but the emperor had wisely made the face resemble mine more closely than his. Only the line of its nose and its ghastly neck beard suggested Nero's trademark ugliness.

Also . . . did I mention that the hundred-foot statue was entirely nude? Well, of course it was. Gods are almost always depicted as nude, because we are flawless beings. Why would you cover up perfection? Still, it was a little disconcerting to see my buck-naked self stomping around, slamming a ship's rudder at Camp Half-Blood.

As we approached the Colossus, I bellowed loudly, "IMPOSTER! I AM THE REAL APOLLO! YOU'RE UGLY!"

Oh, dear reader, it was hard to yell such words at my own handsome visage, but I did. Such was my courage.

The Colossus did not like being insulted. As Mama and her soldiers veered away, the statue swung its rudder upward.

Have you ever collided with a bomber? I had a sudden flashback to Dresden in 1945, when the planes were so thick in the air, I literally could not find a safe lane to drive in. The axle on the sun chariot was out of alignment for *weeks* after that.

I realized the ants were not fast enough fliers to escape the rudder's reach. I saw catastrophe approaching in slow motion. At the last possible moment, I yelled, "Dive!"

We plunged straight down. The rudder only clipped the ants' wings—but it was enough to send us spiraling toward the beach.

I was grateful for soft sand.

I ate quite a bit of it when we crash-landed.

By sheer luck, none of us died, though Kayla and Austin had to pull me to my feet.

"Are you okay?" Austin asked.

"Fine," I said. "We must hurry."

The Colossus stared down at us, perhaps trying to discern whether we were dying in agony yet or needed some additional pain. I had wanted to get his attention, and I had succeeded. Huzzah.

I glanced at Mama and her soldiers, who were shaking the sand off their carapaces. "Thank you. Now save yourselves. Fly!"

They did not need to be told twice. I suppose ants have a natural fear of large humanoids looming over them, about to squash them with a heavy foot. Mama and her guards buzzed into the sky.

Miranda looked after them. "I never thought I'd say this about bugs, but I'm going to miss those guys."

"Hey!" called Nico di Angelo. He and Will scrambled over the dunes, still dripping from their swim in the canoe lake.

"What's the plan?" Will seemed calm, but I knew him well enough by now to tell that inside he was as charged as a bare electrical wire.

BOOM.

The statue strode toward us. One more step, and it would be on top of us.

"Isn't there a control valve on its ankle?" Ellis asked. "If we can open it—"

"No," I said. "You're thinking of Talos. This is not Talos."

Nico brushed his dark wet hair from his forehead. "Then what?"

I had a lovely view of the Colossus's nose. Its nostrils were sealed with bronze . . . I supposed because Nero hadn't wanted his detractors trying to shoot arrows into his imperial noggin.

I yelped.

Kayla grabbed my arm. "Apollo, what's wrong?"

Arrows into the Colossus's head. Oh, gods, I had an idea that would never, ever work. However, it seemed better than our other option, which was to be crushed under a two-ton bronze foot.

"Will, Kayla, Austin," I said, "come with me."

"And Nico," said Nico. "I have a doctor's note."

"Fine!" I said. "Ellis, Cecil, Miranda—do whatever you can to keep the Colossus's attention."

The shadow of an enormous foot darkened the sand.

"Now!" I yelled. "Scatter!"

36

I love me some plague
When it's on the right arrow
Ka-bam! You dead, bro?

SCATTERING WAS THE EASY PART. They did that very well.

Miranda, Cecil, and Ellis ran in different directions, screaming insults at the Colossus and waving their arms. This bought the rest of us a few seconds as we sprinted for the dunes, but I suspected the Colossus would soon enough come after me. I was, after all, the most important and attractive target.

I pointed toward Sherman Yang's chariot, which was still circling the statue's legs in a vain attempt to electrocute its kneecaps. "We need to commandeer that chariot!"

"How?" Kayla asked.

I was about to admit I had no idea when Nico di Angelo grabbed Will's hand and stepped into my shadow. Both boys evaporated. I had forgotten about the power of shadow-traveling—the way children of the Underworld could step into one shadow and appear from another, sometimes hundreds of miles away. Hades used to love sneaking up on me that way and yelling, "HI!" just as I shot an arrow of death.

He found it amusing if I missed my target and accidentally wiped out the wrong city.

Austin shuddered. "I hate it when Nico disappears like that. What's our plan?"

"You two are my backup," I said. "If I miss, if I die . . . it will be up to you."

"Whoa, whoa," Kayla said. "What do you mean *if you miss?*"

I drew my last arrow—the one I'd found in the grove. "I'm going to shoot that gorgeous gargantuan in the ear."

Austin and Kayla exchanged looks, perhaps wondering if I'd finally cracked under the strain of being mortal.

"A plague arrow," I explained. "I'm going to enchant an arrow with sickness, then shoot it into the statue's ear. Its head is hollow. The ears are the only openings. The arrow should release enough disease to kill the Colossus's animating power . . . or at least to disable it."

"How do you know it will work?" Kayla asked.

"I don't, but—"

Our conversation was ruined by a sudden heavy downpour of Colossus foot. We darted inland, barely avoiding being flattened.

Behind us, Miranda shouted, "Hey, ugly!"

I knew she wasn't talking to me, but I glanced back anyway. She raised her arms, causing ropes of sea grass to spring from the dunes and wrap around the statue's ankles. The Colossus broke through them easily, but they annoyed him enough to be a distraction. Watching Miranda face the statue made me heartsick for Meg all over again.

Meanwhile, Ellis and Cecil stood on either side of the Colossus, throwing rocks at his shins. From the camp, a volley of flaming ballista projectiles exploded against Mr. Gorgeous's naked backside, which made me clench in sympathy.

"You were saying?" Austin asked.

"Right." I twirled the arrow between my fingers. "I know what you're thinking. I don't have godly powers. It's doubtful I'll be able to cook up the Black Death or the Spanish Flu. But still, if I can make the shot from close range, straight into its head, I might be able to do some damage."

"And . . . if you fail?" Kayla asked. I noticed her quiver was also empty.

"I won't have the strength to try twice. You'll have to make another pass. Find an arrow, try to summon some sickness, make the shot while Austin holds the chariot steady."

I realized this was an impossible request, but they accepted it with grim silence. I wasn't sure whether to feel grateful or guilty. Back when I was a god, I would've taken it for granted that mortals had faith in me. Now . . . I was asking my children to risk their lives again, and I was not at all sure my plan would work.

I caught a flash of movement in the sky. This time, instead of a Colossus foot, it was Sherman Yang's chariot, minus Sherman Yang. Will brought the pegasi in for a landing, then dragged out a half-conscious Nico di Angelo.

"Where are the others?" Kayla asked. "Sherman and the Hermes girls?"

Will rolled his eyes. "Nico convinced them to disembark."

As if on cue, I heard Sherman screaming from somewhere far in the distance, "I'll get you, di Angelo!"

"You guys go," Will told me. "The chariot is only designed for three, and after that shadow-travel, Nico is going to pass out any second."

"No, I'm not," Nico complained, then passed out.

Will caught him in a fireman's carry and took him away. "Good luck! I'm going to get the Lord of Darkness here some Gatorade!"

Austin hopped in first and took the reins. As soon as Kayla and I were aboard, we shot skyward, the pegasi swerving and banking around the Colossus with expert skill. I began to feel a glimmer of hope. We might be able to out-maneuver this giant hunk of good-looking bronze.

"Now," I said, "if I can just enchant this arrow with a nice plague."

The arrow shuddered from its fletching to its point.

THOU SHALT NOT, it told me.

I try to avoid weapons that talk. I find them rude and distracting. Once, Artemis had a bow that could cuss like a Phoenician sailor. Another time, in a Stockholm tavern, I met this god who was smoking hot, except his talking sword just would *not* shut up.

But I digress.

I asked the obvious question. "Did you just speak to me?"

The arrow quivered. (Oh, dear. That was a horrible pun. My apologies.) *YEA, VERILY. PRITHEE, SHOOTING IS NOT MY PURPOSE.*

His voice was definitely male, sonorous and grave, like a bad Shakespearean actor's.

"But you're an arrow," I said. "Shooting you is the whole point." (Ah, I really must watch those puns.)

"Guys, hang on!" Austin shouted.

The chariot plunged to avoid the Colossus's swinging rudder. Without Austin's warning, I would have been left in midair still arguing with my projectile.

"So you're made from Dodona oak," I guessed. "Is that why you talk?"

FORSOOTH, said the arrow.

"Apollo!" Kayla said. "I'm not sure why you're talking to that arrow, but—"

From our right came a reverberating *WHANG!* like a snapped power line hitting a metal roof. In a flash of silver light, the camp's magical barriers collapsed. The Colossus lurched forward and brought his foot down on the dining pavilion, smashing it to rubble like so many children's blocks.

"But that just happened," Kayla said with a sigh.

The Colossus raised his rudder in triumph. He marched inland, ignoring the campers who were running around his feet. Valentina Diaz launched a ballista missile into his groin. (Again, I had to wince in sympathy.) Harley and Connor Stoll kept blowtorching his feet, to no effect. Nyssa, Malcolm, and Chiron hastily ran a trip line of steel cable across the statue's path, but they would never have time to anchor it properly.

I turned to Kayla. "You can't hear this arrow talking?"

Judging from her wide eyes, I guessed the answer was, *No, and does hallucinating run in the family?*

"Never mind." I looked at the arrow. "What would you suggest, O Wise Missile of Dodona? My quiver is empty."

The arrow's point dipped toward the statue's left arm. *LO, THE ARMPIT DOTH HOLD THE ARROWS THOU NEEDEST!*

Kayla yelled, "Colossus is heading for the cabins!"

"Armpit!" I told Austin. "Flieth—er, fly for the armpit!"

That wasn't an order one heard much in combat, but Austin spurred the pegasi into a steep ascent. We buzzed the forest of arrows sticking out of the Colossus's arm seam, but I completely overestimated my mortal hand-eye coordination. I lunged for the shafts and came up empty.

Kayla was more agile. She snagged a fistful but screamed when she yanked them free.

I pulled her to safety. Her hand was bleeding badly, cut from the high-speed grab.

"I'm fine!" Kayla yelped. Her fingers were clenched, splattering drops of red all over the chariot's floor. "Take the arrows."

I did. I tugged the Brazilian-flag bandana from around my neck and gave it to her. "Bind your hand," I ordered. "There's some ambrosia in my coat pocket."

"Don't worry about me." Kayla's face was as green as her hair. "Make the shot! Hurry!"

I inspected the arrows. My heart sank. Only one of the missiles was unbroken, and its shaft was warped. It would be almost impossible to shoot.

I looked again at the talking arrow.

THOU SHALT NOT THINKEST ABOUT IT, he intoned. *ENCHANT THOU THE WARPED ARROW!*

I tried. I opened my mouth, but the proper words of enchantment were gone from my mind. As I feared, Lester Papadopoulos simply did not possess the power. "I can't!"

I SHALT ASSIST, promised the Arrow of Dodona. *STARTEST THOU: "PLAGUEY, PLAGUEY, PLAGUEY."*

"The enchantment does *not* start *plaguey, plaguey, plaguey!*"

"Who are you talking to?" Austin demanded.

"My arrow! I—I need more time."

"We don't *have* more time!" Kayla pointed with her wrapped bloody hand.

The Colossus was only a few steps away from the central green. I wasn't sure the demigods even realized how much danger they were in. The Colossus could do much more than just flatten buildings. If he destroyed the central hearth, the sacred shrine of Hestia, he would extinguish the very soul of the camp. The valley would be cursed and uninhabitable for generations. Camp Half-Blood would cease to exist.

I realized I had failed. My plan would take much too long, if I could even *remember* how to make a plague arrow. This was my punishment for breaking an oath on the River Styx.

Then, from somewhere above us, a voice yelled, "Hey, Bronze Butt!"

Over the Colossus's head, a cloud of darkness formed like a cartoon dialogue bubble. Out of the shadows dropped a furry black monster dog—a hellhound—and astride his back was a young man with a glowing bronze sword.

The weekend was here. Percy Jackson had arrived.

37

Hey, look! It's Percy
Least he could do was help out
Taught him everything

I WAS TOO SURPRISED TO SPEAK. Otherwise I would have warned Percy what was about to happen.

Hellhounds are not fond of heights. When startled, they respond in a predictable way. The moment Percy's faithful pet landed on top of the moving Colossus, she yelped and proceeded to wee-wee on said Colossus's head. The statue froze and looked up, no doubt wondering what was trickling down his imperial sideburns.

Percy leaped heroically from his mount and slipped in hellhound pee. He nearly slid off the statue's brow. "What the—Mrs. O'Leary, jeez!"

The hellhound bayed in apology. Austin flew our chariot to within shouting distance. "Percy!"

The son of Poseidon frowned across at us. "All right, who unleashed the giant bronze guy? Apollo, did you do this?"

"I am offended!" I cried. "I am only indirectly responsible for this! Also, I have a plan to fix it."

"Oh, yeah?" Percy glanced back at the destroyed dining pavilion. "How's that going?"

With my usual levelheadedness, I stayed focused on the greater good. "If you could please just keep this Colossus from stomping the camp's hearth, that would be helpful. I need a few more minutes to enchant this arrow."

I held up the talking arrow by mistake, then held up the bent arrow.

Percy sighed. "Of course you do."

Mrs. O'Leary barked in alarm. The Colossus was raising his hand to swat the trespassing tinkler.

Percy grabbed one of the crown's sunray spikes. He sliced it off at the base, then jabbed it into the Colossus's forehead. I doubted the Colossus could feel pain, but it staggered, apparently surprised to suddenly have grown a unicorn horn.

Percy sliced off another one. "Hey, ugly!" he called down. "You don't need all these pointy things, do you? I'm going to take one to the beach. Mrs. O'Leary, fetch!"

Percy tossed the spike like a javelin.

The hellhound barked excitedly. She leaped off the Colossus's head, vaporized into shadow, and reappeared on the ground, bounding after her new bronze stick.

Percy raised his eyebrows at me. "Well? Start enchanting!"

He jumped from the statue's head to its shoulder. Then he leaped to the shaft of the rudder and slid down it like a fire pole all the way to the ground. If I had been at my usual level of godly athletic skill, I could've done something like that in my sleep, of course, but I had to admit Percy Jackson was moderately impressive.

"Hey, Bronze Butt!" he yelled again. "Come get me!"

The Colossus obliged, slowly turning and following Percy toward the beach.

I began to chant, invoking my old powers as the god of plagues. This time, the words came to me. I didn't know why. Perhaps Percy's arrival had given me new faith. Perhaps I simply didn't think about it too much. I've found that thinking often interferes with doing. It's one of those lessons that gods learn early in their careers.

I felt an itchy sensation of sickness curling from my fingers and into the projectile. I spoke of my own awesomeness and the various horrible diseases I had visited upon wicked populations in the past, because . . . well, I'm awesome. I could feel the magic taking hold, despite the Arrow of Dodona whispering to me like an annoying Elizabethan stagehand, *SAYEST THOU: "PLAGUEY, PLAGUEY, PLAGUEY!"*

Below, more demigods joined the parade to the beach. They ran ahead of the Colossus, jeering at him, throwing things, and calling him Bronze Butt. They made jokes about his new horn. They laughed at the hellhound pee trickling down his face. Normally I have zero tolerance for bullying, especially when the victim looks like me, but since the Colossus was ten stories tall and destroying their camp, I suppose the campers' rudeness was understandable.

I finished chanting. Odious green mist now wreathed the arrow. It smelled faintly of fast-food deep fryers—a good sign that it carried some sort of horrible malady.

"I'm ready!" I told Austin. "Get me next to its ear!"

"You got it!" Austin turned to say something else, and a wisp of green fog passed under his nose. His eyes watered. His nose swelled and began to run. He scrunched up his face and sneezed so hard he collapsed. He lay on the floor of the chariot, groaning and twitching.

"My boy!" I wanted to grab his shoulders and check on him, but since I had an arrow in each hand, that was inadvisable.

FIE! TOO STRONG IS THY PLAGUE. The Dodona arrow hummed with annoyance. *THY CHANTING SUCKETH.*

"Oh, no, no, no," I said. "Kayla, be careful. Don't breathe—"

"ACHOO!" Kayla crumpled next to her brother.

"What have I done?" I wailed.

METHINKS THOU HAST BLOWN IT, said the Dodona arrow, my source of infinite wisdom. *MOREO'ER, HIE! TAKEST THOU THE REINS.*

"Why?"

You would think a god who drove a chariot on a daily basis would not need to ask such a question. In my defense, I was distraught about my children lying half-conscious at my feet. I didn't consider that no one was driving. Without anyone at the reins, the pegasi panicked. To avoid running into the huge bronze Colossus directly in their path, they dove toward the earth.

Somehow, I managed to react appropriately. (Three cheers for reacting appropriately!) I thrust both arrows into my quiver, grabbed the reins, and managed to level our descent just enough to prevent a crash landing. We bounced off a dune and swerved to a stop in front of Chiron and a group of demigods. Our entrance might have looked dramatic if the centrifugal force hadn't thrown Kayla, Austin, and me from the chariot.

Did I mention I was grateful for soft sand?

The pegasi took off, dragging the battered chariot into the sky and leaving us stranded.

Chiron galloped to our side, a cluster of demigods in his wake. Percy Jackson ran toward us from the surf while Mrs. O'Leary kept the Colossus occupied with a game of keep-away. I doubt that would hold the statue's interest very long, once he realized there was a group of targets right behind him, just perfect for stomping.

"The plague arrow is ready!" I announced. "We need to shoot it into the Colossus's ear!"

My audience did not seem to take this as good news. Then I realized my chariot was gone. My bow was still in the chariot. And Kayla and Austin were quite obviously infected with whatever disease I had conjured up.

"Are they contagious?" Cecil asked.

"No!" I said. "Well . . . probably not. It's the fumes from the arrow—"

Everyone backed away from me.

"Cecil," Chiron said, "you and Harley take Kayla and Austin to the Apollo cabin for healing."

"But they *are* the Apollo cabin," Harley complained. "Besides, my flamethrower—"

"You can play with your flamethrower later," Chiron

promised. "Run along. There's a good boy. The rest of you, do what you can to keep the Colossus at the water's edge. Percy and I will assist Apollo."

Chiron said the word *assist* as if it meant *slap upside the head with extreme prejudice.*

Once the crowd had dispersed, Chiron gave me his bow. "Make the shot."

I stared at the massive composite recursive, which probably had a draw weight of a hundred pounds. "This is meant for the strength of a centaur, not a teen mortal!"

"You created the arrow," he said. "Only you can shoot it without succumbing to the disease. Only you can hit such a target."

"From *here*? It's impossible! Where is that flying boy, Jason Grace?"

Percy wiped the sweat and sand from his neck. "We're fresh out of flying boys. And all the pegasi have stampeded."

"Perhaps if we got some harpies and some kite string . . ." I said.

"Apollo," Chiron said, "you must do this. You are the lord of archery and illness."

"I'm not lord of anything!" I wailed. "I'm a stupid ugly mortal teenager! I'm *nobody*!"

The self-pity just came pouring out. I thought for sure the earth would split in two when I called myself a *nobody*. The cosmos would stop turning. Percy and Chiron would rush to reassure me.

None of that happened. Percy and Chiron just stared at me grimly.

Percy put his hand on my shoulder. "You're Apollo. We

need you. You can do this. Besides, if you don't, I will personally throw you off the top of the Empire State Building."

This was exactly the pep talk I needed—just the sort of thing Zeus used to say to me before my soccer matches. I squared my shoulders. "Right."

"We'll try to draw him into the water," Percy said. "I've got the advantage there. Good luck."

Percy accepted Chiron's hand and leaped onto the centaur's back. Together they galloped into the surf, Percy waving his sword and calling out various bronze-butt-themed insults to the Colossus.

I ran down the beach until I had a line of sight on the statue's left ear.

Looking up at that regal profile, I did not see Nero. I saw myself—a monument to my own conceit. Nero's pride was no more than a reflection of mine. I was the bigger fool. I was exactly the sort of person who would construct a hundred-foot-tall naked statue of myself in my front yard.

I pulled the plague arrow from my quiver and nocked it in the bowstring.

The demigods were getting very good at scattering. They continued to harry the Colossus from both sides while Percy and Chiron galloped through the tide, Mrs. O'Leary romping at their heels with her new bronze stick.

"Yo, ugly!" Percy shouted. "Over here!"

The Colossus's next step displaced several tons of salt water and made a crater large enough to swallow a pickup truck.

The Arrow of Dodona rattled in my quiver. *RELEASE THY BREATH*, he advised. *DROPETH THY SHOULDER*.

"I *have* shot a bow before," I grumbled.

MINDETH THY RIGHT ELBOW, the arrow said.

"Shut up."

AND TELLEST NOT THINE ARROW TO SHUT UP.

I drew the bow. My muscles burned as if boiling water was being poured over my shoulders. The plague arrow did not make me pass out, but its fumes were disorienting. The warp of the shaft made my calculations impossible. The wind was against me. The arc of the shot would be much too high.

Yet I aimed, exhaled, and released the bowstring.

The arrow twirled as it rocketed upward, losing force and drifting too far to the right. My heart sank. Surely the curse of the River Styx would deny me any chance at success.

Just as the projectile reached its apex and was about to fall back to earth, a gust of wind caught it . . . perhaps Zephyros looking kindly on my pitiful attempt. The arrow sailed into the Colossus's ear canal and rattled in his head with a *clink, clink, clink* like a pachinko machine.

The Colossus halted. He stared at the horizon as if confused. He looked at the sky, then arched his back and lurched forward, making a sound like a tornado ripping off the roof of a warehouse. Because his face had no other open orifices, the pressure of his sneeze forced geysers of motor oil out his ears, spraying the dunes with environmentally unfriendly sludge.

Sherman, Julia, and Alice stumbled over to me, covered head to toe with sand and oil.

"I appreciate you freeing Miranda and Ellis," Sherman snarled, "but I'm going to kill you later for taking my chariot. What did you do to that Colossus? What kind of plague makes you sneeze?"

"I'm afraid I—I summoned a rather benign illness. I believe I have given the Colossus a case of hay fever."

You know that horrible pause when you're waiting for someone to sneeze? The statue arched his back again, and everyone on the beach cringed in anticipation. The Colossus inhaled several cubic acres of air through his ear canals, preparing for his next blast.

I imagined the nightmare scenarios: The Colossus would ear-sneeze Percy Jackson into Connecticut, never to be seen again. The Colossus would clear his head and then stomp all of us flat. Hay fever could make a person cranky. I knew this because I *invented* hay fever. Still, I had never intended it to be a killing affliction. I certainly never anticipated facing the wrath of a towering metal automaton with extreme seasonal allergies. I cursed my shortsightedness! I cursed my mortality!

What I had *not* considered was the damage our demigods had already done to the Colossus's metal joints—in particular, his neck.

The Colossus rocked forward with a mighty *CHOOOOO!* I flinched and almost missed the moment of truth when the statue's head achieved first-stage separation from his body. It hurtled over Long Island Sound, the face spinning in and out of view. It hit the water with a mighty WHOOSH and bobbed for a moment. Then the air *blooped* out of its neck hole and the gorgeous regal visage of yours truly sank beneath the waves.

The statue's decapitated body tilted and swayed. If it had fallen backward, it might have crushed even more of the camp. Instead, it toppled forward. Percy yelped a curse that would have made any Phoenician sailor proud. Chiron and he raced sideways to avoid being crushed while Mrs. O'Leary wisely dissolved into shadows. The Colossus hit the water, sending forty-foot tidal waves to port and starboard. I had never before seen a centaur hang hooves on a tubular crest, but Chiron acquitted himself well.

The roar of the statue's fall finally stopped echoing off the hills.

Next to me, Alice Miyazawa whistled. "Well, that de-escalated quickly."

Sherman Yang asked in a voice of childlike wonder: "What the Hades just happened?"

"I believe," I said, "the Colossus sneezed his head off."

38

After the sneezing
Healing peeps, parsing limericks
Worst God Award? Me

THE PLAGUE SPREAD.

That was the price of our victory: a massive outbreak of hay fever. By nightfall, most of the campers were dizzy, groggy, and heavily congested, though I was pleased that none of them sneezed their heads off, because we were running low on bandages and duct tape.

Will Solace and I spent the evening caring for the wounded. Will took the lead, which was fine with me; I was exhausted. Mostly I splinted arms, distributed cold medicine and tissues, and tried to keep Harley from stealing the infirmary's entire supply of smiley-face stickers, which he plastered all over his flamethrower. I was grateful for the distraction, since it kept me from thinking too much about the day's painful events.

Sherman Yang graciously agreed not to kill Nico for tossing him out of his chariot, or me for damaging it, though I had the feeling the son of Ares was keeping his options open for later.

Chiron provided healing poultices for the most extreme cases of hay fever. This included Chiara Benvenuti, whose good luck had, for once, abandoned her. Strangely enough, Damien White got sick right after he learned that Chiara was sick. The two had cots next to each other in the infirmary, which I found a little suspicious, even though they kept sniping at each other whenever they knew they were being watched.

Percy Jackson spent several hours recruiting whales and hippocampi to help him haul away the Colossus. He decided it would be easiest to tow it underwater to Poseidon's palace, where it could be repurposed as garden statuary. I was not sure how I felt about that. I imagined Poseidon would replace the statue's gorgeous face with his own weathered, bearded mien. Still, I wanted the Colossus gone, and I doubted it would have fit in the camp's recycling bins.

Thanks to Will's healing and a hot dinner, the demigods I had rescued from the woods quickly got back to full strength. (Paolo claimed it was because he waved a Brazilian-flag bandana over them, and I was not about to argue.)

As for the camp itself, the damage might have been much worse. The canoe dock could be rebuilt. The Colossus's footstep craters could be repurposed as convenient foxholes or koi ponds.

The dining pavilion was a total loss, but Nyssa and Harley were confident that Annabeth Chase could redesign the place next time she was here. With luck, it would be rebuilt in time for the summer.

The only other major damage was to the Demeter cabin. I had not realized it during the battle, but the Colossus had managed to step on it before turning around for the beach.

In retrospect, its path of destruction appeared almost purposeful, as if the automaton had waded ashore, stomped Cabin Four, and headed back out to sea.

Given what had happened with Meg McCaffrey, I had a hard time not seeing this as a bad omen. Miranda Gardiner and Billie Ng were given temporary bunks in the Hermes cabin, but for a long time that night they sat stunned among the smashed ruins as daisies popped up all around them from the cold winter ground.

Despite my exhaustion, I slept fitfully. I did not mind Kayla and Austin's constant sneezing, or Will's gentle snoring. I did not even mind the hyacinths blooming in the windowsill, filling the room with their melancholy perfume. But I could not stop thinking of the dryads raising their arms to the flames in the woods, and about Nero, and Meg. The Arrow of Dodona stayed silent, hanging in my quiver on the wall, but I suspected it would have more annoying Shakespearean advice soon. I did not relish what it might telleth me about my future.

At sunrise, I rose quietly, took my bow and quiver and combat ukulele, and hiked to the summit of Half-Blood Hill. The guardian dragon, Peleus, did not recognize me. When I came too close to the Golden Fleece, he hissed, so I had to sit some distance away at the foot of the Athena Parthenos.

I didn't mind not being recognized. At the moment, I did not *want* to be Apollo. All the destruction I saw below me . . . it was my fault. I had been blind and complacent. I had allowed the emperors of Rome, including one of my own descendants, to rise to power in the shadows. I had let my once-great network of Oracles collapse until even Delphi was lost. I had almost caused the death of Camp Half-Blood itself.

And Meg McCaffrey . . . Oh, Meg, where were you?

Do what you need to do, she had told me. *That's my final order.*

Her order had been vague enough to allow me to pursue her. After all, we were bound together now. What I *needed to do* was to find her. I wondered if Meg had phrased her order that way on purpose, or if that was just wishful thinking on my part.

I gazed up at the serene alabaster face of Athena. In real life, she didn't look so pale and aloof—well, not most of the time, anyway. I pondered why the sculptor, Phidias, had chosen to make her look so unapproachable, and whether Athena approved. We gods often debated how much humans could change our very nature simply by the way they pictured us or imagined us. During the eighteenth century, for instance, I could not escape the white powdered wig, no matter how hard I tried. Among immortals, our reliance on humans was an uncomfortable subject.

Perhaps I deserved my present form. After my carelessness and foolishness, perhaps humanity *should* see me as nothing but Lester Papadopoulos.

I heaved a sigh. "Athena, what would you do in my place? Something wise and practical, I suppose."

Athena offered no response. She stared calmly at the horizon, taking the long view, as always.

I didn't need the wisdom goddess to tell me what I must do. I should leave Camp Half-Blood immediately, before the campers woke. They had taken me in to protect me, and I had nearly gotten them all killed. I couldn't bear to endanger them any longer.

But, oh, how I wanted to stay with Will, Kayla, Austin— my mortal children. I wanted to help Harley put smiley faces on his flamethrower. I wanted to flirt with Chiara and steal her away from Damien . . . or perhaps steal Damien away from Chiara, I wasn't sure yet. I wanted to improve my music and archery through that strange activity known as *practice*. I wanted to have a home.

Leave, I told myself. *Hurry*.

Because I was a coward, I waited too long. Below me, the cabin lights flickered on. Campers emerged from their doorways. Sherman Yang began his morning stretches. Harley jogged around the green, holding his Leo Valdez beacon high with the hope it would finally work.

At last, a pair of familiar figures spotted me. They approached from different directions—the Big House and Cabin Three—hiking up the hill to see me: Rachel Dare and Percy Jackson.

"I know what you're thinking," Rachel said. "Don't do it."

I feigned surprise. "Can you read my mind, Miss Dare?"

"I don't need to. I know you, Lord Apollo."

A week ago, the idea would have made me laugh. A mortal could not *know* me. I had lived for four millennia. Merely looking upon my true form would have vaporized any human. Now, though, Rachel's words seemed perfectly reasonable. With Lester Papadopoulos, what you saw was what you got. There really wasn't much to know.

"Don't call me *Lord*," I sighed. "I am just a mortal teen. I do not belong at this camp."

Percy sat next to me. He squinted at the sunrise, the sea breeze tousling his hair. "Yeah, I used to think I didn't belong here either."

"It's not the same," I said. "You humans change and grow and mature. Gods do not."

Percy faced me. "You sure about that? You seem pretty different."

I think he meant that as a compliment, but I didn't find his words reassuring. If I was becoming more fully human, that was hardly a cause for celebration. True, I had mustered a few godly powers at important moments—a burst of divine strength against the Germani, a hay fever arrow against the Colossus—but I could not rely on those abilities. I didn't even understand how I had summoned them. The fact that I had limits, and that I couldn't be sure where those limits *were* . . . Well, that made me feel much more like Lester Papadopoulos than Apollo.

"The other Oracles must be found and secured," I said. "I cannot do that unless I leave Camp Half-Blood. And I cannot risk anyone else's life."

Rachel sat on my other side. "You sound certain. Did you get a prophecy from the grove?"

I shuddered. "I fear so."

Rachel cupped her hands on her knees. "Kayla said you

were talking to an arrow yesterday. I'm guessing it's wood from Dodona?"

"Wait," Percy said. "You found a talking arrow that gave you a prophecy?"

"Don't be silly," I said. "The arrow talks, but I got the prophecy from the grove itself. The Arrow of Dodona just gives random advice. He's quite annoying."

The arrow buzzed in my quiver.

"At any rate," I continued, "I must leave the camp. The Triumvirate means to possess all the ancient Oracles. I have to stop them. Once I have defeated the former emperors . . . only then will I be able to face my old enemy Python and free the Oracle of Delphi. After that . . . if I survive . . . perhaps Zeus will restore me to Olympus."

Rachel tugged at a strand of her hair. "You know it's too dangerous to do all that alone, right?"

"Listen to her," Percy urged. "Chiron told me about Nero and this weird holding company of his."

"I appreciate the offer of assistance, but—"

"Whoa." Percy held up his hands. "Just to be clear, I'm not offering to go with you. I still have to finish my senior year, pass my DSTOMP and my SAT, and avoid getting killed by my girlfriend. But I'm sure we can get you some other helpers."

"I'll go," Rachel said.

I shook my head. "My enemies would *love* to capture someone as dear to me as the priestess of Delphi. Besides, I need you and Miranda Gardiner to stay here and study the Grove of Dodona. For now, it is our only source of prophecy. And since our communication problems have not gone away, learning to use the grove's power is all the more critical."

Rachel tried to hide it, but I could see her disappointment in the lines around her mouth. "What about Meg?" she asked. "You'll try to find her, won't you?"

She might as well have plunged the Arrow of Dodona into my chest. I gazed at the woods—that hazy green expanse that had swallowed young McCaffrey. For a brief moment, I felt like Nero. I wanted to burn the whole place down.

"I will try," I said, "but Meg doesn't want to be found. She's under the influence of her stepfather."

Percy traced his finger across the Athena Parthenos's big toe. "I've lost too many people to bad influence: Ethan Nakamura, Luke Castellan . . . We almost lost Nico, too. . . ." He shook his head. "No. No more. You can't give up on Meg. You guys are bound together. Besides, she's one of the good guys."

"I've known many of the good guys," I said. "Most of them got turned into beasts, or statues, or—or trees. . . ." My voice broke.

Rachel put her hand over mine. "Things can turn out differently, Apollo. That's the nice thing about being human. We only have one life, but we can choose what kind of story it's going to be."

That seemed hopelessly optimistic. I had spent too many centuries watching the same patterns of behavior be repeated over and over, all by humans who thought they were being terribly clever and doing something that had never been done before. They thought they were crafting their own stories, but they were only tracing over the same old narratives, generation after generation.

Still . . . perhaps human persistence was an asset. They never seemed to give up hope. Every so often they *did* manage to surprise me. I never anticipated Alexander the Great, Robin Hood, or Billie Holiday. For that matter, I never anticipated Percy Jackson and Rachel Elizabeth Dare.

"I—I hope you're right," I said.

She patted my hand. "Tell me the prophecy you heard in the grove."

I took a shaky breath. I didn't want to speak the words. I was afraid they might wake the grove and drown us in a cacophony of prophecies, bad jokes, and infomercials. But I recited the lines:

> *"There once was a god named Apollo*
> *Who plunged in a cave blue and hollow*
> *Upon a three-seater*
> *The bronze fire-eater*
> *Was forced death and madness to swallow"*

Rachel covered her mouth. "A limerick?"

"I know!" I wailed. "I'm doomed!"

"Wait." Percy's eyes glittered. "Those lines . . . Do they mean what I think?"

"Well," I said, "I believe the blue cave refers to the Oracle of Trophonius. It was a . . . a very dangerous ancient Oracle."

"No," Percy said. "The *other* lines. *Three-seater*, *bronze fire-eater*, yadda yadda."

"Oh. I have no clue about those."

"Harley's beacon." Percy laughed, though I could not understand why he was so pleased. "He said you gave it a tuning adjustment? I guess that did the trick."

Rachel squinted at him. "Percy, what are you . . ." Her expression went slack. "Oh. *Oh*."

"Were there any other lines?" Percy urged. "Like, except for the limerick?"

"Several," I admitted. "Just bits and pieces I didn't understand. *The fall of the sun; the final verse.* Um, *Indiana, banana. Happiness approaches.* Something about *pages burning.*"

Percy slapped his knee. "There you go. *Happiness approaches.* Happy is a name—well, the English version, anyway." He stood and scanned the horizon. His eyes fixed on something in the distance. A grin spread across his face. "Yep. Apollo, your escort is on the way."

I followed his gaze. Spiraling down from the clouds was a large winged creature that glinted of Celestial bronze. On its back were two human-size figures.

Their descent was silent, but in my mind a joyous fanfare of Valdezinator music proclaimed the good news.

Leo had returned.

❧

39

Want to hit Leo?

That is understandable

Hunk Muffin earned it

THE DEMIGODS HAD TO TAKE NUMBERS.

Nico commandeered a dispenser from the snack bar and carried it around, yelling, "The line starts to the left! Orderly queue, guys!"

"Is this really necessary?" Leo asked.

"Yes," said Miranda Gardiner, who had drawn the first number. She punched Leo in the arm.

"Ow," said Leo.

"You're a jerk, and we all hate you," said Miranda. Then she hugged him and kissed his cheek. "If you ever disappear like that again, we'll line up to *kill you*."

"Okay, okay!"

Miranda had to move on, because the line was getting pretty long behind her. Percy and I sat at the picnic table with Leo and his companion—none other than the immortal sorceress Calypso. Even though Leo was the one getting punched by everyone in camp, I was reasonably sure he was the *least* uncomfortable one at the table.

When they first saw each other, Percy and Calypso had hugged awkwardly. I hadn't witnessed such a tense greeting since Patroclus met Achilles's war prize, Briseis. (Long story. Juicy gossip. Ask me later.) Calypso had never liked me, so she pointedly ignored me, but I kept waiting for her to yell "BOO!" and turn me into a tree frog. The suspense was killing me.

Percy hugged Leo and didn't even punch him. Still, the son of Poseidon looked disgruntled.

"I can't believe it," he said. "Six months—"

"I told you," Leo said. "We tried sending more holographic scrolls. We tried Iris messages, dream visions, phone calls. Nothing worked.— Ow! Hey, Alice, how you doing?— Anyway, we ran into one crisis after another."

Calypso nodded. "Albania was particularly difficult."

From down the line, Nico di Angelo yelled, "Please do not mention Albania! Okay, who's next, folks? One line."

Damien White punched Leo's arm and walked away grinning. I wasn't sure Damien even knew Leo. He simply couldn't turn down a chance to punch someone.

Leo rubbed his bicep. "Hey, no fair. That guy's getting back in the line. So, like I was saying, if Festus hadn't picked up on that homing beacon yesterday, we'd still be flying around, looking for a way out of the Sea of Monsters."

"Oh, I hate that place," Percy said. "There's this big Cyclops, Polyphemus—"

"I know, right?" Leo agreed. "What is up with that guy's *breath?*"

"Boys," Calypso said, "perhaps we should focus on the present?"

She did not look at me, but I got the impression she meant *this silly former god and his problems.*

"Yeah," Percy said. "So the communication issues . . . Rachel Dare thinks it's got something to do with this company, Triumvirate."

Rachel herself had gone to the Big House to fetch Chiron, but Percy did a reasonable job summarizing what she had found out about the emperors and their evil corporation. Of course, we didn't know very much. By the time six more people had punched Leo in the arm, Percy had brought Leo and Calypso up to speed.

Leo rubbed his new bruises. "Man, why does it not surprise me that modern corporations are run by zombie Roman emperors?"

"They are not zombies," I said. "And I'm not sure they run *all* corporations—"

Leo waved away my explanation. "But they're trying to take over the Oracles."

"Yes," I agreed.

"And that's bad."

"Very."

"So you need our help.— Ow! Hey, Sherman. Where'd you get the new scar, dude?"

While Sherman told Leo the story of Crotchkicker McCaffrey and the Demon Peach Baby, I glanced at Calypso.

She looked very different from what I remembered. Her hair was still long and caramel brown. Her almond-shaped eyes were still dark and intelligent. But now, instead of a *chiton* she wore modern jeans, a white blouse, and a shocking-pink ski jacket. She looked younger—about my mortal age. I wondered if she had been punished with mortality for leaving her enchanted island. If so, it didn't seem fair that she had retained her otherworldly beauty. She had neither flab nor acne.

As I watched, she stretched two fingers toward the opposite end of the picnic table, where a pitcher of lemonade sweated in the sunlight. I had seen her do this sort of thing before, willing her invisible aerial servants to whisk objects into her hands. This time, nothing happened.

A look of disappointment crossed her face. Then she realized I was watching. Her cheeks colored.

"Since leaving Ogygia, I have no powers," she admitted. "I am fully mortal. I keep hoping, but—"

"You want a drink?" Percy asked.

"I got it." Leo beat him to the pitcher.

I had not expected to feel sympathy for Calypso. We'd had harsh words in the past. A few millennia ago, I had opposed her petition for early release from Ogygia because of some . . . ah, drama between us. (Long story. Juicy gossip. Please *do not* ask me later.)

Still, as a fallen god, I understood how disconcerting it was to be without one's powers.

On the other hand, I was relieved. This meant she could not turn me into a tree frog or order her aerial servants to toss me off the Athena Parthenos.

"Here you go." Leo handed her a glass of lemonade. His expression seemed darker and more anxious, as if . . . Ah, of course. Leo had rescued Calypso from her prison island. In doing so, Calypso had lost her powers. Leo felt responsible.

Calypso smiled, though her eyes were still touched by melancholy. "Thank you, babe."

"*Babe?*" Percy asked.

Leo's expression brightened. "Yeah. She won't call me Hunk Muffin, though. I dunno why.— Ow!"

It was Harley's turn. The little boy punched Leo, then threw his arms around him and broke down sobbing.

"Hey, brother." Leo ruffled his hair and had the good sense to look ashamed. "You brought me home with that beacon of yours, H-Meister. You're a hero! You know I never would've left you hanging like that on purpose, don't you?"

Harley wailed and sniffled and nodded. Then he punched Leo again and ran away. Leo looked like he was about to get sick. Harley was quite strong.

"At any rate," Calypso said, "these problems with the Roman emperors—how can we help?"

I raised my eyebrows. "You *will* help me, then? Despite . . . ah, well, I always knew you were kindhearted and forgiving, Calypso. I meant to visit you at Ogygia more often—"

"Spare me." Calypso sipped her lemonade. "I'll help you if *Leo* decides to help you, and he seems to have some affection for you. Why, I can't imagine."

I let go of the breath I had been holding for . . . oh, an hour. "I'm grateful. Leo Valdez, you have always been a gentleman and a genius. After all, you created the Valdezinator."

Leo grinned. "I did, didn't I? I suppose that was pretty awesome. So where is this next Oracle you— Ow!"

Nyssa had made it to the front of the line. She slapped Leo, then berated him in rapid Spanish.

"Yeah, okay, okay." Leo rubbed his face. "Dang, *hermana*, I love you, too!"

He turned his attention back to me. "So this next Oracle, you said it was where?"

Percy tapped the picnic table. "Chiron and I were talking about this. He figures this triumvirate thingie . . . they probably divided America into three parts, with one emperor in charge of each. We know Nero is holed up in New York, so we're guessing this next Oracle is in the second dude's territory, maybe in the middle third of the U.S."

"Oh, the middle third of the U.S.!" Leo spread his arms. "Piece of torta, then. We'll just search the entire middle of the country!"

"Still with the sarcasm," Percy noted.

"Hey, man, I've sailed with the most sarcastic scalawags on the high seas."

The two gave each other a high five, though I did not quite understand why. I thought about a snippet of prophecy I'd heard in the grove: something about Indiana. It might be a place to start. . . .

The last person to come through the line was Chiron himself, pushed in his wheelchair by Rachel Dare. The old centaur gave Leo a warm, fatherly smile. "My boy, I am so pleased to have you back. And you freed Calypso, I see. Well done, and welcome, both of you!" Chiron spread his arms for a hug.

"Uh, thanks, Chiron." Leo leaned forward.

From underneath Chiron's lap blanket, his equine foreleg shot out and implanted a hoof in Leo's gut. Then, just as quickly, the leg disappeared. "Mr. Valdez," Chiron said in the same kindly tone, "if you ever pull a stunt like that again—"

"I got it, I got it!" Leo rubbed his stomach. "Dang, for a teacher, you got a heck of a high kick."

Rachel grinned and wheeled Chiron away. Calypso and Percy helped Leo to his feet.

"Yo, Nico," Leo called, "please tell me that's it for the physical abuse."

"For now." Nico smiled. "We're still trying to get in touch with the West Coast. You'll have a few dozen people out there who will definitely want to hit you."

Leo winced. "Yeah, that's something to look forward to. Well, I guess I'd better keep my strength up. Where do you guys eat lunch now that the Colossus stepped on the dining pavilion?"

Percy left that night just before dinner.

I expected a moving one-on-one farewell, during which he would ask my advice about test taking, being a hero, and living life in general. After he lent me his help in defeating the Colossus, it would have been the least I could do.

Instead, he seemed more interested in saying good-bye to Leo and Calypso. I wasn't part of their conversation, but the three of them seemed to reach some sort of mutual understanding. Percy and Leo embraced. Calypso even pecked Percy on the cheek. Then the son of Poseidon waded into Long Island Sound with his extremely large dog and they both disappeared underwater. Did Mrs. O'Leary swim? Did she travel through the shadows of whales? I did not know.

Like lunch, dinner was a casual affair. As darkness fell, we ate on picnic blankets around the hearth, which blazed with Hestia's warmth and kept away the winter chill. Festus the dragon sniffed around the perimeter of the cabins, occasionally blowing fire into the sky for no apparent reason.

"He got a little dinged up in Corsica," Leo explained. "Sometimes he spews randomly like that."

"He hasn't blowtorched anyone important yet," Calypso added, her eyebrow arched. "We'll see how he likes you."

Festus's red jewel eyes gleamed in the darkness. After driving the sun chariot for so long, I wasn't nervous about riding a metal dragon, but when I thought about what we'd be riding *toward*, geraniums bloomed in my stomach.

"I had planned to go alone," I told them. "The prophecy from Dodona speaks of the bronze fire-eater, but . . . it feels wrong for me to ask you to risk your lives. You have been through so much just to get here."

Calypso tilted her head. "Perhaps you *have* changed. That does not sound like the Apollo I remember. You definitely are not as handsome."

"I am still *quite* handsome," I protested. "I just need to clear up this acne."

She smirked. "So you haven't completely lost your big head."

"I beg your pardon?"

"Guys," Leo interrupted, "if we're going to travel together, let's try to keep it friendly." He pressed an ice pack to his bruised bicep. "Besides, we were planning to head west anyway. I got to find my peeps Jason and Piper and Frank and Hazel and . . . well, pretty much everybody at Camp Jupiter, I guess. It'll be fun."

"*Fun?*" I asked. "The Oracle of Trophonius will supposedly swallow me in death and madness. Even if I survive that, my other trials will no doubt be long, harrowing, and quite possibly fatal."

"Exactly," Leo said. "Fun. I don't know about calling the whole quest thing *Apollo's trials*, though. I think we should call it *Leo Valdez's Victory Lap World Tour*."

Calypso laughed and laced her fingers in Leo's. She may not have been immortal anymore, but she still had a grace and easiness about her that I could not fathom. Perhaps she missed her powers, but she seemed genuinely happy to be with Valdez—to be young and mortal, even if it meant she could die at any moment.

Unlike me, she had *chosen* to become mortal. She knew that leaving Ogygia was a risk, but she had done it willingly. I didn't know how she'd found the courage.

"Hey, man," Leo told me. "Don't look so glum. We'll find her."

I stirred. "What?"

"Your friend Meg. We'll find her. Don't worry."

A bubble of darkness burst inside me. For once, I hadn't been thinking of Meg. I'd been thinking about myself, and that made me feel guilty. Perhaps Calypso was right to question whether or not I'd changed.

I gazed at the silent forest. I remembered Meg dragging me to safety when I was cold and soaked and delirious. I remembered how fearlessly she fought the myrmekes, and how she'd ordered Peaches to extinguish the match when Nero wanted to burn his hostages, despite her fear of unleashing the Beast. I had to make her realize how evil Nero was. I had to find her. But how?

"Meg knows the prophecy," I said. "If she tells Nero, he will know our plans as well."

Calypso took a bite of her apple. "I missed the whole Roman Empire. How bad can one emperor be?"

"Bad," I assured her. "And he is allied with two others. We don't know which ones, but it's safe to assume they are equally cutthroat. They've had centuries to amass fortunes, acquire property, build armies . . . Who knows what they are capable of?"

"Eh," Leo said. "We took down Gaea in, like, forty seconds. This'll be easy squeezy."

I seemed to recall that the *lead-up* to the fight with Gaea had involved months of suffering and near misses with death. Leo, in fact, *had* died. I also wanted to remind him that the Triumvirate might well have orchestrated all our previous troubles with the Titans and giants, which would make them more powerful than anything Leo had ever faced.

I decided that mentioning these things might affect group morale.

"We'll succeed," Calypso said. "We must. So we will. I have been trapped on an island for thousands of years. I don't know how long this mortal life will be, but I intend to live fully and without fear."

"That's my *mamacita*," Leo said.

"What have I told you about calling me *mamacita*?"

Leo grinned sheepishly. "In the morning we'll start getting our supplies together. As soon as Festus gets a tune-up and an oil change, we'll be good to go."

I considered what supplies I would take with me. I had

depressingly little: some borrowed clothes, a bow, a ukulele, and an overly theatrical arrow.

But the real difficulty would be saying good-bye to Will, Austin, and Kayla. They had helped me so much, and they embraced me as family more than I had ever embraced *them*. Tears stung my eyes. Before I could start sobbing, Will Solace stepped into the light of the hearth. "Hey, everybody! We've started a bonfire in the amphitheater! Sing-along time. Come on!"

Groans were mixed in with the cheers, but most everyone got to their feet and ambled toward the bonfire now blazing in the distance, where Nico di Angelo stood silhouetted in the flames, preparing rows of marshmallows on what looked like femur bones.

"Aw, man." Leo winced. "I'm terrible at sing-alongs. I always clap and do the 'Old MacDonald' sounds at the wrong time. Can we skip this?"

"Oh, no." I rose to my feet, suddenly feeling better. Perhaps tomorrow I would weep and think about good-byes. Perhaps the day after that we would be flying toward our deaths. But tonight, I intended to enjoy my time with my family. What had Calypso said? *Live fully and without fear.* If she could do it, then so could the brilliant, fabulous Apollo. "Singing is good for the spirits. You should never miss an opportunity to sing."

Calypso smiled. "I can't believe I'm saying this, but for once I agree with Apollo. Come on, Leo. I'll teach you to harmonize."

Together, the three of us walked toward the sounds of laughter, music, and a warm, crackling fire.

GUIDE TO APOLLO-SPEAK

Achilles   the best fighter of the Greeks who besieged Troy in the Trojan War; extraordinarily strong, courageous, and loyal, he had only one weak spot: his heel

Admetus   the king of Pherae in Thessaly; Zeus punished Apollo by sending him to work for Admetus as a shepherd

Aeolus   the Greek god of the winds

Agamemnon   king of Mycenae; the leader of the Greeks in the Trojan War; courageous, but also arrogant and overly proud

agora   Greek for *gathering place*; a central outdoor spot for athletic, artistic, spiritual, and political life in ancient Greek city-states

Ajax   Greek hero with great strength and courage; fought in the Trojan War; used a large shield in battle

ambrosia   food of the gods; has healing powers

amphitheater   an oval or circular open-air space used for performances or sporting events, with spectator seating built in a semicircle around the stage

Aphrodite   the Greek goddess of love and beauty

apodesmos   a band of material that women in ancient Greece wore around the chest, particularly while participating in sports

Apollo   the Greek god of the sun, prophecy, music, and healing; the son of Zeus and Leto, and the twin of Artemis

Ares   the Greek god of war; the son of Zeus and Hera, and half brother to Athena

Argo   the ship used by a band of heroes who accompanied Jason on his quest to find the Golden Fleece

Argonauts   a band of heroes who sailed with Jason on the *Argo*, in search of the Golden Fleece

Artemis   the Greek goddess of the hunt and the moon; the daughter of Zeus and Leto, and the twin of Apollo

Asclepius   the god of medicine; son of Apollo; his temple was the healing center of ancient Greece

Athena   the Greek goddess of wisdom

Athena Parthenos   a giant statue of Athena; the most famous Greek statue of all time

ballista (ballistae, pl.)   a Roman missile siege weapon that launched a large projectile at a distant target

Batavi   an ancient tribe that lived in modern-day Germany; also an infantry unit in the Roman army with Germanic origins

Briseis   a princess captured by Achilles during the Trojan War, causing a feud between Achilles and Agamemnon that resulted in Achilles refusing to fight alongside the Greeks

Bunker Nine a hidden workshop Leo Valdez discovered at Camp Half-Blood, filled with tools and weapons; it is at least two hundred years old and was used during the Demigod Civil War

Caesar Augustus the founder and first emperor of the Roman Empire; adopted son and heir of Julius Caesar (*see also* Octavian)

Calliope the muse of epic poetry; mother of several sons, including Orpheus

Calypso the goddess nymph of the mythical island of Ogygia; a daughter of the Titan Atlas; she detained the hero Odysseus for many years

Camp Half-Blood the training ground for Greek demigods, located in Long Island, New York

Camp Jupiter the training ground for Roman demigods, located between the Oakland Hills and the Berkeley Hills, in California

Cassandra the daughter of King Priam and Queen Hecuba; had the gift of prophecy, but was cursed by Apollo so that her predictions were never believed, including her warning about the Trojan Horse

catapult a military machine used to hurl objects

Cave of Trophonius a deep chasm home to the Oracle Trophonius; its extremely narrow entrance required a visitor to lie flat on his back before being sucked into the cave; called "The Cave of Nightmares" due to the terrifying accounts of its visitors

Celestial bronze a rare metal deadly to monsters

centaur a race of creatures that is half-human, half-horse

Ceres   the Roman god of agriculture; Greek form: Demeter

Chiron   a centaur; the camp activities director at Camp Half-Blood

chiton   a Greek garment; a sleeveless piece of linen or wool secured at the shoulders by brooches and at the waist by a belt

Chrysothemis   a daughter of Demeter who won Apollo's love during a music contest

Circe   a Greek goddess of magic

Cloacina   goddess of the Roman sewer system

Clytemnestra   the daughter of the king and queen of Sparta; married and later murdered Agamemnon

Colosseum   an elliptical amphitheater in the center of Rome, Italy, capable of seating fifty thousand spectators; used for gladiatorial contests and public spectacles such as mock sea battles, animal hunts, executions, re-enactments of famous battles, and dramas

Colossus Neronis (Colossus of Nero)   a gigantic bronze statue of Emperor Nero; was later transformed into the sun god with the addition of a sunray crown

Cretan   of the island of Crete

Crommyon   a village in ancient Greece where a giant wild sow wreaked havoc before it was killed by Theseus

cuirass   leather or metal armor consisting of a breastplate and backplate worn by Greek and Roman soldiers; often highly ornamented and designed to mimic muscles

Cyclops (Cyclopes, pl.)   a member of a primordial race of giants, each with a single eye in the middle of his or her forehead

Cyrene a fierce huntress with whom Apollo fell in love after he saw her wrestle a lion; Apollo later transformed her into a nymph in order to extend her life

Daedalus a skilled craftsman who created the Labyrinth on Crete in which the Minotaur (part man, part bull) was kept

Daphne a beautiful naiad who attracted Apollo's attention; she was transformed into a laurel tree in order to escape him

Demeter the Greek goddess of agriculture; a daughter of the Titans Rhea and Kronos; Roman form: Ceres

dimachaerus a Roman gladiator trained to fight with two swords at once

Dionysus the Greek god of wine and revelry; the son of Zeus; activities director at Camp Half-Blood

Domus Aurea Emperor Nero's extravagant villa in the heart of ancient Rome, built after the Great Fire of Rome

Doors of Death the doorway to the House of Hades, located in Tartarus; doors have two sides—one in the mortal world, and one in the Underworld

drakon a gigantic yellow-and-green serpentlike monster, with frills around its neck, reptilian eyes, and huge talons; it spits poison

dryads tree nymphs

Erebos a place of darkness between earth and Hades

Eros the Greek god of love

Erythaea an island where the Cumaean Sibyl, a love interest of Apollo, originally lived before he convinced her to leave it by promising her a long life

Fields of Punishment   the section of the Underworld where people who were evil during their lives are sent to face eternal punishment for their crimes after death

Gaea   the Greek earth goddess; mother of Titans, giants, Cyclopes, and other monsters

Germani (**Germanus**, sing.)   tribal people who settled to the west of the Rhine river

Golden Fleece   this hide from a gold-haired winged ram was a symbol of authority and kingship; it was guarded by a dragon and fire-breathing bulls; Jason was tasked with obtaining it, resulting in an epic quest

Gorgons   three monstrous sisters (Stheno, Euryale, and Medusa) who have hair of living, venomous snakes; Medusa's eyes can turn the beholder to stone

Great Fire of Rome   a devastating fire that took place in 64 CE, lasting for six days; rumors indicated that Nero started the fire to clear space for the building of his villa, Domus Aurea, but he blamed the Christian community for the disaster

greaves   shin armor

Greek fire   an incendiary weapon used in naval battles because it can continue burning in water

Grove of Dodona   the site of the oldest Greek Oracle, second only to the Delphi; the rustling of trees in the grove provided answers to priests and priestesses who journeyed to the site

Hades   the Greek god of death and riches; ruler of the Underworld

harpy   a winged female creature that snatches things

Hebe the Greek goddess of youth; daughter of Zeus and Hera

Hecate goddess of magic and crossroads

Hephaestus the Greek god of fire and crafts and of blacksmiths; the son of Zeus and Hera, and married to Aphrodite

Hera the Greek goddess of marriage; Zeus's wife and sister

Hermes Greek god of travelers; guide to spirits of the dead; god of communication

Herodotus a Greek historian known as the "Father of History"

Hestia Greek goddess of the hearth

hippocampi (**hippocampus**, sing.) half-horse, half-fish creatures

hippodrome an oval stadium for horse and chariot races in ancient Greece

Hittites a group of people who lived in modern Turkey and Syria; often in conflict with Egyptians; known for their use of chariots as assault weapons

House of Hades a place in the Underworld where Hades, the Greek god of death, and his wife, Persephone, rule over the souls of the departed

Hunters of Artemis a group of maidens loyal to Artemis and gifted with hunting skills and eternal youth as long as they reject men for life

Hyacinthus a Greek hero and Apollo's lover, who died while trying to impress Apollo with his discus skills

Hypnos the Greek god of sleep

ichor   the golden fluid that is the blood of gods and immortals

imperator   a term for *commander* in the Roman Empire

Imperial gold   a rare metal deadly to monsters, consecrated at the Pantheon; its existence was a closely guarded secret of the emperors

Iris   the Greek goddess of the rainbow, and a messenger of the gods

Julian dynasty   the time period measured from the battle of Actium (31 BCE) to the death of Nero (68 CE)

karpoi (*karpos*, sing.)   grain spirits

kouretes   armored dancers who guarded the infant Zeus from his father, Kronos

Kronos   the youngest of the twelve Titans; the son of Ouranos and Gaea; the father of Zeus; he killed his father at his mother's bidding; Titan lord of fate, harvest, justice, and time; Roman form: Saturn

Labyrinth   an underground maze originally built on the island of Crete by the craftsman Daedalus to hold the Minotaur

Laomedon   a Trojan king whom Poseidon and Apollo were sent to serve after they offended Zeus

Lepidus   a Roman patrician and military commander who was in a triumvirate with Octavian and Marc Antony

Leto   mother of Artemis and Apollo with Zeus; goddess of motherhood

Lupercalia   a pastoral festival, observed on February 13 through 15, to avert evil spirits and purify the city, releasing health and fertility

Lydia a province in ancient Rome; the double ax origi-
nated there, along with the use of coins and retail shops

Marc Antony a Roman politician and general; part of the
triumvirate, with Lepidus and Octavian, who together
tracked down and defeated Caesar's killers; had an
enduring affair with Cleopatra

Marsyas a satyr who lost to Apollo after challenging him
in a musical contest, which led to Marsyas being flayed
alive

Medea a follower of Hecate and one of the great sorcer-
esses of the ancient world

Midas a king with the power to transform anything he
touched to gold; he selected Marsyas as the winner
in the musical contest between Apollo and Marsyas,
resulting in Apollo giving Midas the ears of a donkey

Minos king of Crete; son of Zeus; every year he made King
Aegus pick seven boys and seven girls to be sent to the
Labyrinth, where they would be eaten by the Minotaur;
after his death he became a judge in the Underworld

Minotaur the half-man, half-bull son of King Minos of
Crete; the Minotaur was kept in the Labyrinth, where
he killed people who were sent in; he was finally defeated
by Theseus

Mithridates king of Pontus and Armenia Minor in northern Anatolia (now Turkey) from about 120 to 63 BCE;
one of the Roman Republic's most formidable and
successful enemies, who engaged three of the prominent generals from the late Roman Republic in the
Mithridatic Wars

Mount Olympus home of the Twelve Olympians

myrmeke a giant antlike creature that poisons and paralyzes its prey before eating it; known for protecting various metals, particularly gold

Nemesis the Greek goddess of revenge

Nero Roman emperor from 54 to 68 CE; the last in the Julian dynasty

New Rome a community near Camp Jupiter where demigods can live together in peace, without interference from mortals or monsters

Nike the Greek goddess of strength, speed, and victory

Nine Muses Greek goddesses of literature, science, and the arts, who have inspired artists and writers for centuries

Niobe daughter of Tantalus and Dione; suffered the loss of her six sons and six daughters, who were killed by Apollo and Artemis as a punishment for her pride

nosoi (*nosos*, sing.) spirits of plague and disease

nymph a female nature deity who animates nature

Octavian the founder and first emperor of the Roman Empire; adopted son and heir of Julius Caesar (*see also* Caesar Augustus)

Odysseus legendary Greek king of Ithaca and the hero of Homer's epic poem *The Odyssey*

Ogygia the island home—and prison—of the nymph Calypso

omphalus stones used to mark the center—or navel—of the world

Oracle of Delphi a speaker of the prophecies of Apollo

Oracle of Trophonius   a Greek who was transformed into an Oracle after his death; located at the Cave of Trophonius; known for terrifying those who seek him

Ouranos   the Greek personification of the sky; father of the Titans

palikoi (*palikos*, sing.)   twin sons of Zeus and Thaleia; the gods of geysers and thermal springs

Pan   the Greek god of the wild; the son of Hermes

Pandora   the first human woman created by the gods; endowed with a unique gift from each; released evil into the world by opening a jar

Parthenon   a temple dedicated to the goddess Athena located at the Athenian Acropolis in Greece

Patroclus   son of Menoetius; he shared a deep friendship with Achilles after being raised alongside him; he was killed while fighting in the Trojan War

pegasus (**pegasi**, pl.)   a winged divine horse; sired by Poseidon, in his role as horse-god

Peleus   father of Achilles; his wedding to the sea-nymph Thetis was well attended by the gods, and a disagreement between them at the event eventually lead to the Trojan War; the guardian dragon at Camp Half-Blood is named after him

Persephone   the Greek queen of the Underworld; wife of Hades; daughter of Zeus and Demeter

phalanx (**phalanxes**, pl.)   a compact body of heavily armed troops

Phidias   a famous ancient Greek sculptor who created the Athena Parthenos and many others

Polyphemus   the gigantic one-eyed son of Poseidon and Thoosa; one of the Cyclopes

Poseidon   the Greek god of the sea; son of the Titans Kronos and Rhea, and brother of Zeus and Hades

praetor   an elected Roman magistrate and commander of the army

Primordial Chaos   the first thing ever to exist; a void from which the first gods were produced

Prometheus   the Titan who created humans and gifted them with fire stolen from Mount Olympus

Pythia   the name given to every Oracle of Delphi

Python   a monstrous serpent that Gaea appointed to guard the Oracle at Delphi

Rhea Silvia   the queen of the Titans, mother of Zeus

Riptide   the name of Percy Jackson's sword; *Anaklusmos* in Greek

River Styx   the river that forms the boundary between earth and the Underworld

Saturnalia   an ancient Roman festival celebrating Saturn (Kronos)

satyr   a Greek forest god, part goat and part man

shadow-travel   a form of transportation that allows creatures of the Underworld and children of Hades to use shadows to leap to any desired place on earth or in the Underworld, although it makes the user extremely fatigued

Sibyl   a prophetess

Sibylline Books   a collection of prophecies in rhyme written in Greek; Tarquinius Superbus, a king of Rome, bought them from a prophetess and consulted them in times of great danger

siccae a short curved sword used for battle in ancient Rome

Sparta a city-state in ancient Greece with military dominance

Stygian iron a magical metal, forged in the River Styx, capable of absorbing the very essence of monsters and injuring mortals, gods, Titans, and giants; has a significant effect on ghosts and creatures from the Underworld

Talos a giant mechanical man made of bronze and used on Crete to guard its shoreline from invaders

Tantalus According to legend, this king was such a good friend of the gods that he was allowed to dine at their table—until he spilled their secrets on earth; he was sent to the Underworld, where his curse was to be stuck in a pool of water under a fruit tree, but never be able to drink or eat

Tartarus husband of Gaea; spirit of the abyss; father of the giants; a region of the Underworld

Theodosius the last to rule over the united Roman Empire; known for closing all ancient temples across the empire

Thracian of Thrace, a region centered on the modern borders of Bulgaria, Greece, and Turkey

Titan War the epic ten-year battle between the Titans and the Olympians that resulted in the Olympians taking the throne

Titans a race of powerful Greek deities, descendants of Gaea and Ouranos, that ruled during the Golden Age and were overthrown by a race of younger gods, the Olympians

trireme   a Greek warship, having three tiers of oars on each side

triumvirate   a political alliance formed by three parties

Trojan War   According to legend, the Trojan War was waged against the city of Troy by the Achaeans (Greeks) after Paris of Troy took Helen from her husband, Menelaus, king of Sparta

Troy   a Roman city situated in modern-day Turkey; site of the Trojan War

Tyche   the Greek goddess of good fortune; daughter of Hermes and Aphrodite

Typhon   the most terrifying Greek monster; father of many famous monsters, including Cerberus, the vicious multi-headed dog tasked with guarding the entrance to the Underworld

Underworld   the kingdom of the dead, where souls go for eternity; ruled by Hades

Zephyros   the Greek god of the West Wind

Zeus   the Greek god of the sky and the king of the gods

The Knights Templars
In England

The Knights Templars In England

Thomas W. Parker

The University of Arizona Press

Tucson   1963

L. C. Catalogue Card Number 63-11983
Copyright ©1963
The Board of Regents of the Universities and
State College of Arizona. All rights reserved.

F.A.H.

Discipulo et Amico

Preface

MUCH has been written about the Knights Templars as an international military order and about their trial and the dissolution of their order, but little has been done systematically or in detail on their organization and activities in individual countries. This work seeks to fill this gap for England by presenting a survey of the history of the Templars there from the time of their appearance in the third decade of the twelfth century to their dissolution in the early years of the fourteenth. In order to give balance and perspective to them and their activities, brief consideration is given to the Templars on the Continent and in the Holy Land as well; however, chief attention is directed to their organization, privileges, holdings, and political and economic activities in England. Because of the nature of the source materials, the particular activities the Templars engaged in, and the reliance of the order upon the crown for support, the treatment of the subject is oriented toward their relations with the English kings.

Except for the Inquest of 1185 and a few minor documents, primary source materials must be gleaned mainly from the miscellaneous references in the Public Records and in the various volumes of the Rolls Series. Secondary authorities are surprisingly few. There are only three general works of note: the lengthy and detailed essay on the Templars in England in the twelfth century written by Beatrice Lees as an introduction to her edition of the Inquest;[1] the doctoral dissertation of Clarence Perkins[2] which is chiefly concerned with a discussion of the privileges and the trial of the Templars in England; and the introductory chapters of J. Bruce Williamson's study of the Temple in London.[3]

Tucson, Arizona   T.W.P.
January, 1963

Contents

The Knights Templars
In England

Introduction

T HE KNIGHTS TEMPLARS were the most colorful, the most powerful, and the most widely known of the crusading orders of the Middle Ages. Accordingly, their history is to a large degree a part of the history of the Crusades; and in this sense, the struggle for the faith and the Holy Land receives major emphasis in any discussion of the order and its activities. But the Templars were concerned with political and economic as well as with religious and military matters. Indeed, their power and accomplishments as feudal lords and bankers seem as great as, if not greater than, their achievements and contributions as soldiers of Christ and His Church, as can be seen both in the general history and in the specific affairs of the order in the various areas where the Templars were active, whether in the states of the Holy Land or in the states of western Europe.[1]

Since the Templars have unfortunately left no specific or official history of their order, such information as we possess must be pieced together from the incomplete and not always impartial or accurate records and reports which have survived from the Middle Ages. All that the Templars themselves have left are copies of their Rule and a limited collection of charters. Several historical writers of the High Middle Ages, both in the Holy Land and in western Europe, provide valuable but not very extensive material. In addition, the public records of individual countries, especially England and France, furnish considerable but controversial political and financial data; and papal records abound with references to the order.

In England, the major concern of this study, information on the Templars has to be drawn chiefly from references in the public records, the accounts of contemporary historical writers, and such Templar records as still survive. Though most of the order's English records have disappeared, a few important charters and a number of miscellaneous documents do exist. The reason for the disappearance of the records is not wholly known. Especially on the local level, probably the mere passage of time accounts for the loss of many of them, while on the national level, destruction by fire seems the probable explanation. At the time of the dissolution of the order and the subsequent assignment of former Templar lands to the Knights Hospitallers, full records seem to have existed at New Temple in London, the central office and depository of the order, and at local preceptories. These records, at least in part, formed the basis for the claims and counter-claims of the king, individual nobles, and the Hospitallers.[2] Later, at the time of Wat Tyler's insurrection (summer, 1381), when the rebels attacked and destroyed much property in London, New Temple was among the buildings ravaged and burned.[3] There is no indication that either the Hospitallers, who were to hold the Temple for many years, or the Apprentices of the Law, who have occupied it since at least the last quarter of the fourteenth century, disposed of any of the Templar records.

Origins of the Templars

Of the precise origin of the Templars, little is known beyond brief mention by several medieval writers.[4] To this, modern historians have been able to add little, if anything.[5] Apparently, the origin of the Order of the Temple is to be found in the determination of two Frankish knights in the East — Hugh of Payens (in Champagne) and Geoffrey of St. Omer (in Artois) — who, being distressed by the sufferings of Christian pilgrims, decided to devote their lives to the protection and aid of these people as they made their way from Asia Minor and the sea ports of the eastern Mediterranean to the Holy City. It was in 1118 that these two men, renouncing all worldly ambition and choosing to live like monks, went to Arnulf, Patriarch of Jerusalem, and before him took vows of poverty, chastity, and obedience and formally announced their noble and useful purpose. Soon, however, another duty — which was to become their chief purpose — was added: to do battle against the infidel, whether or not Christian pilgrims were threatened.

From its dwelling place, the new order received its name; for, lacking a place to live, Hugh and Geoffrey, and the six or seven other men who had joined them, were given a residence within the precincts of his own palace area and near the church known as the Temple of Solomon, by Baldwin II, King of Jerusalem. From this, the Templars (*Templarii*) became known first as "the poor fellow soldiers of Christ and of the Temple of Solomon" (*Pauperes Commilitiones Christi et Templi Salomonis*) and later as the "Knights of the Temple of Solomon of Jerusalem" (*Fratres Militiae Templi Salomonis Ierusalem*).[6]

The first few years of their existence provided no indication of the importance the Templars were to assume. It was at the end of nine years, when there were still only nine members,[7] that the Templars turned to

Bernard, Abbot of Clairvaux, for aid and advice. Baldwin II, writing on behalf of this worthy new order and praising its cause (1127), begged the saintly and influential abbot to help by encouraging the pope to confirm the order and to approve a rule for it.[8] Responding favorably, the great Cistercian advocated the cause of the Templars and indicated a willingness to help them draw up a rule.[9] Meanwhile, Hugh, received by Honorius II, was assured of papal sympathy and instructed to present a petition to the church council which had been called to meet at Troyes in 1128. The Council approved the new order, entrusted the revision and amplification of its existing rule to Bernard, and decreed that their new constitution and rule should be put into effect after being finally sanctioned by the pope and the patriarch of Jerusalem.[10] When both Honorius and Stephen, pope and patriarch respectively, subsequently gave their approval, the Templars' fortune took a decided turn for the better.

Because of their fame arising from their soldierly skill which brought victory in battle and their religious enthusiasm which set an example of self-sacrifice, and in addition, because of Bernard's words of praise which were as unstinting as they were influential,[11] the Templars soon found themselves besieged by recruits and patronized by kings, popes, princes, and other lords, both lay and ecclesiastical. Both in the east and the west, these gifts and privileges, as well as recruits, now came to them in great number. William of Tyre gave testimony of this growth when he said: "There was not a prince in western Europe who did not contribute to their maintenance, and in wealth they were the equals of kings."[12] Later (1244) in a similar vein, Matthew Paris wrote, ". . . the Templars in Christendom [have] nine thousand manors . . . besides the emoluments and various revenues arising from their brotherhoods, and from procurations, all of which are increased by their privileges."[13]

𝔓apal 𝔓riuileges

Especially important among the many and extensive privileges bestowed upon the Templars over a period of more than a century and a half were those granted by the popes, practically all of whom from Celestine II to Clement V issued bulls — many of them still surviving — on their behalf.[14] Among the major privileges granted to the order as a whole by the various popes were the following: First an exemption from payment of clerical taxes of all sorts.[15] This meant that regular tithes, on the one hand, and special levies of twentieths, fifteenths, and the like, for the Crusades, on the other, were not to be collected from the Templars. Second, a requirement that the clergy urge Christians to contribute to the Templars.[16] This meant special encouragement to fundraising activities on behalf of the Templars and provision of funds without effort on their part. Third, a reservation of offerings collected on certain days in certain churches for the Templars.[17] This provided a sort of compulsory support of the Templars in addition to the voluntary contributions just mentioned. Fourth, an authority to open churches in order to hold services and collect offerings even in places under the interdict.[18] This somewhat surprising concession provided still more revenue for the Templars. Fifth, a right to have their own chaplains, to build their own chapels (*oratoria*), and to bury the dead in their own churchyards.[19] These grants meant the Templars could go their own way in religious matters irrespective of the regular and secular clergy and helped to make the Templars practically independent of all churchmen except the pope.[20] Sixth, an exemption from excommunication and interdict.[21] This meant that neither the Templars nor their vassals or tenants could be proceeded against by the usual religious means and thus further removed the order from dependence upon the ordinary religious groups. Seventh, a requirement that all prelates uphold and protect the rights, persons, and goods of the Templars.[22] This further strengthened the Templars' immunity from unfriendly action by their critics and rivals and promoted respect for their privileges. In addition to the grant of other lesser privileges,[23] too numerous to mention here, papal grants and confirmations of land, other property, and money were many and extensive.[24] The net effect of these papal privileges was to put the Templars under the special protection of the popes and to render them practically immune from all other jurisdiction, lay or ecclesiastical. Thus we note that the order had been raised to a position of extraordinary power, influence, and privilege. To these papal gifts and privileges were added those given by temporal rulers — for example, the specific and additional privileges received by the Templars in England which will be considered in the next chapter.

It is not in the least surprising to find that the rights and privileges of the Templars were not always respected and that considerable resentment and opposition arose — as is clearly evident in the numerous papal bulls which so often restated the provisions of earlier ones and which repeatedly directed recognition and acceptance of the Templars' privileges.[25] Upon occasion, however, it was necessary for the popes to check, or to seek to check, the Templars' tendencies toward excessive greed, arrogance, and independence.[26] In short, the financial rights and exemptions, the ecclesiastical privileges and immunities, and their own actions and attitudes made the Templars powerful and independent and aroused rivalry and hatred which would one day return to plague them. Yet, in the early years, and indeed, throughout much of their history, the Templars were well thought of, especially because of their very real achievements against the infidel.[27]

Organization

The organization and rule of the Templars had much in common with those of most western monastic orders of the Middle Ages, but it was the Cistercian order that the Templars used as their chief model,[28] a not unexpected choice in view of the prominence of the Cistercians in the early twelfth century and especially in view of the willingness of Bernard of Clairvaux to help the new group draw up its rule and to support its program. Quite naturally, the specific details of organization, especially those of a military nature, had to be worked out slowly on the basis of necessity and experience. Not until 1163, when Pope Alexander III issued *Omne datum optimum,* mentioned above, was a definite and centralized organization officially established. But this was in large part a confirmation of the system which had evolved in the preceding half-century during which the order had gained great power and risen to a level of wide influence both in the east and the west. The Templars' organization, as revealed in the papal bull and in the Rule of the order, must now be briefly examined.[29]

The chief official of the Templars, chosen by a complicated electoral procedure and serving for life, was the Grand Master whose headquarters were in Jerusalem and whose powers were extensive, including, as they did, leadership in battle, appointment and supervision of officials, administration of the order's property, and discipline of individual members. Though limited to some degree by the Council of the order, in which he had one vote and in which the principle of majority vote prevailed, he, nonetheless, by his power of appointment and of determining who should be called to sit in council, must often have dominated both the Council and the order.[30] Second in command was the Seneschal who was supreme in the absence of the Grand Master.[31] Below the Seneschal was the Marshall, a sort of minister of war and normally the immediate subordinate of the Grand Master on campaign.[32] Below these officers was the Commander of the Realm of Jerusalem who served as the Master of the Province of Jerusalem and also as the Grand Treasurer of the whole order.[33] Strictly limited in his spheres of activity and jurisdiction, but still one of the chief officials of the order, was the Commander of the City of Jerusalem whose task it was to defend Christian pilgrims and to provide them with food and horses in the Holy Land.[34]

Initially the organization and rule of the order pertained to Templars in the Holy Land alone; but in time, as the order expanded into Europe, the organization, somewhat modified, was applied there, too.[35]

At the head of each province, a large territorial area often coterminous with a state or kingdom, was a Provincial Master — also called Grand Preceptor or Grand Prior — who was to the province what the Grand Master was to the whole order. Though apparently appointed technically by the Grand Master — at least in the early years — the provincial master was probably to a large degree free of his actual or direct control. In turn, the provincial master was responsibile for the appointment and supervision of subordinate officials in his province and was expected to consult with his provincial council before deciding important matters or undertaking major activities. Each province was divided into preceptories which served as the basic administrative units and as the recruiting stations of the order. The individual preceptories were often local manors which had come into the hands of the Templars and had thereby been transformed into religious houses. The term preceptory, therefore, is used to refer both to the territory and to the office for the management of the territory. The powers and importance of any individual preceptor would vary according to the size and wealth of his preceptory as well as according to the ability and personality of the preceptor himself. Subordinate to the preceptors, but essential to the effective functioning of the preceptory, must have been the business agents and estate stewards as well as the serfs who worked the Templar lands.[36]

Alongside the officials of the order where the chapters which shared in the administration of the order and in the determination of policy. A general chapter, or chapter for business, was held, apparently at least once each year, usually at Jerusalem, except in the later years, after the capture of that city by the Moslems and the withdrawal of the Christians from the Holy Land, when it of necessity met elsewhere. This chapter, over which the Grand Master presided, served as the supreme assembly of the order; and it was expected that its advice and counsel would be followed by the Grand Master.[37] Its specific membership, apart from the chief officials of the order, was left to the discretion of the Grand Master who was to admit only those he knew "to be worthy and profitable to give advice."[38] This general chapter was to be concerned with such matters as these: the admission of new brothers; the grant, confirmation, or sale of Templar land; decision on matters of war and military activities; the dispatch of envoys to foreign powers; the request for aid for the order and for the Holy Land; administration during the absence of the Grand Master; and the discussion of matters of general interest and importance to the order.[39]

There was another type of chapter, too — one concerned with discipline primarily — which met frequently, perhaps weekly, and which all Templars in a given preceptory were to attend.[40] At these meetings, the brothers were expected to confess their sins voluntarily, but if they did not, the other brothers were expected to denounce them; and at these meetings, the proper penance for offenses was to be assigned.[41] At first, the penance seems to have been largely left to the discretion of the Master; but in time, the most usual offenses, together with their penalties, were listed in the Rule.[42]

In addition to the general and disciplinary chapters meeting in Jerusalem, there were provincial chapters and local chapters[43] — the former dealing with the business of the order in the province, and the latter dealing with local matters in each preceptory and especially with matters of discipline.[44] Unfortunately, practically nothing is known about these provincial and local chapters.

Classes of Membership

There were at least five classes of brothers recognized by the Templars in their Rule. The first and highest class was that of the knights *(fratres milites, frères chevaliers)* who could be distinguished by their garment, a white mantle with a red cross.[45] Upon joining the order, the knight surrendered his property, took the monastic vows,[46] and agreed never to leave unless to join another religious order having a stricter rule.[47] Few in number[48] and necessarily of noble and legitimate lineage,[49] the knights served as mounted warriors and as officials of the order. The sergeants or esquires *(clientes, frères sergens; armigeri, écuyers),* who made up a second class, were required to be of free birth.[50] Prohibited from wearing the white mantle, they instead wore black or brown robes.[51] Some of these men served as light-armed troops, and the younger of them were often assigned as squires to older knights. In addition to military service, however, the sergeants might serve as minor officials, supervisors of local administration, and attendants or assistants of the great dignitaries of the order.[52] With this group may be associated the *frères casaliers* who managed and protected the smaller Templar houses and farms *(casaux).*[53] A third class was composed of chaplains *fratres capellani, frères chapelains).* In the beginning, the order relied upon outside priests to render spiritual services — especially confession and the mass — to them;[54] but not too many years had passed before the Templars were authorized to have their own priests who in time became full members of the order and were wholly independent of diocesan authority.[55] A group of manual laborers, artisans, domestic servants, and workers of the soil who performed the countless obvious and necessary tasks and services required within the order formed a fourth class of craftsmen and menials *(frères de métier).*[56] No doubt, the great majority of persons calling themselves Templars fell into this category — in modern terms, they might be referred to as "lay brothers." A number of men of rather uncertain position formed the fifth class, a group of associates of the order *(affiliés)* or temporary members. For example, married men *(frères mariés, confrères)* were permitted to join under certain conditions; crusaders in the Holy Land were allowed to join for a time only *(fratres ad terminum, frères à termine);* and men might, for the salvation of their souls, be received into the order at the point of death.[57] Women, of course, were denied membership though they might be associated with the order as wives of associate members.[58] These classes of membership existed throughout the order, both in the east and in the west.

The life of the Templars was both religious and military. Indeed, the union of these two spheres of activity was the reason for the existence of the order; and the degree to which the Templars adhered to this life was to be, in large measure, the degree to which they succeed or failed. As a religious and military group, the Templar order admitted neither children nor women.[59] As a religious group, its members lived the communal and restricted life of monks bound by vows of poverty, chastity, and obedience, and emphasizing prayer, silence, and moderation in food and drink as well.[60] As a military group, it emphasized constant training, rigid discipline, mastery of tactics and strategy, careful maintenance of equipment, and victory in battle.[61] For support, since charity was not enough, the Templars were permitted by their Rule, as well as by the heads of the church and the state, to possess property,[62] institutional rather than personal, and to receive tithes.[63]

The Templars and the Crusades

This is not the place for any lengthy discussion of the history of the Templars in the east or of the Crusades,[64] but it is necessary to refer briefly to the Templars outside of England and to their participation in the Crusades in order to give some balance and perspective and a fuller meaning to the activities and position of the English Templars.

The First Crusade and the establishment of the Christian states in the east — Jerusalem, Edessa, Tripoli, and Antioch — in a sense necessitated the existence of a military order. After Jerusalem had been captured (July, 1099) and Ascalon had fallen (August, 1099), many crusaders assumed their purpose had been achieved and their aid was no longer needed. The departure of many of them for their homes in Europe left scarcely enough troops to garrison the few towns held by the Christians and left almost defenseless against recurring Arab raids the weak Kingdom of Jerusalem, over which Godfrey of Bouillon and then, within a year, Baldwin I, ruled. Fortunately for themselves, the Christians had found the Moslem world upon which they had descended disunited after the death (1092) of the powerful sultan Malik Shah. But since the rivalry of the Moslem leaders and the disunity of the Moslem states could not be counted upon as being permanent, there was an urgent need for large numbers of Christian recruits and pilgrims. Unfortunately, the needed aid and services were not forthcoming. It was in this setting and under these conditions that the Templars came into being.

The Order of the Temple was not exactly the first, nor was it the last, of the crusading orders to come into existence. The Knights Hospitallers, who had been formed some years earlier in the Holy Land as a group to aid the sick and the needy, soon became a military organization. Their first wholly military action — and the Templars' as well — seems to have been the assistance given in the 1130's to Baldwin II, King of Jerusalem, against his daughter, Alice of Antioch.[65] Like the Templars, who became their chief rivals, the Hospitallers received privileges and gifts from popes, kings, and others. Later, in 1197, a third military crusading order, the Teutonic Knights, appeared in the Holy Land.

The chief concern of the Templars in the east was military — to wage war against the infidel. For many years, their bravery, tenacity, and achievements were a constant example to their fellow Christians and a terror to their enemies. As time passed, the Templars assumed other interests as well — possession of large estates, accumulation of portable forms of wealth, participation in trade, and rivalry with the Hospitallers and the Patriarch of Jerusalem. Though individual activities of the Templars and the motivation behind certain of these activities may have been justifiably suspect upon occasion, nonetheless, the Templars in the east remained throughout basically faithful to their original purpose and repeatedly appear in the front rank, with their Grand Master as one of the chief leaders, in the many campaigns against and battles with the Moslems.

As early as 1136, at the Battle of Aleppo, the Templars, not yet the great military power they were soon to become, fought valiantly under the command of Fulk of Anjou in his unsuccessful contest with Zengi, Atabeg of Mosul, a new and powerful Moslem leader. Real impetus to the increase in power and numbers of the Templars came after Zengi's capture of Edessa in 1144 — an event which called forth the preaching of the Second Crusade by St. Bernard and others, led Pope Eugenius III to authorize the Templars to wear the red cross on their garments, and brought numerous men and gifts to the order. Though much had been hoped for, nothing of note came of the Second Crusade.

Louis VII of France and Conrad III of the Holy Roman Empire, failing in the seige of Damascus (1148), abandoned plans to beseige the key city of Ascalon and returned to Europe instead. Although some persons blamed the Templars for the Christian defeat at Damascus,[66] Louis, writing to Suger, Abbot of St. Denis, spoke well of the Templars, saying he could not have "existed even for the shortest time" without their assistance.[67] With the departure of the French and German kings and their armies, the task of securing fortresses and of guarding the frontiers was more and more assigned to the Templars who successfully seized control of Ascalon and Gaza (1149), fortress cities along the coast, which they were to hold for some years.

The rise to power of Saladin, a Moslem of great talent and fame, and a man dedicated to the expulsion of the Christians from the east, was a most portentous development. In 1177, the Christians, with the Templars in the forefront, had temporarily checked the Moslem forces at Ascalon. The next year, Saladin's attack on Jacob's Ford, an important Templar fortress on the northern frontier of the Latin Kingdom of Jerusalem, was unsuccessful; but shortly thereafter (1179), Saladin was victorious in an open battle near the Ford. For the next several years, there existed an uneasy truce between the Moslems and Christians. This ended in 1187, when Saladin launched a new and decisive campaign against the Christians and their holdings after the repeated violations of the truce by Reginald of Chatillon, one of the prominent Christian lords whose hatred of the Moslems knew no bounds and whose political ambitions had not been satisfied. The key battle (July 4) was fought outside Hattin,[68] west of the Sea of Galilee, after the Master of the Temple had unwisely convinced Guy, King of Jerusalem, to take the offensive on the sun-scorched, waterless plain. The Christians were overwhelmingly defeated, and the king, the Masters of the Templars and Hospitallers, together with many of their men, as well as numerous lords and nobles, were captured. Most of his captives Saladin generously released, but his hatred of the crusading orders was so intense that all Templar and Hospitaller prisoners, perhaps two hundred in number, were executed forthwith. Following up his victory, Saladin proceeded immediately to further attacks, capturing many Christian cities along the coast, including Acre, and finally, on October 3, 1187, Jerusalem itself. Only Tyre, Antioch, Tripoli, and a few other Latin possessions remained in Christian hands.

The fall of Jerusalem called forth the Third Crusade so familiarly associated with the colorful English king, Richard, the Lion-Hearted. In June of 1191, several months after the arrival of Philip Augustus of France and many months after his departure from England, Richard finally reached the Holy Land. Despite the rivalry of the two kings and their failure to cooperate in the seige of the city, Acre surrendered to the Christian forces in July. This favorable event gave Philip, who pleaded ill health, reason to hasten back to France while Richard, still desiring to regain control of Jerusalem, stayed on for another year. Not much attention was given to the Holy City, however. For, the Templars and Hospitallers, envious of the able and popular English leader and concerned with strengthening their own positions and regaining control of lands they had lost to Saladin, convinced Richard to direct chief attention to Ascalon and Jaffa — cities which fell to the Christians in 1192. Seizing the opportunity offered by the fall of Jaffa, Richard made a truce with Saladin (September 2, 1192), which permitted Christians to visit the Holy City, and then set out for Europe and further adventure, making his way initially in the guise of a Templar.

The crusade sent by Henry VI, Holy Roman Emperor, (1197) was of little importance. Some minor successes were achieved with the aid of the Templars and others, but the early death of the emperor ended western interest in the campaign. Even less successful for the Holy Land was the Fourth Crusade (1202-04) so avidly promoted by Pope Innocent III. Instead of proceeding to the proposed attack on Egypt, which might have checked Moslem power and thereby made easier the recovery of the Holy Land, the crusaders launched an attack on Constantinople, which served to bring advantages not to the Holy Land but to Venice. Nor was the Fifth Crusade (1218-19) successful. Directed against Egypt, this crusade, in which the Templars played a key role, resulted in the capture of Damietta, an important Egyptian frontier outpost, which was promptly lost when the flooding of the Nile necessitated withdrawal.

The crusade of Emperor Frederick II (1228-29) improved the Christian position in the east despite the bitter opposition of the Templars and Hospitallers.[69] After initially refusing to fight under the command of the emperor, who had been excommunicated by Pope Gregory IX, the two military orders finally did render some degree of cooperation and assistance. Though facing great odds, Frederick fought effectively and was able to conclude a ten-year treaty with Al Kamil, the Sultan of Egypt. According to the treaty terms, the Christians were to regain Nazareth, Bethlehem, Jaffa, and all of Jerusalem except the Temple and Mosque of Omar; and Frederick was to see to it that no Christian disturbed any of Al Kamil's possessions. This favorable treaty, along with the emperor's success where the Templars had failed and his open contempt and disrespect for them, was strongly resented by the Templars who must have seen in Frederick an immediate threat to the maintenance of their own power and influence in the east. In anger, they informed the Sultan of Frederick's proposed visit to the alleged place of Christ's baptism. Al Kamil, however, rejected the treachery intended and sent their letter to Frederick, thus giving the emperor additional reason for wanting to humble the proud Templars. Frederick, however, was unable to do anything about the Templars because the crusade which Pope Gregory IX was preaching against him required his immediate return to Europe. The Holy City remained in Christian hands for a decade before it again fell to the Moslems.

Louis IX of France, a devoted and eager if not very successful crusader, undertook two campaigns which he hoped would regain control of the Holy Land for the Christians. His first crusade (1248-54), warmly supported by the Templars, was directed against the Moslem ruler in Egypt. After capturing Damietta, in the Nile delta, the French king moved southward, unsuccessfully beseiging the stronghold of Mansourah. In the retreat from there, Louis himself was captured and was briefly held prisoner by Baibars, Sultan of Egypt; and Damietta was again taken by the Moslems. Louis remained in the east for several more years and was aided by the Templars financially as well as militarily.[70] After his departure, the rivalry between the Templars and Hospitallers broke out into open warfare, thereby further weakening the Christian position in the east. Indeed, by 1268 the Christians retained control of little more than Tyre, Acre, and Tripoli. In 1270, because of the Christian losses in the east, Louis IX again took the cross. But his attention this time was turned to North Africa where he had been erroneously informed the Bey of Tunis was willing to be converted to Christianity. Prince Edward of England joined in the proposed crusade, and after the death of Louis, proceeded to the Holy Land where, with the cooperation of the Templars and others, he made several raids into the area around Acre.

Participation in the major crusades does not represent the only military activity of the Templars. An important — perhaps the most important — part of their activity involved garrison duty in the fortresses and frequent skirmishes with the enemy along the frontiers of the Christian kingdoms in the east.[71] It certainly would be no exaggeration to say that the Templars, aided by the Hospitallers and Teutonic Knights, apart from being the first line of defense in time of war, rendered their most valuable service as defenders of the persons, lands, and possessions of the eastern Christians in the years when the religious fervor and military spirit of their fellow Christians waned. Had it not been for the constant vigilance of the military orders, the loss of Christian holdings in the east would have occurred long before the end of the thirteenth century.

The final struggle in the Holy Land was soon to come. The Moslems, determined to drive the Christians out of the east, continued their campaign with vigor during the 1280's. When Acre, the last Christian stronghold in the east was attacked, the Christians, led by the Master of the Temple, resisted as best they could. During the last hours of the seige, eleven Templars, under cover of darkness, escaped by sea with the wealth of the order to Cyprus while a small band of determined Templars remained behind and fought to the death.[72] With the fall of Acre (May 28, 1291), Christian possession of territory in the Near East ended and the Crusades as such were over. In the long run, the purpose of the Templars had not been achieved; and without persons and property to protect in the east, the need for the military orders was no longer urgent — especially was this true inasmuch as no organized or sustained effort to regain the Holy Land was undertaken. Though there was much talk about campaigns against the Turks, and though this talk increased when the Turks soon began extending their power into Europe, the idea and fervor of the crusades were not to revive, and projects of reconquest never really got beyond words.[73]

While the Templars were active in the east, they were busy in Europe as well, seeking recruits and amassing wealth, supposedly for the campaign against the infidel. Many Templar houses had been established in France, England, Germany, Italy, and Spain;[74] and as the houses and wealth of the order increased, the provincial organization, referred to above, was worked out for the practical supervision of these areas and the effective utilization of their men and resources. France seems to have been the chief area; and Paris, the chief center in the west. Indeed, as time passed, the Templars tended to concentrate increasingly in the west where individual members not only achieved positions of great political influence as diplomats and as counsellors to kings and princes but also successfully engaged in economic activities as brokers of international exchange and lenders of money as well as supervisors of agricultural production. With power and wealth came abuses which were probably greater in number and seriousness in the west than in the east. It will not prove wholly surprising to find the Templars, after having been driven from the Holy Land, ultimately attacked, tried, and convicted by their rivals and former supporters in the west.

chapter two

The Templars in England

Origins

OF THE INTRODUCTION and settlement of the Templars in England little is known.[1] After attending the Council of Troyes (1128), which had formally recognized his new order, Hugh de Payens, the first Grand Master, journeyed to Normandy. There Henry I, the English monarch, received him with honor, and after presenting him with gifts of gold and silver, sent him to England and Scotland where, besides being given additional treasures of gold and silver for the Holy Land, it is said, he enlisted an undetermined number of men for service in Jerusalem.[2] Whether or not a Templar unit was actually established in England and whether or not grants of land were made at this time to the new order cannot be known for certain though it seems probable. All that can be ascertained is that grants of land, both royal and private, were made to the Templars in England during the reign of King Stephen, the earliest being that of Temple Cressing in Essex, made in 1137 by Matilda, his wife, in a charter issued at Évreux in northern France.[3] From this time on, grants and confirmation of grants of land and privileges to the Templars appear with increasing frequency. Stephen, as well as Matilda, was generous to the Templars. Generous, too, were the rivals of Stephen in the contest for the control of England following the death of Henry I. Thus, from approximately 1135 on, it can be said that the rise of the Templars to power and wealth in England proceeded in rapid fashion.

At least two reasons for the success of the Templars during this period of civil strife may be cited. One the one hand, the Templars profited from the crusading sympathies of the time. Stephen of England was a member of a distinguished crusading family, being the son of that Stephen of Blois who had been an important leader on the First Crusade; and Matilda, his wife, was a member of a Boulogne family closely associated with the crusading movement. Interestingly enough, Hugh de Payens was from Champagne, an area controlled by Stephen's family;

and Godfrey of St. Omer, another of the original founders of the Templars, was a vassal of the Count of Boulogne. In England, as elsewhere, enthusiasm for the crusades and generosity to crusaders existed among the various groups in society. On the other hand, the Templars seem to have played shrewd politics during the period of civil turmoil, serving both parties and winning rewards from both sides, as charters and documents favoring the Templars, about sixty of which have survived, attest.[4] Unfortunately, just what the Templars did in the wars cannot be ascertained. Nor can their donors, be they of Stephen's party or of his rival's party, even be determined with certainty in many instances. It was not the Templars alone, however, who profited from the troubles of the reign of Stephen. William of Newburgh stated that more religious houses were founded in the troubled reign of Stephen than during the one hundred preceding years.[5] Though his statement may not be literally true, his emphasis is well taken.

About two years after her original grant of Temple Cressing, Matilda gave the Templars Temple Cowley in Oxfordshire; and another two years later, in 1141, Uphall in Essex.[6] Stephen not only subsequently confirmed these grants[7] but himself made grants to the order — for example, land and mills at Dinsley in Hertfordshire *(ca.* 1142).[8] His rival, the Empress Matilda, daughter of Henry I and wife of Geoffrey of Anjou — whose family had also long been associated with the crusades — at this same time granted pasture in Shotover Forest to the Cowley Templars.[9] The Sandford Cartulary and documents in the Inquest of 1185 record a number of additional grants by various persons in this period.[10] Hence, by 1142, when Stephen had won out in the contest for the control of England, the Templars had acquired a goodly number of holdings in southeastern and south-central England. The next decade witnessed a marked increase in Templar holdings — and privileges — in England. The record reveals Stephen confirming grants to the Templars — for example, grants of land by Gilbert, Earl of Pembroke, in Berkshire;[11] the grant by Matilda of the manor and half-hundred of Witham in Essex;[12] the grant by William Marci of lands within London;[13] and the grant of Robert of Ferrer of the manor of Bisham in Berkshire.[14] Finally, shortly before his death (1154), Stephen issued a general charter to the Templars confirming to them all their liberties and gifts which they had been in seisin of at the previous Easter.[15] All this shows that, though the details are incomplete and often imprecise, the Templars were firmly established in England by 1154 and that they must already have obtained lands, privileges, and exemptions of importance. This was the foundation on which the Templars were to build their great edifice of power, wealth, and influence.

Organization

The general organization of the Templars in the East and in the provinces, as it is revealed in their Rule and as it gradually evolved, was discussed in the preceding chapter. Here the concern is with the provincial and local organization in England — a subject about which little is known.[16] This lack of information is partly due to the small number of Templar records in England; but it may also in part be due to the fact that there is relatively little to know. After all, England was a remote province which developed later than and was less involved in the crusading movement than many of those on the continent.[17] Precise details on the Templar organization in England, then, cannot be given.

The same five classes that existed elsewhere among the Templars also existed in England.[18] Most important, though fewest in number, were the knights who had to be of noble lineage; more numerous than the knights were the sergeants, or serving brothers, who were free-born men; and fewest in number were the chaplains, or priests, of the order. At the bottom of the social scale were the manual workers and craftsmen, a numerous group without whose practical skills the Templar organization could not function. Also recognized as part of the Templar order were the associates who might join the order on a temporary basis, usually during the last years of their lives.

The total membership of the Templars can be estimated only at the time of their dissolution when presumably their number was greatest. If Perkins, who has carefully examined the records dealing with their imprisonment and trial, is right, their number was remarkably small and certainly far smaller than many another religious group in England. After eliminating duplication in names, he concludes there were 144 Templars in England in their last years, including 15 to 20 knights, 8 to 16 priests, and 108 to 121 sergeants or serving brothers.[19] These figures omit, however, associate members whose status is not wholly clear and whose numbers cannot possibly be determined. Regardless of the accuracy, or inaccuracy, of these figures, the point is clearly made that one must avoid any notion of the Templars as a numerous group. For the sake of clarity, it should be pointed out that the many tenants of the Templars, who were in no sense members of the order — although they were quite willing to claim and exercise Templar privileges — are properly excluded from consideration here.

With time, definite units, offices, and officials emerged in the provinces; their exact evolution, however, cannot be traced. Indeed, whether England was always a separate province *(ballia)* or whether it was in the earliest years appended to the French province is unclear. Most of the time, however, England, including Scotland and Ireland, formed a separate province[20] under a master or grand preceptor whose usual title was *Magister Militiae Templi in Anglia*. Whether the Master served on a temporary basis or held office for life is not always clear; and for the early years, not even the names of the men who held the mastership can be determined. But with the coming of the thirteenth century, some degree of consistency in organization is to be found, and a satisfactory list of masters can be drawn up.[21] There is some uncertainty about the manner of appointment of the Master in England. Initially he may well have been named by the Grand Master of the order;[22] but the brief tenure and rapid turnover of the Grand Mastership during the years of warfare in the east, the many other urgent problems the Grand Master had to deal with, and the slowness and difficulty of communication between Jerusalem and England, make it doubtful that this was consistently or effectively done. Inasmuch as the Master in England frequently came from distinguished noble families associated with the administration of the king — for example, Richard de Hastings and Geoffrey Fitz Stephen — and since the Templars themselves stood to profit if their masters were on good terms with the crown, the possibility of royal appointment or intervention must be considered. However, there is no evidence to suggest that the king was ever directly responsible for or even ever actively intervened in the selection of a master. Most likely, the Master in England came to be chosen by the English Templars, probably by the knights and officials only,[23] who were wise enough to select a person not apt to be disapproved of by either the Grand Master or the king. If, as is likely, the Master in England had to take the same oath as did the provincial masters on the continent, he had to:

> . . . promise to Jesus Christ . . . and to His Vicar, the Sovereign Pontiff and his successors, perpetual obedience and fidelity; . . . defend . . . the mysteries of faith; . . . be submissive and obedient to the Master-general of the Order in conformity with the statutes prescribed by . . . St. Bernard; . . . at all times in case of need pass the seas to go and fight; . . . not sell the property of the Order, nor consent that it be sold or alienated; . . . always preserve chastity; . . . be faithful to the king of [England]; . . . never surrender to the enemy the towns and places belonging to the Order; [and] aid and defend [the religious] by words, by arms, and by all sorts of good offices. . . .[24]

From the central headquarters of the order at the preceptory in London, where the annual chapters were held,[25] the master exercised general supervisory powers over the officials, members, and property of the order. Being, like other great feudal lords, an itinerant rather than a sedentary ruler, he frequently travelled from preceptory to preceptory with his staff and attendants, supervising his subordinates, attending to the business of the order, and living off the proceeds of the order's estates.[26] It was the master also, who, on behalf of the order, often through one of his agents, accepted the many donations which were usually given "magistro et fratribus Milicie Templi in Anglia."[27]

Below the master, directly responsible to him, and evidently appointed by him, were the preceptors *(preceptores)* or commanders, each of whom was charged with the discipline and training of the Templars and with the supervision and administration of Templar properties in his preceptory *(preceptoria)*.[28] The most important of these officials were the preceptors of Ireland and Scotland who, though often referred to as master in their respective areas, were actually subordinate to the master at London.[29] The miscellaneous information which survives pertains to preceptories more than to preceptors and does not permit accurate lists of preceptories (or of preceptors) to be compiled for most of the period. By the time of the dissolution, however, the number of preceptories had reached approximately forty;[30] but the number of preceptors was considerably less, due apparently to the fact that one perceptor might simultaneously exercise jurisdiction over more than one preceptory.[31] Though specific information is lacking on the point, it would seem reasonable to assume that a major preceptory was run by a knight and that the great majority of preceptories were headed by a sergeant, or serving brother.

The Templars also had procurators *(procuratores)* — men serving as business agents or lawyers — whose task it was to represent the order, or individuals in the order, in such matters as the receipt and acceptance of donations of all kinds, the transfer and sale of land and goods of all sorts, and in the defense or prosecution of cases involving the Templars. In such references as can be found, the procurators were always themselves members of the order.[32]

In addition to the officials mentioned thus far, the Templars must have maintained a large, trained clerical staff, at least at their central headquarters in London. Though no specific indication of such is given in the records, the composition of documents, the attestations of clerks and chaplains, the use of seals, and the like, make this assumption necessary since most of the Templars were illiterate.[33] There may of course have been some Templars who could read and write, in addition to their priests, but it is impossible to ascertain if any of these clerks employed at New Temple or elsewhere were themselves members of the order.[34]

Like many other religious organizations, the English Templars met together in chapter, sometimes at London, and sometimes in local areas. Since the composition and dates of the chapters are not specified in the source materials, one can only speculate on the membership and frequency of the meetings. When, upon occasion, the "whole chapter" *(totum capitulum)* is mentioned as meeting in London,[35] it is conceivable that all the Templars in the English province were summoned. For the most part, however, it would seem more likely that the London chapter was normally attended by the master and the preceptors only. Addison[36] suggests that there were two types of chapters — one general and the other particular. The general chapter, he says, was composed of the master and preceptors, met once a year at London, dealt with matters pertaining to the Holy Land, received accounts of their stewardship from the various officials, and framed rules and regulations for the management of Templar properties. The particular chapter, he says, met irregularly at the different preceptories which the master visited; admitted new members; made appointments to vacant benefices; dealt with the purchase, sale, or exchange of land; and imposed penalties on erring brothers. Addison's distinction is reasonable and helpful, but is perhaps an over-simplification. Only in part can what he says about the activities of the chapters be verified by historical references,[37] and the point that a distinction was made between the two types of chapters cannot be documented. Most references to the chapters simply use the term "capitulum" without a preceding adjective. Hence, what is known of the chapter in England must be based upon the assumption, which is in general acceptable, that the English chapters, both in composition and business, were modelled after those discussed in the Rule.

Little is known about the preceptory *(preceptoria* or *domus)*, the basic unit of organization in England, or about the manner in which it functioned. Chief among the preceptories was the Temple at London,[38] the central headquarters which administratively set the pattern, policies, and procedures for the other preceptories to follow. In a sense, the London center was the mother house; and the other preceptories were cells.[39] Economically, the Templar organization was overwhelmingly based on the manorial system, many preceptories being in fact manors transformed by the grant of their donors into religious houses — e.g., Temple Cressing in Essex, Temple Cowley in Oxfordshire, and Temple Guiting in Gloucestershire. Beginning in the twelfth century and fully emerging in the thirteenth, the preceptory became the acknowledged local center through which the Templars administered their many holdings and rendered their obligations as feudal landlords. In addition to the preceptors, who supervised the Templar properties, there were obviously estate stewards and other officials who were directly concerned with the actual production of crops. Lees suggests that many of these men may have been members of middle-class Anglo-Norman families and knights of the order able to deal as equals with the clergy and with the squires and gentry of the countryside.[40] Forming the great bulk of the persons on the Templar lands and doing the actual work were the manorial specialists and peasants — men who had no direct ties to the Templar order.

The lands constituting these preceptories, probably from the beginning, represented many types of rural economy — the small manors,[41] the large honors,[42] the great fiefs,[43] the lesser fiefs,[44] ecclesiastical states,[45] and scattered manorial holdings.[46] But the bulk of Templar possessions was composed of grants of small units of land and small sums of rent made by persons or groups of humble status — units ranging from one-half acre to two acres, to ten or more acres,[47] and rents ranging from twelve pence to forty shillings.[48] Kosminsky in his recent studies, based primarily on the Hundred Rolls for 1278-79, groups the manors of England into large (over 1,000 acres of arable land), medium (between 500 and 1,000 acres), and small (less than 500 acres)[49] and finds that the church held manors in each of these categories.[50] However, his research — agreeing with the data presented here — further shows that the lands of the Templars (and Hospitallers) consisted for the most part of small manors and countless petty holdings and rental rights on the manors of other lords.[51] To illustrate, he found the Templars had four medium, twelve small, and no large manors in the area covered by the 1278-79 survey.[52] Specifically, in Duxford (Cambridgeshire), the Master of the Temple in England held his demesne from seven different persons in differing proportions.[53]

Both with respect to the lands and crops and the manner of production, it would seem that what had been before continued under and after the Templars[54] — another instance of the persistence and relative imperviousness to change of the manorial system. The type of economic activity engaged in depended upon the resources and customs of the area. Accordingly, some areas produced grain and legumes; some areas were used mostly for pasturage of cattle or sheep; and on most estates were forests which provided wood and game animals. On the Templar manors and other holdings were laborers in the fields, herdsmen, gardeners, millers, artisans of various sorts, and others.[55] Over all, regardless of specialization, was imposed a degree of centralized control aiming at a common goal — the increase of revenue for financing the Holy War.

The tenants of the Templars as seen in the Inquest of 1185, like the tenants seen in the Extents and Hundred Rolls, fell into three main groups:[56] those who rendered services only *(opera et servitia);* those who rendered services and/or paid a money rent *(opera vel redditus);* and those who paid a money rent only *(reditus assissae).* In most counties examples for each of the three groups can be cited. Generally speaking, however, it can be said that services were most consistently demanded and were most common in such areas as Yorkshire,[57] that money payments were common in areas around London,[58] and that the payment of service and/or money was found in all areas where the Templars had holdings.[59] A tendency toward and preference for money can be seen in such areas as Essex, Kent, Warwickshire, Oxfordshire, and Hertfordshire where such statements as these are found in the Inquest: ". . . *et si non dederit den [arios] faciet quolibet ebdomeda tocius anni ij opera [ciones] . . .;*"[60] "*. . . pro xxx d. vel predictam operacionem . . .;*"[61] "*. . . pro virgata terre x sol. et quieti sunt de omnibus aliis consuetudinibus ville . . .;*"[62] "*. . . ij d. vel iiij galli [nas] ad electionem illorum . . .;*"[63] "*. . . quiete ab omnibus serviciis pro iiij sol. . . .;*"[64] or "*. . . tenet pro xviij d. pro omni servicio. . . .*"[65]

This matter of commutation of payments from services to money is one of the most significant and controversial subjects in the economic history of the Middle Ages. Some writers, such as Lipson, Cunningham, and Ashley, are quite conservative in their views when they hold that commutation was often temporary and irregular and was not very extensive, and that, though it may have begun before the Norman Conquest, it did not become very noticeable till the thirteenth century, and did not become widespread till the fourteenth and fifteenth centuries.[66] Kosminsky in his studies of the agrarian history of England in the thirteenth century has come to a more positive conclusion, holding that commutation had increased — more rapidly and more easily on the small than on the large manors — until by the thirteenth century money rent had become the predominant form of rent in England.[67] Furthermore, he maintains that the lord could often demand money payment instead of service and that part of the dues shown as services were actually levied in money so that "the actual role of money rents was greater, perhaps much greater, than the sources indicate."[68] This is not to deny, however, that there was also a trend away from commutation back to the exaction of labor services apparent in the thirteenth century and later, especially on the large manors and on ecclesiastical estates.[69] Current research also suggests that the view expressed by such men as Nabholz[70] that the rise of a money economy played a major role in breaking down or altering the manorial system is a simplification which must be extensively qualified.

The records of the Templars, primarily the Inquest, provide us with no wholly decisive evidence on commutation, but they do indicate that commutation was definitely going on as early as the last part of the twelfth century in all the areas in which the Templars held land, and they do suggest that the Templars showed a preference for money payments in many instances, a wholly reasonable preference in view of their need for cash or other portable wealth for the support of their activities in the Holy Land.

In addition to their ordinary feudal tenants, who no doubt held the great bulk of their lands, the Templars came, increasingly as time passed, to depend for the performance of many needed services upon corrodaries, who in return received pensions (or corrodies) from the Templars. These corrodaries might include clerics[71] who would perform religious services for the Templars or laymen[72] who would render various types of manual labor — such as carpentry, work in the fields, care of animals, and odd jobs around the manor or Templar buildings. Corrodaries might also be persons or institutions, lay or ecclesiastical, who transferred land to the Templars[73] — sometimes for their lifetime, sometimes for a stated period of years, and sometimes for an indefinite period — or who gave to the Templars a sum of money[74] and in return were to receive pensions or annual payments. In the case of an individual, a corrody might involve the guarantee that the donor and his wife could remain on their former property, or on a specific estate, for the remainder of their lives and that they would receive certain stated necessaries — e.g., 2 or 3d. per days for food, 10s. yearly for a robe, 40d. per year for shoe leather, 5d. annually for miscellaneous items, a tallow candle nightly, firewood as needed, and a groom assigned by the preceptor to serve them.[75] In case of an institution, a corrody commonly involved the payment of a specified sum yearly.[76] Monastaries and nunneries apparently found it convenient upon occasion to transfer to the Templars lands, tithes, or rents in return for an assured yearly payment. For the Templars, the grants by individuals and by institutions offered the opportunity, through efficient management, to increase their holdings and revenue. Thus, as the terms of the agreements and the great popularity of the corrodies suggest, the system proved attractive for both parties concerned. Most of the data on the Templar corrodaries comes from the last years of the Templars' existence, but the complexity and universality of the system indicate a development dating far back in Templar history. The great document on this subject is the "corrodia petita de domibus Templariorum"[77] which was drawn up at the time of the dissolution of the order, when the Templars' property was in the King's hands, so that Edward II would know which claims to corrodies were valid and which were not.

So far the preceptorial organization in England, to the degree that it can be known from the incomplete and miscellaneous nature of surviving evidence, has been briefly examined. Despite the fact that more problems are raised than solved by existing records, it seems justifiable to suggest that, on the one hand, local variation was a dominant characteristic of Templar tenure and of their agricultural productivity and that, on the other hand, where some degree of similarity in tenure and productivity existed it may have been partly due to such administrative uniformity as the Templars were able to impose.

Before leaving the Templar organization in England, one must give some attention to the London center. Though the London holdings in one sense formed just another preceptory, the fact that the central headquarters were there made the London unit in fact far more important than the other preceptories. It may well be, as some suggest, that the origins of the London holdings are to be traced back to grants made to Hugh de Payens when he visited England in 1128.[78] The first area in the city held by the Templars was at Holborn where were built, in the parish of St. Andrew, their house and their church — the latter being constructed of stone brought from Caen in Normandy, and being circular in form like the Church of the Holy Sepulchre at Jerusalem.[79] When, shortly, their growing wealth and numbers made the Holborn holdings inadequate, the Templars sold these holdings, sometime between 1155 and 1162, to Robert de Chesney, Bishop of London, for one hundred marks and a small annual rent.[80] They then proceeded to establish themselves on a new site on the north bank of the Thames River where new and elaborate buildings were constructed.[81] To distinguish between the two centers, the Holborn unit was referred to as Old Temple *(Vetus Templum)* and the Thames unit as New Temple *(Novum Templum)*. Whether these new holdings were obtained by gift or by purchase and whether or not any buildings already existed on the Thames site are unknown. Desiring to make their London headquarters impressive and indicative of their growing wealth and power, the Templars began the construction of New Temple, a large and magnificent Gothic church, round in shape, with simple pointed arches and large window areas.[82] Dedicated on February 10, 1185, by Heraclius, Patriarch of Jerusalem,[83] probably in the presence of King Henry II, who was then in London and held the Templars in high esteem,[84] New Temple provided a fitting structure for the honor of God and St. Mary and the glory of the Templars, dominating as it did its immediate environs. In time, several small chapels were built nearby and two large halls — a "hall of priests," connected with the Temple by a cloister, and, a short distance away, a "hall of knights."[85] The former was probably where the Templars' business was conducted; and the latter, where the knights resided. Across the river, on the south side of the Thames, was a large field, approximately fifteen acres in size, known as Fickettscroft,[86] which may well have been used by the Templars for their military exercises. Associated with the London house also were mills, ponds, roads, gates, forges, and piers[87]— all of which provided needed services or revenues — and offices and clerks for the transaction and recording of matters of all kinds. This importance of New Temple as a political, administrative, and financial center, not only for the Templars, but for the crown and laymen as well, will be shown in detail in the next chapter.

Privileges

It is with much truth that Sir Edward Coke, writing in the sixteenth century, said the Templars had "so great and so large privileges, liberties, and immunities for themselves, their tenants, and farmers, etc., as no other Order had the like."[88] In examining these privileges, it will be convenient to divide them into groups — political, economic, jurisdictional, and religious — and to make an effort to specify what they consisted of, from whom they were obtained, how effectively they were maintained, and how unique or widespread they were.

The religious privileges, since they were mostly granted by the papacy, applied throughout Christendom and, as seen in the preceding chapter, included, among other things, the right of the Templars to have their own priests and to receive special collections or offerings, and exemption of the Templars from ecclesiastical taxation of all sorts and from all but papal excommunication and interdict. In addition, the popes supported most of the activities of the Templars, granted indulgences for aid to the order and its cause, and used their influence with both the clergy and laity on the Templars' behalf. As also seen above, these extensive privileges did not go unresented by the clergy and were not always maintained unimpaired as papal orders directing recognition of and compliance with them indicate. Many other religious groups, including the Knights Hospitallers, the rivals of the Templars, also received comprehensive privileges; but probably no group received quite so many or quite such extensive ones.

The Templars were equally favored by laymen, including first and foremost the kings of England and secondarily the great and lesser lords. Since the privileges granted by the king were the more important and since the lay lords were in many instances only following the lead of the king, the concern here will be largely limited to the grant of privileges by the crown. The first charter granting the Templars privileges and liberties, as well as confirming the grants of land and gifts already made, was issued by King Stephen in 1154[89] and was later confirmed by Henry II, his successor.[90] The first really comprehensive grant of privileges by the crown was that of Richard I (1189) who went well beyond the mere confirmation of the charters of Stephen and Henry II.[91] A decade later (1199), John issued his own charter of privileges to the Templars,[92] but it was essentially the same as that of Richard. Two charters (1227 and 1253) were issued by Henry III.[93] The first one, in large part a reissuance of John's charter, confirmed all donations made to the Templars by his predecessors and by other benefactors and added new privileges of his own. The second charter, known only from Edward II's confirmation of it (1280),[94] was an extension of the first and was maintained, with reservations, throughout the reign of Edward I and in the early years of the reign of Edward II.

Any of a number of reasons can be given for the grant of privileges to the Templars — piety, favoritism, and mutual advantage; but the most fundamental reason would seem to be an effort by the crown to preserve the strength and revenues of the Templars for the cause of the Holy Land.[95] Indeed, while the Templars were concerned primarily with the Holy Land, their troubles in England, and elsewhere, were not insuperable; but after the Holy Land had been lost, their difficulties increased and the reason not only for their privileges but even for the continued existence of the order itself was questioned.

The royal privileges granted to the Templars were political, economic, judicial, and jurisdictional in nature and scope. Since they tend to overlap the one with the other, no effort will be made to fit any one privilege, or set of privileges, into a single category. However, for the sake of convenience and clarity, six privileges — or sets of privileges — will be discussed here.

First, the Templars were exempt from secular taxation. This exemption was at certain times national, at other times local, and sometimes both.[96] Exemption from taxes on land, such as Danegeld,[97] carucage,[98] and tallage,[99] was repeatedly given. The right to maintain in each community one free guest *(hospes)*— i.e., a tenant of their choice — immune from tallage was common.[100] Exemption from special assessments made on behalf of the Holy Land[101] and from levies on movable property — e.g., tenths,[102] fifteenths,[103] twentieths,[104] and thirtieths[105]— was repeatedly granted, as was exemption from scutage[106] and from military service.[107] Second, the Templars were excused from payment of tolls in markets, at fairs, on bridges, and on highways.[108] In addition, they were at times permitted to import and export wine without payment of customs duties[109] and, similarly in time of peace, were not required to pay the export duty on wool going to Flanders.[110] Third, the Templars tended to be exempted from many ordinary feudal burdens and to be given special privileges instead. For example, they were granted freedom from amercements and fines for themselves[111] and free warren in their demesne lands.[112] Furthermore, they were granted freedom from assarts,[113] from waste and regard in the forests,[114] from murage,[115] from frankpledge,[116] and from *corvées*[117] — such as work on parks, castles, bridges, and buildings. Fourth, the Templars were exempted in time of war from seizure of their agricultural produce — such as grain and hay — by royal officials.[118] Fifth, the Templars received widespread judicial and jurisdictional privileges. They were permitted to hold their own courts with full jurisdiction over their tenants and other persons on their estates,[119] including specifically the power not only to try and punish their own vassals and villeins, but also to try and punish thieves, trespassers, breakers of the peace, and other malefactors found on their properties.[120] In addition, the Templars were permitted to retain the chattels of felons and fugitives, to exact fines and amercements on their vassals and tenants, to receive back from the Exchequer any amercements collected by royal officials from their vassals, and to impose drowning and hanging ("pit and gallows") upon wrongdoers.[121] They were also exempted from attendance at and responsibility to the courts of the shires and hundreds[122] and were granted quittance of summons of the courts of eyre and common pleas.[123] Finally, as chief of these judicial and jurisdictional privileges, they could be impleaded only before the king or his chief justice.[124] Sixth, all the rights given to the Templars, including those mentioned above and many others of less importance, were to be maintained even if they were not utilized.[125]

For practical purposes, since these many rights and privileges granted to the Templars applied to their vassals and tenants as well,[126] a very considerable group and number of people were involved. To indicate possession of these rights, the Templar houses, and those of their tenants, were marked with a cross.[127] Needless to say, when persons not legally entitled to the Templar privileges erected crosses on their property, special royal action had to be taken to check the practice.[128]

Having indicated some of the privileges granted to the Templars by royal charters and noted in contemporary documents and realizing the extent of these privileges, one must ask whether or not they were maintained and exercised unimpaired. The answer to this question, as the following paragraphs will show, must be a qualified one. At times, the privileges were in large measure held intact; but at other times, they were not. What is more, the Templars sometimes had to pay dearly for recognition of their privileges; and most of the time, they could maintain them only by constant vigilance and frequent resort to legal action. The degree to which the king — and the pope — supported the Templars was, in large measure, the degree to which the Templars were able to maintain their rights and privileges.

28   *The Knights Templars in England*

The Templars repeatedly found it necessary to appeal for support to the king and to the pope in order to gain and maintain their privileges.[129] Both the king[130] and the pope[131] directed that the rights and privileges of the Templars be respected, but the repetition of the appeals and of the orders for compliance suggests that the royal officials and the clergy did not always obey. Moreover, the king himself was inconsistent on the matter and upon occasion, especially when money was involved, followed the course most advantageous to the crown. Similarly, the popes, as in the struggle between Innocent III and King John over the appointment of Stephen Langton as Archbishop of Canterbury (1207), might limit Templar privileges when advantageous.[132] In addition, legal suits, the outcome of which are often unknown, were instituted by the Templars and others over claims and counterclaims of rights and privileges.[133]

Public records – especially the Pipe Rolls in which there are literally over a thousand references – abound with data alluding to the status of Templar privileges.[134] Though many of the entries are unclear or indefinite, others are obvious and significant. It is clear that the Templars were frequently pardoned by the king from payment of taxes and fines (a voluntary payment to the king for the grant of charters of rights, privileges, exemptions, land transfers, and the like). For example, they were pardoned from payments of fines for amercements,[135] essarts,[136] frankpledge,[137] disseisin,[138] murder,[139] hunting,[140] waste and regard in the forest,[141] false presentation,[142] and the like. They were also pardoned from the payment of such taxes as scutage and tallage.[143] Perhaps as frequently as they were pardoned, however, the Templars were compelled to pay fines and taxes to the crown. For example, they were called upon to make fine with the king for amercements,[144] essarts,[145] frankpledge,[146] murder,[147] waste and regard in the forest,[148] hunting,[149] default,[150] and the like, and were also compelled to pay scutage and tallage.[151] In addition to these payments, and highly indicative of the uncertain status of their privileges, the Templars repeatedly found it necessary to give the kings – especially John – large sums of money in order to maintain and guarantee their privileges. For example, in 1199-1200, the Templars paid 400 marks to John, gave him a palfrey, and were listed as owing £1,000 for confirmations of their charters and for quittance of amercements due at the Exchequer.[152] In 1201, they again gave him a palfrey, this time for royal protection and the right to be impleaded only before the king or his chief justice.[153] In 1209, for an unknown reason, they paid him 4,000 marks.[154] In 1210, John exacted money from the Templars, as well as from other religious groups, apparently for reinstatement of their privileges or for contribution to the recovery of Normandy.[155] Again, in 1216, for some unspecified reason, the Templars gave John 200 marks and two horses.[156] Later, under Henry III, in 1226 and 1244, the Templars paid still other fines to the king.[157] From this information, it would appear that, on the one hand, the Templars probably contributed their share of the "voluntary" payments expected by the king; and on the other, that they found it necessary to make additional contributions in order to retain royal support.

Exemption from[158] and payment of[159] taxes varied from time to time. Henry III, on one occasion, having allowed his sheriffs to demand and take carucage from the Templars, ordered them to return the amounts collected or to leave the matter for later settlement.[160] At the same time, however, he wrote the Master of the Templars to consult with his brethren on how they should answer the king on this matter.[161] Though the outcome is not known, it would not be without precedent to find that the Templars decided to make a monetary gift to the king in order to encourage him to support the principle of their exemption from such exactions. Scutage and tallage were sometimes paid by the Templars,[162] and sometimes were not.[163] Upon occasion, when either had been exacted unjustifiably, the money was returned.[164] The issue involved, which never was settled, seems to have been a dual one — whether or not the tenants of the Templars were liable for scutage and whether or not all the lands of the Templars and their tenants, or only certain of them, were exempted from tallage. Interestingly enough, evidence exists to indicate that, at least upon occasion, the Templars were permitted to exact tallage from their tenants whenever the king levied tallage upon his subjects.[165] As a rule, the Templars' exemption from aids for the Holy Land seems to have been fairly consistently maintained. In one case, when an aid had been collected, it was ordered returned;[166] and in another case, when a proposal to levy such an aid on the Templars (and Hospitallers) was made,[167] nothing came of it except that the Templars were authorized to collect such an aid from their own tenants.[168] The special levies authorized by the popes in the form of tenths, fifteenths, twentieths, thirtieths, and the like, did not usually apply to the Templars or to several other religious orders.[169] A goodly number of times, however, at least on certain of their holdings, the Templars were compelled to pay these special levies,[170] at least until such time as the matter could be brought to the attention of the king who might order the amount paid refunded.[171] Under Henry III and Edward I, it appears that the Templars' exemption was often most effectively recognized and upheld after making fine with the king.[172] The resentment against the violation of the privilege of having a free guest *(hospes)* in each community proved an especially troublesome matter as will be indicated below in Chapter IV.

Since the public records and other source materials provide little direct evidence on the subject, it is necessary to show great caution in making any statements regarding the maintenance of or infringement upon the commercial privileges of the Templars. The absence of information to the contrary suggests that the exemption of the Templars from payment of tolls levied by the king and his officials must have been quite universally maintained. When it came to the payment of local tolls, however, it would seem that the Templars, like all other persons, were excused only if exempted by the proper local authorities. The only violations of the grant of royal commercial privileges which have been found deal with the improper collection of stallage[173] from the Templars and the improper exaction of money from the perquisites of a market.[174] Only after the dissolution of the order, are the king's officials found collecting the tolls and revenues of a Templar fair.[175] In the delicate field of foreign trade, the privileges regarding customs duties and the amount of goods which could be exchanged were temporary and localized from the start. When the Templars engaged in trade which the king considered proper, they experienced no difficulties; but when they engaged in trade which he considered unauthorized, their special privileges were cancelled.[176] Though royal officials frequently seized the goods of private individuals, if those goods were needed by the king, there survives a record of only one instance in which they unjustly seized Templar goods — specifically wool.[177]

The exemption of the Templars from ordinary feudal burdens and their independence from royal and other courts were not clear-cut. As has been indicated above, the Templars were sometimes pardoned from feudal burdens; but as often they seem to have been required to assume their share of them. In addition to the burdens already discussed, the exemption, on the one hand, and the requirement, on the other, for work on *corvées* by Templar tenants might be mentioned.[178] The right of the Templars to maintain their own courts and to be immune from all prosecution except before the king and his chief justice was often enough maintained.[179] But, nonetheless, the Templars were upon occasion brought before the assize courts, the courts of eyre, and the county courts, as the king's grant of pardon of fines imposed by such courts reveals.[180]

Of considerable importance and frequent use were royal letters of protection and safe-conduct issued for periods ranging from several months to three years. These letters were obtained by the Templars for their security in England as well as abroad and pertained in some instances to the individual Templar, usually the Master in England,[181] and in other instances to all the Templars and their lands and possessions.[182] The value and need for these letters was made especially obvious during the contest between Pope Boniface VIII and King Edward I over royal taxation of the clergy. Because of the issuance of the bull *Clericis laicos* (1296) and the subsequent refusal of the English clergy to contribute to the national tax levy, Edward withdrew the English clergy from the protection of the king's law and ordered the lay fees of the clergy, together with their goods and chattels, seized by the sheriffs. This meant that the clergy, including the Templars, could be proceeded against with impunity and that their lands and chattels were temporarily lost to them. The Templars soon came to terms with the king (February 22, 1297) and were received back into his protection, and their goods were returned to them.[183] The other religious groups likewise bowed to the royal will, and Boniface found it necessary to alter his instructions to the English clergy.

In summary, regarding the privileges of the Templars, it may be said that they were varied in nature; that they were not uniformly maintained; that such maintenance of them as was obtained was due to papal, and especially to royal support; that, though the kings made lavish grants of privileges and repeatedly ordered compliance with them, the actual enforcement of them was sporadic; that the kings demanded much in return for their grants and assistance; that the maintenance of the Templar privileges probably reached its height in the first half of the reign of Henry III; and that from the latter half of Henry III's reign on, and especially during the reign of Edward I, who was seeking to centralize the royal administration and to curtail privileges of both lay and clerical magnates and groups, the maintenance of their privileges proved increasingly more difficult to achieve.

Holdings

Starting with the limited holdings represented by such grants as those of Stephen and Matilda, discussed above, the English Templars consistently and quite rapidly expanded their property until they became numbered among the great landlords of the realm. An accurate survey of their holdings, however, cannot be given. The content and chronological coverage of surviving sources are too incomplete; the identification of place names cannot always be made with certainty; the multiplicity of land units and the local variation in size of the same basic unit hinders precision; and the indefiniteness and miscellaneous character of the documentary data prevent a comprehensive treatment. Furthermore, since the Templars were constantly acquiring, selling, and transferring land, it is frequently impossible to determine whether a particular estate belonging to the order in the period was actually still in their possession at another time. Yet some sort of survey must be attempted.

The sources for such a survey are limited. The earliest comprehensive material is to be gotten from the Inquest of 1185 which Geoffrey Fitz Stephen, then Master of the Temple in England, wisely had made. His reason, according to the opening statement of the Inquest was to make a record of Templar lands, possessions, and income so that no harm or disadvantage might befall the order.[184] Actually, this meant he was taking precautions in anticipation of trouble arising from the envy of the secular clergy — especially of the bishops — at the growing power and wealth and increasing prominence of the Templars.[185] The Inquest shows that Templar holdings were already, by 1185, extensive; that their greatest concentration was in Yorkshire and Lincolnshire; that they were let out in units ranging from less than an acre to eighty acres for varying rents and services; that they were given over to the production of grain, cattle, sheep, and the like; and that they were rented for cash whenever possible. The Inquest, however, is not complete as it lacks data on holdings in and around London and in Cambridgeshire. These two omissions can be compensated for, however — the former, by references in the Public Records, and the latter, by the Sandford Cartulary, drawn up between 1265 and 1274, which deals in detail with Templar holdings in Cambridgeshire. Unfortuntely, demesne land, which was not always rented out and which may have amounted to about one-half of the arable land, was not reported in the Inquest.[186] There are other difficulties too. Except for the convenient use of acres in some cases — but even acres may vary in size from area to area — it is very hard to make sense out of the land units. Messuages are repeatedly referred to, evidently meaning a house and the small plot of land on which it was located. Especially troublesome are the units which vary in size from region to region — for example, carucates may be 120, 160, or 240 acres in size; hides, 64, 96, or 120; virgates, 15, 24, or 30; and bovates, 20, 24, or 30.[187] Tofts, however, appear to be regularly units of twelve acres. In addition, indefinite units such as crofts, cotlands, meadows, gardens, woodlands, vills, and pastures are widely used. To add further to the confusion, it is sometimes unclear whether or not certain areas are being counted twice in the returns from the counties. Despite these deficiencies and difficulties, the Inquest is a most useful and revealing document.

Equally as important as a source for Templar possessions in England is the Hospitaller Report of 1338, one section of which deals with former Templar lands currently in the hands of the Knights of the Hospital of St. John of Jerusalem.[188] This report to the Grand Prior of the order was drawn up by Prior Philip de Thame, an efficient manager and supervisor, who had been sent from Italy to straighten out the financial difficulties which the English Hospitallers had fallen into under the priorship of Thomas Larcher. The change in the financial condition from a debit to a credit status was not due solely to the able leadership of de Thame, however. Perhaps equally important was the actual transfer of many of the former Templar estates to the Hospitallers — a goal toward which the prior's predecessor had worked long and diligently.[189] Like the Templar Inquest, the Hospitaller Report records the lands, possessions, and income of the order. In some respects, it is clearer than the Inquest — for example, the lands are carefully listed by county; and the areas, many of which are expressed in acres, are given. But the Report is much less detailed than the Inquest, and like the Inquest, is also incomplete. Though certain Templar lands which the Hospitallers claimed but had not yet obtained are specifically indicated,[190] there are still additional holdings known to have been in their possession at this date which were omitted.[191] Nonetheless, the survey of 1338 was reasonably complete and accurate.

In addition to these two primary sources, valuable information on Templar holdings can be obtained from the Public Record collection and from Dugdale's *Monasticon*. The data in the Public Records tend to be miscellaneous, being references to gifts and/or confirmations of gifts, transfers of land, and court cases involving the Templars. Insofar as the Templars in twelfth century England are concerned, the *Monasticon* has been in large measure superseded by Miss Lees' edition of the Inquest together with other documents pertaining to that century; but it remains of some value for the twelfth century and is indispensable for the thirteenth. Yet another source of information on Templar goods, lands, and income, is the survey made by the king's officials in 1308. Because this document still exists in manuscript form only, references to it here must be made on the basis of secondary works.[192]

The following survey of Templar holdings in England represents a combination of material gained from the above sources. To attempt to be complete would be folly — the surviving data and the limits of space and interest prevent it. It is deemed important here not to list every known area held by the Templars but only to indicate the major holdings in the various counties. Furthermore, it should be remembered that for the most part the Templars' holdings were small and irregular rather than large and consolidated units. In making this survey, special emphasis will be placed on the preceptories which, though varying in size, wealth, and importance, regularly consisted of at least a manor, a manor house, a chapel, and a number of outbuildings and formed the basic administrative units of the Templars. Since the Templars were most active and numerous in Yorkshire and Lincolnshire, it is fitting to start with these two counties.

In Yorkshire there were ten preceptories and several houses of almost equal importance. Indeed, Templar interests were so concentrated in this county that it was early found necessary to appoint a Chief Preceptor in Yorkshire[193] to supervise the vast estates, the varied activities, and the large income of the order there. The oldest preceptory in Yorkshire was Temple Hirst, the origins of which are to be found in Ralph de Hastings' grant of the manor of Hirst to the Templars in 1152.[194] Penhill and Temple Cowton, growing out of initial gifts of land by Roger Mowbray (*ca.* 1142) and greatly enlarged by grants of subsequent donors, became preceptories sometime after 1185.[195] The origin of the preceptory of Temple Newsam is to be found in a grant of land made by William de Villiers — a leading noble of the realm like Hastings and Mowbray — sometime before his death in 1181.[196] The grant of Westerdale, which early became a preceptory, was confirmed by King John in 1203 and included a moiety of the advowson of Beeford Church as well as its own estates and chapel.[197] The preceptory of Ribston and Wetherby seems to have started with a grant by Robert de Ros, a noble, of the manor, vill and mills of Ribston, along with the advowson of the church of Walshford. To this was later added the vill and church of Hunsingore, the vill of Wetherby, and a number of smaller areas[198] which made Ribston and Wetherby one of the wealthiest Templar units. Sometime prior to 1258, the Templars were given the manor and church of Copmanthorp which were added to the castle mills below York, which had earlier (before 1185) been donated to the order by Roger Mowbray. Another church and additional lands were subsequently obtained and were attached to the above units to form the preceptory of Copmanthorp.[199] The origin of the Faxfleet unit, a wealthy one, and the areas under its jurisdiction are unknown.[200] Nor is much known about two other wealthy preceptories, Foulbridge and Whitley.[201] On the basis of their average net income expressed in pounds for the years 1308 to 1338, when Templar possessions were in the king's hands, the Yorkshire preceptories would be ranked in the following order:[202] Ribston and Wetherby (£ 270), Foulbridge (£ 208), Faxfleet (£ 115), Temple Hirst (£ 111), Temple Newsam (£ 108), Temple Cowton (£ 97), Westerdale (£ 55), Copmanthorp (£ 43), Whitley (£ 27) and Penhill (£ 24). In addition to these units, there were several Templar houses — e.g., Alveston, Cave, and Etton, worth £ 19, £ 31, and £ 19 respectively, each of which possessed extensive lands and had its own church—which never became preceptories but were more important than many a preceptory in another county.[203] All of these estates with the exception of Faxfleet, Temple Hirst, and Temple Newsam, passed ultimately to the Hospitallers.[204]

In Lincolnshire, there were five preceptories, four of them among the richer and more powerful houses of the English Templars. Eagle, supposedly founded by a grant of King Stephen, included lands and churches in adjacent areas as well as the manor and church of Eagle[205] and in 1308 was listed as worth £125. Willoughton, founded by a noble in the reign of Stephen, and enlarged greatly by subsequent grants by other lords, included nearly the whole vill of Willoughton with a moiety of the advowson of the church there and churches in five and lands in eight other communities[206] and brought in £261 in 1308. Aslackby, established apparently in 1164, included lands, subsequently increased, and the church of the area[207] and was valued at £78. Temple Bruer, founded late in the reign of Henry II,[208] in an area then considered wasteland, became, thanks to subsequent gifts and hard work, one of the largest, richest, and most prominent Templar houses in England including several churches, at least one market, extensive arable lands, and huge pasture areas used for grazing sheep. While in the king's hands, it returned by far the largest income (£325) of any of the Templar estates in Lincolnshire. South Witham, the origin of which is uncertain,[209] appears to have been a small house of unknown value and cannot be compared with the other preceptories in the county. Indeed,, when the Hospitallers took it over, they wisely subordinated it to Temple Bruer.[210] For a time, Mere, just outside the city of Lincoln, may have been a preceptory; but if so, it was early placed under the jurisdiction of Eagle and later under Willoughton.[211] Each of these preceptories — together with the lands, churches, and mills associated with them — ultimately came into the possession of the Hospitallers.[212]

In the counties to the north and west of Yorkshire and Lincolnshire, the Templars had no preceptories and only very small holdings.[213] In Northumberland, the Templars held lands at Thornton worth £47; in Westmorland, at Temple Sowerby of unknown value; in Nottinghamshire, at Flaufor, and in addition, small churches at Markham and Sibethorp, and mills at Bekingham, the total returns of which were £52 in 1308; and in Lancashire, small areas not specifically identified.

In the counties near or bordering Wales and in southwest England, the Templars held only small estates which, however, were more numerous than those in the counties just mentioned. In Shropshire, several hundred acres were held in the area of Staunton and Halston;[214] and it is possible that a preceptory existed at Halston.[215] In Worcestershire, the Templars had several minor holdings – e.g., the advowson of Bromsgrove, which they claimed to have held since the time of Richard I; a messuage at Feckenham where they raised sheep and cattle; land at Temple Broughton, part of which had been granted to them by Henry III; and the manor of Temple Laughern, which they had purchased in 1249.[216] In Herefordshire, there were enough holdings to form two preceptories:[217] one at Garewy worth £106, and another at Upleden worth £60. In the southwestern counties, the chief center was at Temple Combe in Somerset,[218] a preceptory in a cattle and sheep raising area which returned £78 in 1308. In Wiltshire, there were a number of holdings, the largest of which were Temple Rockley – probably a preceptory – and Chiryton which together contained over five hundred acres, not including pasture for well over a thousand sheep,[219] but returned only £20 according to the royal survey. In addition, the Templars had small holdings at Connerton in Cornwall, Templeton in Devonshire, and Wileton in Somerset.[220] The chief of these holdings – Upleden, Garewy, Rockley, and Combe – came into the hands of the Hospitallers, and probably the lesser ones did, too.[221]

In the eastern and southeastern counties, Templar holdings were greatest in Essex, Kent, and Sussex. Essex, as seen above, was the site of the first establishments of the Templars in England, and Temple Cressing, the gift of Queen Matilda, was the preceptory in that area.[222] Closely associated with Cressing was Witham – the manor, market, church, and pasture lands – which similarly received royal favor.[223] The two estates together, consisting of well over one thousand acres, returned £77 in 1308. Reyndon, Sutton, Uphall, and Rivenhall were additional Templar centers in this county.[224] In Kent, Temple Ewell, worth £26, served as the preceptory and was closely associated with the Templar manors at Strood, Dertford, and Waltham.[225] In Sussex, though no information was returned in the Inquest, the Templars already held an estate at Shipley[226] and soon were to hold Saddelscomb and minor estates elsewhere.[227] Shipley was definitely a preceptory and possible Saddelscomb was also. The two of them together returned £45 in 1308. In the other eastern and southeastern counties, Templar holdings were few in number and small in size. In Norfolk and Suffolk, the Templars held practically no land in the twelfth century and not very much in the thirteenth.[228] Indeed, their estates here were so small and of such limited value that they appear to have been appended to the Cambridgeshire holdings and to have returned about £15 per year only. Apart from the manor of Widflete, which they rented from 1161 on, the Templars held practically nothing in Surrey except part of the manor of Merrow which returned £ 17 in 1308.[229] In Berkshire, the Templars had a preceptory at Temple Bistlesham, appraised at £ 55 per year, and possessed subordinate houses at Bisham, Templeton, Wescott, and Clewer[230] which probably date from the late twelfth or early thirteenth century. In Hampshire, land was held in North, South, and Milford Baddesley, the various holdings making up the preceptory of Baddesley which was in existence by 1240.[231] Generally speaking, all these lands in the eastern and southeastern counties, except Saddelscomb,[232] eventually came into the hands of the Hospitallers.

The holdings of the Templars in the counties in central England, or the Midlands, were second in number and importance only to those in Yorkshire and Lincolnshire. Not all the counties were equally significant, however, as the following paragraphs will show. To facilitate treatment here, the counties will be divided into three groups on the basis of geography and revenue: first, Leicester, Warwick, Gloucester, and Oxford; second, Cambridge, Hertford, and Middlesex; and third, Rutland, Northampton, Huntington, Bedford, and Buckingham.

The first of these groups of counties was the most important both in number of holdings and in revenue. In Oxfordshire, the Templars began their acquisitioins with the grant in 1136 by Matilda of the manor of Cowley[234] which, enlarged by later donations, came to be known as Temple Cowley and early became a preceptory of considerable value. In the 1150's, the manors of Sibford Gower, Merton, and Hensington were obtained.[235] These were followed by the grant of land and a church at Broadwell by 1185, the manors of Littlemore and Warpsgrove in the early years of the thirteenth century, the manors of Horspath and Overhorspath in 1225, and the manor of Sandford-on-Thames in 1239-40.[236] Sandford soon became a preceptory and exercised jurisdiction over Templar holdings in Hampshire and Berkshire as well as in southern Oxfordshire. The wealth of the properties in this county is indicated by the returns of 1308 which credit Temple Cowley with £ 60, Sandford with £ 58, Broadwell with £ 46, and Merton with £ 44. In Gloucestershire, there were numerous small holdings; but the chief center was at Temple Guiting, the original grants of which — lands, mills, and the advowson of the church — were made in the middle of the twelfth century.[237] Guiting, returning £ 206 in 1308, was clearly one of the chief Templar preceptories in England. In addition, in the southern part of the county, Bristol served as a financial center not only for its immediate area but also for the counties of Cornwall, Devon, Somerset, and Dorset.[238] Before the dissolution of the order, however, Bristol appears to have been subordinated to Temple Combe in Somerset.[239] In Leicestershire, the holdings which became the preceptory of Rothley started with a small grant of land by a noble in the time of John (probably in 1203) to which Henry III (1231) added the manor of Rothley and the advowson of its church.[240] At the dissolution, this preceptory, worth £195, included lands in thirteen neighboring areas, several mills, large pastures for grazing sheep, and five dependent chapels.[241] Numerous small holdings belonged to the Templars in Warwickshire, chief among which were lands at Sherborne, Warwick, and Fletchamstead.[242] But the major center was the preceptory of Balsall[243] which returned £104 in 1308.

In the second group of counties, Middlesex claims pre-eminence as the county in which the central headquarters of the Templar order in England was located. As has been indicated above, New Temple, London, served as a preceptory for the area as well as the central headquarters of the order. In addition to their chapels and lands in the suburbs of London and their lands and mills along the Thames, the Templars held small estates at Lilleston, Hamstede, Hendon, Crawnford, Hakeneye, and Charring.[244] But none of these holdings, including New Temple, brought in much revenue inasmuch as only £85 was reported in 1308. In Cambridgeshire, which was omitted from the Inquest, the Templars held numerous estates which, for the most part, were subordinated to the three preceptories of the county – Denney (worth £37 in 1308), Duxford (worth £22), and Great Wilberham (worth £59). Some of the individual grants go back to the twelfth century, but most of them seem to have been made in the thirteenth.[245] Templar properties in Hertfordshire, among the oldest holdings of the order in England, appear to have been about the same in number and value as those in Cambridgeshire. Lands, churches, mills, and markets at Hitchin, Preston, Dinsley, Weston, and Baldock date back to 1147-48 when they were given to the Templars by such great lords as Gilbert de Clare, William Marshall, and Bernard de Balliol and were confirmed by King Stephen.[246] These initial grants, and subsequent additions to them, were consolidated under Temple Dinsley which probably had become a preceptory by the end of the reign of Henry II. Another important center in this county, about which very little is known, was Langenok[247] which by 1308 was worth £55 as compared to Temple Dinsley's £60.

In the third group of counties in central England, Templar holdings were small in number and value: the church of Stretton and lands at Melton Mowbray and Stonesby in Rutland;[248] lands at Blakesley, Guilsborough, and Harrington in Northamptonshire;[249] a variety of holdings in Huntingdonshire of which Ogerston-Washingley and Sibeston,[250] worth £25 together, were the most important; the manors of Swanton, Stocton, and Sharnbrook, worth about £17 each, and land, a mill, and a church worth £13, in Bedfordshire;[251] and lands at Radnage—granted by John in 1212 — Marlow, Temple Wycombe, Ham, Loudwater, Calverton, and Bulstrode, worth less than £30 all together, in Buckinghamshire.[252] None of these counties had a preceptory except Buckingham where Bulstrode had become one by 1278. The origin of most of the holdings in this group of counties is difficult, if not impossible, to determine, and the disposition of them after the dissolution of the Templars is not always clear either. But in general, they, like most of the Templar properties, ultimately came into the possession of the Hospitallers.[253]

To be complete, something must be said of the Templar holdings in Ireland, Scotland, and Wales. It is estimated that 13 manors, 21 churches, and miscellaneous parcels of land, returning a total of £411 in 1308, were held in Ireland.[254] In Scotland, where information on the Templars is more controversial than abundant, property returning a total of £25 was held at Blantrodok, Culthur, Templiston, and Berwick-on-Tweed.[225] In Wales, land worth £3 was held at Lammadoch.[256]

Although much more could be written on the holdings of the Templars, enough has been given to suggest that they were extensive and profitable. It would be interesting and pertinent to determine the size and value of the Templar properties, but the lack of essential information and the inconsistency of such data as survives makes the task impossible. One can only say that Templar holdings varied in size from a plot of a few acres to huge estates — like Balsall, Upleden, and Cressing — between five hundred and one thousand acres,[257] and in revenue from petty sums of a few pence to large sums — as at Temple Guiting, Ribston-Wetherby, and Temple Bruer—of over £200 or £300 per year.[258] To this it can be added that the Templars were among the great landholders of the realm though it is doubtful if they held as much land as such other religious groups as the Benedictines, Augustinians, and Cistercians.[259]

Recruitment and Training

Practically nothing is known of the manner in which the Templars obtained their members or of the numbers of men involved. In their Rule, only a few items of information are to be found: the basic requirements for membership,[260] the procedure and vows of initiation,[261] the animals and equipment allowed to individual Templars according to their rank and assignments,[262] and the modification of the dominant western ideas and practices of war by eastern or Turkish influences.[263] All that can be said is that the Templars were a relatively small and elite group, that they were at the start and remained till the end predominantly cavalrymen, and that their valor and *espirit de corps* — as shown time and again in the wars and skirmishes in the Holy Land —

had won for them a reputation which must have provided them with more candidates for membership than they could normally accept. Yet, there must also have been times — as, for example, after certain campaigns in which their numbers had been decimated[264] — when they direly needed new members, perhaps more than they could obtain.

Nor is information on their training available. Obviously, the Templars were initially thoroughly trained in western methods of warfare. This meant that chief reliance in war was put on the charge of the heavy-armed cavalry whose knights *(milites),* wearing helmets, hauberks, and coats of chain mail, equipped with swords, lances, and triangular shields, and riding large but slow horses, launched all-out attacks upon the infidel, not so much in a single, mass formation as in successive squadrons of one hundred to one hundred and fifty men each.[265] The way for the cavalry charge was usually prepared by the preliminary activities of the light-armed foot soldiers *(pedites)* who, equipped with spears, clubs, and bows, were stationed in front of the cavalry, between it and the enemy forces.[266] So long as the knights could mount their attack and could maintain their formation, they were likely to drive all before them. And when it came to hand-to-hand combat following the charge, the more lightly armed Turks proved inferior to the more heavily armed Franks. But the Turks, relying chiefly on their light-armed cavalry, especially on mounted archers — bearing shields, lances, swords, and clubs as well — and riding smaller and faster horses, enjoyed greater speed and maneuverability than the Crusader forces. Because of their ability to attack, retreat, reorganize, and attack again so easily, the Turks were able to do great damage to the Christians and often to upset the latter's plans and formations. In imitation, the Templars, and other Christian groups and leaders as well, organized their own light-armed cavalry troops, which, equipped primarily with bows and arrows, proved highly effective and became a vital part of Christian armies employing modified western tactics.[267] These troops, known as Turcopoles, were recruited from the native population, being often offspring of parents of different religions, and were used for reconnaissance work as well as for fighting as regular light-armed cavalry units.

It would be interesting to know what sort of training was given the Templars in the West, but lack of information permits us only to wonder whether or not the lessons of the eastern campaigns and the new methods employed by the Templars were brought back to their recruits and brothers in Europe.[268] That some sort of training was given is inevitable in view of the military nature and purpose of the order and the likelihood that many a Templar would be sent East. Though the existence of training fields or parade grounds cannot be determined with complete certainty, Fickettscroft in London, across the Thames from New Temple, must have been such a field;[269] and other preceptories may well have had such facilities as well. Without doubt, the Master of the Temple in England was in over-all charge of military training. This task, however, was probably directly under the supervision of the preceptors who in turn relied upon lesser persons — perhaps the heads of the individual houses — to do most of the actual work. Though tournaments might have formed a convenient means of testing their training, there is no indication that the Templars participated in them. The only references which can be found are those in which a Templar is one of a small group of persons sent by Henry III to stop a proposed tournament at Northampton and an actual tournament at York.[270]

When a Templar became sick or too old and infirm to fulfill his duties, he was well taken care of.[271] In England, there were two centers for such persons — one at Eagle, in Lincolnshire,[272] and the other on the Isle of Ely, associated with the preceptory of Denney, in Cambridgeshire.[273]

Though information is limited, enough is known to state that the Templars first came to England about 1128, that they were few in number but great in wealth, that their privileges were very extensive in theory but were limited in actual practice, and that the Templar units and organizations were centralized under the Master at New Temple but were allowed considerable local autonomy.

chapter three

Political and Economic Activities

IN THE PRECEEDING CHAPTER, some consideration was given to the political and economic activities of the Templars, primarily as reflected in their organization, privileges, and land holdings. It is now necessary to examine these activities, and the administrative as well, in some detail, as they pertain to the crown — for which there is considerable information — and to other persons or groups — for which there is little material. The Templars will be found as officials, envoys, and advisers of the crown; they will be found represented in Parliament; and they will be found the recipients of royal gifts and favors excluding the privileges discussed in the preceding chapter. It will also be apparent that they actively engaged in agriculture, trade and commerce, and banking. New Temple, their central headquarters in England, will be seen to be a place of lodging for both lay and clerical persons, of assembly for political and ecclesiastical meetings, of deposit for valuables and money, of monetary exchange and banking activity, of convenience from which royal business of various kinds was carried on, and of burial.

Political Activities

The earliest official position given a Templar by the English kings was that of royal almoner. Roger, a Templar serving as an almoner to John, acted in addition as a royal agent entrusted with the regulation of sea-borne commerce between England and Gascony.[1] Under Henry III, there were at least three different Templars serving as royal almoners. Geoffrey, who held this position from 1234 to 1239, handled a great variety of other tasks for the king as well.[2] As keeper of the king's wardrobe, he held inquiries regarding certain lands and issued licenses and letters of protection as well as writs pertaining to the king's business.[3] That he did a thorough job is suggested by Matthew Paris' statement that his dismissal was an event longed for because of his "arrogance."[4] Another Templar, also named Roger, was dismissed as royal almoner by Henry III in 1253 when the Templars and Hospitallers refused to provide the king with the five thousand marks which had been promised to Richard de Clare if the latter would have his eldest son marry the daughter of the Count of Angoulême.[5] And in 1241, John, a Templar, serving as almoner, was sent by Henry III to stop a proposed tournament at Northhampton.[6] Perhaps Richard, a Templar in King Alexander of Scotland's Council,[7] had been royal almoner in that country. A chance reference to a certain Morinus, a Templar, serving as almoner to Hugh, Bishop of Lincoln,[8] suggests that the Templars may also have been almoners to persons other than kings. As almoners, at least as almoners of the king, they served as individuals and not as Templars as is shown by Henry III's promise to Robert de Sanford, Master of the Temple in England, that the Templar order should not be bound to answer for anything done by Geoffrey as royal almoner.[9]

Frequently the Templars were used as messengers and envoys of the king. John and Henry III repeatedly sent them *"ad partes transmarinas"*[10] as well as to persons and places in England. Sometimes the reason for their dispatch is not given; but when it is, it can be seen that important matters were often entrusted to them. Under Henry II in 1164, two Templars were sent to treat with the Archbishop of York at the Council of Clarendon regarding the possible appointment of the archbishop as papal legate.[11] And it was from a Templar that Henry received the message that Louis VII of France was concerned about the delay in the marriage of Richard and Alice, the son and daughter respectively of the English and French kings.[12] Under Henry III, Templars were often sent, along with other persons, on missions for the king. The Master of the Temple in England, Alan Martel, was sent (1224) to deal with Louis of France on the subject of a truce[13] and, almost immediately thereafter, to look into the possibility of effecting an agreement with Leopold, Duke of Austria, for marriage of King Henry to the duke's daughter.[14] A decade later, Robert de Sanford, then Master in England, was one of the royal representatives in the negotiations leading to the king's marriage to Eleanor, daughter of Count Raymond of Provence, and was a member of the royal party designated to escort her to England.[15] In 1252, Roscelin de Fos, Master of the Temple in England, was in charge of discussing violation of the truce in Gascony; of negotiating an agreement between Simon de Montfort, Henry III's governor of the duchy, and the leaders of the Gascons who were dissatisfied with his administration; and of conserving the truce he succeeded in making.[16] Two years later (1254), the king sent a Templar to Scotland on matters pertaining to the queen of that country.[17] In the same year, when in southern France, Henry directed that certain royal valuables be brought to him by either a Templar or a Hospitaller.[18] Shortly thereafter, a

Templar was one of six royal envoys sent to Italy to deal with Pope Alexander IV on Sicilian affairs.[19] Between 1261 and 1265, on four separate occasions, a Templar was sent, along with one or two other persons, to discuss terms of peace between France and England.[20] During this period, a Templar is also found as a royal envoy to an English noble.[21] Under Edward I and Edward II, the use of Templars as royal messengers and envoys seems to have been discontinued.

There is little information on the use of Templars in England as envoys and messengers by persons other than the king. In 1234, Templars were used as messengers between Richard, son of William Marshall, Earl of Pembroke, and the Irish nobles, in Richard's campaign in Ireland;[22] and in 1235, Emperor Frederick II sent a delegation, including two Templars, to ask for the hand of Isabella, Henry III's sister, in marriage.[23] Quite probably a more thorough search of the sources, though they are concerned primarily with royal affairs, would provide additional examples.

On two occasions, the kings of England found it desirable to entrust disputed areas to the safekeeping of the Templars. In the first instance (1158-61), Henry II of England and Louis VII of France, arguing over possessions of the castles of Néaufles and Gisors in the Vexin, agreed that when Henry's two sons were married to Louis' two daughters – all four were small children – the castles should be handed over to Henry, but that in the meantime, the Templars were to hold them in safekeeping. This they did until Henry, in considerable haste, had his older son, Henry, married to Louis' older daughter, Margaret. For handing the castles over to Henry at this point, the Templars were rebuked by the French king but were rewarded by the English.[24] Later, in 1186, they seem to have had a part in the arrangement by which Queen Margaret of France renounced her claim to the castles.[25] In the second instance, when, en route to the Holy Land, a disagreement between Richard of England and Philip of France arose over which of the two kings should raise his banner over the Sicilian city of Messina, it was decided to entrust the city to the Templars.[26]

On a number of occasions, the Templars are found as advisers to the king. Richard de Hastings, Master of the Temple in England, along with the Bishops of Salisbury and Norwich and the Earls of Leicester and Cornwall, played a prominent part in the Becket controversy (1164).[27] Apparently he and the others sought to effect a reconciliation between the archbishop and the king by urging Thomas to yield to Henry II. Aymeric de St. Maur, Master of the Temple in England, showed himself a faithful adviser to John for over a decade.[28] In the crucial phase of John's dispute with Innocent III, it was two Templars, who had been sent to the king by Pandulph, the papal legate, who arranged for the meeting leading to John's submission. These two Templars, doubtlessly after consultation with Aymeric, advised the king to submit and accompanied him to the Preceptory of Ewell, near Dover, from which John left to submit to Pandulph and receive his realm back as a fief of the papacy.[29] Indeed, the gold mark which John offered the church when absolved from excommunication was borrowed from none other than Aymeric.[30] This same Templar advised John in the contest with the barons which led to the issuance of *Magna Carta*. It appears that Aymeric was one of those lords who, though on the side of John at Runnymede, advised the beleaguered king to sign the proposed charter of liberties and rights.[31] Certainly the liberties and rights of the Templars are to be considered among those confirmed and guaranteed by this charter[32] and also by the earlier charter of rights and liberties of the clergy which, interestingly enough, had been signed by John in January at New Temple.[33] Specific instances in which the Templars served as advisers to Henry III are not readily found; but in view of the great favor he showed to the Templars and in view of his frequent visits to New Temple, it is quite probable that such masters as Alan Martel, Robert de Sanford, and Roscelin de Fos, who were sent on many a royal mission,[34] may also have served as royal advisers. Under Edward I and Edward II, however, there is no evidence to prove nor reason to suspect that the Masters of the Temple served as royal advisers.

Since the preceding paragraphs do not quite give a complete picture of the political relations of the Templars with the crown, a few additional points should be mentioned. Under Stephen, when the Templars, whether from wisdom or necessity, were playing both sides in the years of civil strife, one of their number is found in the list of witnesses to the charter which provided for settlement between Stephen and the Empress Matilda whereby the latter's son, Henry of Anjou, was to succeed to the English crown.[35] As part of his penance for the Becket murder, Henry II promised, among other things, to pay the Templars the sum necessary to maintain two hundred knights for the defense of the Holy Land for a year.[36] In the hope that Henry could also be convinced to come east at the head of a large force, an impressive delegation from Jerusalem — consisting of the Patriarch, the Prior of the Hospitallers, and the Grand Master of the Templars, who died in Italy en route — was sent to England. But the king, relying upon a convenient opinion of Parliament (1185), finally rejected the request on the grounds that reasons for his remaining in England were more compelling than those for his going to the Holy Land.[37] However, in his will, Henry remembered the Templars, Hospitallers, and several other religious groups in England, with five thousand silver marks each.[38]

The relations of Richard with the Templars, which are as colorful as they are popular, are more a part of the history of eastern than of English affairs. From the incident at Messina, referred to above, it is clear that a number of Templars, some of whom no doubt left England with the king, accompanied Richard all the way east. While in the Holy Land, Richard found the Templars loyal allies, as was especially proved at Ascalon.[39] When it came time for Richard to return to Europe, even though he had not been able to accomplish all he had wanted to, it was in a boat provided by Robert de Sable, Grand Master of the Templars that he set out for the west (October 9, 1192).[40] Wearing the habit of a Templar, and accompanied by four Templars and a number of attendants, he sailed first to Corfu and then to the northern shore of the Adriatic Sea where he finally landed in the area of Aquileia and Venice. Retaining his Templar disguise and accompanied initially by several priests and two Templars, but later by only one attendant — in order to make capture less likely — the English monarch proceeded inland through territory belonging to his enemy, Leopold, Archduke of Austria. Recognized and captured at a small town near Vienna, he was held prisoner for thirteen months, first by the Archduke and then by Emperor Henry VI, before being brought to trial on a variety of charges at a diet at Worms. At his trial, Richard defended himself with such vigor and eloquence that he was finally put up for ransom — 100,000 silver marks.[41] To this ransom, laity and clergy in England without distinction were compelled to contribute (1193). Privileges and immunities were suspended. The English Templars doubtlessly had to pay their share — as William of Newburgh said, even the Cistercians had to pay.[42]

John, and his son, Henry III, as has been shown above, relied heavily upon the Templars for a variety of services and for advice. Furthermore, both kings were frequent guests at New Temple and at other Templar houses where they carried on royal business.[43] Indeed, the close relationship between the Templars and the crown reached its height in the first half of Henry's reign. Indicative of this royal favor were Henry's choice (1236-37) of New Temple as his burial place — a choice with which his bride concurred — and his bequest of £8 sterling for three chaplains to say mass there daily.[44] Actually, however, upon death, Henry's body, though claimed by the Templars, was not entombed at New Temple but rather in the church of the shrine of Edward the Confessor.[45] Like Henry II, his grandfather, Henry III assumed the cross (1252) but did not actually undertake a crusade although the Templars, Hospitallers, and Teutonic Knights had been instructed to make preparations for the king's passage.[46] While in Paris (1254), it was at the Old Temple there, the Templars' headquarters in France, that Henry chose to stay.[47] Also suggestive of the close ties between Henry and the Templars is the gift of a crystal vase allegedly containing a portion of the blood of Christ which William de Sonnac, Grand Master of the order, sent him in 1247.[48]

The political relations of Edward I and Edward II with the Templars were limited, though both monarchs had frequent financial dealings with them. It should be pointed out, however, that the Templars rendered military service to Edward I in his campaign against Scotland (1298-99)—the Master of the Temple, Brian de Jay, and presumably certain other members of the order, being summoned for this campaign.[49] Indeed, Brian de Jay and another Templar were killed in the crucial battle of Falkirk.[50] Interestingly, too, this same Brian de Jay — apparently while still Preceptor of Scotland and just before his selection as Master in England — had earlier (1296) been called to do fealty to the English king. [51] As this is the only notice of the sort, it raises but does not answer the question of whether or not the Templars regularly rendered fealty to the king. Most likely, the demand for fealty from the Preceptor of Scotland was part of Edward's general policy of seeking to bring all the important lords of that country more directly under his authority, an especially urgent matter inasmuch as Scotland had recently (1295) allied itself with France. In the absence of additional data, then, one cannot assume that fealty was normally demanded of the master and preceptors in England. Apart from their arrest, trial, conviction, and dissolution — which will be dealt with below in Chapter IV — the political relations between the Templars and Edward II are limited to one insignificant event, namely, that they, along with the Hospitallers, should furnish three carts for the king's use, with recompense to be made out of the funds of the king's wardrobe.[52]

The political prominence of the Templars, and of other religious orders and their heads as well, is shown by the regular attendance of the Master of the Temple in England at sessions of Parliament. From 1295 to 1306, he was summoned by name, along with other leading clerics and lay lords, to be present;[53] but unfortunately, exactly what he did at these sessions cannot be determined.

Associated with the political activities of the Templars, but to a lesser degree than with their economic activities, is the administrative role of New Temple. As suggested above, various kings made frequent visits to New Temple — and to other preceptories upon occasion as well — and, during their residence there, carried on royal business as close and patent letters clearly reveal.[54] The subject matter of these letters was as varied as similar royal correspondence written elsewhere: the election of clerical officials, the assignment of church benefices, the holding of assizes, the issuance of letters of safe-conduct and protection, the licensing of merchants and goods, the collection of taxes, the grant of royal gifts and privileges, and the like.

New Temple was repeatedly used as a convenient place for political and ecclesiastical meetings. The council, led by Simon de Montfort, which discussed what should be done regarding Henry III's misrule, met at New Temple in 1260.[55] The parliament which met in November, 1272, upon the death of Henry III, to recognize Edward, abroad on a crusade, as the new king, and to make the necessary arrangements for carrying on the government until his return, was held at New Temple.[56] And in 1299, Parliament was summoned by Edward I to assemble at New Temple.[57] A number of times, when Henry III was king, New Temple was used as the place where those who wished to see him should come.[58] On at least nine occasions between 1256 and 1299, the English clergy, either the prelates alone or the prelates and the lower clergy jointly in convocation, met at New Temple to discuss their various problems and to decide upon a course of action.[59]

Both clerics and laymen found New Temple a convenient place of lodging. Besides the kings who frequently stayed there, prominent clerics like the archbishops of York, Cologne, and Toledo were lodged there.[60] Papal legates seem to have made it a point to stay there — Martin, legate of Innocent IV, for example, resided there for several years (1244-46).[61] And foreign diplomats, such as envoys of the King of Castile, were put up at New Temple.[62] The church even served as a burial place for a number of prominent persons — William Marshall, first Earl of Pembroke; his son, William, second Earl of Pembroke; and his great grandson, Gilbert, fourth Earl of Pembroke.[63] As mentioned above, it had originally been planned that King Henry III and his wife should be buried there.

New Temple was used for other administrative purposes, too. Upon occasion, the great seal of the realm was deposited there for safekeeping,[64] as were royal vestments[65] and valuables—e.g., a large book belonging to the queen[66]— and royal records and charters.[67] Even wine and herring belonging to the king and set aside for charitable or hospitable purposes were found there.[68] And, as will be indicated below, New Temple served both as a place where agreements of all sorts were made and as a place where copies of those agreements were filed.[69]

In view of all of these activities and services engaged in by the Templars, it is not surprising to find them the recipients of favors and gifts. The privileges granted them by kings and popes and the lands given them by kings and laymen have already been discussed. A few additional gifts from the crown can, however, be cited. For almost every year under Henry II, Richard I, and John, the Pipe Rolls authorize annual grants of alms to the Templars ranging from one-half mark to four marks — one or two marks being the rule.[70] Since these grants were authorized for approximately thirty of the counties of England and for such cities as London, Winchester, and Waltham, and since they were made with great consistency, though the sums tend to be smaller under John than under Henry II and Richard I, the total sum involved was considerable. To these gifts of alms are to be added under Henry III and Edward I frequent grants, usually of fifty marks, made to the Master in England rather than to individual houses.[71] Especially under Henry III, annual gifts of wine and venison are repeatedly made to the Templars. These grants, which actually started under Henry II and John,[72] include one, two, or three casks *(dolia)* of wine[73] and five to ten deer from the royal forests[74] and are usually made to the Master and Brothers of the Temple at the time of their annual chapter meeting. Sometimes, however, the grants are made to a particular preceptor[75] and for some other reason.[76] In addition, the Templars are repeatedly authorized to use two to seven oaks per year from the king's forests for construction and repair of mills, windmills, and the like.[77] Individual and non-periodic grants were also made — e.g., the grant of a silver chalice worth five marks for use in religious services,[78] the grant of vestments for the same purpose,[79] the grant of fish for stocking a pool,[80] the grant of one hundred silver marks for an undisclosed purpose,[81] and the payment for construction of a chapel at New Temple.[82] Without doubt extensive grants, apart from land, were also made by persons other than the kings; but surviving forces do not provide much specific evidence on this point.

Economic Activities

The economic activities of the Templars were varied and far-reaching, extending as they did to agriculture, trade and commerce, and financial transactions. Other religious orders and many lay groups were involved in these activities, too. Some religious groups, for example, engaged in agriculture to a greater degree; and some lay groups, in trade and commerce; but few groups, lay or clerical, were involved actively in all three fields simultaneously, and none of them (except possibly the rising Italian bankers) were as deeply involved in financial transactions as the Templars.

Unfortunately, there is no way of determining the total income of the Templars from their economic activities at any one time or in any one area. Their land, churches, and mills listed in the Inquest of 1185 provided an annual income of £857. Not surprisingly, Lincolnshire and Yorkshire, where most of the Templar holdings were located, provided the largest part (£81 and £47 respectively) of the total. But the total figure given in the Inquest omits demesne holdings, which probably were equal to those rented out, as well as services and payments in kind, which were numerous. Furthermore, the Inquest itself did not include all the Templar lands, nor even all the counties in which they had property.[83] The most comprehensive survey that is available is the one made by royal officials in 1308 at the time of the arrest of the Templars and the seizure of their goods. But this survey, too, is incomplete. It purports to give the income received by the king from the Templar properties — lands, mills, and churches — in his.keeping. However, the value of crops and animals, the revenue from trade and commerce, the profit from financial transactions, and the income from perquisites of court are not included. Adding up the figures from the reports of the sheriffs and keepers, as given by Perkins,[84] one gets a total income of £4,351 — a considerable sum for the period even though much of the Templar wealth is not included in it. Again, Yorkshire and Lincolnshire, reporting £1,130 and £934 respectively, provided nearly half the total. Oxfordshire, Leicestershire, Warwickshire, Essex, and Gloucestershire follow in that order, with amounts ranging from £268 to £216. Below them, between £167 and £116 are the counties of Hereford, Hertford, Cambridge, Shropshire and Stafford (jointly), and Somerset and Dorset (jointly). The remaining counties varied from the £72 of Sussex to the £2 of Cornwall.

Agriculture

The earliest and most extensive of the economic activities of the Templars was agriculture. Such information as we have on the subject, which is surprisingly little, is gained from legal documents, such as the Inquest, corrody agreements, and miscellaneous references in the public records and in narrative sources. The division of lands and methods of production, as is to be expected, were based primarily on the manorial system and the modifications in it which the Templars retained when control fell to them. This meant, on the one hand, that land was divided into arable, pasture, garden, and waste; and on the other, that it was utilized largely on the basis of the two- or three-field system.[85] That strip farming was widely used, and that at the same time some degree of consolidation was going on, is suggested by the rental units of land varying in size from an acre or two at rates ranging from several pence to several shillings, depending upon the quality of the soil — as is revealed in the Inquest — and by the large units of one hundred or more acres repeatedly referred to in the Hospitaller's Report of 1338. Especially noteworthy were the vast areas of pasture, much of it former waste land, especially in Lincolnshire and Yorkshire, which the Templars reclaimed.

The exact role played by the Templars in agricultural production and management is open to question. The preceptors no doubt exercised a general supervision over agriculture as well as over other matters in their preceptories. The small houses and farms *(casaux),* which the Templars themselves occupied, were managed by the *frères casaliers,*[86] whom we might in some respects compare with the lay brothers of other orders.[87] Perhaps more often than not, the *frères casaliers* personally worked the land along with a few peasants. The larger estates, under the responsibility of the preceptor or certain *frères sergens* designated by him, were usually rented out to lay lords who left the actual work to the usual manorial officials, specialists, and peasants.[88]

Since some consideration was given to specific Templar holdings, rents, and commutation of feudal fees and services into monetary payments in the preceding chapter, the major concern here will be with the crops and livestock raised on the Templar estates. Since the Templars tended to maintain the specialty of the region in which they acquired land, certain areas were devoted to the growing of grains; others, to the pasturage of livestock; and still others, to the utilization of water and water rights.

Grain — wheat, oats, rye, and barley — was raised throughout the areas held by the Templars, but especially in the Midlands and Essex.[89] In only a few instances, in the inventories of Templar movables made by the royal keepers,[90] is a specific indication of the grain raised found. At Hanningfield (Essex), 31 acres were planted to wheat; 7, to rye; and 52, to oats. At Rothley (Leicestershire), the granaries contained 166 quarters of grain; at Copmanthorp, Temple Newsam, and Temple Hirst (Yorkshire), the amounts were 180, 712, and 274 quarters respectively. The question arises of whether or not the Templars produced grain for sale. Rogers, writing in general terms, says that because the market value of grain tended to be low in the Middle Ages, landlords were better off to use their surplus production for fattening livestock than for sale.[91] But Gras, whose work supersedes Rogers' on this subject, disagrees saying that English landlords sold grain on the local market from the twelfth century onward and on the foreign market after the middle of the thirteenth century[92] and specifically shows that the sale of their surplus was encouraged by the fact that the price of wheat rose from 4½d. to 22½d. per bushel between 1150 and 1350, a five-fold increase.[93] Furthermore, in the south and east of England surplus grain —

not only wheat but oats and barley as well — was sold as early as the first decade of the thirteenth century as the well-known Pipe Rolls of the See of Winchester for the years 1208 and 1209 clearly show;[94] and by the end of the thirteenth century, both the total amount of grain raised and the percentage of the total production sold had increased.[95] This information, plus the one specific reference to their sale of grain,[96] makes it certain that the Templars, who specialized in the growing of grain and who were constantly in need of cash, did produce grain for sale. The same regions that raised grain seem also to have raised legumes — peas and beans being the only ones listed in the sources — as repeated references to "messuagium cum gardino" or "manerium cum gardino" suggest.[97] And certain areas, especially the county of Kent,[98] where small garden plots were very numerous, seem to have specialized in the raising of fruit as well as legumes.

The grazing of livestock — cattle, sheep, and swine — on their meadows, pastures, and forest lands constituted a major part of the Templars' agricultural program. All of these animals were valuable for their meat, hides, and manure; but cattle were most valuable for dairy products and sheep for wool. Wherever the Templars had reasonable amounts of land they kept their own flocks though certain counties, such as Yorkshire, Lincolnshire, Essex, and Wiltshire which had already become especially famous for grazing, had far more than others. The following list, based on the very small portion of the inventories made at the time of the arrest of the Templars which have been published[99] and upon the Report of the Hospitallers[100] after they had gained control of most of the Templar estates, gives some indication of the numbers of cattle and sheep on Templar lands: Ribston, Copmanthorp, Temple Hirst, and Temple Newsam (Yorkshire), 20, 22, 90, and 97 cattle respectively; Eagle (Lincolnshire), 20; Cressing and Witham (Essex), 32; Lockridge and Rockley (Wiltshire), 16 and 17 respectively; Swanton (Bedfordshire), 35; Feckenham (Worcestershire), 10; and Rothley (Leicestershire), 15. Rockley, Lockridge, and Chiryton (Wiltshire), 900, 300, and 260 sheep respec·tively; Cressing and Witham (Essex), 600; Eagle (Lincolnshire), 400; Temple Combe and Lopene (Somerset), 200 and 100 respectively; Temple Newsam and Temple Hirst (Yorkshire, 1,036 and 644 respectively; Feckenham (Worcestershire), 60; and Rothley (Leicestershire), 525. The approximate number of sheep at a given Templar preceptory, or in a given county, can be theoretically estimated on the basis of the number of sacks of wool sold at any given time — assuming that it took about two hundred fleeces to make one sack.[101] In 1298, the Master of the Templars complained to the king that his officials had taken forty-nine sacks in Yorkshire without payment or provision for payment.[102]

and in 1308, the king's officials seized thirty-eight sacks in Lincoln-shire.[103] On the basis of this data, wholly inadequate as it is, it can be estimated that the Templars had at least 9,800 sheep in Yorkshire and 7,600 sheep in Lincolnshire. Without doubt these figures are decidedly low. If more information were available, it might also be possible to find out whether or not the Templars, like so many owners of great estates, pastured the flocks of strangers in return for a share of the animals or a payment in money.

For swine, horses, and oxen, which the Templars must have had in considerable numbers, practically no information is available. The Inquest occasionally refers to *pannagium* (the privilege of feeding pigs);[104] and the Templars, like many others, held forest lands. In the reports of the keepers of Templar lands, some mention of swine is made – e.g., there were 30 at Temple Newsam, 22 at Temple Hirst, 40 at Swanton, and 45 at Rothley.[105] Of horses, there is even less mention although obviously the Templars needed many, especially for military and training purposes. In one reference, it is stated that 30 palfreys and 3 sumpter horses, valued at £78, were taken into the king's hands by the royal keepers.[106]

Associated with agriculture were the Templar mills which proved highly profitable. Exactly how many there were cannot be determined though the Inquest of 1185 lists eighty-one. Most of these were grain mills to which the Templar tenants, and many others in the area, brought their crops to be ground. The Templars themselves seem to have run many of them; and the others were rented out at annual rates usually ranging from five shillings to five marks,[107] depending upon the size and value of the mill. The Castle Mills at York, however, were especially valuable and were rented at fifteen and one-half marks annually.[108] Some of the mills, one at Barton in Gloucestershire and one at Temple Newsam in Yorkshire, appear to have been used for fulling purposes[109]— the earliest such known in English history.[110] Whether or not the Templars and their tenants participated directly in the production of cloth is uncertain, but it seems likely that they did – at least the probability is sufficient to warrant further investigation.[111]

The millponds and the rivers on which Templar mills were located also provided fish, as did the bays along the coast and the sea. Probably fishponds of one sort or another existed on all the larger Templar estates.

In general, it can be said that the Templars were orthodox and efficient in the production of agricultural goods and in the management of their properties. Perhaps earlier and to a greater extent than other lords, they sought to convert their agricultural produce and their income from rents into cash;[112] but just how successful they were in this and exactly how much money they obtained cannot be determined.

Trade and Commerce

Wool, wine, dairy products, grain, fish, hides, salt, timber, and metals were among the standard items of medieval trade. In varying degrees, all the great English estates of the twelfth and thirteenth centuries produced for purposes of sale and exchange as well as consumption.[113] The old generalization that medieval economy, including that of the religious orders, was in essence self-sufficient is now universally recognized as a gross oversimplification. The Templar estates certainly were not self-sufficient; not only basic commodities such as wine, fish, and timber, but also luxury items such as fine cloth, special horses, leather, and metal ware were needed. For the Templars, as for most others, most of these goods were to be obtained through exchange and purchase at local or regional markets and fairs or by trade with foreign merchants. In payment for these goods, the Templars could offer wool, grain, and cash to the foreign merchants, and grain, fish, and livestock to the local merchants.

Wool, the chief commodity the Templars could offer for sale and exchange, was sold by grade—good, medium, and lock—either to agents of the king or to foreign merchants, Flemish or Italian. In 1298, royal agents of the king contracted to buy 16 sacks, 27½ stone of wool from the Templars in Lincolnshire for £134 15s. 7½d.; 6 sacks, 18½ stone of good wool and 3 sacks, 22 stone of medium wool at Temple Bruer; 2 sacks, 25 stone of good wool and 1 sack, 12½ stone of medium at Willoughton; and 1 sack, 16½ stone of good wool and 17 stone of medium at Eagle.[114] At the same time, they purchased 3½ sacks of wool for 22 marks 10 shillings from the Templars at Wilberham in Cambridgeshire and 5½ sacks for 44 marks from the Templars at Temple Guiting in Gloucestershire.[115] In addition, the royal agents took without payment or provision for payment 49 sacks of wool in Yorkshire and 24½ sacks in Lincolnshire.[116] The price the crown promised to pay for the wool purchased in Lincolnshire and Cambridgeshire was £10 per sack for good wool and six marks (£4) for medium wool.[117] These prices compare favorably with those the Cistercians were receiving at the same time and would appear to be in line with the standard rate paid for English wool in the late thirteenth century.[118] No specific prices were quoted for inferior (lock) wool, probably because the variation in quality was so great.

Foreign merchants also purchased Templar wool, probably at such major fairs as the one at Boston.[119] As royal licenses indicate, the Templars were active in shipping their wool abroad, especially to Flanders, through the ports of Boston and Southhampton, usually free of customs duties,[120] and without limitation except in time of war between England and Flanders.[121] The value of this exemption is immediately apparent when one remembers the export duties put on wool by Edward I — 7s. 6d. per sack in 1275, 5 marks in 1294, and 3 marks in 1297.[122] Unfortunately no figures are given on the amount of wool shipped abroad, and no contracts survive to indicate the terms of sale. It would be interesting to know whether or not the Templars, like the Cistercians and some other religious groups, found it necessary, in their need for cash, to commit their clips to foreign merchants for years in advance.

The finest wool in England was produced in such areas as Lincolnshire, Shropshire, and Herefordshire; high quality wool was raised in much of Yorkshire, the Lindesey region of Lincolnshire, and the Cotswold Hills of Gloucestershire; and the Midlands tended to provide medium grade wool. In each of these areas, but especially in the undeveloped northern counties, the Templars held sizable lands; and in all of them except Shropshire, they pastured large flocks of sheep and maintained major preceptories. However, the Cistercians certainly, and perhaps the Premonstratensians and the Gilbertines as well, were more famous and important in this respect than the Templars.[123]

Wine was the second major item in the foreign trade of the Templars, an import as wool had been an export. So far as can be determined, the exchange was to a large degree limited to the Templar houses in Poitou and Gascony.[124] The ships which plied the seas between the English ports of Dover, Portsmouth, and Boston and the Angevin ports of La Rochelle and Bordeaux were often owned by the Templars[125] — one of them, fittingly was named "La Templère."[126] In general, provided their ships and cargoes did not fall into the hands of the king's enemies,[127] did not carry goods belonging to other persons,[128] and did not go to other than English ports,[129] the Templars were granted freedom from customs duties both for exports and imports.[130] On one occasion, in 1242, when he found the Templars violating these terms by taking other persons' wines to places other than England, Henry III temporarily cancelled the Templars' commercial exemptions.[131] It might be added, too, that John and Henry III, and perhaps some of the other monarchs as well, found it convenient to purchase wine for the royal household from that imported by the English Templars.[132]

In addition to wine, the Templars were permitted to import and export free of tolls and customs other goods *("alias res et merchandisas")*.[133] What these goods were, is at no time specified. Perhaps they included grain, fish, and dairy products; and possibly, in view of the Templars' many commercial associations, such things as spices, silk cloth, and armor. Two Templars, by name Roger and Thomas, were employed at different times by Henry III in his naval service as officials entrusted with the regulation of commerce both of seaports and on the high seas. In this capacity, probably more administrative than commercial they aided the bailiffs of the port cities in the inspection of vessels and cargoes and even stopped ships and seized goods at sea.[134] They also were commissioned to procure win for the king.[135] And for a time, Thomas was put in charge of one of the king's larger ships sailing between England and southern France on royal business.[136]

Markets and fairs were a regular medium for the exchange of goods in the Middle Ages and were a convenient source of profit to the owner. It is not surprising, therefore, to find that the Templars obtained from the kings, who claimed exclusive jurisdiction over the issuance of such franchises, the grant of markets and fairs on certain of their properties.[137] The first such grant to the Templars, made by Stephen, was a weekly market (on Sunday, later changed to Tuesday) at Witham (Essex). This was followed by John's grant in 1199 of a weekly market (on Wednesday) at Baldock (Hertfordshire) and an annual fair of four days — later changed to three (September 20-23) at the same place. It was Henry III, however, who made the largest number of such grants to the Templars. He authorized them to establish a weekly market (on Wednesday) at Newburgh (Yorkshire), and both weekly markets (usually on Sunday) and annual fairs, usually of three day's duration, at Wetherby (Yorkshire, July 24-26), Walnesford (Essex, August 28-30), Balsall (Warwickshire, April 22-24 and September 20-22), and Kirkeby (Lincolnshire, July 24-26). Some years after his original grant, Henry III cancelled the market and fair at Walnesford but substituted a weekly market (on Thursday) and an annual fair (June 23-25) at Werriby, in the same county, instead. Edward I also made several grants of markets and fairs and subsequently changed one of them. He granted a weekly market (on Monday) and an annual fair at Rothley (Leicestershire, June 10-12) and at Southcave (Yorkshire, June 2-5) and then substituted a weekly market (on Wednesday) and an annual fair (June 10-12) at Gaddesby (Leicestershire) for the one at Rothley. Under Edward I, also, a weekly market (on Thursday) and an annual fair (July 24-26) at Bruer (Lincolnshire), originally granted by Henry III but hitherto not made use of, was authorized. Though the profit from these markets and fairs is unknown and though none of them were among the most celebrated and wealthy ones, they must, nonetheless, have proved both profitable and convenient to the Templars.

Financial Activities

When we think of English finances in the late Middle Ages, the Templars, the Italians, and the Jews come quickly to mind. The Jews were active both before and after the Templars, but they seem to have been little more than pawnbrokers and money-lenders of limited means; and the Italian merchants and bankers did not become important until the late thirteenth century, especially as they took over the collection of papal revenues and as they enlarged their own resources. But during most of the twelfth and thirteenth centuries in England, neither the Italians nor the Jews could be ranked in financial power or influence with the Templars.

In a period of rapid economic development, it was the Templars, with their center at New Temple, London, to whom the Angevin kings, papal legates, great and small lay and ecclesiastical lords, merchants, and others in England turned for guidance and aid. There were several reasons for this: the traditional sanctity of centers of religion and the strength of their buildings, the confidence and security associated with the Templars as outstanding men of religion and arms, the abundance of their riches, the international scale of their operations, the conveniences and permanence of their houses, and the independence of the order from most lay and ecclesiastical authorities. To kings and feudal lords who were almost constantly on the move and who had few, if any, persons to whom they could turn for financial aid or places where they could safely store their wealth, the use of the Templars and their facilities must have seemed the answer to their problems.

The financial activities[138] of the Templars were numerous and varied, simple and complex, successful and unsuccessful. Knowledge of them, despite the general absence of their account books and of other pertinent data and the need to rely upon brief and often incomplete entries in the public records and upon occasional references in the chronicles, is sufficient to present a general picture showing that the Templars engaged in the exchange of money, the acceptance of valuables and cash for deposit and disbursement, the lending of money, the international transfer and transportation of funds, the issuance and use of credit instruments, and the trusteeship of future interests. From these many activities, it is apparent that in an age before the appearance of banks proper the Templars engaged in most of the activities normally associated with banking. And, in addition, they served as financial officials of the kings and fiscal agents of the popes.

Evidence for the exchange of money by the Templars is indirect. References are made to the import and export of specie; to the receipt and disbursement of money in terms of English pounds and of pounds

Tournois; and to dealings with French, Flemish, and Italian merchants. Obviously these transactions could only have been performed by the exchange and evaluation of money, both domestic and foreign. The deposit and disbursement of cash and valuables made New Temple both a treasury and a bank. Hundreds of entries in the public records dating from the last years of Henry II to the early years of Edward II, but mostly from the reign of Henry III, indicate the large scale of these operations. However, since these references are in a large part incidental and unsystematic, there is no necessary relationship between what was paid in and what was paid out; and, though funds may have been deposited for a certain purpose, they were not always so used. Consequently, the true scope and method of these transactions cannot be determined.

The term treasury *(thesaurium)* was often used in the Middle Ages to mean a storehouse where valuables of various kinds were placed for safekeeping.[139] New Temple served as a treasury in this sense for the kings, for members of the royal family, and for important men in the realm. Except for one reference to John depositing the royal jewels in New Temple (1204-1205),[140] all the surviving data pertaining to the royal family date from the reign of Henry III. In 1232, Henry placed royal jewels worth three thousand marks (£2,000) there for safekeeping.[141] Some of them were withdrawn in 1242.[142] Later (1254), the remaining jewels were ordered transferred to the queen at Portsmouth[143] and were finally (1261) sent to Queen Margaret of France who, after taking careful inventory, had them deposited temporarily with the Templars at Paris.[144] In 1264, however, the royal jewels were returned to London for safekeeping at New Temple.[145] The treasure of Hubert de Burgh, former justiciar, and his wife, Margaret, was stored at New Temple.[146] Chests of valuables belonging to Simon the Norman (1242),[147] for a time keeper of the royal seal, to an unnamed merchant of Ghent (1259),[148] and to the Bishop of Rochester (1278)[149] were also kept there. The above examples are known either because they involved the crown or because something out of the ordinary occurred. There must have been many other instances of which no record has survived.

Taxes, both royal and papal, after being collected and stored locally, were frequently transported in strong carts under guard to New Temple for deposit and safekeeping.[150] So, for example, tenths,[151] fifteenths,[152] twentieths,[153] thirtieths,[154] fortieths,[155] carrucage,[156] the tallage of the Jews[157] and of cities such as London and Lincoln,[158] subsidies for the Holy Land,[159] issues of eyre,[160] revenue from Ireland,[161] and clerical contributions to the crown[162] — as well as income derived by the king from ecclesiastical benefices[163] — were deposited or ordered to be deposited there by John, Henry III, and Edward I. Sometimes, however, the treasury at Westminster or in the Tower of London was cited as an alternate place of deposit.[164] Papal procurations,[165] subsidies for the Holy Land,[166] and Peter's pence[167] were frequently stored at New Temple though they were sometimes entrusted to the Hospitallers, Cistercians, and Italian merchants as well.[168] There is no way of knowing just how much money might have been on deposit at any one time; but the fact that taxes (e.g., £2,900 and £1,388, the thirtieth of only the two centers of Nottingham and Bristol[169] in 1238) and the extensive deposit of funds by many persons were entrusted to the Templars make it obvious that very large sums of money were involved. Indeed, in 1307 just before their downfall, the amount of money in New Temple was so large that Edward II was able to seize the enormous sum of £50,000 at one time.[170]

The question of the safety of the deposits at New Temple inevitably arises. Though the money and other valuables were normally secure, a number of exceptions can be cited. After the fall from power of Hubert de Burgh, Henry III, having learned of his former justiciar's great wealth in the custody of the Templars, and being in need of money as usual, summoned the Master of the Temple and demanded that Hubert's treasure be handed over (1232). This the Master said he could not do without the permission of the depositor. Though Henry seems to have been ready to use torture to get Hubert's approval and to use force to get the treasure from the Temple, neither was necessary as the prisoner consented to the king's demand.[171] Ten years later (1242), the treasure of Simon the Norman, recently dismissed as keeper of the royal seal, was ordered removed from New Temple.[172] This seizure appears to have been made over the strong protest of the Templars as Henry's guarantee that they should not be questioned about the matters suggests. In 1254, Richard of Cornwall, then serving as regent for his brother, King Henry, who was in Gascony and in immediate need of money, invaded the treasuries both at New Temple and at Westminster and may have carried off certain valuables.[173] The Poitevins, forced to withdraw from England because of their unpopularity (1258), left behind at New Temple a large sum of money which was confiscated and expended "at the option of the king and barons for the benefit of the kingdom."[174] About the same time, the fortune of William de Valence, which Paris says was of "astonishing magnitude," was seized by King Henry, William's half-brother.[176] In 1263, when his misrule had caused the barons led by Simon de Montfort, Earl of Leicester, to seize control of the government and when Henry and the queen had taken refuge in the Tower of London, the young Prince Edward and Robert

Walerand, the king's seneschal, went to New Temple to obtain badly needed funds. Demanding to see the queen's jewels, Edward and Walerand were admitted to the Temple treasury where they broke open a number of chests and carried off a large sum of money belonging to others — variously reported as £1,000 or £10,000.[176] Some years later, in 1277, after a band of robbers had broken into the Templar treasury,[177] and at a time when many of the barons and knights of the realm were departing for the campaign in Wales, it was suggested by a group of prelates meeting at New Temple and by the king that the papal tenth then being collected should be entrusted to Italian firms like the Ricciardi, instead of being deposited at New Temple.[178] At one point (1295), Edward I temporarily appropriated funds the Templars were about to send to Cyprus but, on the earnest demand of the pope, restored them.[179] And finally, in 1307, Edward II had £50,000 in silver, plus gold and jewels, which had been deposited in their treasury by Bishop Langton, his father's treasurer, seized and handed over to his favorite, Piers Gaveston.[180]

These examples certainly prove that the Temple and its treasure were neither inviolable nor impregnable. Yet most of the cases of violation involved the king, against whom the Templars dared not take too positive a stand lest they be deprived of valuable privileges and immunities or be restricted in their possessions and activities. What happened to the Templars could and did happen to others. For example, the goods of the Jews were repeatedly seized, and the loans of Italian bankers were sometimes repudiated. Yet, the Templars' record of one hundred and twenty years of active financial operations was one in which losses and confiscations were rare and security the rule. It is doubtful if depositors could have found more trustworthy persons or a safer place for their wealth.

Money was regularly, and on a large scale, deposited at New Temple, sometimes for safekeeping, but more often for use. If for safekeeping only, it was usually stored in strong boxes under double lock and key (with one key for the depositer and another for the Treasurer of the Temple) or the instructions for deposit directed that the money "be kept under seal,"[181] or some such phrase. Normally this sort of deposit was held until the depositor showed up in person to reclaim possession. The principle and practice here is identical with the storage of valuables, such as jewels, mentioned above. On the whole, most deposits would either be (1) general — in which case the funds were disposed of according to specific directions of the depositors as they were received — or (2) conditional — in which case the disposition was indicated at the time of deposit and the funds were not to be used for any other purpose.[182] The Templars were careful in the handling of these general accounts and normally released funds only upon written instructions bearing the signature or seal of the depositor as well as the date, the name of the payee, and the sum involved.[183] This authorization fulfilled the chief function of our check and has been referred to as a primitive form of check though there was no transfer or endorsement possible.[184] That the Templars insisted upon this procedure is well illustrated when King Henry III was informed that Hubert de Burgh's money could not be handed over to him without the depositor's authorization.[185] As a further safeguard, the Templars often demanded that the person obtaining the money sign a statement of receipt.[186] In the case of the conditional accounts, care was taken to see that the terms were fully met, or if a change of terms was to be made, that the change was agreed upon by all parties concerned.[187]

Deposits might also be classified as regular or irregular. If the former, the money was not to be touched except by order of the depositor; if the latter (e.g., the open account of the King of France and possibly of the King of England), the management of the funds seems to have been left to the discretion of the Templars with the possible consequence that a sum of money supposedly deposited for a given purpose (e.g., a special levy for a proposed crusade) might actually be used for some other purpose (e.g., payment of a royal debt to Italian merchant-bankers.)[188]

Under certain conditions, it would seem that funds could be transferred without the actual movement of specie from one account to another — not only between accounts of a given house but also between accounts of different Templar houses. This seems clearly to have been the case in many of the transactions of the London and Paris Temples which will be discussed below. The details of the procedure are lacking; but from what is known of the Templars and of other financial groups in this period, or a little later, the transfer may well have been effected either on the basis of written statements or on the basis of oral agreements made by the parties concerned in the presence of the appropriate Templar official.[189]

To the question of whether or not the Templars paid interest on money deposited with them, no positive answer can be given. There seems to be no evidence that they did although it was not unusual for bankers to do so under the form of a gift or bonus.[190]

The kings, royal officials, members of the royal family, lay and ecclesiastical lords, religious organizations or units, merchants, widows, and the like — practically all classes of persons and corporations — had accounts with the Templars at one time or another. Public authorities carried the largest and most active accounts and, at least upon occasion, even overdrew their balances in their general or current accounts. When this happened, the Templar treasurer might permit the overdraft in view of funds in the client's conditional accounts or might make short-term loans available to cover the shortage.[191]

Henry II in 1182 and again in 1188 deposited money with the Templars for use on his projected crusade to the Holy Land.[192] John entrusted 20,000 marks[193] on one occasion, 10,000 marks on another, 7,000 marks on still another, and other sums totalling at least £5,000 to the Templars.[194] From time to time he ordered the Templars to pay out certain sums — e.g., 1,000 marks to Emperor Otto IV, his nephew (1212); 8,500 marks again to Otto (1213); 9,000 marks to the Earl of Salisbury and Falkes de Breauté a Norman adventurer in the king's service, for official purposes; 6,000 marks to Pandulph, the papal legate; and 3,000 marks to be sent to the Bishop of Rochester.[195] For Edward I and Edward II, there are very few references — probably because they turned increasingly to the Italian bankers in financial matters, especially for loans. Yet, the Templars still appear as custodians of royal revenue and as bankers to the crown. So, for example, Edward I used £2,000 from the tallage of the Jews on deposit at New Temple to cover expenses for his visit to Paris (1274) on his way home from the Holy Land. On two different occasions (1276) he withdrew 1,000 marks each; and he repeatedly ordered the Treasurer of New Temple to pay out various sums from tenths and the like entrusted to the Templars for expenses of the royal household, for repair and construction work at the Tower of London, and so forth.[196]

The numerous and sizable deposits and disbursements of Henry III suggest the close relationship which existed between him and the Templars. Indeed, as will be indicated below, Henry came to use New Temple as a royal treasury and the treasurers of New Temple as royal treasurers. Since a complete listing of Henry's financial dealings with the Templars would take many pages, only representative examples will be cited here. Sometimes individual sums, apart from the revenue from the tax levies referred to above, were deposited without indicating their purpose — so for example, £1,000 in 1225, 1226, and 1246;[197] £700 in 1224;[198] £510 in 1221;[199] £200 in 1223;[200] 5,000 marks in 1247;[201] 2,000 marks in 1224 and 1247;[202] 1,400 marks in 1224;[203] and 1,000 marks in 1226 and 1240.[204] Sometimes funds were deposited for a definite purpose — so, for example, 10,000 marks in 1237 for payment of the remainder of the dowry of his sister, Isabella, wife of Emperor Frederick II;[205] 1,000 marks for papal tribute in 1222, 1239, 1246, 1247 and 1250;[206] 3,300 marks for expediting the king's business at the Roman Curia in

1225;[207] 300 marks, £1,000 and £200 for Simon de Montfort in 1245, 1250, and 1251;[208] 1,500 marks for the Count of La Marche in 1224;[209] 2,000 marks for the Holy Roman Emperor in 1235;[210] the same amount for his mother-in-law, the Countess of Provence, in 1224;[211] £1,000, 10,000 marks, 6,000 marks and 2,000 marks for Richard, Earl of Cornwall, in 1225, 1237, 1238, and 1245;[212] 500 marks for Ferrand, Count of Flanders, in 1229-30;[213] the same amount for the king's affairs in Gascony in 1221, 1222, and 1224;[214] and 400 marks for use in Wales in 1231.[215] These sums were to be held until proper certification by the king or his officials directed their release.

As the following examples attest, other persons had sizable accounts at New Temple, too. At the time the barons forced him to leave England (1258), William de Valence, the king's half-brother, had a large but unstipulated sum subsequently increased by deposit there during his absence of the revenues from his estates.[216] The Earl of Pembroke had on deposit an undisclosed sum for the use of Simon de Montfort (1245).[217] Hubert de Burgh, a powerful noble and former high official of the realm, had £150 in cash in the Templar treasury in 1232.[218] Falkes de Breauté on one occasion (1226) deposited 40,000 marks there — most of it apparently belonging to the king.[219] Various Poitevins in their hasty flight from the country left behind their deposits in New Temple (1258).[220] That merchants and magnates of the realm had funds there is proved by the fact that some of the money seized by Prince Edward in 1263 belonged to them.[221] Also, on the basis of royal Scottish records from Edinburgh (1282), certain English magnates had deposited money at New Temple apparently to be used to win the support of the Scottish king in their contest with Henry III.[222] Moreover prominent clerics like Walter de Merton and John Bradfield, Bishops of Rochester (prior to 1278), and Walter Langton, Bishop of Lichfield and Coventry (1307), had funds there.[223] So did the Bishop of Exeter who in 1227 collected the 4,000 marks which W. Bruer, his uncle, had bequeathed to him and had deposited in New Temple.[224] This is obviously an incomplete list as it is composed only of those persons whose funds were recorded in the rolls because they came into the hands of the king.

Associated with the deposit and disbursement of funds was the use of New Temple as a place for the payment of debts of all kinds. Sometimes, the money involved seems to have been paid through the Templar bank; but at other times, the Temple seems to have been used merely because of its convenient location. To determine which category any particular case falls within is frequently impossible. Kings and prominent persons paid debts at New Temple. For example, Henry III promised to pay Prince Louis of France 6,000 marks there for his withdrawal from England (1218);[225] Peter, Duke of Brittany, 6,572 marks (1234);[226] Richard of Cornwall, King of Germany, 250 marks (1226);[227] his uncle, Thomas of Savoy, 500 marks (1253);[228] and his wine merchant, £500 (1270).[229] Prince Edward was to pay £200 to an unknown creditor there for two years (1256-57);[230] another £200 annually for five years to his uncle, Archbishop Boniface (1256-62);[231] a total of £1,000 owed to his mother over a period of years starting in 1269;[232] and £10,000 Tournois, starting the same year, to King Louis IX of France for funds lent to him for his crusade.[233] Other payments made at New Temple included those of the Count of Salisbury, who paid money owed to the city of Bordeaux (1226);[234] the Count of Warren, who had agreed to pay an undesignated creditor £20 annually for an unstated period (1227);[235] Richard de Clare, Earl of Gloucester, who paid 1,000 marks as surety for Prince Edward (1253);[236] a certain John of Balun, who paid 140 marks to Guy de Lusignan, Henry III's half-brother (1257);[237] Henry, the nephew of King Henry, who repaid a loan of 200 marks (1259);[238] various persons who paid sums of varying amounts owed to William de Valence, another of Henry III's half-brothers (1259-70);[239] William de Valence himself, who paid 3,500 marks to Richard de Clare in three installments for custody of certain lands and tenements (1270);[240] and John and Hugh le Despenser, prominent lay lords, who paid Eleanor, consort of Prince Edward, £220 in 1271 and William of Camp Bello 1,600 marks in 1282.[241]

Clerics also found New Temple a convenient place for the payment of debts. A certain Arnold de Bosco paid the Bishop of Norwich £120 there in 1259;[242] the Abbot of St. Albans paid a debt of 115 marks there (1252);[243] and Hugh of Gloucester paid the Abbot of La Couture ten marks per year there, starting in 1206.[244] The Prior of the Cluniacs at Bermondesey owed Adam of Stretton 700 marks to be paid off at New Temple in seven annual installments, starting in 1271;[245] and Ralph of Grendon owed the Bishop of Bath and Wells £200 to be paid there (1290).[246] Additional cases involving clerics could be cited.[247]

Merchants frequently used New Temple as a convenient place for the payment of debts owed to them and often specifically designated New Temple in their contracts as the place of payment.[248] Henry III repaid loans to Florentine and Sienese merchants there[249] — as did such members of the royal family as Queen Eleanor and Prince Edward;[250] such clerics as Fulk, Archbishop of Dublin, the Abbot of St. Albans, and Anthony Bek, Bishop of Durham;[251] and numerous private citizens whose names are otherwise unknown.[252] This use of New Temple — and the chief fairs of England, which were also so used — as a place for the repayment of debts owed to foreign merchants must have served as a precedent for the Statutes of Acton Burnell (1283, 1285) by which Edward I and his council decreed that merchants could register their loans before the mayors of London, Bristol, and York and that official action would be taken to promote repayment at the agreed upon time and place.

Because of its convenient location, ordinary debts between private citizens were often paid at New Temple. Numerous examples of this could be cited;[253] but for the purpose of illustration, it is only necessary to indicate that the men and sums involved ranged from the £900 which Simon of Pateshull, a financial official of the king, owed to John Gifford (1268)[254] to the twelve and one-half marks which John, son of Alan, paid to Thomas of Aldeham (1267).[255]

Some of these debts were repaid in a single payment; and some, on an installment basis. Information is available on this payment of private debts at New Temple because both debtors and creditors found it to their mutual advantage to appear before the officials of the Chancery to have their oral agreements recorded.[256] Consequently, the contracts became a part of the public records, with copies frequently being made and sent to New Temple.[257] Then, when the debt was paid, a new entry was inserted by the clerks of the Chancery to that effect or the words "Cancelled because the debt was paid" were inscribed after the original entry.[258]

Lending money was another of the financial activities of the Templars. The loans, probably made out of funds deposited with them[259] as well as out of their own revenues, seem to have been granted usually in rather small sums and for short terms, often ranging from one month to one year. The loan was often granted on the basis of a promise to pay on a given date although collateral or guarantees of a stronger sort — for example, jewels or control of revenue from certain properties — were sometimes demanded. Though complete details of the contracts entered into are lacking,[260] penalties, as will be seen, were exacted for failure to pay on the due date. On the basis of surviving records, the English kings are found to have been by far the chief and most frequent of the Templars' clients.

The earliest financial services the Templars rendered John involved more than a mere loan. On the king's instructions, they arranged for as well as paid the ransom of William Brewer (1204), Petrus de Arcanaca and Gaufridus de Moher (1205), and Gerard d'Athies (1206), subjects of John captured on the continent.[261] These services were followed by a loan of 1,500 marks in 1206 for repayment of a debt owed to Philip Augustus of France.[262] There is no indication of whether or not these loans were repaid. John again borrowed from the Templars — 1,100 marks from the English Templars[263] and 1,000 marks from the Templars of Poitou[264] in 1215 and another 1,000 marks from the Templars of Aquitaine[265] in 1216. These sums were used to bring troops from the continent to England and to pay them for their services in John's struggle with his barons.[266] Always direly in need of money and consequently without funds to repay, John proved a poor risk. Aymeric de St. Maur, then Master in England and one of John's advisers, apparently did not press very hard for repayment; but the Templars on the continent were more determined. Finally, in view of their persistent demands for repayment, John ordered a part of his revenue from his fiefs in Gascony handed over to the Master of the Temple at Poitiers;[267] and his revenues from the city of Bordeaux, to the Templars at Aquitaine.[268] At the time of his death, these loans still had not been completely repaid as is shown by the arrangements to continue payment made by William Marshall and Hubert de Burgh,[269] who were heading the government of England during the minority of John's son and heir, Henry III.

The chief royal client of the Templars was Henry III. In 1221, he borrowed the 500 marks needed for making peace with France, promising to repay at the rate of £120 per year out of the income from the royal manor of Godmanchester.[270] Three years later (1224), another 300 marks were borrowed; and this time, "full seisin" of the manor was assigned to the Templars until the total debt should be discharged.[271] In 1225, Henry is listed as owing the Templars 330 marks.[272] Whether this was a new loan or the loan of the preceding year with an increase in sum due to non-payment is unclear. In 1234, reference is made to two loans obtained from Robert de Sanford, then Master in England — the first, a royal order for repayment of an earlier loan of £200; and the second, a new loan of 300 marks to be repaid within the year.[273] The next year, what amounted to still another loan, this time totalling £1,000 — to be repaid out of income from royal lands at the rate of £200 per year for five years — was arranged for payment by the Templars of money Henry owed to Hugh de Lusignan, Count of La Marche.[274] Five years later, in 1239, in order to raise 1,000 marks for the use of Thomas, Count of Flanders, Henry again went to Robert de Sanford and borrowed the necessary amount.[275] In 1244, 500 marks were paid to Hugh of Stocton, Treasurer of New Temple, for a loan which the Templars of Paris had made the previous year to a certain Roger, Henry's representative abroad.[276] In 1247, the king, on behalf of Guy de Lusignan, obtained a loan from the Templars of Jerusalem in the amount of £1,000;[277] and in the same year, he requested the Templars at Paris to lend Gaucher de Chastilon £400 to be repaid at the rate of £100 per year.[278] The first payment seems to have been delayed, however, a year beyond its due date.[279] Then, not until 1260, over a decade later, is there specific evidence that Henry again borrowed from the Templars. At this time, he obtained £2,800 Tournois from the Templars at Paris to be repaid within the year.[280] This was soon followed (1262) by another loan, this time for £700, from the French Templars.[281] And in 1268, he paid the Templars of Paris 2,000 marks on a loan of £28,189 Tournois which his son, Edward, had obtained in the Holy Land and in France.[282] Though the loans indicated here may not have been the only ones he obtained from them, they are sufficiently large and numerous to show how often and how heavily Henry III relied upon the Templars for financial aid.

Edward I also borrowed on occasion from the Templars. In 1274, he paid the balance of the huge loan (£24,974 Tournois) he had received in the Holy Land; the next year, £200 or £300 Tournois for the sum borrowed from the Templars in Paris for the conduct of certain royal business in France; and four years later 3,355 marks for other money he had borrowed in the east.[283] In 1299, evidently pressed for cash by the Frescobaldi, merchants of Florence, he resorted to the device of transferring his debt of 2,000 marks to them to the Templars whom he promised to repay at an early date.[284] In general, however, Edward I, unlike his father, did not find it necessary to borrow repeatedly from the Templars — not because he did not need money, but more likely, because he preferred to do business with the Italian merchants who had become important as money lenders some time after the middle of the thirteenth century.[285] For Edward II, there is no evidence of loans obtained from the Templars.

Loans were also made to people other than kings though there is little surviving evidence of this. That Hubert de Burgh, at the time of his imprisonment (1233), was in debt to the Templars is known by the fact that King Henry permitted the Master of the Temple to speak to Hubert about the debt — no amount is indicated — but about nothing else.[286] On one occasion (1279), on orders of the king, the Templars lent the Bishop of Bath and Wells £69 17s. 7d. and £49 5s. 2½d. out of royal funds on deposit at New Temple.[287] In several instances, the Templars are shown as creditors of Italian banking houses. Thus, in 1304, merchants of the Mozzi company of Florence owed the English Templars 2,000 marks; and in 1305, merchants of the companies of the Galerani of Siena and the Frescobaldi of Florence owed them 879 marks, a sum which was paid shortly thereafter at New Temple.[288] Other cases involve only small loans: 30 marks owed them by John de Erde of Kent (1306);[289] £10 owed them by Bartholomew of Badlesmore (1306);[290] and 300 marks repaid them by Stephen de Burgherssh, a knight (1307).[291]

The question now arises of whether or not the Templars profited from their lending transactions. Since canon law and the prevailing Christian attitude were opposed to usury,[292] one might well conclude that the Templars certainly were not apt to have practiced openly what their religion forbade. Furthermore, inasmuch as surviving documents invariably provide for the repayment of the same sum as borrowed, one might also assume that loans were made without the expectation of profit. However, that the Templars should have foregone all remuneration is neither reasonable nor likely in view of what we know of commercial activity in the Middle Ages.

It might be truthfully argued that the Templars received good-will, gifts, privileges, and protection in return for their loans; but they received these things without lending money, too. However, the specific exemption from import and export duties on wine and wool and the grant of gifts in land and cash, both of which have been mentioned above, may have been a more direct reward. So, too, protection, especially by the crown, was very valuable as the following incident of 1304 suggests.[293] Certain merchants of the Mozzi company of Florence, in return for a loan of 1,300 marks from the English Templars, issued letters promising the sum would be paid by members of their society in Paris. Before the sum was paid, it was reported to the king that other merchants of the same company, still in London, who owed the Templars 700 marks for wool, seemed to be preparing to leave without paying. Thereupon Edward ordered his sheriffs to seize all members of the company in England and, after ascertaining by oath of other merchants what goods the Mozzi had in the area, to seize and hold these goods until further order. Though the outcome of the case is not known, the implication certainly is that the crown seriously intended to protect and aid the Templars.

A few explanatory remarks are necessary before responding to the specific question "Did the Templars exact usury?" The whole complicated issue of usury was evolutional in definition and interpretation and becomes rather technical, involving considerations of both act and intent.[294] Gathering together statements from the early Latin Church Fathers and from such early councils as that of Nicaea, and supporting prohibitions of Charlemagne found in his Capitularies, Gratian[295] treated the issue briefly, directing attention initially to a prohibition of usury to all clerics, but later applying the prohibition to laymen as well. For Gratian and most canonists of the late Middle Ages, usury consisted primarily of demanding back more than was given — i.e., receiving something in excess of the principal, whether open or hidden. Technically speaking, the canonists and theologians tended to hold that usury pertained only to a loan *(mutuum)* and not to other contracts unless a loan was implicit in them.[296] What their discussion of principles and cases adds up to is this: a person certain of making a profit commits usury; one not certain of making a profit does not. As Hostiensis explained it, it is wrong for a lender of money to make a profit on a loan because ownership and risk have been transferred to the borrower and for the lender to do so would be to pay him for what is not his.[297] Rather, where a loan is made, it should be granted out of a feeling of Christian charity and not out of the motive of gain. This amounts to a refusal to recognize that the creditor is inherently running a risk in lending out his money and may be justified in demanding recompense. Moreover, even the lender who does not demand a sum in addition to the principal from his debtor but only hopes for gain – e.g., an unsolicited gift from his debtor – becomes guilty of usury.[298]

Yet, there were instances in which canon lawyers sanctioned the receipt of something in excess of the principal. Two such instances are pertinent to the present discussion. The first was that of the "free gift" *(gratis dans, donum)* made by the debtor to the creditor on a wholly voluntary and unsolicited basis.[299] So long as the creditor neither expected nor hoped for such a gift, he was held free to accept it. The second was the penalty exacted by the creditor from the debtor for his failure to repay his loan on time *(poena nec in fraudem),* provided no fraudulent intent was involved and provided that the penalty was designed to serve only as an incentive for prompt repayment.[300] The idea involved here is clearly based on the assumption that non-payment has caused the creditor to suffer an unjustifiable loss and is similar to the Roman law concept of *"interesse"* (or damages) which became due to the injured party when the other party to a contract defaulted. Roman law *interesse, id quod interest* involved determination of (1) the difference between the creditor's present situation and what it would have been if the loan had not been made – i.e., actual damages *(damnum emergens)* – and (2) compensation for the gain which was lost to the creditor by the debtor's failure to repay – i.e., lost profit *(lucrum cessans).*[301] *Interesse* as it pertained to actual damages suffered was acceptable to most medieval canonists. Indeed, from the 1220's on, due to the treatment of the subject by the Roman legist Azzo in his glosses on the Code of Justinian, the single word *interesse* came to be used by the canonists to refer not to something paid in addition to the principal of a loan but to the difference to be made up to the injured party (the creditor) by the defaulting party (the debtor) who had failed to meet his obligations.[302] But *interesse* as it pertained to profits lost was not widely accepted by medieval canonists before the fourteenth century.[303] Hence the term *"interesse"* is not to be equated with our term "damages." Similarly, usury refers technically only to unauthorized receipts in excess of the principal of a loan and not to all receipts in excess of the principal.

Many a medievalist specializing in economic history has held that the bankers of the Middle Ages did not lend money without charging interest. They have pointed out that it was easy to conceal their profits within rates of exchange wherein a loan might be made in one currency but made repayable in another at a value in excess of the original grant, that interest could be hidden by levying it at the time the loan was made or by adding it to the total due in such fashion that the debtor repaid a sum larger than the amount he actually received, and that penalities for late payment might be agreed upon with the informal understanding that repayment would not be made on the due date so that the debtor would be open to assessments for damages as determined by the creditor.[304] Only Piquet, however, makes an explicit statement that the Templars found ways to get around the Church's prohibition[305] though he can hardly prove this in a documentary manner.

Illustrative of the theory of damages or compensation for losses in operation is the example preserved in a document incorporated by Matthew Paris into his history.[306] In this particular document, the merchants of Cahors demand as compensation for losses the payment every two months of one mark for every ten marks borrowed if the loan was not repaid on time – 60% interest per year. But because the canonists held that the setting of specific rates determined purely by the time of delay created a presumption of usury, it became common, as notarial records show,[307] to stipulate penalties as being double the sum lent if the terms of the contracts were not met. But for the Templars, there are no surviving contracts with precise and detailed terms showing that they did, and if so by what means, get around the restrictions laid down by the Church. It is reasonable to assume, however, that Templar contracts and methods were not markedly different from those of secular business men. It appears that John's original loan (1215) of 1,000 marks from the Templars of Poitou had grown by 1218 to 1,157 marks.[308] Exactly what was meant when Henry III assigned the English Templars "full seisin" of the manor of Godmanchester until "full satisfaction" had been obtained[309] is uncertain, but a sum in excess of the original loan may well have been involved. On the surface, the Templars appear to be involved in a mortgage, prohibited to the clerics by Pope Alexander III (1163) – i.e., they appear to be granting a loan, or the extension of a loan, on the security of a piece of property placed in their hands to retain until the debt had been paid, with the fruits of the property accruing to them and not being used to reduce the principal of the debt.[310] But that this is necessarily the correct interpretation is open to question. In January of 1260, having borrowed £2,800 Tournois from the Templars at Paris and having promised payment "within the month of Easter next," Henry III agreed that if the debt was not paid by then, he would "make good all losses, interest, and expenses" occasioned by the default, accepting the word of the Templars as to the amount of the loss.[311] The terms of this loan are not markedly different from those Henry agreed to in a contract with certain Florentine merchants by which he promised under penalty of 200 marks, in addition to losses, interest, and expenses to repay by a certain date at New Temple the 780 marks borrowed. Incorporated in this same loan was an earlier unpaid loan of £100 and a payment of 80 marks "of the king's gift for their grace in lending."[312] It is conceivable, though there seems to be no specific evidence, that the Templars were accustomed to receive such "gifts" for their grace in lending. The most explicit evidence that the Templars received something in excess of the principal for their loans is to be found in the acquittance issued by William Beaulieu, Grand Master of the order (1274), to Edward I for repayment of a loan (£24,974 Tournois) made to him in the Holy Land and for receipt of an additional £5,333 6s. 8d. Tournois "tam super principali quam super custibus, dampnis, et interesse"[313]— the extra payment being due to the king's failure to fulfill the terms of the original contract.

The material cited here, although it is not as precise and detailed as one might wish, is nonetheless pertinent and convincing evidence that the Templars were compensated for their lending and that they did receive sums in excess of the principal of their loans. But the evidence does not prove that the Templars were guilty of practicing usury in the sense of the term as defined and discussed by the canonists. It only shows that the Templars received what today would be called interest and damages. Furthermore, had there been any grounds at all for a belief that the Templars engaged in usurious activities, such a charge would surely have been included in the indictment drawn up against them at the time of their arrest and trial.

The international transfer and transportation of funds was another of the useful activities engaged in by the Templars. Carrying money over long distances was at best a precarious operation in the Middle Ages, and especially before the widespread use of gold coins, was a laborious task, as details in the public records show. Until credit instruments came into existence, only persons who were reliable and capable of defending themselves could be used. During the era of the Crusades, there was probably no group safer or more reliable than the Templars. The direct and specific instances in which the English Templars actually transferred and transported funds at a distance are not too numerous though the implication of many passages is that they did do so. Quite possibly the English Templars, rather than carry funds for the Holy Land directly to the east, normally brought them to the Temple at Paris, the headquarters of the order in western Europe, whence they were taken east. Yet, in 1241, the king ordered that money which had been raised in England for the Holy Land should be delivered to a Templar and a Hospitaller "to be taken at first passage" to Richard, Earl of Cornwall, in the Holy Land.[314] Whether this involved the transportation of the cash or the use of letters of credit is uncertain.

Most information from England, however, is limited to the carrying of money for the king between England and France. In 1228, Aymeric, Master in England, was ordered by Henry III to have an unstated sum taken to the Paris Temple for ultimate payment to citizens of St. Emilio for certain claims they had against the crown.[315] The £200 which Henry agreed to pay annually for five years (starting in 1235) to the Count of La Marche at the Paris Temple for the Isle of Oleron was to be carried there "at the peril of the king."[316] In 1238, three or four Templar knights were ordered by the king to accompany two royal clerks, no doubt to guarantee the safe conduct of the money, delivering 6,000 marks to Paris for the use of Richard of Cornwall.[317] In 1254, a Templar, Alan of Kent, was ordered to take £1,500 in February and £1,460 in March "safely except for the peril of sea, fire, and thieves" to Alphonse, Count of Toulouse, at Paris in payment of damages committed by Henry's troops during his recent campaign in Gascony and an additional 4,671 marks in August and 4,000 marks in October to Gascony for the king's use there.[318] In the same year, Henry III, while still in southern France, sought to borrow money for a pilgrimage to Pontigny and directed that it be sent to him by a Templar, a Hospitaller, or other sure messenger.[319] And in the next year (1255), three Templars took money owed by the king to three citizens of Toulouse and returned with the jewels the king had deposited as collateral.[320] There are other examples where the English Templars may have transported specie from one place to another,[321] but the matter is not certain. Likewise, though it is most probable that they did so, there is no specific evidence in English sources of the Templars transporting papal funds to Rome, except via the Temple at Paris.[322] All that can be said is that in the years before the appearance of credit instruments and in the early stages of their development, it is most likely that the Templars carried funds, their own and those belonging to others, with a considerable degree of regularity and with great reliability. To obviate the need for the actual physical transfer of specie, credit devices were needed.

The widespread use of credit in the late Middle Ages, beginning in the Italian city-states as early as the eleventh century and spreading rapidly in the period of the Crusades and thereafter, is now a familiar subject,[323] though the precise distinctions between the different forms of credit instruments used and the technical points in their actual operation are not wholly known or agreed upon.[324] Similarly, there is no questioning that the Templars employed credit instruments, but there is considerable doubt regarding the type and working of the ones they used. This uncertainty is due to the fact that we do not have the Templars' contracts and correspondence which would give precise details but must rely primarily upon brief instructions and requests, mostly royal, directed to the Templars.

For the Templars in England, only two examples involving specific and unquestionable use of credit instruments have been found. The first, dated 1255, is a reference to a letter of credit for twenty-five marks issued to three English Templars going abroad on a mission for the crown.[325] What is involved here is simply an authorization for them to use this letter to meet their expenses and a guarantee to any person honoring the letter that the sum stated will be paid. The second, dated 1304, is a reference to a letter obligatory (or possibly an *instrumentum ex causa cambii*) worth seven hundred marks issued in favor of the English Templars by the Mozzi of Florence upon purchase of wool worth that amount.[326] To receive actual payment of the sum, the Templars had to present the letter at the offices of the company in Paris. Since there are many examples in the public records of the use of letters of credit by the crown, it would seem likely that the Templars used them quite regularly despite the small number of specific references found.

There are many transactions — e.g., long distance payments or transfers between Templar houses, especially between the London and Paris Temples — which seem to assume the use of credit even though the references contain no statement to this effect and no indication of the procedure to be employed. The typical transaction is one in which money would be deposited at New Temple and the appropriate Templar house on the continent would be expected to discharge that sum to the designated party abroad. Before discussing the instruments and procedures of credit which might have been used, a number of examples of the transactions involved must be given.

The settlement (1186) between Henry II and his son's widow, Margaret, to be discussed below, involved sums handled by the Templars of England and France. In 1213, John allotted 2,000 marks at New Temple for the use of the Earl of Salisbury, then in Flanders, to be obtained from the Paris Temple.[327] In 1218, it was provided that the 2,150 marks which Henry III still owed Louis of France for his departure from England should be paid by the Templars of Paris after deposit of the sum at New Temple.[328] The same arrangement was made three years later for 500 marks which Henry owed Philip Augustus.[329] Similarly, in the same year, another 500 marks were deposited at New Temple for Henry's affairs in Germany.[330] In 1221 and 1224, two payments of 500 marks each were made, apparently at London, to be credited to the Templars of La Rochelle who were to pay out the thousand marks for the execution of the king's affairs there.[331] In 1226, money owed by the Count of Salisbury to the city of Bordeaux was deposited at New Temple for payment by the Templars at Bordeaux.[332] An especially good example is the payment by Henry to his step-father, Hugh de Lusignan, Count of La Marche. In 1224, 1,500 marks were brought to New Temple for payment to the Count by the Master of the Temple *"citra montes"*;[333] and in 1235, it was arranged that Henry should deposit £200 yearly for five years in London and the Temple at Paris should pay the count that sum for the same period.[334] In the same year (1235), there are two references – one of 2,000 marks and the other of 10,000 marks – to payments in England for funds to be made available to the emperor by the Templars on the continent.[335] The 3,000 marks to be paid by the Temple at Bordeaux (1242) for the truce expenses[336] was most likely a credit transaction. In 1266, Henry deposited at New Temple 250 marks for the use of Richard of Cornwall, King of the Germans, who was to obtain the money from the Templars on the continent.[337] Perhaps the best example of all is the arrangement whereby the £70,000 Tournois owed Louis IX of France by Prince Edward of England were to be repaid in installments of 5,000 marks twice a year by deposits at New Temple and disbursements by the Templars of Paris.[338] There are other examples, but these are enough to suggest the sort of credit transactions involved and to show the need to work out some system for the balance of deposits and disbursements between the various Templar houses.

Credit and exchange operations in the late Middle Ages took a variety of forms:[339] letters of credit and contracts of exchange as well as simple letters designed to meet specific current situations. A common type of letter of credit was a formal document issued by a king (or some other prominent person whose financial position was known and respected) authorizing the bearer(s) to incur indebtedness of a given amount which would be paid off later by the king upon presentation of the letter by the person (or his representative) who had honored it before the proper official at the royal court. That the Templars were acquainted with this device, which so conveniently obviated the need for carrying large amounts of specie, has already been shown. However, surviving materials do not permit one to say whether or not the Templars issued such letters in their own name.

A variety of contracts of exchange[340] were employed in this period. The simplest was the *cambium minutum* which involved on-the-spot exchange of coins and was usually limited to petty exchange between money-changer and client. In their capacity as bankers, the Templars engaged in this activity, probably not so much in England as on the continent. More complicated was the *instrumentum ex causa cambii,* the prototype of the bill of exchange, which involved the extension of credit in the form of a loan, the transfer of funds, and the exchange of currency. Commonly used in the thirteenth and early fourteenth centuries to cover a multiplicity of transactions, and normally involving only two parties (the creditor and the debtor), the *instrumentum* recorded the loan of money in one currency (e.g., English pounds) and called for its repayment in another currency (e.g., pounds Tournois) at a definite time and in another place. Clauses of indemnity for expenses and damages in the case of delayed repayment and the posting of collateral were familiar provisions in these contracts. Hundreds of contracts of this kind made by Italian merchants survive because the two parties concerned agreed to terms in the presence of a notary who wrote them down and entered them in the records of such cities as Genoa. Many of the loans made by the Templars, such as some of those extended to Henry III and Edward I discussed above, may well have fallen into this category since all the necessary elements of the *instrumentum* were present. This type of contract may also have been employed in the transfer of funds from England to the continent or from the continent to England without the actual shipment of specie since the funds involved could easily have been expressed in terms of credit and exchange. An additional incentive for the use of the *instrumentum* was the fact that it was looked upon by canon lawyers as an operation of exchange and not as a loan *("cambium non est mutuum")* and as such did not come under the restrictions pertaining to usury.

The *cambium per litteras,* or true bill of exchange, also involved a loan, a transfer, and an exchange of currency, but it was more complicated than the *instrumentum,* involving four parties (two at the place of issue and two at the place of payment), two payments, and two bills of exchange — one of change and one of rechange. This type of contract made possible for the first time, according to Usher,[341] systematically doing business between parties not present in the same place, and like the *instrumentum* had the advantage of not falling in a category of transaction subject to prosecution for usury. The English Templars had nothing to do with this type of contract since its details were not worked out by the Italian merchants who created it until the last half of the thirteenth century, and since they did not introduce its use into England before the middle of the fifteenth century, long after the Templar order ceased to exist. Furthermore, the bill of exchange was not usually handled by banks of deposit and transfer but rather by merchants who found it useful in their purchase and exchange of goods.

Most likely what the Templars ordinarily used in lending and transfer operations were separate letters for each individual transaction, working out and improving upon details and techniques with time and experience.[342] So, for example, the English Templars may have sent a letter to the Paris Temple requesting that house to pay out a certain sum, at a given time or at stated intervals, to a specified party, for a particular purpose. Then, quite likely, the Paris Temple sent back a letter of confirmation and execution. Over an extended period, the requests, deposits, and disbursements between houses may have been reasonably well balanced so that the facilities and commitments would not get too far out of line. However, if they should, the transfer of specie or of credit could easily and speedily be effected.

Like modern bankers, the Templars also accepted responsibilities of trusteeship. By this is meant that they became involved with the administration of what might be called future interests — e.g., dowries, revenues, pensions, and wills. As has been indicated above, the castles of Gisors and Néaufles were held in trust by the Templars (1158-61) until the marriage of Henry and Margaret, the son and daughter of Henry II and Louis VII respectively.[343] In 1259, the Templars stood guarantee for Louis IX of France in his promise to pay Henry III, in accordance with the treaty just made between the two monarchs, the cost of maintaining five hundred knights for two years.[344] The dowry of Berengaria, the wife of the late King Richard, as agreed upon between her and John — £1,000 per year — was to be paid at New Temple and entrusted to the Templars.[345] In 1214, John sent £2,500 to the Templars of La Rochelle, to be paid in five annual installments to Alice, Countess of Angoulême, as her dowry.[346] Similarly, the dowries of Isabella, sister of Alexander III of Scotland (1228),[347] of Eleanor, King Henry's sister and wife of the Emperor, Frederick II (1239),[348] and of Alice, daughter of William de Valence and fiancée of Gilbert, son of Richard de Clare (1255),[349] were handled through the Templars. The income from properties of absentee owners — e.g., those of William de Valence[350] and Guy de

Lusignan[351]— were frequently entrusted to the Templars for deposit in New Temple. Pensions were also paid through the Templars. In 1186, after the death of her husband, it was agreed that Margaret of France should receive an annual pension of £2,750 — the sum being paid through the French Templars — at the expense of the English crown in return for withdrawal of her claim on certain lands.[352] John, in order to strengthen his own position on the continent, sent £30,000 to the Templars of La Rochelle for the payment of £6,000 annually to Ralph, Count of Eu, for his neutrality.[353] Other pensions paid for the king by the Templars included those of John's uncles, Thomas and Amadeus of Savoy; Peter Saracen, Vicomte de Thouars; Hugh, Bishop of Ostia; a certain Hubert Huese; and Ferrand, Count of Flanders.[354] A pension of £400 per year, in the absence of her husband, William, was authorized to be paid by the Templars to Joan de Valence (1258).[355] And a pension of £20 yearly for life was to be paid to Bayamund de Vicia by arrangement made by William, Abbot of Malmesbury, with the Templars.[356] After the deaths of the Earl of Salisbury (1227), of W. Bruer (1227), and of the Bishop of Ely (1257), the execution of their wills, insofar as certain debts and other financial matters were concerned, was entrusted to the Templars.[357] Though additional examples could be cited, those given here are sufficient to indicate the type and scope of trusts engaged in by the Templars.

Since their record books have not survived, practically nothing is known of the system of accounting used by the English Templars. However, it must have been essentially the same as that used in France where some information is available because of the survival of a part of the Journal of the Paris Temple covering the period from March 9, 1294 to July 4, 1296.[358] An examination of the cash book, the most comprehensive and informative of the surviving documents, shows that the Templars divided their receipts into two major classes: those pertaining to their own business and goods and those pertaining to the transactions of their clients. In the first category, are the returns or surpluses turned in from time to time by the preceptors or commanders of the various houses for crediting to the Treasurer or Master of the Paris Temple representing the order in France and the disposition to be made of those amounts. In the second, are the receipts and expenditures of individual clients, most important of whom was the king. From the cash book, entries were made into the appropriate accounts or books, perhaps as many as twelve different ones. So, for example, there are the *liber regis* in which records of the king are entered, the *magnus liber* in which entries pertaining to other clients and to the Templars themselves are kept, the *liber ad debemus* in which deposits for payment on

a given future date are listed, and the *liber ad debetur* in which information concerning various clients of the Templars and the debtors of
those clients is recorded. Beween the various accounts, however, there
is so much overlapping of subject matter that it is often difficult to
understand why a certain item of information is found in one book
instead of another. The same is true for the keeping of records on the
income and expenditures of their own order, for which the Templars
at Paris kept at least five separate accounts: the *liber in magnis fratrum,*
the *liber pilosus,* the *parvus liber novus,* the *parvus liber vetus,* and the
liber in parvis ad vad-[imonia]. Though the Templars kept a great many
separate accounts, they could easily extract from them a credit and
debit statement, and did in fact do so three times a year for their major
clients. At Candlemas (February 2d), Ascension (in April or May),
and All Saints (November 1st), the king received such a statement in
two parts: a General Account or summary of totals of receipts and
expenditures and a series of Appendices in which was given a detailed
breakdown of receipts showing types, sources, and amounts credited to
his account and of expenditures showing individual sums listed by major
categories with a final statement of the credit or debit balance clearly
indicated.

The great weakness of the Templars' system of accounting was their
failure to keep a general account which would have provided themselves with an analysis of their financial position as a whole at any given
time.[359] Though the material for a balance sheet was available, such a
record was never compiled. Consequently ignorance of their precise
overall financial condition must have caused many a business decision to
be made on the basis of incomplete and inadequate data, if not on the
basis of chance.

Despite the lack of as much explicit information as might be desired,
the foregoing discussion of the Templars as a financial group has shown
that their organization was well worked out, their activities were varied,
their methods were basically sound and successful, and the scope of
their operations was broad. Although most of these things were not
wholly apparent till the thirteenth century, they presuppose an evolu-
tionary development extending well back into the preceding century.[360]
This financial activity is especially interesting inasmuch as the Templars
were not professional traders or bankers but rather seem to have been
drawn into banking because of their wealth and international connec-
tions. On a comparative basis, the Templars are to be seen as financial
leaders, especially in banking and credit activities, and with few peers
or significant rivals during much of the period. It is doubtful if most
writers, excluding Delisle and Piquet, have given the Templars as much

credit as they deserve for the breadth and depth of their financial activities and for the influence they had on the development of medieval finance and credit operations. This is true despite the fact that England was an economic backwater and that the Italian merchants were performing in various areas on the continent the services the Templars were performing in England.

Financial and Administrative Use of the Templars and of New Temple

So far, a considerable amount of material has been introduced to show the activities of the Templars as bankers. Now it remains, in order to complete the general picture, to show that the Templars were used as financial officials and agents by the kings of England and by various popes and that New Temple was used as a center for the administration of some of the financial activities of the kings.

As royal officials, the Templars served as collectors, receivers, and keepers of the king's revenue, and as auditors for the crown. Tenths, fifteenths, and other such levies, both lay and ecclesiastical, were frequently collected by a local committee composed of one Templar, one Hospitaller, and one or two other persons. The use of Templars as royal collectors first appeared in 1184;[361] and the policy of using a Templar and a Hospitaller jointly was laid down at the time of the first Saladin tithe (1188).[362] Interestingly enough, the bad precedent which was then set by Gilbert of Ogerstan,[363] a Templar who was found guilty of embezzlement of some of the funds — for which he was severely punshed by the Master of the order — seems not to have limited the practice as the collections of subsequent years show.[364] If the example from Bristol is a guide, the same local committees which collected the funds were responsible for seeing to it that they were safely conducted to New Temple for deposit.[365] Another duty assigned the Templars by the king was the auditing of accounts. So, for example, the Master of the Temple in Ireland, along with the Archbishop of Dublin and two royal officials, audited the accounts of the Justiciar of Ireland in 1242, 1250, and 1281;[366] in 1253 and 1279, along with the Prior of the Hospitallers in Ireland, and two royal officials, he audited the accounts of the Treasurer of the Exchequer of Dublin;[367] and in 1252, he audited the account of Simon de Montfort for the administration of Cusac castle.[368] Except for one occasion (1285), when the account of the Templars for the twentieth then deposited at New Temple was audited by order of Edward I by a merchant of Lucca,[369] there is no indication that the Templar accounts were themselves checked. Royal confidence in the financial knowledge and experience of the Templars is further suggested by

Edward I's appointment of Richard de Herdewyk and Richard de Fetham, preceptor and treasurer of New Temple, to a committee of three — Richard de Boclaunde, sacristan of St. Paul's Cathedral, London, being the other member — to determine adjustments necessary for the conversion from the old money to the new (1294).[370]

Since the Templars were so involved in the collection and receipt of royal revenue, it is not surprising to find them serving — at least from 1238 to 1242, and most likely for a longer time than that — as keepers of the king's revenues, along with such other persons as certain Hospitallers and the royal constables at the Tower of London.[371] Indeed, at one time, as indicated above, Geoffrey the Templar served as keeper of the wardrobe — the only Templar ever to hold that position.[372] Nor is it surprising to find certain of the treasurers of New Temple serving as royal treasurers.

Use of Templars as messengers and officials through whom royal funds were paid or transported has already been dealt with — Roger,[373] Thomas,[374] and Geoffrey[375] being the best known examples. Likewise, the use of Templars as agents for the collection and receipt of papal revenues has already been covered.

Important, but not wholly clear, was the relationship of the New Temple Treasury to the Exchequer and the Wardrobe which by the end of the reign of Henry II were the two major financial offices of the English government. The former had come to enjoy a certain degree of independence from the king and had its own treasury at Westminster, subsequently moved to London; and the latter, wholly under the control of the king, served as his private treasury, normally accompanying him wherever he went. By the time of Henry III, the Wardrobe was gaining in power and importance though income still seems to have been deposited without much distinction in either the Wardrobe or the Exchequer.[376] In view of this trend, Henry III found it desirable to establish treasuries, in the sense of storehouses or places of deposit, for the Wardrobe at the Tower of London and at New Temple so that regular and permanent places for the deposit and safekeeping of royal income would be provided.[377] The practical wisdom of this move is suggested by the fact that New Temple served as a royal treasury for approximately a century. Whether or not New Temple ever became a treasury in the sense of a center for the determination and administration of royal financial policy is unclear. If certain references are to be taken literally, it would seem that it did for a brief period. At least, the Wardrobe, whose officials helped determine and administer royal financial policies, seems to have been temporarily established at New Temple (1225). For, in that year, royal orders directed the deposit of funds *"in garderoba domini regis apud Novum Templum Londonie.*"[378] Usually, however, royal orders merely called for the deposit of income at New Temple and for the disbursement of funds *"de thesauro nostro [qui est] in domo Novi Templi Londonie.*[379] The reasons for the choice of New Temple as a royal treasury would seem to have been these: its permanence and convenient location, the physical strength of the Templars and their buildings, the known financial competence of the Templars, the piety of King Henry III and his strong sympathy for the Templars, and especially the need for such a financial center in the years before royal administrative institutions had evolved sufficiently to assume full control of all royal functions and responsibilities.

The question arises of who was in charge of royal funds deposited at New Temple. That normally the treasurer of New Temple was is shown by the great number of royal orders addressed to him directing him to accept deposits of various sorts, to pay out certain sums of money to a named official or private person, or to permit a particular official or individual to have what is necessary to accomplish the specific tasks designated in official letters.[380] A number of times, however, other persons seem to have been in charge — for example, the Bishops of Bath and Salisbury in 1225;[381] Peter Chaceporc, Keeper of the Wardrobe, in 1247;[382] the treasurer of the Hospitallers in 1270-71;[383] and Joseph de Chauncey, the king's treasurer, in 1276.[384] These instances, however, seem to be the exceptions rather than the rule. The important thing to note is that the treasury at New Temple remained directly under the control of the king and was not under the control of the officials of the Wardrobe or of the Exchequer in the sense that deposits and disbursements were made on the basis of royal orders rather than on the basis of orders of Wardrobe or Exchequer officials. This qualification has to be added, however: when the Exchequer deposited certain of its funds at New Temple, as it occasionally did, those funds remained under the control of the Exchequer as is indicated by certain orders sent from the officials of the Exchequer to New Temple directing payment of the indicated sums "out of our treasury which is in the New Temple in your custody."[385]

The closeness of the Templars to the crown and the reliance of the kings upon the services of the Templars are especially manifest in the use of two of the treasurers of New Temple as royal treasurers and keepers of royal funds at the Tower of London. Hugh of Stockton, treasurer of New Temple from approximately 1229 to 1242, and Robert of Sicklinghall, treasurer of New Temple from approximately 1245 to 1260, were repeatedly used during their terms as royal treasurers by Henry III.[386] Under Edward I, however, the Templars, though they still were of service to the crown and though they continued to accept on deposit the revenues of the kingdom, declined in importance, probably because Edward was building his own administrative staff and was turning to Italian bankers who may have been more willing to lend large amounts of money than the Knights.

Conclusion

The survey of political, administrative, and economic activities of the Templars given in this chapter reveals the interrelationship of these activities and the variety of Templar undertakings. Most of their activities, except for those that were wholly within the sphere of their own affairs, were closely associated with those of the crown. In all three fields, they served the kings of England, with very few exceptions, with distinction. Honesty and efficiency must have characterized their actions or else their services would not have been so sought after or so relied upon.

In political affairs, the Templars were mainly used as representatives of the king in missions abroad and as advisers to the king. In these capacities, however, they were merely a few of the king's many envoys and councillors. Accordingly, though they were powerful and influential, they were no more so than many other groups, clerical or lay.[387] In administrative affairs, the Templars played a more prominent role. In their capacity as financial agents of the crown and in the use which the king made of their treasury and offices at New Temple, they became for a time a direct part of the king's administration, thus contributing significantly to the development of the royal administration. In economic affairs, the Templars played their most important role. Wealthy from their own lands and goods which they managed efficiently, constantly active in trade and commerce which they profited from, and deeply concerned with matters of finance in which they engaged effectively and creatively, the Templars became expert accountants, outstanding administrators, and active promoters of credit and credit instruments. In a very real sense, during the late twelfth and all of the thirteenth centuries, they were the greatest bankers in England, easily overshadowing the Jews but being eventually themselves overshadowed by the Italian merchants. It is not surprising, then, to find that for almost a century much of the financial business of the English crown passed through the hands of the Templar order whose men and facilities were freely used by all the kings from Henry II through Edward II. But the height of their influence was reached under Henry III whose favors to them and whose use and reliance upon them were great.

Though details cannot be gone into here, it is safe to say that the Templars were active in the political, administrative, and economic affairs of other countries, too. In no state was this more apparent than

in France where the kings seem to have relied upon the Templars to an
even greater degree than did the English kings.[388] In the field of finances,
this reliance was most noticeable and most significant. Throughout the
thirteenth century, under Philip II, Louis IX, Philip III, and Philip IV,
the treasury of the Templars at Paris was intimately associated with the
crown as existing documents show. M. Delisle even contends that for
all practical purposes the Templar treasury was also the royal treasury
and that the Templar treasurers were royal treasurers as well.[389] More
cautious, M. Piquet says only that the royal treasury was at the Temple.[390]
This situation continued till Philip the Fair, at the end of the thirteenth
century, established a sort of private treasury at the Louvre which he
used in conjunction with the Temple treasury.[391] And it was under the
same king that the French Templars, perhaps too powerful and too
influential, fell from favor to disgrace. But it might be asked for France
as for England whether a private organization of a religious and military nature like the Temple could continue to manage effectively the
complicated financial affairs of the crown and whether the Templars
could, had they chosen, compete with the activities and ambitions of
the Italian banking houses.[392]

It is necessary now to turn to a consideration of the forces and events
which led to the arrest, trial, and dissolution of the Templars, first in
France, and then in England and the other countries of western Europe.

chapter four

Trial and Dissolution

The Fall of the Templars in France

THE CONDEMNATION of the Knights Templars, which the distinguished historian Henry C. Lea has called "the great crime of
the Middle Ages,"[1] constitutes one of the most interesting and dramatic
chapters in the history of medieval Europe and serves as an especially
good example of "man's inhumanity to man." The trial and dissolution
of the order, reflecting the age-old rivalry between church and state,
involved considerations of economic and political advantage to a greater
degree than elements of religion and morality. In the recurring struggle
between church and state in France, where currently the ambitious and
ruthless king, Philip IV (the Fair), was vying for control with the
weak and vacillating pope, Clement V, the Templars, caught between
the two parties, were destined to be sacrificed. Indeed, for some time
the Knights Templars had been a source of uneasiness to the rulers
of both the church and the state. This uneasiness increased with the loss
of the Holy Land and with the settlement of the Templars, with their
great wealth and power, on a more permanent basis in the states of
Europe. In no country was this tension more obvious than in France;
but the attack on the Templars, though it started in France, was not to
be limited to that country. It was to extend to all areas where Templars
were found.

In citing reasons for the fate which befell the Templars, one must
distinguish between alleged and real reasons. The practice of heresy,
idolatry, immorality, and all sorts of indignities and irregularities was
given as their motive by many who wanted to see the Templars
destroyed.[2] A more fundamental reason for the attack, however, was
the hostility and rivalry which the Templars had aroused because of
their extensive privileges and immunities, their apparent power and
influence, their arrogance, and their occasional perfidy. The Knights
Hospitallers, the Teutonic Knights, the various monastic orders, and
the secular clergy were all envious and perhaps even fearful of the Templars. The bitter rivalry between the military orders had repeatedly been

brought out into the open, and the attitude of many of the secular clergy was well expressed by those bishops who had regularly protested the exemption of the Templars from their jurisdiction and had been understandably concerned over the growth of Templar wealth and power. Secular rulers, too, had good reason to be disturbed at the growth in their realms of Templar wealth and power over which they had no control. Moreover, now that the Templars were no longer actually fighting the infidel, their continued existence seemed less compelling. But the crucial and the immediate reason for the attack on the Templars was financial — Philip the Fair's pressing need for money.[3] Philip had already dealt with this problem in a variety of ways, but without lasting success. He had, for example, taxed the clergy, confiscated goods of his vassals, robbed the Lombards, seized the wealth of the Jews, imposed new levies on trade and property, and devalued the currency over fifty per cent in a decade. The Templars, who had both land and money, seemed a desirable victim to Philip.

The details of Philip's plans and the execution of them, significant and enlightening as they are, cannot be carefully gone into here.[4] Suffice it to say that Philip's campaign, though filled with risk and moments of seeming failure, succeeded in the long run. However, the steps in this campaign against the Templars in France must be mentioned briefly as a contrast to what happened in England. Seizing upon rumors unfavorable to the Templars which had been circulated almost periodically over the last four or five decades, Philip's lawyers, led by William de Nogaret, drew up a long list of charges against the order, a copy of which was forwarded to Pope Clement V who, however, took no immediate action and referred to the charges as beyond belief.[5] Pressed with the threat of initiating proceedings to condemn Boniface VIII, his predecessor, and with the demand to make Philip's brother, Charles of Valois, Holy Roman Emperor, Clement soon consented to an investigation of the Templars.[6] Philip, having gained his point, and being determined both to prevent the pope from conducting the inquiry and to prevent the Templars from organizing a defense, had secret instructions for the arrest of the Templars prepared and delivered (September, 1307) to his seneschals and to certain other royal officials.[7] These letters, not to be unsealed, on pain of death, until October 12th, directed the royal officials, effective October 13th, to imprison the Templars, to seize their goods, to make an inventory of their possessions, and to hold everything at the discretion of the king. All this proceeded as planned — a remarkable demonstration of the effective organization and force Philip had created. At this point, a propaganda campaign against the Templars was undertaken. The clergy and people of France were informed of the charges against the order and were told, untruthfully, that Clement had consented to the king's action and that Philip had acted only after being requested by William of Paris, chief inquisitor in France — who was also private confessor to the king — to help stamp out the heretics and idolators.[8] The French clergy, both secular and regular, largely dominated by the crown, fell into line and openly denounced the alleged evils of the Templars. And the French nobility, perhaps partly in hope of political and economic concessions, but more probably in fear of Philip, in view of the king's earlier successes, did not protest. The Templars, being now officially informed of the charges against them, were examined — at times by Philip's political agents, at times by representatives of the Inquisition, and at times by both[9] — and were promised leniency if they confessed but death if they did not. To facilitate the process, torture was used openly and effectively.[10] Under these conditions, a number of "free and spontaneous" confessions were obtained although many of them were later repudiated as having been obtained under duress. Armed with these depositions of heresy, immorality, and indecency, Philip intended to force Clement to make further concessions. But Clement, when he learned what Philip had done, denounced the action in the strongest possible terms, declaring the seizure of the Templars an unjustifiable interference in the rights of the papacy and expressing the opinion that there was no truth to the charges. Furthermore, as an indication of papal anger and determination, William, Inquisitor of Paris, was deposed.[11] For the moment, then, it looked as though Clement meant to stand his ground. Just what would have been his next step is uncertain, but it is likely he meant to have the Templars examined under more favorable conditions. Philip, however, filled with rage at Clement's hostile action and having no intention of conceding to the pope, determined to bring to bear enough pressure to compel Clement to renounce his recent statements and to permit Philip to proceed with his campaign against the Templars. Vigorously pressing anew his plans for the condemnation of Boniface, pointedly insisting that the secular arm had come to the aid of the ecclesiastical at the latter's request, dramatically stressing the evidence of heresy and wrongdoing, and shrewdly acquiring the specific support and approval of the archbishops of France, Philip forced the pope to give in. In a new bull — *Pastoralis praeeminentiae*[12] — issued November 22, 1307, Clement submitted, not only saying that since his bull of a month earlier new and convincing evidence of the guilt of the Templars had been laid before him but also going on to praise Philip for his zeal as a faithful son of the church and devoted defender of the holy faith.

Philip had obviously won — the Templars were to be examined.

However, since the matter had not yet been agreed upon, Philip, in his determination to gain papal acquiescence to a trial procedure not inimical to his own interests, resorted to the tactic of summoning a carefully selected Estates-General — which met in May, 1308 — whose duty it was to support him and to arouse the people. By mid-July, Philip had obtained from Clement a satisfactory compromise solution: the trials of the Templars were to be conducted in each diocese by the bishop and six lesser clerics, with the services of inquisitors available at the discretion of the local bishop. It was also agreed that the goods of the Templars were to be entrusted to curators, half of whom were to be named by the bishops and half by the king. These concessions were balanced by Clement's announcement that the goods of the order were to be reserved solely for the use of the Holy Land and that the results of the inquiry were to be submitted to a church council which would meet at Vienne and would decide the fate of the Templars.[13]

Accordingly, episcopal commissions of inquiry were set up in each of the dioceses of France, and papal commissions of investigation were established at such key centers as Paris where an especially important investigation was held. There William Imbert, Inquisitor of France, and his colleagues, together with representatives of the king who were always present, examined Jacques de Molay and other Templars (November, 1309 to March, 1310).[14] When Molay, claiming he could be tried before the pope alone, refused to assume the defense of the order, the task fell to two Templar priests, who did most of the work, and two knights.[15] All this was preliminary to the trial proper which began in April, 1310. The first group of witnesses at the formal trial was composed, except for a few Templars or former Templars, of secular clerics and laymen who testified to the guilt of the order.[16] The second group to testify consisted of the imprisoned Templars who, one after another, denied the charges alleged against them and their order and publicly repudiated their earlier confessions of guilt as the product of torture.[17] Philip became understandably concerned as his case against the Templars seemed to be collapsing. From a reluctant pope, he hastily gained approval of the appointment of a certain Philip de Martigny, Bishop of Cambrai and brother of one of the king's most trusted ministers, to the vacant archpishopric of Sens which had jurisdication over the diocese of Paris. The new archbishop, within a month of his appointment, summoned a provincial council to met at Paris (May, 1310) to deal with the Templar matter. Promising leniency for those who confessed and life imprisonment or death for those who made no confession or retracted confessions already made, the council, working rapidly and diligently, interrogated the Templars and handed fifty-four of them over to the secular arm as relapsed heretics.[18] Meanwhile, the papal commission, though it continued to sit at Paris and to hear the Templars, was limited in its activities by the action of the provincial council; and individual Templars, mindful of what had happened to their brothers after denying the charges against the order and renouncing their individual confessions before the provincial council, were hesitant to testify before it. Finally, in June of 1311, the papal commission at Paris adjourned and transmitted its records without comment for the use and guidance of the Council of Vienne.

The Council of Vienne,[19] which finally assembled in October of 1311, was presided over by Pope Clement, who, as seen above, had, as early as November of 1307, committed himself to the guilt of the Templars and who had openly supported the use of torture against them. When the council members, despite papal orders, seemed hesitant to condemn the Templars without a hearing, a select committee — which also proved reluctant — was appointed to consider the matter. Though Clement had held earlier that the Templars should be permitted to defend themselves, he nonetheless had no Templars brought before the council. Indeed, when, in November, six renegade Templars, shortly increased by two, did show up requesting permission to defend their order and claiming to represent between fifteen hundred and two thousand of their brothers who had taken refuge in the mountains of the Lyonnais, they were imprisoned without being heard. The months dragged on without progress or decision, with Philip the Fair anxiously awaiting the outcome and appearing with a small army first at Lyons and then at Vienne. Finally, Clement issued a bull — *Vox in excelso,*[20] dated March 22, 1312 — to the effect that, though the evidence did not justify the definitive condemnation of the Templars, yet, the order had been so scandalized that no honorable man could hereafter enter it and that its possessions could not be maintained unimpaired. In view of this, he said, it was expedient for the Holy See to abolish the order provisionally. The council approved this bull in April of 1312; and in short order (May 2, 1312), also ratified another bull — *Ad providam*[21]— which abolished the Templar order irrevocably and declared excommunicated any person presuming to enter the order or to wear its habit. Hence, the Order of the Knights of the Temple was abolished without being convicted, even without being heard.

It still remained to dispose of the persons and the property of the Templars. According to Clement's recent bull — *Ad providam* — the property was assumed by the Holy See and was declared transferred to the Knights Hospitallers, with exceptions in the Iberian peninsula. All those who failed to hand over the property within a month after summons were to be pronounced excommunicated. The disposition of the persons of the Templars, except for the chief officers who were reserved for papal decision, was to be determined by provincial councils which were to summon all Templars — knights, sergeants, and chaplains — to appear within one year before their bishops for examination and sentence under pain of excommunication for non-appearance. The unrepentant and relapsed were to be dealt with locally, with the severest penalties being authorized; and the penitent were to be placed in former houses of the order or in monasteries where they were to be decently maintained out of the proceeds of the order. This policy was general and was to be applied throughout Europe. How well this directive was carried out in France, and elsewhere, is not wholly certain; but enough is known to say that some of the Templars died in their dungeons, some were burned as relapsed heretics, some wandered about Europe as homeless vagabonds, and some worked as manual laborers.[22] Meanwhile, the fate of the leaders of the order was decided by a commission of cardinals appointed by Clement. On March 9, 1314, in Paris, Jacques de Molay, the Grand Master, and three other high officers, heard their fate: perpetual imprisonment. But de Molay and Geoffrey de Charney, Master of Normandy, arising before the assembled throng, proclaimed the innocence of the order and denounced the charges and confessions as fictitious and false. Thereupon, these two men were handed over to the provost of Paris, a royal official, and on order of an infuriated king and council, were, on the same day, burned as heretics without having been held for the formal decision of the church.[23]

What happened to Templar property in France cannot be dealt with in detail here. Apparently the treasure of the order fell into Philip's hands and was never accounted for;[24] and the landed estates, despite a pretense of being surrendered to the pope, were retained by Philip till his death. (Interestingly — and prophetically for some — Philip and Clement both died within a year of the execution of de Molay.) The revenues from the estates and the debts owed the Templars were also collected by Philip. By the final settlement in France (1317),[25] the French king was to retain all claim to the income of landed estates which the crown had held for ten years and was to retain most of the movable goods which had belonged to the Templars; but the remaining Templar lands and goods were to go to the Hospitallers who were to assume the expenses of the imprisoned Templars. Meanwhile, rulers, great lords, religious houses, and former donors seized or claimed Templar lands and goods wherever and whenever the occasion permitted. Only after extended and costly legal suits did the Hospitallers gain sound title to part of the former Templar possessions in France.

𝔗𝔥𝔢 𝔗𝔯𝔦𝔞𝔩 𝔬𝔣 𝔱𝔥𝔢 𝔗𝔢𝔪𝔭𝔩𝔞𝔯𝔰 𝔦𝔫 𝔈𝔫𝔤𝔩𝔞𝔫𝔡

As in France, the Templars in England were effectively prosecuted. But the dissimilarities of the campaign against them in England were of greater significance than the similarities. Instead of the ruthless prosecution which was carried on by the French king, his officials, and many of the French clergy, the trial of the Templars in England was characterized by relative leniency and proceeded largely in accordance with the principles and procedures of English law which were more advantageous to the accused than those practiced in France. The English Templars were also aided by a popular attitude which was not nearly so hostile as that in France and by a king who seemed less than convinced of their guilt and who was less determined in his policies and actions than the French monarch.

Uncertainty regarding the status and future of the Templars in England first arose in October of 1307 when Philip the Fair, King of France, dispatched Bernard Peletin, a trusted messenger, to King Edward II, his future son-in-law, with a secret communication enumerating the alleged wickedness and crimes of the Knights Templars and urging Edward to take action against them as he, Philip, had already done in France.[26] Edward's reaction was not what Philip had hoped for. Instead of immediately proceeding against the Templars in his realm, Edward defended them. In his letter in reply (October 30, 1307), Edward dismissed Philip's charges as "incredible" to himself, his priests, earls, barons, and others of his council.[27] Furthermore, writing on behalf of the order to the kings of Portugal, Castille, Aragon, and Sicily (December 4, 1307), Edward pointed out the great reputation of the Templars for devotion and probity, recalled their distinctive services to the faith, urged his fellow monarchs to turn deaf ears to the slanderers who were moved more by greed and envy than by zeal for righteousness, and called on them to permit no injury to the Templars or their property unless the alleged wrongs were lawfully established.[28] Edward also sent a letter to Pope Clement (December 10, 1307) in which, expressing amazement and horrer, he declared that the great esteem in which the master and brothers of the Temple were held by him and by all his kingdom prevented him from believing the charges.[29] Further, suggesting that the charges might well be the work of evil-disposed persons who were turning the good deeds of the order to works of perversity for their own advantage, he urged the pope by some fair inquiry to clear the order of the charges being brought against it. But Edward's letter to the pope was to be of no avail; for, as previously noted, Clement had already committed himself to the guilt of the order.[30] Though Edward had not yet received a copy of Clement's recent bull — *Pastoralis prae-eminentiae* — he soon learned that in this papal dispatch Clement, after speaking of the crimes of the Templars and of the action taken against the order in France, asserted that the Grand Master — as well as many of the brothers — had publicly and spontaneously confessed certain of the charges and that he himself had examined a knight of the order of high birth and authority who had fully and freely confessed. Because of these things, Edward was instructed with caution and secrecy to arrest all of the Templars in his kingdom on one day and to take their property into safe custody.[31]

Adhering to his initial conviction but briefly, Edward in short order turned against the Templars.[32] To determine motives for human actions is always difficult. In this case, there seems no reason to assume that Edward actually became convinced of their guilt. On the one hand, his original statements and the subsequent failure of the examinations of the Templars in England to produce positive proof would make such an assumption doubtful; on the other hand, his hesitation, as a monarch and as a Christian, to challenge the formal policy and decision of a pope seems a probable reason for his change of attitude. His realization of the problems involved in pursuing a policy opposed by the papacy and his knowledge of what had happened to certain earlier kings who had done so must have influenced him. The possibility of gains for the crown must also have been considered. At any rate, his subsequent action, as will be indicated below, shows that some of the wealth and property of the Templars went to the crown.[33] In addition, his impending marriage to Isabelle, daughter of Philip the Fair, may well have caused him to think twice about following a policy not in agreement with that of the strong-willed French monarch.

By December 20, 1307, sealed instructions of arrest and confiscation, to be effective January 8, 1308, had been drawn up and sent by sworn clerks to the sheriffs of England, the justices of Wales and Chester, the Keeper of Scotland, and the Justiciar of Ireland.[34] Only after each official involved had taken an oath to keep the contents secret were the writs opened and their contents disclosed. In accordance with the royal directive, between January 8th and 11th, approximately one hundred and fifty Templars in England were arrested; and their property was taken into the king's hands. Though some Templars escaped,[35] it is not known how many. The prisoners, apparently treated considerately, were taken to a central castle in each county to be held pending further order, being, according to royal command, guarded "in a fitting place" and not confined "in a hard and vile prison."[36] It was also provided that each Templar was to receive for his support a liberal allowance, to be taken out of the income from the land of the order, of four pence per day.[37] William de la More, Master of the Temple in England, was taken to Canterbury Castle where he was given clothes and equipment, was authorized a daily stipend of two shillings, and was permitted the company and services of any two Templars he desired.[38] Shortly, on May 27, 1308, at the intervention of the Bishop of Durham,[39] one of the greatest lords in England, he was released on his honor and was not again imprisoned until six months later (November 28th), due probably to papal insistence.[40]

The charges brought against the Templars in England were essentially identical with those brought against them on the continent, the eighty-seven articles listed by Clement[41] serving as the basis for the examinations. The charges fell into five major classes. Heresy, including idolatry, was the major charge. The Templars were accused of denying Christ, God, Mary, and the saints (article 1); rejecting the crucifixion (article 5); worshiping a statue (articles 37, 46-57) or a cat (articles 14-15); disbelieving in the sacrament of Holy Communion (articles 16-19); failing to have their priests consecrate the host in the celebration of mass (articles 20-23); and permitting the Grand Master or the local masters to grant absolution from sin (articles 24-26). Disrespect and profanation, as represented by spitting and stamping on the cross at reception (articles 9-11), were alleged. Improper action, as represented by confessing only to their own priests (article 74), and greed, as represented by a concerted effort to increase the wealth of the order by every possible means (articles 77-78), were charged. Indecency, as represented by kissing (articles 30-33) and homosexual practices (articles 40-45), was stressed. And secrecy, as represented by the holding of secret initiations (articles 69-73) and chapters (articles 36-39), was alleged.

The basic procedure to be followed in examining the English Templars was set down by Clement in his bull of August, 1308,[42] in which the archbishops and bishops of England, in conjunction with the papal inquisitors, were directed to secure evidence on the charges listed. After the individual brothers had been examined, provincial councils were to be summoned to determine the guilt or innocence of the order and the disposition of its individual members. However, because of delay, the trial itself did not begin for well over a year.

It was not until September 13, 1309, twenty months after the arrest of the Templars in England, that the papal inquisitors finally arrived.[43] On the next day, new royal writs were sent to the sheriffs to arrest all the Templars in their counties — meaning, apparently, those Templars

who for some reason were still at large — and to send them without
delay, together with those already in custody, from the county prisons
to the Tower of London or to York and Lincoln castles.[44] On the same
day, writs were sent to the constables of these three strongholds to
receive the prisoners, to keep them safely, and to produce them on request for examination.[45] The boards of inquiry — composed of the Archbishops of Canterbury and York; the Abbot of Lagny (in France) and
the French notary, Sicard de Vaur, papal inquisitors; and the Bishops
of Durham, Orleans, Lincoln, Chester, and London[46]— were now almost
ready to begin work. But first, on September 22, 1309, before the actual
examination of the Templars had begun, the Archbishop of Canterbury,
acting in accordance with papal orders, had had published and read in
all the churches of the country a papal bull in which Clement declared
his conviction that the Templars were guilty and announced the excommunication of all persons, regardless of rank, station, or profession, who
should aid or counsel the Templars and the imposition of the interdict
on all cities, castles, and places which might harbor any of the accused.[47]

What is known of the trial of the Templars in England pertains
chiefly to the examination at London. Most of the prisoners were concentrated there,[48] and the examination of them falls conveniently into
five phases. During the first phase — between October 21 and November
17, 1309[49]— forty-three Templars were questioned on a number of
matters, but primarily on the procedure used by their order for confession and absolution. In this initial phase in which no torture was applied,
most of the Templars denied the alleged charges and failed to make any
specific confessions of wrongdoing though their testimony suggested a
degree of unclearness in the matter of confession and absolution.[50]
When a number of outside witnesses also failed to provide any significant or incriminating evidence, it became rather apparent that the desired
confessions would not be obtained without the use of torture. Accordingly, at a meeting of the southern provincial council at Lambeth at the
end of November, where the papal bull calling for a general council to
meet at Vienne was read, the inquisitors requested permission to proceed
"secundum constitutiones ecclesiaticas."[51] On December 11 (1309), the
appeal of the bishops was called directly to the attention of Edward who,
four days later, conceded by issuing orders to the custodians of the Templars to allow and assist the prelates and inquisitors to do as they wished
with the bodies of the prisoners "according to ecclesiastical law."[52]
Nonetheless, there was still considerable hesitation on the part of the
royal officials to proceed in this fashion — at least Edward's order had
to be repeated.[53]

In the second phase of the examination at London — from the end of January into March of 1310 — two stages can be observed. Initially, thirty-four Templars were questioned, again apparently without torture being used and with no confessions obtained.[54] Shortly (February 8th), new royal writs were issued ordering the jailors to obey the prelates and inquisitors so as to help them deal with the Templars "according to ecclesiastical law" and appointing William de Dien to oversee the employment of torture.[55] Then, a month later, solitary confinement was authorized and the orders to use torture were repeated.[56] Even so, no headway was made inasmuch as those Templars who were again examined failed to confess.[57]

In June (1310), the inquisitors drew up a statement addressed to the Archbishop of Canterbury[58] in which they attributed their lack of success to their inability to find persons to carry out the torture which had been authorized and recommended the following ways by which the Templar affair could more quickly be brought to a successful conclusion: removing the prisoners from the care of the king's officials; putting the men on a bread and water diet; making public the confessions from France so as to arouse public indignation to the point that torture could be applied *"sine scandalo populi"*; and transferring the Templars to Ponthieu, an English possession on the continent, where torture could be more fully and freely applied. After some time had passed without any action on these recommendations being taken by Edward, Clement wrote the king (August 6th) to the effect that he had heard reports that the crown had prohibited the application of torture as contrary to the laws of England and that the work of the inquisitors had thereby been impeded.[59] At the same time, the pope wrote to the English bishops condemning them for negligence and urging them to aid the inquisitors.[60] In response to these papal criticisms, Edward, on August 26th — and again, in slightly modified form, on October 23d — ordered the Templars in the Tower to be delivered to the sheriffs of London whenever requested by the inquisitors for the application of ecclesiastical law.[61] Meanwhile, the southern provincial council which had again met at Canterbury (September 22, 1310) ordered that the Templars should be examined further and should be tortured provided no mutilation, permanent dismemberment, or effusion of blood resulted.[62] It would seem that the bishops were concerned on the one hand lest no confessions be obtained; and on the other, lest popular opinion be aroused against the use of torture.

Edward, occupied with his campaign in Scotland, cooperated so that the third phase of the examination at London — October through December, 1310 — was conducted more in accord with papal wishes. From Scotland, he directed the Constable of the Tower to deliver the Templars in his keeping to the sheriffs of London when the prelates and inquisitors desired, to permit the inquisitors to do as they pleased with the bodies of the prisoners, and to receive the Templars back when their examination was over.[63] The Templars handed over to the sheriffs were now confined in prisons attached to the city gates where it seems the sterner treatment was meted out.[64] Edward, in instructing the Mayor, aldermen, and commonalty of London to obey his orders, stated that he was allowing the proceedings against the Templars *"ob reverentia Sedis Apostolicae."*[65] Similar letters were sent (November 22d) to the Constable of Lincoln ordering him to hand over the Templars in his custody to the bailiffs of Lincoln for imprisonment in the city gates there.[66] Finally, on December 12th, Edward ordered the Templars hitherto detained at Lincoln to be transferred to London where all the Templars in the southern province were being collected in anticipation of the meeting of the southern provincial council which would determine the guilt or innocence of the order in England.[67] During this period, the Templars were re-examined,[68] and torture was probably employed; but still, there is no indication that any confessions were obtained. Clement, again making known his dissatisfaction with the course of affairs in England and indicating his lack of confidence in the efficacy of ecclesiastical law as applied in England, suggested (December 23d) — but to no avail — that Edward follow the recommendation of the inquisitors that the whole matter be transferred to Ponthieu where their work could be carried on without hindrance.[69]

Meanwhile, during the spring and summer of 1310, the Templars at York were examined.[70] Though the papal bull of accusation had been heard there with astonishment by all concerned,[71] the royal officials made the prisoners available to the designated ecclesiastics who proceeded to interrogate them as directed by Clement. The use of torture, as authorized by papal and royal letters, caused extended debate at the meeting of the northern provincial council which seemed quite uncertain as to whether it was to be applied by lay or clerical officials.[72] In fact, torture does not appear to have been used against the Templars at York at all, and perhaps as a consequence not a single confession of guilt was obtained.

The fourth phase of the trial at London — beginning in March and lasting throughout April (1311) — provided no more convincing or incriminating evidence against the Templars than the earlier phases. When re-examination of the Templars, after several months of more rigorous treatment, produced admissions of irregularities on only the most trivial of points, the inquisitors turned to outside witnesses — approximately sixty in number, only six of whom were not ecclesiastics —

most of whose testimony was second or third hand and of little credibility.[73] For example, one priest testified that another priest had told him that a certain Templar had confessed to every single crime now charged against the order. However, both the priest and the Templar concerned, being dead, were unavailable for confirmation or denial. A certain knight affirmed that his grandfather, who had died after becoming a Templar, was believed to have been murdered by his brothers for refusing to take part in heretical practices. And a Franciscan testified that he had been told by a woman, who had been told by a man, who had been told by someone else, that a servant of the latter's acquaintance had been put to death when caught watching the Templars worship an idol. On April 22, 1311, after the present phase of the examination had been completed and the testimony of outside witnesses had been heard, the Bishops of London and Chichester and the papal inquisitors finally offered the Templars eight days to prepare and to present any defense they might desire.[74] The invitation was rejected with the comment that the aid of anyone who could give them competent advice was denied them — the reference being without doubt to the bull of Clement which the Archbishop of Canterbury had had read throughout England back in September, 1308. Instead, at the end of the eight days, William de la More, Master of the Temple in England, joined by other Templars, replied that the Templars believed all the doctrines of the church, denied all heresy and iniquity alleged against them, and called for all except their enemies to come forward to speak of the good conduct and activities of the order.[75]

The subsequent treatment of the Templars is somewhat unclear. Arrests of renegade Templars were pressed anew;[76] stricter confinement was practiced; and the use of torture was again authorized by the king.[77] It must be stressed, however, that there is no evidence to suggest that any Templar in England died from torture as so many had in France. During the fifth and last phase of the examination at London — late June and early July (1311) — three confessions were gained. Stephen de Stappelbrugge, a renegade Templar who had only recently been captured (June 10th), under imprisonment and probably under torture, confessed (June 23d) the truth of many of the charges. Especially, he said there were two initiations: one was good and proper; the other was *"contra fidem"* and involved denying Christ and spitting on the cross.[78] Thomas Tocci de Thoroldsby, another renegade Templar who had just been arrested, confessed initially that the Templars were urged not to confess to priests outside the order. On June 29th, after a lapse of four days during which it is quite probable that torture was used against him, he further admitted that the Templars renounced Christ, spat beside the cross, favored the Moslems over the Christians in the Holy Land, and permitted their lay officials to exercise priestly functions.[79] And on July 1 (1311), John de Stoke, a chaplain of the order and recently treasurer at New Temple, London, after having initially denied all the charges against the order, admitted that the Templars denied Christ and were told that Christ was an imposter. To the other charges and questions, however, he pleaded ignorance.[80] Whether or not torture was applied to him cannot be ascertained. With the testimony of these men, the public examination of the Templars in England was concluded. Although very little specific or convincing evidence had been gained either from the Templars themselves or from the non-Templar witnesses, it was evidently the best and most that could be obtained under existing conditions and was deemed sufficient for present purposes by those in positions of authority.

Hence, the "trial" of the Templars in England had been completed; and the decision of guilt or innocence would normally follow. But, as seen above, the final decision had already been made; and it now remained only for the general council at Vienne, and the local provincial councils in England, to announce the disposition of the Templars and their goods in accordance with papal mandates.

Disposition of Templar Property in England

The question of what should be done with the lands of the Templars in England proved to be a major problem. A considerable amount of confusion and conflict arose both with respect to the establishment of a policy and the practical implementation of it.[81] For present purposes, the problem can be most effectively treated by discussing briefly the three periods through which it passed.

The first period (1308-12) was one of indecision by both pope and king. At one time, Clement argued that their lands should be held in safekeeping for the Templars until a definite decision was reached on their guilt or innocence;[82] at other times, he maintained that the lands should be held for use in the recovery of the Holy Land.[83] Edward initially seems to have expected that he would acquire a goodly portion of the Templar lands for the crown; later, however, he was willing to satisfy himself with the use of the income from the Templar lands and possessions of only a few of the Templar estates.

In January, 1308, at the time of their arrest of the Templars, the king's sheriffs, in accordance with royal mandate, had seized the property of the Templars as well as their persons.[84] As the months passed and the trial of the Templars did not begin, Edward seems to have begun to dispose of the property at will. As early as October 4, 1308,

Clement, concerned over a report that the king had transferred or sold certain Templar properties, wrote to Edward ordering that possession or control of the property should be entrusted to certain prelates and certain other fit and proper persons.[85] In his reply, Edward asserted that he had thus far done nothing improper with the possessions of the order, that he had no intention of doing anything he had no right to do, and that he would deal with the goods in a manner acceptable to God.[86] Clement subsequently (February 25, 1309) advised Edward to transfer the goods to the papal commissioners designated to handle them — the archbishops of Canterbury and York and the bishops of Lincoln and Durham — and urged him to aid the commissioners regain lost goods, but there is no evidence that Edward paid any attention to this order.[87]

Edward soon proceeded to the task of the appraisal and supervision of the Templar wealth. As early as February 10, 1308, he ordered his sheriffs, under whose control the goods had been placed, to learn by inquisition of local juries the extent and value of the Templar possessions.[88] A year later, on March 4, 1309, the treasurer and barons of the exchequer were ordered to have another survey made so as to learn the annual value of the property "in demesnes, services, rent, villenages, and all other issues"[89] and were further directed to commit the properties of the Templars "to faithful men who will answer to the king for the value appraised."[90] This meant — as was gradually done during the rest of the year — that the sheriffs were to be relieved of their control over Templar property and that special keepers were to be appointed instead. Furthermore, by 1310, though the title as such was not officially used, there had emerged a general keeper of all Templar lands — Roger de Wingfield, clerk of the king's wardrobe[91] — whose task it was to supervise the local keepers and to see that accounts were made directly to the king's central officials.[92]

In the meantime, it would appear that certain persons followed the king's lead in taking over various Templar estates — or perhaps they had even anticipated his action. In order to check these seizures, Edward appointed special agents to inquire into the value of the property carried off and ordered the sheriffs to summon juries to get at the truth.[93] Perhaps the fact the public records provide scanty information on this subject means the trend was checked, at least for the time being.

It is possible to trace in considerable detail what Edward did with the Templar properties held in his name. First, he had the revenue of the Templars — including the debts owed to them[94] — paid into the royal treasury or wardrobe for use as he might direct.[95] For example, there are royal orders to the officials of the exchequer to pay out given sums for services rendered,[96] for specified debts,[97] and for bounties due the

Scotch refugees of his recent campaign.[98] What is more, even the grain,[99] timber,[100] and livestock[101] of the Templars were used or sold as the king desired. Second, the king granted Templar lands and revenues to various persons. For example, he dispensed churches, vicarages, prebends, and the like;[102] he gave lands as dowries, as royal favors, and in return for services rendered to him;[103] and he assigned the use of revenue from Templar possessions.[104] Third, without equivocation, Edward paid the Templars the regular allowance authorized for their subsistence both when imprisoned and when confined to monasteries.[105] Fourth, the king recognized lawful claims against the Templars. For example, Templar corrodies and pensions were recognized after their validity had been determined;[106] expenses for necessary repairs of Templar property were allowed;[107] rent owed by the Templars for lands they held of others was paid;[108] and debts to or debts contracted on behalf of the Templars were honored.[109] Moreover, individuals who could produce proper authority for holding former Templar lands were permitted to retain them.[110] Fifth, the king, and other lords as well, under certain circumstances were assigned Templar lands as escheats and were permitted to exact feudal reliefs of their tenants.[111]

Some indication of the amount of money the king received from the Templar property can be given. The careful work done on this problem by Perkins[112] suggests that for the period 1308 to 1313 the king received a net income from Templar goods of £9,256 — £8,840 being derived from England; £390 from Ireland; £25, from Scotland — or an average of £1,542 per year.[113] Using such figures as are available on the total annual income of the crown for these years, based on wardrobe receipts, Perkins estimates that the Templar income constituted approximately four per cent of the total normal annual income.[114] These figures suggest that the Templar possessions provided the king with a considerable amount of money but that this sum was by no means of decisive importance. It must be noted, however, that these figures do not include the movable goods—for which we do not even have probable estimates— possessed by the Templars and used or disposed of by the king.

Not much information is available on either the amount or the value of the Templar movables — i.e., cash, grain, livestock, clothing, household equipment, agricultural implements, armor, weapons, ecclesiastical robes and objects, books, and the like. Not only is complete data missing, but only parts of the inventories which do exist in manuscript form have so far been utilized.[115] The impression one gets, however, is that the Templar movables were far less than the king and his officials had anticipated. For example, instead of great treasures of gold, silver, and jewels at New Temple, London, the royal officers found only ecclesiastical movables worth £121 and other movables worth £68.[116] At some key manorial centers, such as Faxfleet and Foulbridge in Yorkshire, the movables were of greater value, being worth £290 and £254 respectively.[117] Even more surprising is the fact that the total cash seized from all the preceptories in England amounted to only £36.[118] Two possibilities suggest themselves: either some Templars may have escaped with or secretly disposed of the valuables of the order or the Templars did not possess extensive movable property. It is true that a few Templars did escape, but a rigorous search by the king's officials and the inquisitors produced only nine.[119] The one known instance of a Templar bribing his keeper to permit him to escape involved the rather small sum of forty florins.[120] Two cases,[121] the only such known, were concerned with a definite effort on the part of the king to acquire Templar movables allegedly in the hands of private citizens. In the one, a certain man and his wife were ordered by the king to account for twenty-three shillings— a small sum — supposedly left with them by a Templar. In the other, the outcome of which is also unknown, the king demanded that a chest of money, said to contain the rather large sum of one hundred marks sterling and two hundred gold florins, which the Templars had supposedly left in Warwickshire, be produced. Then, there is also the royal order instructing the new sheriff of Gloucester to secure those Templar possessions, including movables, which his predecessor had not yet obtained.[122] It would be unwarranted, on the basis of this information, to argue that any appreciable number of English Templars escaped or that much Templar wealth was successfully sequestered. It is more reasonable to argue that the Templars' movable goods were actually quite limited. Very likely, the Templars in England lived relatively simple and unostentatious lives and sent the greater part of their portable wealth to the Templar headquarters in the Holy Land or in Cyprus.

The second period (1313-24) was concerned with a struggle to see whether or not the Knights Hospitallers were actually going to come into possession of the Templar properties. The position of Clement, as taken at the Council of Vienne, was that with the condemnation of the Templars their goods should be transferred to the Hospitallers. Accordingly, on May 16, 1312, Edward was directed by a papal bull to deliver the property of the Templars in England to the Hospitallers forthwith.[123] This, however, the king was reluctant to do[124] and instead, for over a year, did nothing except to order (August 1st) the Prior of the Hospitallers to cease his efforts to gain control of the Templar possessions until parliament again met.[125] Ultimately, but under protest, Edward did yield, pointing out that he was doing so only from fear of dangers to himself and his realm if he refused,[126] referring probably to his fear of ecclesiastical censures. But at the same time, he insisted that his own rights and those of his subjects should not be prejudiced by any restitution of such lands and goods as might be effected and that he and his subjects should be allowed to sue for their rights in the proper courts. It was not until November 28, 1313, a year and a half after Clement's order, that Edward specifically instructed his keepers to hand over the lands to the Hospitallers.[127] Having transferred the lands concerned, Edward, on February 8, 1314, ordered the Prior of the Hospitallers henceforth to pay out of the revenue of former Templar property in his possession the regular allowance of four pence per day for each Templar placed in a monastery to do penance, except for Himbert Blanke, the ranking Templar in England, who was to receive two shillings per day.[128] Always watching out for his own interests, Edward, before he had ordered the transfer of the Templar lands, had made sure that his keepers, or others involved, had first been instructed to hand over to the king's representatives all the movables (especially the livestock) of value.[129]

With the removal of direct royal control, there appears to have been a scramble for the Templars' lands involving both the lesser and the great lords. Certainly the Hospitallers got some of the property without much difficulty;[130] but lacking most of the records of the Templars, they were hard put to defend their claims and to protect what they did obtain.[131] Even as late as August 1324 and August 1325, the Hospitallers complained of not having received the Templar charters.[132] Matters were further complicated when the great lords—including such men as Thomas of Lancaster, Robert de Holand, John de Mowbray, Guy de Beauchamp, and Aymer de Valence[133]— seized and claimed certain lands as heirs of the original donors or as lords by escheat. These actions on the part of the secular lords were not only tolerated by the king[134] but were practiced by him as well.[135] Meanwhile, Clement attempted without much success to aid the Hospitallers by ordering the king, the nobles, and the clergy to assist the order in gaining possession of their legitimate properties.[136] Edward assumed a rather indifferent attitude, pointing out that he himself had given up the Templar lands and could proceed against his lords only according to the law and custom of his realm.[137] Nor did the clergy as a whole seem very anxious to help despite the papal bulls and the strong efforts of Archbishop Reynolds.[138] Thus the matter dragged on for several years until May 23, 1322, when John XXII, a more determined pope than Clement, ordered the bishops to unite in parliament in order to expel the lay occupants of the Templar estates and to use ecclesiastical censures to enforce the restitution of the lands.[139] After some delay and much discussion, Parliament, on March 26, 1324, finally decreed that no lord had any title or right to Templar lands or appurtenances by escheat or otherwise;[140] however, as a concession to the lay lords involved, the statute recognized the right of individuals to prosecute their claims in the proper courts. In executing this statute, King Edward, on May 16th following, ordered his sheriffs to seize Templar properties in his name so that they could be delivered to the Hospitallers,[141] but with the proviso that all movables on the estates were to be returned to their owners and that the Hospitallers were to pay for the crops already sown.[142] By July 1, 1324, the royal keepers in the different counties had been instructed that they must permit the sheriffs to hand over the land;[143] and some time later, the sheriffs and others concerned were told to deliver Templar charters and records to the Hospitallers as well.[144] Thus, the decision to grant the Templar lands to the Hospitallers had definitely been made, but it still remained to enforce and implement the decision.

The third and last period (1325-38) was concerned with the concerted efforts of the Hospitallers to get actual possession of the lands (and records) guaranteed to them by pope, king, and parliament. In some instances, certain lands were handed over without any apparent difficulty;[145] in other instances, litigation, which had already been resorted to, was continued or pressed anew even though it proved time-consuming and costly.[146] In 1328, Philip de Thame, Prior of the Hospitallers in England, wrote to the Grand Prior of his order that for the current year he had received only £458 from the Templar lands.[147] Ten years later, this income had increased to £1,441 per year[148] — a sum still less than the average income of £1,542 for the years 1308-13 when the Templar property was in the hands of the king.[149] When the king, the great lords, and royal officials still proved reluctant to give up certain Templar lands under their control, the Hospitallers, in their effort to gain actual possession of the larger part of the Templar lands and to win the necessary support of influential persons, began to employ a new and more successful method — a method which might be called bribery. After granting certain former Templar lands and/or revenues, without restrictions and in perpetuity, to the king,[150] to influential lords and officials like Hugh le Despenser and Hugh the Younger,[151] and to lesser, but nonetheless important, people at the royal court,[152] they found it easier to acquire the bulk of the lands they had so long and unsuccessfully sought. They now found that royal orders (1332-33) directing the sheriffs to again take former Templar lands into the king's hands on behalf of the Hospitallers resulted in the prompt delivery of them.[153] Furthermore, in 1335, Edward III, a more determined ruler than his father, explicitly confirmed the parliamentary statute of 1324,[154] thereby giving the Hospitallers both moral and legal support. Within a couple of years — by

1338 specifically — the Hospitallers had obtained at least nominal possession of most of the Templar estates not ceded to the king or such important persons as the Despensers.[155] Though some difficulties remained and some court cases still arose,[156] they were few in number and tended to turn out satisfactorily. By and large, these lands which the Hospitallers had gained were to remain in their possession until the dissolution of religious houses by Henry VIII in the sixteenth century.

In summary, then, it can be said regarding the Templar property in England that, though the king was unable to take over any great part of the lands, he was able to dispose of the movable goods and to use the revenue from the lands for some years. Ultimately, however, the great bulk of the property of the Templars did pass to their rival religious-military order, the Knights Hospitallers.

Elsewhere in Europe, the Templar lands were disposed of in various ways. In Portugal, Aragon, and Castille, where the Hospitallers received none of the lands, they were handed over to other military orders, many of them newly established.[157] In France, Italy, and Germany, the Hospitallers had experiences somewhat similar to those they had in England,[158] finally acquiring part of the former Templar property only after long delay and considerable effort. Especially to be noted is the fact that the Hospitallers in France, as indicated at the end of the first section of this chapter, fared far worse than the Hospitallers in England in their attempts to gain possession of former Templar properties.

Disposition of the English Templars as Individuals

The problem of deciding what should be done with the Templars as individuals proved far less troublesome and time-consuming than the problem of deciding what should be done with their property. At the end of their interrogation in the summer of 1311, the Templars were informed by their inquisitors that if they would publicly admit their inability to clear themselves of the accusations levied against them and would agree to submit to the provincial councils, they would be received back into the church.[159] By the middle of July (1311), after abjuring their alleged errors, most of the prisoners at London were formally received back into the church. The southern provincial council meeting at Canterbury then ruled that the men be assigned singly or in small groups to various monasteries to do penance and directed that payments of money, at the rate of four pence per day for each Templar — to be taken out of the income from the order's properties — be made for their maintenance in these monasteries.[160] Similar arrangements for the abjuration of errors, assignment to monasteries, and payment of expenses were made by the northern provincial council (July 29, 1311) for the prisoners at York.[161] Within a reasonable time, the English Templars were placed in a great number of different monasteries throughout the country where they apparently spent the remainder of their lives and conducted themselves in a humble and proper manner.

Only two Templars still remained imprisoned — Master William de la More and Himbert Blanke, Preceptor of Auvergne — both of whom had refused to abjure errors they said they had never committed.[162] More, broken in health, died in the Tower of London (December 20, 1312) before his case could be referred to the pope and council at Vienne;[163] and references to Blanke, who had been ordered retained in prison pending further instructions,[164] disappear from the records.

In Scotland, where two Templars had been arrested and examined, both denied all the charges except that the master had some power in the matter of absolution.[165] Forty-one outside witnesses, all ecclesiastics, were heard, apparently without providing any significant evidence against the prisoners or their order.[166] In Ireland, where fifteen Templars were arrested, no noteworthy results were obtained despite the fact the prisoners were examined up to three times.[167] As in Scotland, the testimony of outside witnesses, thirty-seven ecclesiastical and four lay, provided no significant evidence of heresy or wrongdoing.[168]

Regarding the trial of the Templars in England, it can be said that the proceedings, procedure, and results were less severe than in France and that the English Templars were treated fairly well during their years of incarceration and examination. Though torture was sanctioned, it was applied sparingly, without enthusiasm, and with little success. The few confessions gained, whether resulting from torture or not, proved contradictory and unreliable in content. On the matter of orthodoxy or unorthodoxy, the only point that can be conceded is that the Templars' practice of confession and absolution, though unclear to the Templars themselves, differed somewhat from the system becoming increasingly common in the west. Even the testimony of outside witnesses — of which there were 157, all but 33 of whom were ecclesiastics[169] — was neither very credible nor very damaging. In general, the Templars in England, as will be shown in the next section of this chapter, had been fairly popular and apparently remained so inasmuch as there is no adequate evidence to show that any noteworthy hostility toward the order developed even during the trial. Though the Templars may well have been guilty of misdeeds of one sort or another, the case presented against them as individuals and as an order must be labeled "not proved."[170] Indeed, much of the evidence cited against them would today be dismissed as unreliable and irrelevant by any legally trained or fair-minded person. The greatest disadvantage, and the most damaging factor against the

Templars, was their penchant for secrecy which made possible so many of the charges raised against them and so many of the tales told about them. It was with telling wisdom, insight, and pathos that Himbert Blanke, Preceptor of Auvergne, when asked by the inquisitors at London why secrecy was maintained if nothing but good was done under its cover, answered "through folly."[171]

To make the record more complete, passing reference to the fate of the Templars elsewhere must be indicated.[172] Though Clement persisted in his insistence on the guilt and condemnation of the order throughout Europe, he was not always successful in getting his desires executed. In Aragon, where the Templars defended themselves with arms, it was two years before they were finally arrested and tried. As in England, the use of torture was, to a degree, resisted by the king and *cortes*. The final decision, as reached by the provincial council of Tarragona (November 4, 1312), was an unqualified acquittal of the order and a recommendation that the Templars should reside in the dioceses where their property lay.[173] In Castille and Portugal, the Templars were arrested with dispatch and secrecy and after a trial, the details of which have been lost, were pronounced innocent by a provincial council at Salamanca. In addition, in Portugal, a new order, which some people claim represents a continuation of the Templar order, was established by the king and approved by the pope.[174] In Italy, in the areas most directly under the control of the pope and of Charles of Anjou, King of Naples and cousin of Philip the Fair, the Templars were arrested, tortured, tried, and convicted; but in other areas, very considerable difficulties were encountered in the attempt to arrest, torture, try, and convict them. In Cyprus, where the outcome of the trial is unknown, no significant evidence against the order was gained despite the use of torture. And finally, in Germany, where the number of Templars was not great and where such Templars as were captured refused to give evidence against the order, two separate trials were held, with the Templars in each instance being in essence found not guilty.

The final decision regarding the fate of the Templar order, as seen above, was actually made by Pope Clement V though it was supposed to have been left to the Council of Vienne. But, when the members of the council hesitated to do as the pope wanted, Clement took it upon himself to abolish the order and to assign its property to the Knights Hospitallers. Similarly, the final decision regarding the fate of the individual Templars, as also seen above, was actually made by the pope though it was supposed to have been left to local provincial councils. But, as few of these councils ever met, it was Pope Clement V and John XXII who ordered all former Templars sent to monasteries.[175]

𝔓opular Attitude 𝔗oward the 𝔗emplars in 𝔈ngland

In discussing the downfall of the Templars in England, considerable attention must be given to the matter of their popularity or unpopularity even though evidence on this point is difficult to find and more difficult to evaluate. Yet, such information as is available, much of it of an indirect and of a very minute sort, does provide at least a qualified answer to the question raised. Most of the material to be discussed below will tend to be unfavorable in varying degrees for two reasons: the nature of the available data and the need to determine whether or not this unpopularity was an important factor in bringing about or in hastening the fall of the order. For the sake of simplicity, clarity, and brevity, the criticisms of the Templars will be dealt with in a topical manner.

The secrecy of the order aroused a considerable amount of curiosity, suspicion, and distrust from which the Templars certainly did not profit. It permitted fantastic tales to be circulated about them and gave some of the witnesses at the trial an opportunity to make rash and unsupported statements against them.[176] It may well be, as Perkins says, that their secrecy was the chief cause of their unpopularity[177] – but even if it was not, it was at least a major cause.

The pride of the Templars, which was proverbial, aroused great antagonism and assuredly did not help them in their hour of trouble. The best known reference to this pride is the pointed statement attributed to King Richard I. Though there exist various versions, differing only in minor detail, the gist of the story is this: Richard, on a military campaign in France, was rebuked by a French priest, Fulk de Neuilly by name, for having three daughters who cost him dearly; and he was advised by the priest that it would be to his advantage to rid himself of those daughters because only thus could he expect to find favor with God. When Richard denied having three daughters, Fulk informed him that the daughters he meant were Pride, Luxury, and Avarice. With quick wit and insight – so the story goes – he replied that he would forthwith marry off these daughters. Pride he would marry to the Templars [or Hospitallers] "who are as proud as Lucifer himself;" Luxury, to the Black Monks [or the prelates of the church]; and Avarice, to the White Monks.[178] There are other indications of Templar pride, too. Pope Innocent III, in 1208, sternly denouncing their short-comings, wrote the Templars that their unbridled pride had led them to abuse their enormous privileges.[179] Frederick II, Holy Roman Emperor, writing to Richard of Cornwall (1244), complained that the pride of the Templars was responsible for the defeat of the Christians by the Kharizmians.[180] King Henry III (1252), replying to a complaint of the Hospitallers regarding some injury committed against them, stated that the prelates, and especially the Templars and Hospitallers, had such great revenues that they had become swollen with pride.[181] William of Tyre maintained that in his own day (i.e., in the last half of the twelfth century) the Templars, having abandoned their former humility, had by their actions become obnoxious to everyone.[182] Matthew Paris and Roger of Wendover said essentially the same thing, though in different words.[183] Similarly, Walter Mapes, an out-spoken critic of religious groups alluded disapprovingly to the pride of the Templars.[184] To these references can be added the suggestion of H. C. Lea that the many men of the lower class who were admitted to the order as sergeants, or serving brothers, may have assumed the airs of the knightly class, to which they did not really belong, and may have conducted themselves in a more haughty manner than they should, thereby arousing further hostility.[185]

Insolence, closely akin to pride, was not unknown to the Templars and was manifested in a variety of ways and forms. Royal domain and jurisdiction were infringed upon and violated by the Templars as a bull of Honorius III (1222), in reference to the situation in the French possessions of the English king indicates. In this bull, the Templars are called upon, among other things, to cease doing the following: usurping royal domain by erecting their crosses on houses not belonging to them, preventing customary dues from being paid the crown, disregarding the customs of the king's manors, and involving the king's officials in troublesome law suits.[186] A bull of Innocent III (1208) complained that the Templars, upon receipt of a gift or contribution, were so bold as to bury in their church yards even persons under excommunication.[187] The continuous rivalry between the Templars and the Hospitallers – a rivalry frequently involving outright warfare – led Walter Mapes to attribute the misfortunes of the Christians in the East to the corruption of the military orders[188] and caused Matthew Paris (1259) to assert that the Templars' call for members in Europe to be sent to the Holy Land was designed "to take fearful vengeance upon the Hospitallers by force of arms."[189] Paris, in the same passage, further added that he feared that the peace and stability of Christendom would be destroyed "through their extreme fury." In 1253, the Templars (and Hospitallers) dared to refuse to give Henry III, much to his anger, the money promised to Richard de Clare.[190] And Clement IV (1265), reproaching the Templars for their ingratitude, warned them that only the papacy could sustain them against the hostility of the bishops and princes.[191] How right Clement was, the Templars were later to learn.

The Templars were upon occasion accused of treachery – sometimes with reason and sometimes without. In 1170, Thomas Becket, Archbishop of Canterbury, was warned by a friend not to trust or to take the advice of two Templars in the particular matter before him because of their deceit.[192] Writing in reference to the situation in 1244, Matthew Paris remarked that people were uncertain whether or not to believe reports sent to Europe by the Templars (or Hospitallers) because Christians "always suppose them to conceal some fraud and . . . [to] . . . have some wolfish treacheries under a sheep's clothing."[193] Indeed, he went on to say, had there not been fraud and treachery, the many brave western knights would have successfully routed the infidel in their recent encounters.[194] The same author, in a speech attributed to the Sultan (1246), at a time when the envoys of the Templars and Hospitallers were seeking to procure the release of Christian captives, recorded that the Sultan called the Templars (and Hospitallers) "wretched" *(miseri)* because they sought to betray the emperor, Frederick II; because they rejected the efforts of Richard of Cornwall, brother of the English king, to bring peace between the two orders; and because they broke the peace made by the same Richard.[195] In a speech of the Count of Artois (1250), reported also by Paris, the Count, when advised by the Templars to let the soldiers rest and then to proceed only with caution in the attack on Mansourah – good advice as events turned out – made a bitter attack saying:

> See the ancient treachery of the Templars! the long-known sedition of the Hospitallers. . . . This is what we were told long ago; and truly has the augury been fulfilled; the whole country of the East would long ago have been gained, had not we seculars been impeded by the deceit of the Templars, Hospitallers, and others calling themselves religious men. See, the chance of capturing the sultan is open to us, and the ruin of all paganism is imminent, as well as the lasting exaltation of the Christian faith, all of which this Templar, who is here present, endeavors to impede by his fictitious and fallacious arguments. For the Templars and Hospitallers, and their associates, fear that, if the country is reduced to submission to the Christian power, their domination, who fatten on its rich revenues, will expire. Hence it is that they poison, in divers ways, the Christians who come hither girt for the cause of the cross, and, confederating with the Saracens, put them to death by various means. Is not Frederick, who has had experience of their treachery, a most certain witness in this matter?[196]

And again, according to Matthew Paris, Richard of Cornwall (1241) would not commit Ascalon to the Templars, nor would he entrust to them money left behind for the completion of a castle, because of their quarrels with and attacks on other Christians.[197]

As the record occasionally indicates and as reason suggests, certain of the economic exemptions of the Templars aroused resentment and hostility. Being exempted from royal tolls, and sometimes from local tolls as well,[198] the Templars must have been hated and opposed upon occasion by those merchants whom they could undersell at the different markets and fairs, if they so chose. The Templars' exemption, in varying degrees, from certain types of taxes also provided grounds for resentment.[199] For example, the king had granted the Templars (and Hospitallers) exemption from tallage for one man per city, a privilege which with time had been extended, apparently without specific authorization, to additional persons. The dissatisfaction of the townsmen at this extension can be seen, at least in the city of Bristol, in a quarrel, continuing in an off-and-on manner from the reign of John into the reign of Edward I, which arose between the two groups because the townsmen wanted the Templars to pay their "fair share" of the tallage due the king.[200] The fact the Templars were generally exempted from a variety of fees, fines, aids, services, and the like, associated with the land[201] must also have aroused a considerable amount of envy and hatred even though not expressed in such manner as to leave a record of the details either in judicial proceedings or in popular literature.

Various of the judicial privileges accorded the Templars, especially those tending to increase the order's power and independence, aroused antagonism in men of importance, both lay and clerical. The keystone of Templar judicial privileges was the one stating that members of the order could be impleaded only before the king or his chief justice.[202] By using this privilege to their own advantage, the Templars were able to postpone trials and to exhaust their opponents both in time and money as a case which arose in Ireland well illustrates. There the Abbot of St. Mary's monastery in Dunbrody, after having begun (1278) a suit against the Master of the Temple in Ireland over the ownership of seven carucates of land, found himself faced with one delay after another, arising apparently from the Master's claim that he could be impleaded only before the king or his chief justice. Finally, in 1291, after over twelve years of arguing in the courts and after the Abbot had petitioned Parliament for redress, pleading poverty from the extended legal proceedings, a settlement was reached according to which the Master of the Temple was to give the Abbot one hundred marks in return for the latter's acknowledgment of Templar ownership of the land.[203] Hundredors of various counties repeatedly made complaints against the Templar judicial privileges and their misuse. Specifically, they complained that the Templars hindered justice by forbidding their tenants to appear before any but Templar courts,[204] prevented the arrest of persons guilty of crime by receiving them on their property,[205] oppressed people under their jurisdiction by imposing excessive fines or by summoning them to London,[206] and unjustly and without warrant assumed rights of court.[207] Even the crown came face to face with Templar usurpation of rights of court from time to time. For example, Henry II, on one occasion, deemed it necessary to fine a royal servant for going before a Templar court and not before a royal court;[208] and Edward I was especially active in an attempt to check private jurisdiction, including that of the Templars, exercised at the expense of the crown.[209]

The wealth of the Templars did not add to their popularity. Though the extent of this wealth, at least in England, was grossly exaggerated,[210] it was, nonetheless, great enough and sufficiently believed in to have some adverse effect. Both William of Tyre[211] and Matthew Paris[212] put great stress on this wealth, as also did Walter Mapes.[213] It was common knowledge – and it was certainly true, as seen in the two preceding chapters – that the Templars possessed numerous estates, both large and small; that they received a considerable revenue from rent, fees, and services associated with their lands; that they had a goodly income from grain, wool, and the like; that they acquired large sums of money or other valuables yearly as gifts and tithes; and that they profited handsomely from their banking activities. Though it is reasonable to assume that their wealth aroused envy and hatred, yet direct and positive evidence to this effect is hard to find. Rather, it was avarice or greed, which is so closely related to wealth, that evoked open and bitter antagonism and criticism.

Though the charges were often of a general and undocumented nature, the Templars were repeatedly accused of unbounded avarice. Jacques de Vitry wrote, "You profess to have no individual property, but in common you wish to have everything."[214] William of Tyre, in one passage, accused the Templars of delivering Naziredden, a captured Moslem leader, to his enemies for 60,000 pieces of gold though he was on the point of becoming a Christian.[215] Matthew Paris charged that the Templars prolonged the war with the Saracens merely to have a pretext for raising more money.[216] And the well known incident of the Templar purchase of Cyprus (1191) from Richard I for 25,000 silver marks and the sale of it the next year to Guy de Lusignan for the same price after the order had flagrantly misruled the island and exacted excessive taxes[217] was cited as proof of their greed. In addition, the Templars were accused of practicing usury as a means of further satisfying their avarice. So, for example, during their trial, a certain John de Lyndeseye, Rector of the Church of Ratbon in Scotland, swore that he knew the Templars were usurers;[218] and a certain William de Brasl, a witness in Ireland, gave similar testimony.[219]

The best and most concrete illustration of Templar avarice, of which only a few of the many instances need be mentioned here, was their great hunger for land. It is not always easy, however, to distinguish between a voluntary grant to the Templars – of which there must have been thousands – and Templar seizure or covetousness. The repetition of the charges that the Templars illegally seized certain lands and made improper claims to other lands – even seizure of royal lands without warrant are referred to[220]–suggests that the Templars did not always cease their practice despite the complaints and accusations. Nor did Edward I's Statute of Mortmain (1279), designed to limit or prohibit further alienation of land to clerical groups, prevent the Templars from continuing to acquire land, sometimes by special royal authorization of grants in mortmain[221] and sometimes through grants by corrodaries and pensionaries.[222] A Hospitaller charter of 1354 from Hawkerstown, Scotland, referring to an incident of the thirteenth century, well illustrates this hunger for land.[223] On the death of a certain man, who had allegedly conveyed the patrimony of his wife to the Templars for his own lifetime in return for maintenance by them, the Templars claimed the land as theirs. When the deceased man's wife challenged the claim and took the matter to court, where the decision was rendered in her favor, she was twice forcibly removed by the Templars. Finally, when her son later sought to regain the land, the Templars were said to have had him murdered. If this story is true – and Edwards in his article accepts it as true[224]– or if people then accepted it, or other similar stories, as true, then there is good reason to assume that definite hostility to the Templars arose on the grounds of avarice. The statement of a certain Adam of Wedale, a Scottish monk, at the trial of the Templars in Scotland, provides further information on Templar land hunger in the part which reads:

> This order is defamed in manifold ways by unjust acquisitions, for it seeks to appropriate the goods and property of its neighbors justly and unjustly with equal indifference, and does not cultivate hospitality except towards the rich and powerful, for fear of dispersing its possessions in alms.[225]

Also at the Templars' trial, John de Lyberton, a priest, testified that he had heard another priest, Walter de Alberton, who had been in the service of the order for seven years, say that the Templars were avaricious to acquire property for their order.[226] The same idea is brought out by Walter Mapes, who, speaking in general about the greed of the Templars (and Hospitallers), accused them of viciously exploiting the poor and humble by convincing them to hand over their lands to the military orders.[227] It is not surprising, then, to find the Templars' greed for land as one of the charges listed against the order by Pope Clement.[228]

Associated with this land hunger was a steady increase in the number of Templar tenants, an increase which was due not only to the aggressiveness of the Templars themselves but also to the desire of individual persons wanting to profit from the attractive privileges and exemptions which might be theirs as Templar tenants. As in the case of the excessive alienation of land by mortmain, so in this instance, the practice had become so widespread and of so serious a nature that kings like Henry III and Edward I found it necessary to issue special royal orders limiting the number of persons who might qualify as Templar tenants.[229]

The extensive religious privileges and the large degree of independence granted to the Templars by the popes, which have been discussed in Chapter I above, served to arouse the rivalry and enmity of other clerics and religious groups, both secular and regular. One need only recall that the Templars were exempted from the jurisdiction of the local clergy — being in effect subordinate to the pope alone — were immune to ordinary excommunication, were excused from paying most clerical taxes and other levies, and were given the right to collect regular and special contributions throughout Christendom. The bitterness and envy these and other privileges elicited from the clergy are clearly reflected in the testimony, only a small portion of which has been cited earlier in this chapter, of hostile ecclesiastics at the Templars' trial.

Lastly, there were many minor complaints and criticisms raised against the Templars. For example, they were charged with obstructing water courses or roads, of raising walls, and of enclosing common lands to their own advantage,[230] but it would be difficult to determine whether or not such annoyances as these appreciably contributed to the unpopularity of the Templars.

Having thus far presented the adverse criticism, one must now briefly discuss the evidence favorable to the Templars. That this evidence is limited and often indirect is not unexpected inasmuch as historical records are frequently less complete and informative about the good that is done than about the bad. This is especially true in the case of the Templars because they had no contemporary apologists or known writers of their own, because their opponents — led by Clement V — did a remarkable job of silencing those who might have worked or spoken on their behalf, and because even their organizational records have largely disappeared.

The fame, valor, success, and good repute of the Templars as soldiers and leaders on the field of battle — which were briefly referred to in Chapter I above — are too familiar to need recital or documentation here. It should perhaps be pointed out, however, that many of the writers who severely criticized the Templars upon occasion were generous in their praise of them at other times, as can be observed in the works of Jacques de Vitry, William of Tyre, Walter Mapes, and Matthew Paris.[231] A favorable attitude toward the Templars is certainly attested by the numerous and repeated grants of property, privileges, exemptions, and the like, which were freely made to the order by private citizens, clerical persons, public officials, great lords, and kings over the long period of its existence. Furthermore, the difficult time the papal inquisitors faced in their concerted efforts to find witnesses against the Templars suggests that public hostility was anything but widespread. What is more, as has already been noted, the evidence given by the 157 witnesses against the English Templars, of whom 124 were clerics and only 33 were laymen,[232] was either not very damaging or was of doubtful quality and reliability. A careful search through a goodly amount of the popular literature of the period reveals little, if any, material pertinent or helpful to a solution of the problem of popularity or unpopularity.[233] In an indirect and negative sense, this would seem to mean that though the Templars were not popular heroes they were also not the subject of popular ridicule or hatred. Generally speaking, it seems safe to say that the actions of the kings – about which we have the most information – and other Englishmen indicate not only royal favor and good opinion of the Templars but public approval and esteem as well. To be specific, Edward I (May 13, 1304), writing to Jacques de Molay, Grand Master of the Templars, praised William de la More, Master of the Temple in England, for his "great and laudable services" to the crown and called upon the Grand Master to treat William well and to send him back to England with all speed.[234] Later, in 1307, as seen above, Edward II, who had just succeeded to the throne, initially rejected the charges levied against the Templars by the French king and wrote letters on their behalf to the pope and to certain of his fellow monarchs. It was this same Edward who permitted William de la More, and apparently other Templars as well, to be set free on parole after their initial arrest and imprisonment.[235] All this suggests the Templars were not deemed the evil men the charges asserted them to be but rather were held in high esteem by both the king and his subjects right up to the very moment of their downfall.

To many a reader of Sir Walter Scott's *Ivanhoe*, the Templars were men of unusual arrogance, ambition, hypocrisy, worldliness, and luxury. This characterization, however, is based more on fiction than on fact. In Brian de Bois-Guilbert, a not too typical Templar, is to be seen an exaggeration of those human strengths and weaknesses which are dearer to the heart of a novelist than of a historian. If anything, the picture of Beaumanoir, the aged and proud Grand Master, is closer to the truth than that of Brian, the preceptor and candidate for the Master's chair.

The information which has just been cited and the fact that the Templar order was composed of human beings suggest that the Templars were neither all good nor all bad. Without question, there were adequate grounds for friction and animosity between the Templars and other groups in society because of their extensive privileges, which they did upon occasion abuse or take improper advantage of, and because of their many aggressive and selfish acts. These things most certainly did them no good. However, the privileges which they enjoyed and the questionable actions which they engaged in — political, economic, or religious — were far from unique inasmuch as many other religious groups and many lay lords had received similar ones and had done, or sought to do, the same things. Indeed, the complaints levied against the Templars can be, and were, levied equally well against others.[236] Hence, in most cases the Templars as such were not being exclusively singled out for criticism or reprimand. So, for example, when kings or popes proceeded against the Templars, it was often as one of a number of persons or groups. Furthermore, every instance of censure or criticism can be balanced many times over by instances of praise and commendation.

In England, there is no adequate evidence to suggest any sudden or marked increase in grievances against the Templars or any sudden or marked change in the popular attitude toward the Templars in the years just before the trial. Nor is there any indication, even during the trial, of an effective or of a noticeable campaign against the Templars among the laity. Rather, there is evidence of some popular support. The leniency of the king, his sheriffs, and the keepers of the Templars toward the arrested and accused prisoners suggests a considerable degree of sympathy rather than hostility. As the trial revealed, the most bitter and open critics of the Templars were the clerics, many of whom considered the Templars their chief rivals and all of whom had been as a unit committed by Pope Clement to the guilt and destruction of the order.[237] But even so, the leniency and consideration shown by such important clerics as the Archbishop of York suggest that the Templars' judges were not wholly convinced of the guilt of the order. Indeed, when the exaggeration and bias of their critics, especially the clerical, is compensated for, the Templars appear no worse than many other groups which, though sharing many of the same actual and alleged grievances, did not share the same fate. Finally, the hesitation, secrecy, and delay in the trial of the Templars and the propagandistic efforts undertaken during the period of imprisonment and trial, limited as they were in England, suggest that uncertainty about popular opinion necessitated great caution and care by the public officials and clerics involved. Hence, it would be unwarranted to say that the opinion of the British laity —

and for that matter, of the royal officials or the entire clergy in England as well — was in any significant manner unfavorable to the Templars or that their attitude had much actual effect in determining the ultimate fate of the Templars.

chapter five

Conclusion

Summary and Evaluation

The origin and purpose of the Templars were essentially military. To a considerable degree, as its long record of leadership and achievement both during and between the Crusades attests, the order remained military from its humble beginnings in 1118 to its dramatic dissolution between the years 1307 and 1312. Indeed, not realizing that the fall of Acre had ended the Crusades as a major project, the Templars were still anxious to continue the struggle against the infidel; and Jacques de Molay, the last Grand Master, when summoned to appear before Pope Clement V at Poitiers, presented him with a plan for a new campaign.[1] Yet, during the two centuries of their existence, the Templars had also become very much involved in political and economic activities — as can well be seen in the history of the order in England. These other activities, though less glamorous and exciting, were certainly equally as important as their military exploits.

The Templars first appeared in England toward the end of the reign of Henry I, but it was not until the years of civil strife following his death that they made much headway. Then, from the accession of Henry II to the reign of Edward I, they grew rapidly in power, wealth, and influence. Though initially possessing lands in southeast and south-central England, the Templars came to have their largest, most numerous, and richest holdings in the northern counties of Lincoln and York, which were then, so to speak, frontier regions. There, together with other religious groups, they joined in clearing waste areas and converting them into fields and pastures for the profitable production of grain and the grazing of cattle and sheep. The concentration of Templar estates in the north is probably due to the fact that so many areas in the rest of England had already been taken by other religious orders — for example, the Benedictines, Cluniacs, Augustinians, and Cistercians — who had established themselves in England earlier than the Templars and whose holdings were so extensive that they often made those of the Templars seem small by comparison.[2] The scattered lands of the Tem-

[117]

plars were grouped together for purposes of administration and supervision into preceptories, approximately forty in number, over one-third of which were in the two counties just mentioned. The headquarters of the order, however, were at New Temple in London where the Master of the Temple in England usually resided.

Besides agriculture, which was practiced throughout England and was their major economic concern, the Templars engaged in trade and commerce and in financial operations. Wool, and to a lesser degree, grain, sent to Flanders and France, were the chief exports; and wine from southern France was the chief import. More important than trade and commerce, but less important than agriculture, were the numerous financial activities of the Templars. The exchange of money, the acceptance of cash and valuables for deposit, the transfer of funds, the issuance and use of credit and credit instruments, the execution of trusts, and the grant of loans were systematically and widely engaged in. Indeed, until superseded by the Italian merchants in the last half of the thirteenth century, the Templars were the foremost bankers of western Europe. In England, their chief clients were the kings: Henry II, Richard I, John, Henry III, and Edward I. They had other clients, too, but not much is known about them.

The close relationship of the Templars to the English crown is also to be seen in the grant of privileges to them and in their use as officials and advisers to the kings in matters political and administrative as well as economic. To their religious privileges of exemption from ecclesiastical taxation of all kinds and independence from all ecclesiastical authority save that of the pope, must be added their political privileges — granted to them and repeatedly confirmed by all the kings from Stephan to Edward I — of exemption from secular taxation and ordinary feudal burdens and of jurisdiction over their own lands and persons and over those of their vassals and tenants as well. These privileges made the Templars independent of local ecclesiastical and lay authorities and responsible essentially only to the pope and the king. The kings found the Templars reliable and effective as envoys and advisers and as collectors and keepers of royal revenues; they found them a desirable group to whom to turn in time of financial need; and they found New Temple a convenient and secure treasury for royal funds.

The zenith of Templar power and influence in England came under Henry III, a weak, vacillating, improvident, and pious ruler. Under him, their privileges were more fully maintained than under the other kings; and their influence as royal advisers and their use as royal officials reached their greatest extent. To him they lent more money than to any other monarch; and under him, New Temple and its treasurers were for a time a part of the royal administration. Yet, during the last two decades of Henry's reign and after the mastership of Roscelin de Fos (d. 1253), the power and influence of the Templars in English affairs began to decline. This decline is especially noticeable under Edward I who, instead of turning to the Templars for aid and advice, turned increasingly to the Italian merchants for money and to his own officials for political and administrative service.

The power, influence, and independence of the Templars in England has been greatly exaggerated. Their limited numbers — fewer than one hundred and fifty at the time of their dissolution — their repeated appeals to the king and the pope for maintenance of their privileges, and their reliance upon the crown for support, made it impossible for them to exercise any large degree of independence. They may have been more powerful and influential than their size, actions, and resources warranted; but they were at no time a real threat to the church or state. They did arouse antagonism and hatred among their rivals, the secular and regular clergy and some lay lords; but among the population as a whole, there is no adequate evidence to suggest any widespread or continued unpopularity.

The arrest and trial of the Templars were conducted under questionable conditions. Indeed, many of the charges against them were incredible and obviously suspect; and those who acted as their jailers and judges were not always convinced of their guilt. In England, this doubt on the part of the king, certain of their interrogators, and many members of the church councils which considered their fate is especially apparent. The major charge against them was heresy; but as one historian has said, this was not one of their sins — they were warriors not theologians.[3] They were used and misused by Philip IV of France and by Pope Clement V whose decisions and actions were based not on a careful and impartial examination of the charges and evidence but upon a verdict of guilty which had been determined in advance. In England, where torture was used only sparingly and where none of their members was killed, the Templars fared better than in France though they were nonetheless officially considered guilty. Their lands were initially handed over to the king who succeeded in retaining some of them; but most of them ultimately, after a long struggle, were transferred to the Knights Hospitallers. Their portable wealth, which was never fully accounted for, presumably fell into the hands of the king. And the Templars themselves were assigned to do penance in many different monasteries, only a few being sent to any one house.

The Templars, except for their military character and aristocratic stamp, had much in common with other religious groups and like them formed a bridge between the ideal and the real and serve as an object lesson for the moralist. Beginning as a poor and humble group seeking to serve and defend God and their fellow Christians, they remained wholly loyal to their ideals only briefly. With success came honor, prestige, wealth, privilege, and power. Their original humility and poverty were readily forgotten or ignored, and matters other than defense of God and their fellow Christians received increasing attention. In England, these other activities — political, administrative, and economic — seem to have become their primary concern. This is not to say that the English Templars did not devote themselves to the defense of the Holy Land. They did concern themselves with the Holy Land as their collections of money and recruitment of members suggest. It is only to say that on the basis of surviving evidence the Templars seem to have been less concerned with their crusading activities than with their non-military activities. Quite possibly, many of their contemporaries had a similar impression.

When all is said and done, the Templars contributed much to western civilization as their participation and leadership in the Crusades and their services — political, administrative, and financial — to the kings of England, and to the rulers of other states, indicate. Though they were far from perfect and certainly deserved censure as well as praise, their fate was undeserved. It seems safe to say that they were the victims of forces and circumstances more powerful than themselves. They were also, in part, the victims of that remarkably effective and formidable institution known as the Inquisition. In short, for certain leaders, political and religious, and for certain purposes, likewise political and religious, the Templars were expendable.

The Question of the Continued Existence of the Templars

To the inevitable question of whether or not the Templars continued to exist as an organization, no final answer can be given. There are three modern theories on this subject: the first, that the Templar order was disbanded and did not survive in any sense; the second, that the Templars survived in Portugal as members of a new organization, the Order of Jesus Christ, created by King Dionysius; and the third, that the Templars continued to exist via the Order of Freemasonry.

This is not the place for a detailed discussion of this problem, nor even for an indication of the many difficulties involved. For present purposes, it is only necessary to state that there is much to be said for the first and second views, and little for the third. In a sense the papal bull of dissolution did indeed put an end to the Order of the Knights of the

Temple. But at the same time, there are documents to suggest that in Portugal the Templars did not suffer the fate of their brethren elsewhere and that their lands and possessions were transferred to the new order which was approved in 1319 by Pope John XXII.[4] Apparently former Templars joined this order, but whether or not it was with papal approval is unclear. The association of Freemasonry with the Knights Templars, however, is a different matter. It is claimed that Jacques de Molay, before his death, appointed John Mark Lamernius his successor as Grand Master, and that from that date to the present, the office has never been vacant.[5] Just what happened to the Templars under Lamernius and his successors between the death of de Molay in the early fourteenth century and the uncontroverted existence of Freemasons in the seventeenth century would seem to be a mystery. The few documents which have been presented as proof of the continued existence of the Templars via Freemasonry are, to put it mildly, of doubtful authenticity. A letter by an unnamed writer, quoted in Addison, illustrates the uncritical use of questionable material. This writer refers to a dubious work of a Frenchman writing in the middle of the nineteenth century as proving that the earliest freemason's lodge was probably founded by some recreant and seceding British Templars and that all lodges in the world are offshoots of that early one.[6] Until more convincing evidence is presented, this sort of material can hardly pass for serious history. Much more realistic in their approach to the historical problem of the early origins of Freemasonry are Knoop and Jones who, in their sober and carefully presented study of Freemasonry from its beginnings to 1730, do not even mention the claim that Freemasonry was descended from the Knights Templars of the Middle Ages.[7]

Appendices

Appendix A

A List of the Masters of the Temple in England

Name	Date	Name	Date
Hugh of Argentein	ca. 1140	Amadeus de Morestello	1259-60
Otto (Osto)	ca. 1150	Ambesard	1264
Richard de Hastings	1155-64	Himbert Peraut	1271
Geoffrey Fitz-Stephen	1180-85	Guy de Foresta	1273-74, 1291-94
William Newham	?	Robert de Turvill	1276-90
Aymeric de St. Maur	1200-18	Jacques de Molay	1295
Alan Martel	1218-28	Brian de Jay	1296-98
Robert de Sanford	1229-48	William de la More	1298-1312
Roscelin de Fos	1251-53		

A complete list of the Masters of the Temple in England cannot be drawn up because of lack of evidence. Nor can complete accuracy in the dates of their mastership be attained. The list here includes those men for whom there is definite evidence in the source materials of the period and several men — Hugh of Argentein, Otto, and William Newham — for whom Miss Lees (pp. xliii, xlviii, lix) gives reasonable proof. For other lists, see Addison, *op. cit.*, pp. 457-58 and Williamson, *op. cit.*, p. 671. Cf. also references in the Register of Bishop Sutton, *op. cit.*, pp. 22, 46, 58, 75-77, 89, 91, 105, 110, 137, 147, 173-74, 177, 188-89, and 203.

Appendix B

A List of the Preceptories of the Templars in England

Berkshire
Temple Bistlesham
Buckinghamshire
Bulstrode
Cambridgeshire
Denney
Duxford
Great Wilberham
Essex
Temple Cressing
Gloucestershire
Temple Guiting
Hampshire
Baddesley
Hertfordshire
Garewy
Upleden [or Bosbury]
Herefordshire
Temple Dinsley
Kent
Temple Ewell
Leicestershire
Rothley
Lincolnshire
Aslackby
Eagle
(Mere)
South Witham

Temple Bruer
Willoughton
Middlesex and London
New Temple, London
Oxfordshire
Sandford
Temple Cowley
Shropshire
(Halston)
Somerset
Temple Combe
Sussex
(Saddelscomb)
Shipley
Warwickshire
Balsall
Wiltshire
(Temple Rockley)
Yorkshire
Copmanthorp
Faxfleet
Foulbridge
Penhill
Ribston and Wetherby
Temple Cowton
Temple Hirst
Temple Newsam
Westerdale
Whitley

This list is drawn up on the basis of information presented in Chapter Two. The centers within parentheses are those for which the evidence is not conclusive.

Appenдix C

A List of the Templar Treasurers at New Temple, London

Name	Date	Name	Date
Simon of the Temple	1214-24	Warin	1273-76
Hugh of Stocton	1229-42	William	1288
Robert of Sicklinghall	1239-60	Richard of Feltham	1294
Ralph of Brimsgrave	1259-60	John of Stoke	1308

This list is taken from the article by Miss Sandys ("Financial and Administrative Importance of the London Temple," *op. cit.*, pp. 161-162) in which she has collected the source references from each treasurer. The dates are those in which they are known to have held office.

Appenдix D

A List of Markets and Fairs Granted to the English Templars

Baldock (Hertfordshire). A weekly market on Wednesday and an annual fair of four days[1] – later changed to three[2] – on the vigil, feast, morrow, and following day of St. Matthew the Apostle (September 20-23).[3]

Balsall (Warwickshire). A weekly market on Sunday[4] – later changed to Thursday[5] – and two annual fairs;[6] one on the vigil, feast, and morrow of St. George the Martyr (April 22-24); and the other on the vigil, feast, and morrow of St. Matthew the Apostle (September 20-22).

Bruer (Lincolnshire). A weekly market on Thursday – later changed to Wednesday[7] – and an annual fair on the vigil, feast, and morrow of St. James the Apostle (July 24-26).[8]

Gaddesby (Leicestershire). A weekly market on Wednesday and an annual fair on the vigil, feast, and morrow of St. Barnabas (June 10-12).[9]

Kirkeby (Lincolnshire). A weekly market on Tuesday and an annual fair on the eve, feast, and morrow of St. Jacob (July 24-26).[10]

Newburgh (Yorkshire). A weekly market on Wednesday.[11]

Rothley (Leicestershire). A weekly market on Monday and an annual fair on the vigil, feast, and morrow of St. Barnabas (June 10-12).[12] Both the market and the fair were discontinued in 1306.[13]

Southcave (Yorkshire). A weekly market on Monday and an annual fair on the vigil, feast, morrow, and following day of the Holy Trinity (June 2-5).[14]

Walnesford (Essex.) A weekly market on Sunday[15] – changed to Tuesday or Thursday in 1227[16] – and an annual fair on the vigil, feast, and morrow of the Decollation of St. John the Baptist (August 28-30).[17] Both the market and the fair were discontinued in 1240.[18]

Werriby (Essex). A weekly market on Thursday and an annual fair on the vigil, feast, and morrow of the birth of St. John the Baptist (June 23-25).[19]

Wetherby (Yorkshire). A weekly market on Sunday and an annual fair on the vigil, feast, and morrow of St. Jacob (July 24-26).[20]

Witham (Essex). A weekly market on Sunday[21] – later changed to Tuesday.[22]
Wyham (Lincolnshire). A market.[23]

---

[1] Granted by Stephen, *ca.* 1153-54: Lees, p. 152. Confirmed by John: *Rotuli Cartarum,* 1 John (1199), part II, m. 3 – cited in *VCH: Hertfordshire,* III, 68; also confirmed by Henry III: *CChR,* 11 Hen. III (1227), p. 5. Cf. Dugdale, VII, 838.

[2] Cf. *CPatR,* 6 Ed. II (1312), pp. 536, 537.

[3] The calendar dates given in this appendix are derived from information found in the *Handbook of British Chronology,* ed. F. M. Powicke (London, 1939).

[4] Granted by Henry III, probably in his first year (1216-17): Dugdale, VII, 838.

[5] Cf. *CChR,* 52 Hen. III (1268), p. 112.

[6] Granted by Henry III, probably in his first year (1216-17): Dugdale, VII, 838. Cf. *CChR,* 52 Hen. III (1268), p. 112.

[7] *Ibid.,* 43 Hen. III (1259), p. 19.

[8] Originally granted by Henry II but not used by the Templars till 1259: *ibid.*

[9] This grant, made in 1306, was to replace the market and fair at Rothley, in the same county, which was discontinued: *ibid.,* 34 Ed. I (1306), p. 71; *Rot. Parl.,* I, 182a.

[10] Granted by Henry III, probably in his first year (1216-17): Dugdale, VII, 838.

[11] *Ibid.*

[12] Granted by Edward I in 1284: *CChR,* 12 Ed. I (1284), p. 276; Dugdale, VII, 839.

[13] *CChR,* 34 Ed. I (1306), p. 71.

[14] Granted by Edward I in 1291: *ibid.,* 19 Ed. I (1291), p. 404; Dugdale, VII, 839.

[15] Granted by Henry III, probably in his first year (1216-17): *ibid.,* 838. This is a reinstatement of a grant made by John: *Rotuli Cartarum,* p. 188 – cf. *CChR,* 11 Hen. III (1227), p. 5, 22.

[16] *Ibid.*

[17] See above, n. 15. A fourth day was apparently added at a later date – cf. *ClR,* 25 Hen. III (1240), p. 250.

[18] *CChR,* 25 Hen. III (1240), p. 255; *ClR,* 25 Hen. III (1240), p. 250.

[19] This grant, made in 1240, was to serve as a replacement for the market and fair at Walnesford, in the same county, which was discontinued: *CChR,* 25 Hen. III (1240), p. 255; *ClR,* 25 Hen. III (1240), p. 250.

[20] Granted by Henry III, probably in his first year (1216-17): Dugdale, VII, 838.

[21] Granted by Stephen and confirmed by John: Cf. *CClR,* 11 Hen. III (1227), p. 8; *CChR,* 11 Hen. III (1227), pp. 5, 8.

[22] James L. Cate, "The Church and Market Reform in England during the Reign of Henry III," *Medieval and Historiographical Essays in Honor of James Westfall Thompson,* ed. James L. Cate and Eugene N. Anderson (Chicago, [1938]), p. 60; *VCH: Essex,* II, 177.

[23] This market is known only through a royal pardon of a sum exacted by the officials of the Exchequer in 1293: *CClR,* 21 Ed. I (1293), p. 288.

Notes to Chapters

Footnotes

Abbreviations

Bain	Bain (ed.), *Calendar of Documents relating to Scotland*
Bliss	Bliss (ed.), *Calendar of Entries in the Papal Registers relating to Great Britain and Ireland*
CChanWar	*Calendar of Chancery Warrants*
(C)ChR	*(Calendar of) Charter Rolls*
(C)ClR	*(Calendar of) Close Rolls*
(C)LibR	*(Calendar of) Liberate Rolls*
(C)PatR	*(Calendar of) Patent Rolls*
CRR	*Curia Regis Rolls*
Dugdale	Dugdale, *Monasticon Anglicanum*
DuPuy	DuPuy, *Histoire de l'ordre militaire des Templiers*
Hosp. Rpt.	Larking (ed.), *The Knights Hospitallers in England: . . . the Report of Prior Philip de Thame*
Jaffé, RP	Jaffé and Wattenbach (eds.), *Regesta Pontificum Romanorum*
Lees	Lees (ed.), *The Inquest of 1185*
Pat. Lat.	Migne (ed.), *Patrologiae . . . Latina*
Pipe R	*Ripe Roll*
Quo. War.	*Placita de Quo Warranto*
Règle	Curzon (ed.), *Le Règle du Temple*
Rot. Hund.	*Rotuli Hundredorum*
Rot. Parl.	*Rotuli Parliamentorum*
RLC	*Rotuli Litterarum Clausarum*
RLP	*Rotuli Litterarum Patentium*
RS	Rolls Series: *Rerum Britannicarum medii aevi scriptores*
Rymer	Rymer and Sanderson (eds.), *Foedera, Conventiones, Litterae et . . . Acta Publica*
VCH	*The Victoria History of the Counties of England*
Wilkins	Wilkins (ed.), *Concilia Magnae Britanniae et Hiberniae*

Preface

[1] *Records of the Templars in England in the Twelfth Century: the Inquest of 1185, with illustrative Charters and Documents*, "Records of the Social and Economic History of England and Wales," Vol. IX (London, 1935).

[2] "The History of the Knights Templars in England" (unpublished Ph.D. dissertation, Department of History, Harvard University, 1908).

[3] *The History of the Temple, London, from the Institution of the Order of the Knights of the Temple to the Close of the Stuart Period* (London, 1924), chaps. I-IV.

Chapter One

[1] Among the general histories of the Templars are the following: C. G. Addison, *The Knights Templars* (American ed.; New York, 1874); G. A. Campbell, *The Knights Templars, their Rise and Fall* (London, 1937); Pierre DuPuy, *Histoire de l'Ordre militaire des Templiers, ou Chevaliers du Temple de Jérusalem, depuis son Etablissement jusqu'à sa Decadence et sa Suppression* (Brussels, 1751); Hans Prutz, *Entwicklung und Untergang des Tempelherrenordens* (Berlin, 1888) and *Die geistlichen Ritterorden: ihre Stellung zur kirchlichen, politischen, gesellschaftlichen, und wirtschaftlichen Entwicklung des Mittelalters*

[131]

132   *Notes*

(Berlin, 1908); Amand Rastoul, *Les Templiers, 1118-1312* (4th ed.; Paris, 1908); and Edith Simon, *The Piebald Standard, A Biography of the Knights Templars* (Boston, 1959).
The most complete work in English is that of Addison. The best brief but thorough study of the Templars is Prutz' *Entwicklung.* DuPuy's work is a collection of valuable documents preceded by a general historical essay on the Templars. Rastoul's book is too brief for serious purposes. Both Campbell's and Simon's works are brief, informative, accurate, and readable in the popular sense. Both also lack specific documentation and are clearly written for the general public.
Specific histories of the Templars in individual countries are largely lacking although a number of histories and collections of charters do exist for a number of separate regions in France. Some excellent work has been done on the Templars in England by Lees, Perkins, and Williamson, as referred to in the Preface. Perkins has also written "The Knights Templars in the British Isles," *English Historical Review,* XXV (1910), 209-30.

² See chap. IV below.

³ Thomas Walsingham, *Historia Anglicana, 1292-1422,* in *Chronica monasterii sancti Albani,* ed. Henry T. Riley (RS, No. 28; 2 vols.; London, 1863-76), I, 457: "... ubi plura munimenta, quae juridici in custodia habuerunt, igne consumpta sunt." Walsingham referred to "Temple Barre," but he clearly meant New Temple. This destruction was also noted in *Chronicon Henrici Knighton, vel Cnitthon, monachi Leycestrensis,* ed. Joseph R. Lumby (RS, No. 92; London, 1889), I, 135. Cf. Williamson, *op cit.,* p. 90, n. 1.

⁴ William of Tyre, *Historia rerum in partibus transmarinis gestarum,* ed. A. Beugnot and A. Le Provost, in *Recueil des Historiens des Croisades: les Historiens Occidentaux,* (Paris, 1844), Vol. I, Part I, *Lib.* xii, *cap.* 7; Matthew Paris, *Chronica Majora,* ed. Henry R. Luard (RS, No. 57; 7 vols.; London, 1872-83), II, 144-45 and *Historia Anglorum sive Historia Minor,* ed. Frederick Madden (RS, No. 44; 3 vols.; London, 1866-69), I, 222 and III, 182; Roger of Wendover, *Chronica sive Flores Historiarum,* ed. Henry O. Saxe (5 vols.; London, 1841-44), II, 195-96; Jacques de Vitry, *History of Jerusalem,* tr. Aubrey Stewart, "Palestine Pilgrims' Text Society," Vol. XI, No. 2 (London, 1896), chap. LXV. None of these men lived at the time of the actual founding of the order. William of Tyre (*ca.* 1130-90) is our best source. Born, raised, and spending most of his life in the Holy Land, he was a man of talent, experience, and reliability. He served as royal tutor and advisor, Chancellor of the Kingdom of Jerusalem, and Archbishop of Tyre. As a historian (cf. August C. Krey, "William of Tyre: the Making of an Historian in the Middle Ages," *Speculum,* XVI [1941], 149-66; Emily A. Babcock and August C. Krey, Introduction [pp. 28-34] to their translation of William of Tyre, [*A History of Deeds Done Beyond the Sea,* "Records of Civilization," No. 35; 2 vols.; N. Y., 1943] William was critical of his sources and usually based his statements not upon the account of a single chronicler but upon a careful comparison and consideration of all sources available to him. Jacques de Vitry was only briefly in the Holy Land; and Roger of Wendover took his remarks from the account of William of Tyre.

⁵ Addison, Campbell, Perkins, Prutz, and Williamson, cited in no. 1 above, accept the account of William of Tyre without question.

⁶ William of Tyre, *op. cit., Lib.* xii, *cap.* 7.

⁷ *Ibid.*

⁸ DuPuy, no. 4.

⁹ Henri de Curzon (ed.), *La Règle du Temple* (Paris, 1886), pp. iii and x.

¹⁰ William of Tyre, *op. cit., Lib.* xii, *cap.* 7; DuPuy (no. 5) reproduces the pertinent parts of the *acta* of the council.

¹¹ "Liber de laude novae militiae ad milites Templi," ed. Jacques P. Migne, *Patrologiae cursus completus . . . series Latina* (221 vols.; Paris, 1878-90), CLXXXII, 922-37.

¹² *Op. cit., Lib.* xii, *cap.* 7.

[13] *Chronica Majora,* RS, IV, 291.

[14] Prutz, *Entwicklung,* chap. III; Perkins, "The Knights Templars in England," *op. cit.,* chap. II. Both of these works contains numerous examples and citations of references to papal privileges. Cf. also DuPuy, nos. 6 (documents of twelve different popes), 21, 22, 27, 35, 36, 38.

[15] Perkins (*op. cit.,* p. 13, n. 1) cites more than thirty references to this type of exemption. Cf. *Calendar of Entries in the Papal Registers relative to Great Britain and Ireland,* ed. William H. Bliss (3 vols.; London, 1893-95), I, 229, 232, 268, 429, 432, 444, 551. Very frequently other orders — e.g., Hospitallers, Teutonic Knights, Carthusians, and Cistercians — as well as the Templars are included in certain of these exemptions and privileges. The great charter of privileges of the Templars is *Omne datum optimum* which was first issued in 1162 by Pope Alexander III, was republished in 1172, and was subsequently confirmed by most popes for well over a century. Copies of this bull can be found in Thomas Rymer and Robert Sanderson (eds.), *Foedera, conventiones, litterae et cujuscunque generis acta publica inter reges Angliae et alios quovis imperatores, reges, pontifices, principes, vel communitates* (rev. ed.; 5 vols.; London, 1816), I, 37-38; *Pat. Lat.,* CCI, 1195; DuPuy, no. 21. Cf. also Philipp Jaffé and William Wattenbach (eds.), *Regesta pontificum Romanorum ab condita ecclesia ad annum post Christum natum MCXCVIII* (2 ed.; 2 vols.; Leipzig, 1885-88), no. 14117. In addition, the Rule of the Templars (*Règle,* art. 58), approved in essence by the Council of Troyes and Pope Honorius II, authorized the Templars to receive tithes.

[16] J. Delaville le Roulx (ed.), *Documents concernant les Templiers; Extraits des Archives de Malte* (Paris, 1882), no. 1. Cf. Jaffé, *RP,* nos. 8821, 8829, and others.

[17] *Ibid.,* no. 9193 *et passim.* Cf. Perkins, *op. cit.,* p. 11, n. 3.

[18] A bull of Eugenius III, dated 1145 or 1146, first gave the Templars this privilege: Prutz, *op. cit.,* p. 27 and n. 1, and pp. 259-60, nos. 3 and 10. Perkins, *op. cit.,* p. 9, n. 2, cites fifty-eight instances in which this privilege was in substance repeated.

[19] *Omne datum optimum,* as cited in n. 15 above. Cf. also a bull of Innocent III (1139) in Guigues A. M. J. d'Albon (ed.), *Cartulaire général de l'Ordre du Temple, 1119-1150* (Paris, 1913), p. 375; Prutz, *op. cit.,* p. 260, no. 1, p. 261, no. 16, p. 265, no. 54, p. 266, no. 72.

[20] *Omne datum optimum* emphasized the subservience of the Templars to the papacy alone.

[21] Rymer, I, 334; Delaville le Roulx, *op. cit.,* no. 27; Prutz, *op. cit.,* p. 267, nos. 83 and 84, p. 269, no. 104, and p. 271, no. 122. Cf. Perkins, *op. cit.,* p. 12.

[22] Prutz, *op. cit.,* p. 259, no. 6, p. 262, no. 23, p. 263, no. 32, p. 270, nos. 108 and 110, p. 274, no. 152, and p. 279, no. 201.

[23] Perkins (*op. cit.,* pp. 12, 25) cites a goodly number of these. See also, the registers of individual popes.

[24] Cf. Jaffé, *RP,* nos. 11076, 11814; Delaville le Roulx, *op. cit.,* nos. 29, 30, 32. Perkins (*op. cit.,* p. 12, n. 3) gives twelve examples. Also, Prutz, *op. cit.,* chaps. III and IV, discusses additional privileges to those cited here.

[25] Cf. Perkins, *op. cit.,* pp. 17-18. The bull of Alexander IV, dated 1255 (DuPuy, no. 35), is an especially good example of this.

[26] Cf. *ibid.,* nos. 23, 29; Jaffé, *RP,* no. 15842; and decree of the Lateran Council of 1179 in Roger of Wendover, *op. cit.,* RS, I, 119, and in William of Newburgh, *Historia rerum Anglicarum,* in *Chronicles of the Reigns of Stephen, Henry II, and Richard I,* ed. Richard Howlett (RS, No. 82; 4 vols.; London, 1884-89), I, 221. Cf. Prutz, *op. cit.,* pp. 40-41.

[27] Some discussion of the attitudes toward the Templars in England will be indicated in chapter IV below. Numerous citations could be made showing instances of praise and instances of criticism. The works of Matthew Paris, Jacques de Vitry, William Tyre, and others are filled with references, sometimes favorable and sometimes unfavorable, to the Templars.

[28] Cf. David Knowles and R. Neville Hadcock, *Medieval Religious Houses, England and Wales* (London, 1953), p. 234.

[29] The officials and the basic organization of the Templars, as they existed in the Holy Land, are to be found in the Rule of the order, the best edition of which is that of Curzon (*op. cit.*). The original rule was most likely written in French; but a Latin version, attributed to or inspired by St. Bernard was appended to the records of the Council of Troyes. The Latin version can be found in Curzon, DuPuy, no. 5, and Giovanni D. Mansi (ed.), *Sacrorum conciliorum nova, et amplissima collectio* (new ed.; 31 vols.; Venice, 1759-98), XXI, 358-71. The earliest copies of the rule which survive are two manuscripts of the thirteenth and fourteenth centuries. Both the French and the Latin versions are given in Curzon and are discussed in his introduction. The original rule was apparently quite brief, consisting of seventy-two articles. But in time extensive additions were made until the rule grew to six hundred and eighty articles. Most of the information on the organization and procedure of the order comes from these additional articles.

[30] *Règle*, arts. 79-98 deal with the power of the Grand Master (called Master in the Rule); arts. 198-223 set down the procedure for the election of a Grand Master: On the death of the Grand Master, the Marshall is to summon the Commanders of the Holy Land and to meet and choose a temporary Grand Commander to govern until a new Grand Master has been elected. A date for the election is set far enough in the future so that all the commanders of overseas provinces may participate in person. On the appointed day, the temporary Grand Commander singles out two or three of the most distinguished men of the order from whom the chapter chooses by voice vote a "Commander of the Election." Then one of the knights is selected to serve as his assistant. These two men proceed to choose two more persons; the four then choose an additional two; and so the matter proceeds until twelve men (eight knights and four sergeants) have been selected. Then as a thirteenth member, a brother chaplain is added. These men constitute the "Council of Election" which, meeting apart from the others, and under the presidency of the Commander of the Election, proceed to examine the positions and records of various dignitaries of the order. Finally, by simple majority vote, they elect a new Grand Master. After the electors have rejoined the other Templars, the Commander of the Election calls upon all those present to swear to obey the new master, whoever he may be. Thereupon he turns to the one chosen and says: "*Et nos, el nom dou Pere et dou Fis et dou Saint Esperit, nos avons esleu a Maistre et elisons vos, frere ---- .*"

[31] *Ibid.*, arts. 99-100.

[32] *Ibid.*, arts. 101-09, 173-76.

[33] *Ibid.*, arts. 110-19.

[34] *Ibid.*, arts. 120-24. Other lesser officials existed, too. Cf. arts. 125-81 for their titles and duties.

[35] Direct information on the provincial organization of the Templars is largely lacking in the Rule and must be gained from a study of documents from the individual provinces. Altogether the Templar realm was divided into eighteen provinces. The eastern provinces were: Jerusalem, Tripoli, Antioch, Romania (Morea and Thessaly), and Cyprus; and the western provinces were: England, Normandy, France, Poitou, Aquitaine, Alvernia (Provence), Aragon, Castille, Portugal, Apulia, Lombardy, Germany, and Hungary. In the Rule itself, reference is made to only nine provinces: three in the east and six in the west.

[36] More will be written in the next chapter on this provincial and local organization as it is found in England.

[37] *Règle*, art. 96.

[38] *Ibid.*, art. 36.

[39] *Ibid.*, arts. 36, 85, 87, 92, 106, 125.

[40] *Ibid.*, p. xxviii.

[41] *Ibid.*, arts. 45, 48, 389, 396-404. The holding of frequent "chapters of faults"

was common among many religious communities, and perhaps the Templars were especially influenced by the Cistercian practice.

42 *Ibid.,* arts. 406, 416-656.

43 *Ibid.,* arts. 87, 586, 661. The Rule speaks of the provinces of Jerusalem, Antioch, and Tripoli. Later, additional provinces (cf. n. 35 above) were established. The Rule does not speak specifically of local chapters, but such records as exist, especially in reference to the trial — see chap. IV below — prove their existence.

44 This is also inferred from other records and is in harmony with the content and intent of the Rule.

45 *Règle,* art. 17 *et passim.* During their first decade or so, the Templars had no distinctive habit. The Council of Troyes and Pope Honorius II (1128) authorized them to wear a white mantle, symbolic of purity and innocence. The influence of the white garb of the Cistercians whose great leader, Bernard of Clairvaux, was their special sponsor, may help to explain the choice. Some twenty years later, when the Second Crusade was being preached, Pope Eugenius III authorized the Templars to add a red cross to their mantle. (Cf. William of Tyre, *op. cit., Lib.* xii, *cap.* 7.) Very likely the pope and the Templars selected the red cross because of its association with crusaders since 1095. As the badge and seal of devotion and martyrdom, it clearly proclaimed the Templars' dedication of their lives to the defense of the Holy Land and Christian pilgrims. Cf. remarks of Fucher of Chartres, *Historia Iherosolymitana,* I, iv and Robert the Monk, *Historia Iherosolimitana,* I, 2 in *Recueil des Historiens des Croisades: les Historiens Occidentaux,* Vol. III (Paris, 1866). Karl Erdmann (*Die Entstehung des Kreuzzugsgedankens* [Stuttgart, 1935], p. 49) in his chapter on "Heilige Fahnen" also states that the red cross on a white flag had by the mid-twelfth century become a religious symbol: "... hatte die rot-weisse Kreuzfahne den Charakter eines rein religiösen symbols ..." Members of the order other than Knights, though strictly forbidden to wear the white mantle, were permitted to add the red cross to their black or brown robes.

46 *Règle,* arts. 51, 57, *et passim* (poverty); 70, 71, 675, *et passim* (chastity); and 39, 98, 436, 457, *et passim* (obedience). Only in the case of married men joining the order is it specifically stated that a part of the initiate's property must be given to the order — art. 69. It would not be surprising to find other brothers surrendering their property to the order upon initiation, however.

47 *Ibid.,* art. 429. The Benedictine and Augustinian orders are specifically mentioned as religious houses which former Templars might join. Normally, the only persons to leave the order were those who had been expelled for some serious offense. In a letter of St. Bernard to Pope Eugenius III (DuPuy, no. 11), a Templar is specifically refused permission to enter the Cistercian order.

48 The number of Templars at any one time was apparently small though the influence of the order was great. There seems to be no real way of estimating the numbers of the Templars; and most modern historians — e.g., Prutz, Addison, Lea, and others — mindful of the uncertain reliability of statistics found in medieval documents or in the writings of medieval historians, wisely avoid committing themselves. In chapter IV below, however, some comment on the number of known Templars in England at the time of the dissolution of the order will be made. This matter of the size of Templar membership is a problem which could well be looked into in more detail. Checking over some thirty or more references dealing with the Templars in the Holy Land, one gathers that the Templars were able to muster only between one and four hundred knights for any given campaign or battle. The number of Templars outside the Holy Land at any one time is even harder to estimate. Matthew Paris (*Chronica Majora,* RS, IV, 291), writing in reference to the serious Christian losses in the east at the time of the Battle of Gaza (1244), says, probably referring to their financial ability rather than their actual numbers, that the Temple could easily have raised nine thousand soldiers from its houses outside the Holy Land and equipped them for war at the expense of the order. William of Tyre (*op. cit., Lib.* xii, *cap.* 7), writing in the second half of the twelfth

century, says that there were in his own day three hundred knights and countless lesser members.

49 *Règle*, art. 673: "... l'on li puet demander se il est fiz de chevalier et de dame,
et que ses peres soit de lignage de chevaliers; et se il est de loial mariage."
Cf. also, *ibid.*, arts. 337, 431, *et passim*.

50 *Ibid.*, art. 445.

51 *Ibid.*, art. 68 *et passim*.

52 *Ibid.*, arts. 143, 152, 171, 180.

53 *Ibid.*, arts. 135, 181.

54 Cf. *ibid.*, art. 64.

55 *Ibid.*, arts. 268-71. The papal bull of Alexander III, *Omne datum optimum*,
and bulls of his successors not only authorized but guaranteed the Templars
their own priests independent of all ecclesiastical authority save that of Rome
— cf. n. 19 above.

56 *Règle*, arts. 175, 319, 321, *et passim*.

57 *Ibid.*, arts. 22, 65, 66, 69, 632, *et passim*.

58 *Ibid.*, art. 70. On at least one occasion, however, a married woman seems to
have been admitted in England. A certificate of reception of a sister (Lees, p.
210, chapter no. 5) dating from the period 1189-93 is addressed to Geoffrey
Fitz Stephen, then Master of the Temple in England.

59 *Règle*, arts. 14, 56, 70.

60 *Ibid.*, arts. 10, 15, 16, 279-84 *et passim* (prayer); 8, 31, 32, 42 (silence); 26,
27, 28, 30 (food and drink). Realizing the danger of immoderate abstinence
and the needs of military life, the Templar Rule permitted two regular meals
daily and a third at the discretion of the Master, meat three times a week, and
wine. Fasting was not emphasized to the degree it was in many another religious order. Also, special care and consideration were given to the old and
sick — arts. 33, 60, 61, 190-97.

61 *Ibid.*, arts. 148-55, 161-63, 285, 286, 319, 320, 336-84.

62 *Ibid.*, art. 57: "... et poés avoir terres et homes et vilains et chans tenir et
governer justement ..."

63 *Ibid.*, art. 58: "... nos éguardons a vos qui vivés de vie communal diesmes
avoir."

64 The brief survey of Templar history given in the next few pages relies on the
following standard works: Steven Runciman, *A History of the Crusades* (3
vols.; Cambridge, 1951-54), Kenneth M. Setton (ed.), *A History of the Crusades*, Vol. I: *The First Hundred Years*, ed. Marshall W. Baldwin (Philadelphia, 1955); and René Grousset, *Histoire des Croisades et du Royaume franc
de Jérusalem* (3 vols.; Paris, 1939).

65 Cf. Campbell, *op cit.*, p. 40; Runciman, *op. cit.*, II, 183-84.

66 Cf. Campbell, *op. cit.*, p. 50; Grousset, *op. cit.*, II, 250-70; and Runciman,
op. cit., II, 282-86. Some commentators suggested the Templars had been
bribed by the Moslems to give Louis and Conrad bad advice which led to the
failure of the Christian effort.

67 DuPuy, no. 10.

68 For a brief but thorough discussion of this battle, consult R. C. Smail, *Crusading Warfare (1097-1193)*, "Cambridge Studies in Medieval Life and Thought,"
No. 3, N.S. (Cambridge, 1956) pp. 189-97.

69 Campbell (*op. cit.*, pp. 155-66), Grousset (*op. cit.*, III, 311-14, 318-21), and
Runciman (*op. cit.*, III, 182-87) tell the story of Frederick II and his dealings
with the Templars. Cf. the letter to Richard of Cornwall (DuPuy, no. 34) in
which Frederick makes known his views on the conduct of the Templars.
Grousset is especially severe in his discussion of the Templars' dealings with
Frederick.

70 Jean Sire de Joinville, *Histoire de Saint Louis*, ed. Natalis de Wailly (Paris,
1868), p. 135.

[71] Cf. the pertinent remarks of Smail (*op. cit.,* pp. 60-61, 98-101, 205-15) on the importance of the fortresses.

[72] This was late in May. Cf. Campbell, *op. cit.,* p. 196; Runciman, *op. cit.,* III, 420; and Grousset, *op. cit.,* III, 751-62.

[73] For an excellent analysis of disinterest in further crusades, consult Palmer A. Throop (*Criticism of the Crusade: a Study of Public Opinion and Crusade Propaganda* [Amsterdam, 1940], especially pp. 284-88) who argues that a variety of factors are involved: for example, the unwillingness of the ruling classes in the west to sacrifice their own interests for a distant holy war, the decline in interest and suspicion of papal projects arising from the papacy's diversion of crusades from war against the infidel to campaigns against political enemies in Europe, the new nationalism which led people to support their king and his policies rather than those of the pope, and the resentment against being asked to forego material comforts at home for dangerous and distant wars which had become characterized by repeated Christian defeat.

[74] Prutz (*op. cit.,* pp. 14-20, 58-73) discusses the establishment and development of the Templars in these various areas.

Chapter Two

[1] The works of Addison, Campbell, and Williamson, *op. cit.,* are of little value on the origins of the Templars in England. The best and most thorough discussion of this problem is to be found in Lees, pp. xxxviii-xlvii.

[2] *The Anglo-Saxon Chronicle,* ed. and trans. Charles Plummer (2 vols.; Oxford, 1892-99), *sub anno* 1128, I, 259; Roger of Hoveden, *Chronica,* ed. William Stubbs (RS, No. 51; 4 vols.; London, 1868-71), I, 184; Henry of Huntingdon, *The History of the English from A.D. 55 to A.D. 1154,* ed. Thomas Arnold (RS, No. 74; London, 1879), p. 250. Cf. Paris, *Chronica Majora,* RS, I, 208.

[3] Lees, pp. 145-46; D'Albon, *op. cit.,* no. 124.

[4] Lees, p. xli. Cf. also, pp. xxxix-xl.

[5] *Op. cit.,* RS, I, 53: "Denique multo plura sub brevitate temporis, quo Stephanus regnavit, vel potius nomen regis obtinuit, quam centum retro annis servorum et ancillarum Dei monasteria initium in Anglis sumpsisse noscuntur." Using the data to be found in David Knowles' and R. Neville Hadcock's work (*Medieval Religious Houses, England and Wales,* 3 vols. [London, 1953-59], Vol. I *passim*), it would appear that in the century before 1135 there were 297 monasteries and nunneries established, plus 42 hospitals and 61 secular colleges, for a total of 400 religious houses. Under Stephan (1135-54), there were 253 monasteries and nunneries established, plus 44 hospitals and 5 secular colleges, for a total of 302 religious houses. Cf. also, David Knowles, *The Religious Orders in England* (vols. I-II; Cambridge, 1950-55), II, 256.

[6] Lees, p. 176; D'Albon, *op. cit.,* no. 179; Lees, p. 148; D'Albon, *op. cit.,* no. 256; William Dugdale, *Monasticon Anglicanum,* new ed. John Caley, Henry Ellis, and Bulkeley Badinel (7 vols.; London, 1856), VII, 843.

[7] Lees, pp. 148, 177-78; D'Albon, *op. cit.,* nos. 208, 256.

[8] *Ibid.,* nos. 258, 271; Lees, pp. 212-13.

[9] *Ibid.,* pp. 178-79. Though this is the only charter which can be positively assigned to the Empress Matilda, one cannot rule out the possibility that she made additional grants to the Templars. At least one reference in the Inquest of 1185 (Lees, p. 61) can be found to land granted to the Templars by a supporter of Matilda.

[10] "The Sandford Cartulary," ed. Agnes Leys, *Oxfordshire Record Society Publications,* XIX (1937), 1-177 and XXII (1940), 179-328, nos. 1, 6, 25, 39, 74, 89, 164, *et passim;* Lees, pp. 178, 180, 181, 207, 227-29.

[11] *Ibid.,* pp. 198-99.

[12] *Ibid.,* pp. 149-50.

[13] *Ibid.,* p. 156.

[14] *Ibid.,* pp. 203-04.

138   *The Knights Templars in England*

[15] *Ibid.*, p. 137.

[16] For comparative purposes, see Prutz, *op. cit.*, chaps. I-II, where the evolution of the order in France, the western state for which the most information in available, is discussed.

[17] Cf. Lees, pp. lx-xiv.

[18] See above, Chap. I.

[19] "The Knights Templars in the British Isles," *op. cit.*, pp. 222-24. Knowles and Hadcock (*op. cit.*, p. 27), without citing their evidence, suggest that the number of Templars in England in 1308 was 165, including 6 knights and 118 sergeants; and Knowles, *op. cit.*, p. 256, suggests that the total number of the military orders in England was over 600.

[20] *Calendar of Patent Rolls of Edward I, 1272-1307*, ed. under the superintendence of the Deputy Keeper of the Records (4 vols.; London, 1893-1901), III, 391, 483 [27-28 Ed. I (1298-99)].

[21] See Appendix A below for an incomplete list.

[22] Addison (*op. cit.*, p. 494) says that the masters in the provinces were appointed by the Grand Master of the order and could be removed at his discretion.

[23] A royal order (*Close Rolls of the Reign of Henry III, 1216-1272*, ed. under the superintendence of the Deputy Keeper of the Records (14 vols.; London, 1902-38), III, 183 [19 Hen. III (1235)] and *Calendar of Documents Relating to Ireland*, ed. H. S. Sweetman, Vols. I-V [London, 1875-86], I, no. 2264) instructs the justiciar in Ireland to protect the new master there whom the "council and brethren have chosen." If the Master of Ireland – the Preceptor of Ireland (see below, n. 29) was known as master rather than preceptor – was thus chosen, it would seem logical that the Master of England was similarly chosen. This order of royal protection is unique in that the new master was being protected from the old master who was at the time a fugitive from his order. Ordinarily, the election of a master must have proceeded without any need for royal protection.

[24] Cited by Addison, *op. cit.*, p. 496. This is a copy of the oath taken by the Master in France. No copy of an oath for England survives.

[25] Cf. *ClR*, 21 Hen. III (1237), p. 440. This is only one of many references to the Templars' headquarters and chapter meetings at New Temple, London.

[26] Cf. Lees, p. lxv.

[27] Cf. *ClR*, 16 Hen. III (1231), p. 8; *CPatR*, 21 Ed. I (1293), p. 26. These two entries are typical of the phraseology in hundreds of such grants to the Templars.

[28] Cf. Lees, pp. lxvii-lxxi. The Rule, which is overwhelmingly concerned with the east, does not speak of subordinate provincial officials.

[29] *CPatR*, 25-29 Ed. I (1297-1301), pp. 313, 391, 483, 572; *ibid.*, 30-35 Ed. I (1302-13), pp. 31, 138, 222, 384, 499.

[30] See below, the section of this chapter where an indication of the preceptories is given in the survey of Templar holdings in England and Appendix B.

[31] Perkins ("The Knights Templars in England," *op. cit.*, Appendix D) cites only eighteen known preceptors among the prisoners at the time of the Templars' trial. Addison (*op cit.*, p. 426) refers to the Preceptor of Denney and Dokesworth in Cambridgeshire and the Preceptor of Sandford and Bistlesham in Oxfordshire.

[32] Cf. Lees, pp. 169, n. 8; 170, n. 7; 231, n. 1; 238, n. 10, 244.

[33] If Jacques de Molay, the Grand Master of the order was illiterate – as he himself affirmed at his second interrogation in 1309 (DuPuy, no. 82) – then, it can hardly be expected that many of the other Templars, excluding the chaplains, were literate. Cf. *Règle*, p. xxvi.

[34] In the corrody payments authorized by Edward II while the Templar properties were in his hands, references are found to chaplains and clerks attached to Templar houses – e.g., chaplains: 2 at New Temple, and 1 each at Temple Bruer, Eagle, Wetherby, Upleden, and Garewy; clerks: 5 at New Temple, 2 at

Temple Bruer, and 1 each at Temple Dinsley, Stocton, and Garewy (*CClR*, 5-6 Ed. II [1312-13], pp. 388, 410, 429-30, 482, 512; *ibid.*, 8 Ed. II [1315], pp. 232, 269, 270; and *ibid.*, 5-6 Ed. II [1311-13], pp. 388, 409, 422-23, 473, 482, 483, 492, 510, 516). The task of these chaplains and clerks is not indicated, but they most likely rendered religious and clerical services respectively. There is no way of knowing whether or not this is a complete list of these persons.

[35] Lees, pp. 175, 248, 250.

[36] *Op. cit.*, pp. 494-95.

[37] Cf. Lees, pp. 158, 166, 170, 217, 245, 246, 248; *Règle*, p. xxviii, arts. 11, 36, 328, *et passim; CPatR*, 50 Hen. III (1266), p. 86.

[38] Lees, pp. 169, n. 8; 170; 171; 217, n. 12; 226.

[39] Cf. *ibid.*, p. lxv.

[40] Pp. lxx-lxxi.

[41] Cf. *ibid.*, p. lxxxiii — e.g., Finchingfield in Essex.

[42] *Ibid.*, pp. lxxx, cxvi — e.g., Cressing-Witham and Cowley on the honour of Boulogne.

[43] *Ibid.*, pp. xcvi-vii, cv-vi, cxxii, cxxxvi, clxxii, ccvi, ccx-xii — e.g., the fees of Lacy, Clare, Mowbray, *et al.*

[44] *Ibid.*, pp. cxix, cxlvii, cli, clxxv, cxcix, ccii-v, ccx — e.g., the lands of Harcourt, Basset, Vilers, *et al.*

[45] *Ibid.*, pp. xcvi, 25, 164 — e.g., the benefactions of the Archbishop of Canterbury, of the monks of Bermondesey, *et al.*

[46] *Ibid.*, pp. xxvi, cli.

[47] "The Sandford Cartulary," *op. cit.*, nos. 24, 50, 52, 53, 56, 64, 66, 69, 72, 73, 77, 78, 85, 86, 120, 125, 180-83, 187-91, 193-96, 200-02, 231, 232, 234, 235, 242; Lees, pp. 196, 204, 223, 273.

[48] *Ibid.*, p. 197; "The Sandford Cartulary," *op. cit.*, nos. 185, 306, 328, 410, 446, 468.

[49] E. A. Kosminsky, *Studies in the Agrarian History of England in the Thirteenth Century,* "Studies in Medieval History," Vol. VIII, ed. Geoffrey Barraclough, trans. Ruth Kisch (Oxford, 1956), pp. 98, 270.

[50] *Ibid.*, pp. 112, 116: 20% large, 14% medium, and 66% small.

[51] *Ibid.*, pp. 113, 116.

[52] *Ibid.*, p. 104.

[53] *Ibid.*, — citing *Rot. Hund.*, II, 581.

[54] Some data of a comparative sort can be obtained by examination of certain entries in the Domesday Book, the Inquest of 1185, and the Hospitaller Report of 1338. Some idea of the methods used in the administration of medieval estates can be gotten from N. Denholm-Young, *Seignorial Administration in England* (Oxford, 1937), especially chaps. II and IV.

[55] See the Inquest, *sub verbis.*

[56] Cf. Kosminsky, *op. cit.*, pp. 55-56.

[57] Lees, pp. 117-34.

[58] *Ibid.*, pp. 13-16.

[59] Cf. *Ibid.*, pp. lxxi, lxxxiv, 75-76, 83-84, 86-90, 92, 95-97 *et passim.*

[60] *Ibid.*, pp. 11-12 — as at Finchingfield in Essex.

[61] *Ibid.*, also at Finchingfield.

[62] *Ibid.*, p. 34 — in Leicestershire.

[63] *Ibid.*, p. 36 — in Warwickshire.

[64] *Ibid.*, p. 65 — in Hertfordshire.

[65] *Ibid.*, p. 125 — in Yorkshire.

[66] E. Lipson, *An Introduction to the Economic History of England,* Vol. I: *The Middle Ages* (London, 1915), pp. 89-103; W. Cunningham, *The Growth of English Industry and Commerce during the Early and Middle Ages,* 5th ed.,

Vol. I (Cambridge, 1910), pp. 233-34; W. J. Ashley, *An Introduction to English Economic History and Theory,* Vol. I, 4th ed. (London, 1923), Part I, pp. 20-23, 46-48.

[67] *Op. cit.,* pp. 44, 164, 191-92, 276.

[68] *Ibid.,* pp. 31, 44, 164, 167.

[69] *Ibid.,* pp. 240, 327. Cf. also, the same author's "Services and Money Rents in the Thirteenth Century," *Economic History Review,* V (1935), 24-25; and Hans Nabholz, "Medieval Agrarian Society in Transition," *Cambridge Economic History of Europe from the Decline of the Roman Empire,* Vol. I, ed. J. H. Clapham and Eileen Power (Cambridge, 1941), pp. 504, 508.

[70] *Ibid.,* p. 503.

[71] E.g., *CClR,* 5-6 Ed. II (1311-12), pp. 388, 397, 429, 430 *et passim.*

[72] E.g., *ibid.,* pp. 385, 388, 397, 409, *et passim.*

[73] E.g., *ibid.,* 5 Ed. II (1312), pp. 409, 413, 423, *et passim.*

[74] E.g., *ibid.,* pp. 397, 409, 422, *et passim.*

[75] E.g., *ibid.,* pp. 385, 388, 397, 409, *et passim.*

[76] Cf., *ibid.,* pp. 393, 413, 423, 468, 476, 493, *et passim.*

[77] "Corrodia petita de domibus Templariorum – annis I° et II° Edwardi II[i] et aliis annis sequentibus," ed. Henry Cole, *Documents illustrative of English History in the Thirteenth and Fourteenth Centuries, selected from the Records of the Department of the Queen's Remembrancer of the Exchequer* (London, 1844), pp. 139-230.

[78] Cf. Addison, *op. cit.,* p. 475.

[79] Williamson, *op. cit.,* p. 8.

[80] Léopold Delisle (ed.), *Receuil des actes de Henri II, roi d'Angleterre et duc de Normandie, concernant les provinces françaises et les affaires de France* (3 vols.; Paris, 1916-27), I, 312.

[81] It is often assumed that the Templars did not move to their new headquarters at New Temple until 1185, the date of the dedication of their round church there. However, Williamson (*op. cit.,* p. 9, n. 4) suggests that the date must have been earlier, sometime after 1163, the date of the sale of Holborn church, and before 1185.

[82] The New Temple Church was restored in 1829. For a picture and a sketch of the church, see *ibid.,* frontispiece, and Dugdale, VII, opposite p. 817.

[83] Roger of Wendover, *op. cit.,* RS, I, 133-36; Ralph de Diceto, *Opera Historica,* ed. William Stubbs (RS, No. 68; 2 vols.; London, 1876), II, 27, 32. (The Patriarch of Jerusalem had left the Holy Land with the Grand Prior of the Hospitallers and the Grand Master of the Templars, but only he and the Grand Prior arrived in England since the Grand Master had died at Verona, Italy.)

[84] Henry had summoned his Great Council to meet at the Hospitallers' house of Clerkenwell at this time: Roger of Wendover, *op. cit.,* RS, I, 135.

[85] For details of the Templar buildings in London at the time of the dissolution, see Williamson, *op. cit.,* pp. 70-72.

[86] Cf. *ibid.,* p. 9.

[87] *Ibid.*

[88] Sir Edward Coke, *The Second Part of the Institutes of the Laws of England,* Vol. II (London, 1797), p. 431.

[89] Lees, p. 137.

[90] *Ibid.,* p. 138.

[91] *Ibid.,* pp. 139-40.

[92] *Calendar of Charter Rolls preserved in the Public Record Office,* ed. under the superintendence of the Deputy Keeper of the Records (6 vols.; London, 1903-54), I, 4 [11 Hen. III (1227)] – a confirmation of John's charter.

[93] *Rotuli Litterarum Clausarum in Turri Londinensi asservati,* ed. Thomas D. Hardy (2 vols.; London, 1833-44), II, 171 [11 Hen. III (1227)]; *CChR,* 11

Hen. III (1227), p. 4; Dugdale, VII, 844; and cf. *ClR*, 14 Hen. III (1230), pp. 391-92.

⁹⁴ *CChR*, 9 Ed. I (1280), pp. 237-38.

⁹⁵ Cf. Lees, p. lxxi.

⁹⁶ Cf. Richard Fitzneale, *Dialogus de Scaccario*, ed. and trans. Charles Johnson (London, [1950]), p. 51 (1178); *ClR*, 48 Hen. III (1264), pp. 358-59; *ibid.*, 36 Hen. III (1252), p. 190 in reference to a local grant in Hereford; Johannes de Oxenedes, *Chronica*, ed. Henry Ellis (RS, No. 13; London, 1859), p. 235 (1168).

⁹⁷ Lees, pp. 138 (charter of Henry II, 1154-55), 139-40 (charter of Richard I, 1189); Rymer, I, 49 (charter of Richard I); *CChR*, 9 Ed. I (1280), p. 237 (confirmation of grant of 37 Hen. III).

⁹⁸ *RLC*, 4 Hen. III (1220), I, 428b; *CChR*, 9 Ed. I (1280), p. 237 – confirmation of the charter of 37 Hen. III.

⁹⁹ *Ibid.*, 19 Hen. III (1235), pp. 192-93; *ClR*, 30 Hen. III (1246), p. 412; *ibid.*, 37 Hen. III (1252), p. 428; *CClR*, 32 Ed. I (1304), pp. 145, 202; *CChR*, 9 Ed. I (1280), p. 237.

¹⁰⁰ *ClR*, 13-15 Hen. III (1228-31), pp. 131, 548; *ibid.*, 18 Hen. III (1234), p. 404; *CChR*, 26 Hen. III (1242), p. 267; *ClR*, 36-37 Hen. III (1252), pp. 170-71, 267-68, 384; *CPatR*, 47 Hen. III (1263), p. 281; *Cal. Doc. rel. to Ire.*, I, nos. 312, 2101; *Chartularies of St. Mary's Abbey, Dublin: with the Register of its House at Dunbrody, and the Annals of Ireland*, ed. John T. Gilbert (RS, No. 80; 2 vols.; London, 1884), I, 269 (1192).

¹⁰¹ *RLC*, 8 Hen. III (1224), p. 594b.

¹⁰² *CChR*, 51 Hen. III (1267), p. 62; *CPatR*, 53 Hen. III (1269), p. 330; *Annales de Burton*, ed. Henry R. Luard, in *Annales Monastici* (RS, No. 36; 5 vols.; London, 1864-69), I, 325 (1254); *Annales Monasterii de Wintonia*, *ibid.*, II, 104 (1266); *Annales Monasterii de Waverleia*, *ibid.*, II, 373 (1266); *Chronicles of the Mayors and Sheriffs of London*, trans. Henry T. Riley (London, 1863), p. 162 (1272); *Cal. Doc. rel. to Ire.*, III, no. 873; Bliss, I, 432 (Clement V, 1266), 444 (Gregory X, 1272), 551-52 (Nicholas V, 1291).

¹⁰³ *CClR*, 29 Ed. I (1301), p. 471; *CPatR*, 29 Ed. I (1301), p. 598; Statutes of Westminster, 3 Ed. I (1275), in the *Register of Malmesbury Abbey*, ed. J. S. Brewer (RS, No. 72; 2 vols.; London, 1879), I, 504.

¹⁰⁴ *Les Registres d'Innocent IV publiés ou analysés d'après les manuscrits originaux du Vatican et de la Bibliothèque nationale*, ed. Elie Berger (3 vols.; Paris, 1884-97), nos. 2053, 3551.

¹⁰⁵ *ClR*, 21 Hen. III (1239), pp. 566-67, 569.

¹⁰⁶ *CClR*, 18 Ed. I (1290), p. 67; *The Book of Fees commonly called Testa de Nevill* (3 vols.; London, 1920-31), II, 832 [1242-43, Oxfordshire]; *Magna Carta* in Rymer, I, 131-32.

¹⁰⁷ *ClR*, 48 Hen. III (1264), p. 359.

¹⁰⁸ *CChR*, 11 Hen. III (1227), p. 4; *ibid.*, 9 Ed. I (1280), pp. 237-38 – a confirmation of the grant of 37 Hen. III (1253).

¹⁰⁹ *RLC*, 17 John (1215), I, 238; *ibid.*, 8 Hen. III (1224), I, 599b; *PatR*, 9 Hen. III (1225), p. 517; *ibid.*, 10-12 Hen. III (1226-28), pp. 24, 105, 196-97; *ibid.*, 14 Hen. III (1230), p. 368, 374-75.

¹¹⁰ *RLC*, 15-17 John (1213-14), I, 148b, 214; *ibid.*, 8 Hen. III (1224), I, 609; *ibid.*, 9-10 Hen. III (1225-26), II, 51, 110; *ClR*, 15 Hen. III (1231), p. 519; Rymer, I, 115; *Cal. Doc. rel. to Ire.*, no. 1276.

¹¹ *ClR*, 46-47. Hen. III (1262), pp. 160-61; *CClR*, 21-22 Ed. I (1293), pp. 289, 339; *Cal. Doc. rel. to Ire.*, II, no. 1672; *CChR*, 9 Ed. I (1280), p. 237.

¹¹² *Ibid.*, 32-37 Hen. III (1248-53), pp. 331, 414, 415; *ibid.*, 31 Ed. I (1303), p. 33; *Placita de Quo Warranto temporibus Edw. I, II, et III in Curia receptae Scaccarij Westm. asservata* (London, 1818), pp. 281, 291.

¹¹³ *CChR*, 11 Hen. III (1227), p. 5; *ibid.*, 9 Ed. I (1280), p. 237 – confirmation

of the grant of 37 Hen. III; Rymer, I, 49 (charter of Richard I, 1189); Lees, p. 139 (charter of Richard I, 1189).

[114] *CClR*, 9 Ed. I (1280), p. 237.

[115] *ClR*, 35 Hen. III (1252), p. 534.

[116] *RLC*, 7 Hen. III (1222), I, 558. This grant refers to the privilege as dating back to the time of John. Cf. Assize Roll, p. 325 – cited in *The Victoria History of the County of Hertford*, ed. William Page, Vols. II-IV (London, 1908-14), III, 10.

[117] *Calendar of Documents preserved in France illustrative of the History of Great Britain and Ireland*, ed. J. Horace Round, Vol. I (London, 1899), pp. 91-92 [1 Ric. I (1189)]; Lees, p. 139; *CChR*, 9 Ed. I (1280), p. 237.

[118] *ClR*, 16 Hen. III (1232), p. 92; *CClR*, 25 Ed. I (1297), p. 10; *CChR*, 9 Ed. I (1280), p. 237.

[119] Lees, pp. 137-39; *CChR*, 9 Ed. I (1280), pp. 237-38.

[120] Rymer, I, 49; Lees, p. 139; *ClR*, 36 Hen. III (1251-52), pp. 10, 69.

[121] Lees, p. 140; Rymer, I, 74; *CChR*, 9 Ed. I (1280), pp. 237-38; *Assize Roll*, p. 325 – cited in *VCH: Hertfordshire*, III, 10.

[122] Lees, pp. 137-40; Rymer, I, 49, 78; *RLC*, 7 Hen. III (1223), I, 558; *CChR*, 9 Ed. I (1280), pp. 237-38.

[123] *ClR*, 55-56 Hen. III (1271-72), pp. 397, 427, 553, 562, 563, *CClR*, 9-16 Ed. I (1279-88), pp. 111, 299, 344-45, 364, 407, 413, 471, 539; *ibid.*, 17-22 Ed. I (1288-93), pp. 29, 262, 263, 270, 271, 274, 378; *ibid.*, 30 Ed. I (1302), p. 599.

[124] *Cal. Docs. in France*, p. 92, (10 Ric. I [1198]), *ClR*, 19 Hen. III (1235), p. 110, Cf. *Rotuli de Oblatis et Finibus in Turri Londinensi asservati, tempore Regis Johannis*, ed. Thomas D. Hardy ([London], 1835), p. 175; *Calendar of Fine Rolls preserved in the Public Record Office*, ed. A. E. Bland, Vol. I (London, 1911), p. 95; and *Cal. Docs. rel. to Ire.*, I, no 168.

[125] *CChR*, 9 Ed. I (1280), p. 238.

[126] Cf. Lees, pp. 137-39; *CChR*, 9 Ed. I (1280), pp. 237-38.

[127] Coke, *op. cit.*, p. 431. Cf. Lees, p. 256 (Lincolnshire charter no. 14).

[128] Coke (*op. cit.*, p. 431) stated that the thirty-third chapter of the Statute of 13 Ed. I (1285) prohibited unauthorized use of the Templar cross on penalty of forfeiture of land to the superior lord or to the king. *Statutes of the Realm*, I, 87. Cf. *Historic and Municipal Documents of Ireland,, A.D. 1172-1320, from the Archives of the City of Dublin*, ed. J. T. Gilbert (RS No. 53; London, 1870), p. 255.

[129] The best example of the appeal of the Templars is found in the *Rotuli Parliamentorum; ut et Petitiones et Placita in parliamento tempore Edwardi R. I.* ([London], 1767), p. 2b [5 Ed. I (1276)]. Information on other appeals is gained indirectly from royal and papal orders as cited in nn. 130 and 131 below.

[130] Cf. *RLC*, 11 Hen. III (1227), p. 587; *ClR*, 22 Hen. III (1238), p. 76; *CPatR*, 50 Hen. III (1266), p. 587; *Calendar of Chancery Warrants preserved in the Public Record Office, A.D. 1244-1326*, prepared under the superintendence of the Deputy Keeper of the Records, Vol. I (London, 1927), I, 235 *et passim* [32 Ed. I (1304)].

[131] Rymer, I, 37 (Lucius III, 1183), 189 (Gregory IX, 1228), 333 (Alexander IV, 1255), 335 (Alexander IV, 1256), 497 (Gregory X, 1272).

[132] *Selected Letters of Pope Innocent III concerning England (1198-1216)*, ed. C. R. Cheney and W. H. Semple (London, [1953]), p. 96.

[133] Cf. *Rotuli Curiae Regis: Rolls and Records of the Court held before the King's Justiciar or Justices, from the Sixth Year of King Richard I to the Accession of King John*, ed. Francis Palgrave (2 vols.; [London,] 1835), II, 266 [1 John (1199)]; *Curia Regis Rolls of the Reigns of John and Henry III preserved in the Public Record Office*, ed. C. T. Fowler *et al.* (11 vols.; London, 1922-55), II, 128 [4 John (1202)]; *ibid.*, 8 John (1206), p. 279; *ibid.*, 4 Hen. III (1220),

p. 182; *ClR,* 21 Hen. III (1237), p. 515; *ibid.,* 36 Hen. III (1251), pp. 10, 220; *CClR,* 21 Ed. I (1293), p. 294.

[134] The Pipe Rolls published thus far cover the reigns of Henry II, Richard, and John to the fourteenth year. The Pipe Rolls for the reigns of Henry III, Edward I, and Edward II, since they as yet exist in manuscript form only, have not been used here.

[135] *The Great Roll of the Pipe for the Fifth Year of the Reign of King John,* ed. Doris Stenton, "Publications of the Pipe Roll Society," Vol. XVI N.S. (London, 1938, p. 203 [5 John (1203)]; *ibid.,* 9 John (1207), pp. 59, 63. Cf. also, *Pipe R,* 12 Hen. II (1165-66), p. 121; *ibid.,* 1 Ric. I (1189), pp. 126, 184, 185; *CClR,* 21-22 Ed. I (1293), pp. 289, 339. (These citations, and the subsequent ones, give only a few references by way of illustration and do not pretend to be complete.)

[136] *Pipe R,* 6 Hen. II (1159-60), p. 34; *The Chancellor's Roll for the eighth Year of the Reign of King Richard the First, Michaelmas 1196,* ed. Doris M. Stenton, "Publications of the Pipe Roll Society," Vol. VII N.S. (London, 1930), p. 35 [8 Ric. I (1196)]; *RLC,* 3 Hen. III (1219), I, 398; *CChR,* 11 Hen. III (1227), p. 5.

[137] *Pipe R,* 9 Ric. I (1197), p. 47; *Chancellor's R,* 8 Ric. I (1196), p.233.

[138] *Pipe R,* 3-4 Ric. I (1191-92), p. 14.

[139] *Ibid.,* pp. 187, 272, 290; *ibid.,* 7 Ric. I (1195), p. 9.

[140] *Ibid.,* 6 Ric. I (1194), p. 229.

[141] *Ibid.,* 24 Hen. II (1177-78), pp. 85, 96; *ibid.,* 1 John (1199), p. 11; *ibid.,* 14 Hen. III (1230), p. 255; *CPatR,* 21 Ed. I (1293), p. 56.

[142] *Pipe R,* 3-4 Ric. I (1191-92), p. 278.

[143] See below, n. 163.

[144] *Pipe R,* 14 Hen. III (1230), p. 279.

[145] *Ibid.,* 2 Ric. I (1190), p. 127; *ibid.,* 33 Hen. II (1186-87), p. 79.

[146] *Chancellor's R,* 8 Ric. I (1196), pp. 57, 180.

[147] *Pipe R,* 6 Ric. I (1194), p. 161; *ibid.,* 7 Ric. I (1195), pp. 89, 90.

[148] *Ibid.,* 16 Hen. II (1169-70), p. 133; *ibid.,* 22 Hen. II (1175-76), p. 29; *ibid.,* 31 Hen. II (1184-85), pp. 51, 59, 140; *ibid.,* 2 Ric. I (1190), p. 127; *ibid.,* 10 Ric. I (1198), pp. 73, 164; *ibid.,* 1 John (1194), pp. 156, 175, 257.

[149] *Ibid.,* 5 Ric. I (1193), p. 152; *ibid.,* 1 John (1199), p. 101.

[150] *Ibid.,* 5 Ric. I (1193), p. 51; *ibid.,* 6 Ric. I (1194), p. 112.

[151] See below, n. 162.

[152] *Rot. de Oblatis,* 1 John (1199), p. 73; *ibid.,* 2 John (1200), p. 101; *Pipe R,* 2 John (1200), p. 154; *Rot. de Oblatis,* 1 John (1199), p. 13.

[153] *Ibid.,* 3 John (1201), p. 175; *Pipe R,* 3 John (1201), p. 263.

[154] *Ibid.,* 11 John (1209), p. 30.

[155] *Annales Monasterii de Waverleia, op. cit.,* RS, II, 264; *Annales Monasterii de Bermundeseia, ibid.,* RS, III, 452; Paris, *Chronica Majora,* RS, II, 530.

[156] *Rot. de Oblatis,* 17-18 John (1216), p. 576.

[157] *PatR,* 10 Hen. III (1226), p. 17; *ClR,* 29 Hen. III (1244), pp. 265-66.

[158] *Taxatio ecclesiastica Angliae et Walliae auctoritate P. Nicholai IV, circa A.D. 1291* (London, 1802), pp. 61b, 62b, 167b.

[159] Cf. *ibid.,* pp. 59b, 61, 63b, 299, 310b.

[160] *RLC,* 4 Hen. III (1220), I, 428b.

[161] *Ibid.*

[162] Scutage: *Pipe R,* 14 Hen. III (1230), p. 148; *The Memoranda Roll of the King's Remembrancer for Michaelmas 1230 — Trinity 1231,* ed. Chalfant Robinson, "Publications of the Pipe Roll Society," Vol. XI (Princeton, 1933), pp. 16, 36, 42, 62, 73 [14-15 Hen. III (1230-31)]; *Pipe R,* 9 John (1207), p. 214. Tallage: *ibid.,* 10 Ric. I (1198), p. 7; *ibid.,* 1 John (1199), p. 26; *Memoranda*

R, 1 John (1199), pp. 20, 39; *Pipe R*, 2 John (1199), pp. 100, 126; *ibid.*, 3 John (1201), p. 29; *ibid.*, 8 John (1206), p. 118.

[163] Scutage: *Pipe R*, 3-4 Ric. I (1191-92), p. 151; *Memoranda R*, 1 John (1199-1200), p. 38. Tallage: *Pipe R*, 20 Hen. II (1173-74), p. 23; *ibid.*, 7 Ric. I (1195), p. 110; *ibid.*, 1 John (1199), p. 144; *ibid.*, 3 John (1201), pp. 287, 288; *ibid.*, 7 John (1205), pp. 99, 118; *ibid.*, 8 John (1206), p. 1.

[164] Scutage: *CClR*, 18 Ed. I (1289), p. 67. Tallage: *ClR*, 39 Hen. III (1255), p. 83.

[165] *Ibid.; Ibid.*, 45 Hen. III (1261), p. 389; *ibid.*, 52 Hen. III (1268), p. 483.

[166] *RLC*, 8 Hen. III (1224), I 594b.

[167] Bartholomew de Cotton, *Historia Anglicana*, ed. Henry R. Luard (RS, No. 16; London, 1859), pp. 208-09.

[168] *CPatR*, 40 Hen. III (1256), p. 511; *ibid.*, 44 Hen. III (1259-60), pp. 99, 112.

[169] Bliss, pp. 429 (Clement IV, 1265), 432 (Clement IV, 1266), 444 (Gregory X, 1272), 551-52 (Nicholas V, 1291); *Annales de Burton, op. cit.*, RS, I 325 (1254); Johannes de Oxenedes, *op. cit.*, RS, p. 232; *Annales Monasterii de Wintona, op. cit.*, RS, II, 104 (1266); *Annales Monasteria de Waverleia, op. cit.*, RS, II, 373 (1266); *Chronicles and Memorials of the Mayors and Sheriffs of London*, p. 162 (1272).

[170] *CPatR*, 40 Hen. III (1256), p. 524. Cf. *Reg. d'Inn. IV*, nos. 2777, 5131. A statute of Westminister of 1274 (*Register of Malmesbury Abbey*, RS, I, 504) stated, with regard to the grant by Parliament of a fifteenth to Edward I, that, though the Templars were exempted from the payment, their men, free or villein, were to be taxed.

[171] *CClR*, 17 Hen. III (1233), pp. 284, 293, 300, 301, 303; *CPatR*, 29 Ed. I (1301), p. 606.

[172] *PatR*, 10 Hen. III (1226), p. 17; *CClR*, 34 Ed. I (1306), p. 221.

[173] *CRR*, 8 John (1206), p. 279.

[174] *CClR*, 21 Ed. I (1293), p. 288.

[175] *CPatR*, 6 Ed. II (1312), pp. 536, 538-39, 541, 545-46.

[176] Cf. *ibid.*, 26-27 Hen. III (1242), p. 333.

[177] *CChanWar*, 26 Ed. I (1298), I, 93.

[178] Cf. *ClR*, 24 Hen. III (1240), p. 203 where the Templars' tenants are to help with the construction of a wall, and *ClR*, 35 Hen. III (1251), p. 534 where they are exempted from such service.

[179] *Pipe R*, 17 Hen. II (1170-71), p. 108; *ibid.*, 23 Hen. II (1176-77), p. 43; *Cal. Docs. rel. to Ire.*, I, no. 168; *Rot. de Oblatis*, p. 175; *Pipe R*, 3 John (1201), p. 263.

[180] *ClR*, 37 Hen. III (1252), p. 428; *ibid.*, 38 Hen. III (1254), p. 113; *ibid.*, 48 Hen. III (1264), pp. 357-58; *CClR*, 22 Ed. I (1293), p. 339. Cf. *Cal. of Fine Rolls*, 6 Ed. I (1278), p. 95 where the king orders his sheriff in Yorkshire to proceed against the Templars despite their claim of immunity from prosecution except before the king or his chief justice.

[181] *CPatR*, 1-9 Hen. III (1217-24), pp. 87, 436, 500; *ibid.*, 14-15 Hen. III (1230-31), pp. 338, 433; *ibid.*, 43-50 Hen. III (1259-66), pp. 47, 78, 598; *ibid*, 55 Hen. III (1271), p. 542; *ibid.*, 5-8 Ed. I (1277-80), pp. 233, 381; *ibid.*, 10-20 Ed. I (1282-91), pp. 19, 20, 463; *ibid.*, 32-35 Ed. I (1304-07), pp. 222, 501.

[182] *PatR*, 13 Hen. III (1229), p. 239; *CPatR*, 20 Hen. III (1236), p. 147; *ibid.*, 51 Hen. III (1267), p. 76; *ibid.*, 25 Ed. I (1297), p. 238.

[183] *CClR*, 25 Ed. I (1297), p. 16.

[184] Lees, p. 1.

[185] Cf. *ibid.*, pp. xxx, lvi.

[186] Cf. *ibid.*, p. lxxxiii.

[187] Cf. *ibid.*, pp. lxxix, lxxxiii, cviii, clxxii. Probably the commonest sizes were 240 acres for a carucate; 120, for a hide; 30, for a virgate; and 24, for a bovate. Cf. Ashley, *op. cit.*, Part I, pp. 7-8; Kosminsky, *op. cit.*, pp. 35-36.

[188] *The Knights Hospitallers in England: Being the Report of Prior Philip de Thame to the Grand Master Elyan de Villanova for A.D. 1338*, ed. Lambert B. Larking, "Camden Society Publications," Vol. LXV (London, 1857), pp. 133-99.

[189] Cf. John Kemble in the introduction to the report, *ibid.*, p. lxix.

[190] Cf. *ibid.*, pp. 212-13.

[191] For example, lands in the counties of Surrey, Hertford, Norfolk, Suffolk, Berkshire, and Nottingham are omitted.

[192] The Victoria County Histories, *passim*, and Perkins, "Knights Templars in England," *op. cit.*, Appendix E, provide data taken from the manuscripts. Also very valuable is the list of Templar houses in England and Wales in Knowles and Hadcock, *op. cit.*, pp. 235-39.

[193] *VCH: Yorkshire*, III, 257. Cf. E. J. Martin, "The Templars in Yorkshire," *Yorkshire Archaeological Journal*, XXIX (1930), 366-85 and XXX (1931), 135-56.

[194] Dugdale, VII, 817, 838; Lees, pp. 270-71. Cf. H. E. Chetwynd-Stapylton, "The Templars at Templehurst," *Yorkshire Archaeological and Topographical Journal*, X (1889), 276-86 and 431-43.

[195] *VCH: Yorkshire*, III, 258-60.

[196] *Ibid.*, p. 259. Cf. however, Lees, pp. 263-64.

[197] *Ibid.*, p. 260.

[198] Dugdale, VII, 838; *VCH: Yorkshire*, III, 258. Cf. R. V. Taylor, "Ribston and the Knights Templars," *Yorkshire Archaeological and Topographical Journal*, VII (1882), 429-52; VIII (1884), 259-99; IX (1886), 71-98; and Alfred Brett, "The Manor of Wetherby and Lands within the Manor," *Yorkshire Archaeological Journal*, XXX (1931), 261-73; Knowles and Hadcock, *op. cit.*, pp. 237, 239. Cf. *CChR*, 11 Hen. III (1227), p. 27.

[199] *VCH: Yorkshire*, III, 257.

[200] *Ibid.*, II, 428. Knowles and Hadcock (*op. cit.*, pp. 236, 239) suggest Foulbridge had come into existence by 1226 and Whitley by 1248.

[201] *VCH: Yorkshire*, III, 257-58.

[202] There is no general agreement on the exact income accruing to the crown in 1308. The figures given here and in the following paragraphs, usually in terms of the average net income while in the hands of the king, are taken from Perkins, "The Knights Templars in England," *op. cit.*, Appendix E; Knowles and Hadcock, *op. cit.*, pp. 235-39; and pertinent sections of the Victoria County Histories.

[203] *VCH: Yorkshire*, III, 257.

[204] *Hosp. Rpt.*, pp. 135-43; *VCH: Yorkshire*, III, 257.

[205] Dugdale, VII, 835; *VCH: Lincolnshire*, II, 211.

[206] *Ibid.*, pp. 35, 210-13; Dugdale, VII, 804, 835-36.

[207] *Ibid.*, p. 835; *VCH: Lincolnshire*, II, 211-12.

[208] Lees, pp. 250-51; *VCH: Lincolnshire*, II, 212.

[209] *Ibid.*, p. 312.

[210] *Ibid.*

[211] Lees, p. clxxix.

[212] Dugdale, VII, 801-05; *Hosp. Rpt.*, pp. 144-62.

[213] Cf. Perkins, "Knights Templars in England," *op. cit.*, Appendix E; *VCH: Lancashire*, II, 102; Knowles and Hadcock, *op. cit.*, pp. 235-39; *Hosp. Rpt.*, p. 133.

[214] *Ibid.*, p. 199.

[215] Dugdale, VII, 817. Cf. Addison, *op. cit.*, p. 485.

[216] *VCH: Worcestershire*, III, 31, 117, 377, 505-06; IV, 444-45; *CClR*, 56 Hen. III (1272), p. 556.

[217] *Hosp. Rpt.*, p. 195; Perkins, "Knights Templars in England," *op. cit.*, Appendix E.

146   The Knights Templars in England

Dugdale, VII, 838; *Hosp. Rpt.,* pp. 183-85.
²¹⁹ *Ibid.,* pp. 187-88; Lees, pp. cxxiii, cxxviii, 206-10. Rockley dates back to the late 1150's and was a gift of John Marshall.
²²⁰ Lees, pp. 60-62.
²²¹ *Hosp. Rpt.,* pp. xx-xxii, 133, 179, 183-88, 195, 199; Knowles and Hadcock, *op. cit.,* pp. 235-39.
²²² Lees, p. 145; D'Albon, *op. cit.,* no. 124; Dugdale, VII, 817, 820, 838.
²²³ Granted by Stephen and confirmed by Henry II: Lees, pp. 141, 149-53; D'Albon, *op. cit.,* nos. 482-84; Dugdale, VII, 821, 838; *VCH: Essex,* II, 177.
²²⁴ Lees, p. 148; *VCH: Essex,* II, 177.
²²⁵ Lees, p. 174; *VCH: Kent,* II, 175; *Rotuli Hundredorum temp. Hen. III & Edw. I in Turr' Lon' et in curia receptae scaccarij Westm asservati,* ed. W. Illingworth (2 vols.; London, 1812-18), I, 222.
²²⁶ Perhaps the Templars owned Shipley as early as 1125 or 1139 — cf. Lees, p. 227; *VCH: Sussex,* II, 92.
²²⁷ Dugdale, VII, 817, 820, 834, 840; Lees, pp. 227-28, 232-40; *VCH: Sussex,* II, 92-93.
²²⁸ Cf. Lees, pp. 134-35; *Hosp. Rpt.,* pp. 166-67.
²²⁹ *VCH: Surrey,* III, 358; IV, 149, 165.
²³⁰ Lees, pp. 203-04; Dugdale, VII, 819; *VCH: Berkshire,* II, 133; III, 73, 139, 145-46; IV, 315.
²³¹ Dugdale, VII, 836, 843; *VCH: Hampshire,* II, 105; III, 7, 10; V, 117, 163. *CChR,* 24 Hen. III (1240), p. 251.
²³² *Hosp. Rpt.,* p. 213.
²³³ *Ibid.,* pp. 168-70, 173-75.
²³⁴ Dugdale, VII, 833, 838, 843; Lees, pp. 176-78; D'Albon, *op. cit.,* nos. 178-79; *VCH: Oxfordshire,* II, 106-07.
²³⁵ Dugdale, VII, 833, 834; Lees, pp. 184-89, 190-94; *VCH: Oxfordshire,* II, 106.
²³⁶ *Ibid.;* Dugdale, VII, 833, 842; "The Sandford Cartulary," *op. cit.,* VI, nos. 3, 6, 25, 74; *VCH: Oxfordshire,* II, 106-07.
²³⁷ Dugdale, VII, 823, 836; *VCH: Gloucestershire,* II, 113; Lees, pp. 47-49.
²³⁸ Cf. *ibid.,* p. cxxxii.
²³⁹ *Ibid.; Hosp. Rpt.,* pp. 182-84.
²⁴⁰ Dugdale, VII, 817; *VCH: Leicestershire,* II, 31-32; *CChR,* 15 Hen. III (1231), p. 135.
²⁴¹ *Hosp. Rpt.,* pp. 176-78; *VCH: Leicestershire,* II, 31-32.
²⁴² Lees, pp. cv-cviii; *Hosp. Rpt.,* pp. 179-81; *VCH: Warwickshire,* II, 99.
²⁴³ The original grant at Balsall goes back to Roger Mowbray in the reign of Stephen: Dugdale, VII, 817, 834. Cf. *VCH: Warwickshire,* II, 99-100.
²⁴⁴ Dugdale, VII, 818; Lees, p. lxxxv-lxxxix, 157, 166-68, 172; *Hosp. Rpt.,* p. 95. Cf. *CChR,* 21-22 Hen. III (1237-38), pp. 227, 234.
²⁴⁵ Dugdale, VII, 817, 833; *Rot. Hund.,* II, 454-56; *VCH: Cambridgeshire,* II, 259-63. Grants at Denney go back to 1176-77: Lees, pp. 224-25. Cf. *CChR,* 11 Hen. III (1227), p. 1.
²⁴⁶ Dugdale, VII, 817, 819-20, 832-33; Lees, pp. 211-18; *VCH: Hertfordshire,* III, 10, 18, 66, 68, 174, 176; IV, 445-46.
²⁴⁷ Dugdale, VII, 833; Lees, pp. cxxxvii and n. 6, cxxxviii.
²⁴⁸ *Hosp. Rpt.,* p. 162. Cf. Lees, pp. 79, 87, n. 4.
²⁴⁹ *VCH: Northhamptonshire,* II, 11.
²⁵⁰ Dugdale, VII, 835; *Rot. Hund.,* II, 634, 636, 654; *VCH: Huntingdonshire,* III, 53, 57, 137, 142, 174-75, 198, 218-20, 229.
²⁵¹ Dugdale, VII, 820; Lees, pp. 219-21; *Hosp. Rpt.,* pp. 170-72.
²⁵² *Rot. Hund.,* I 43, 45; *CChR,* 11-12 Hen. III (1228), pp. 5, 77, 79; Dugdale,

VII, 823, 834; *VCH: Buckinghamshire,* I, 346, 391; III, 73, 90, 92, 124, 129, 196, 280; IV, 132, 310.

²⁵³ For the transfer of most of these lands to the Hospitallers, see the *Hosp. Rpt.,* pp. 176, 179, 189-95 (for the first group of counties), 163-67, 172-73 (for the second group), and 162 (for the third group).

²⁵⁴ Lees, p. 142; Perkins, "Knights Templars in England," *op. cit.,* Appendix E.

²⁵⁵ *Ibid.* Cf. David E. Easson, *Medieval Religious Houses, Scotland* (London, 1957), pp. 131-32.

²⁵⁶ Perkins, "The Knights Templars in England," *op. cit.,* Appendix E.

²⁵⁷ Balsall (Warwickshire) included 560 acres; Upleden (Herefordshire), 740 acres; and Cressing (Essex), 800 acres. These figures (*Hosp. Rpt.* [1308], pp. 168, 179, 195) refer to arable lands and do not include meadows, pastures, forests, gardens, and the like. In such areas as Lincolnshire and Yorkshire, where Templar holdings were greatest, the expression used may be one *"manerium"* (e.g., Ribston, Bruer, and Eagle) or so many carucates – which might be 120, 160, or 240 acres – of land (e.g., Copmanthorp, 3; Eagle, 4; Langenok, 4; and South Witham, 8). Cf. *ibid.,* pp. 136, 143, 154, 160, 172. Hence, the actual area of many estates cannot be given precisely.

²⁵⁸ Temple Guiting (Gloucestershire), £206; Ribston-Wetherby (Yorkshire), £270; and Temple Bruer (Lincolnshire), £325 – Perkins, "The Knights Templars in England," *op. cit.,* Appendix E.

²⁵⁹ Cf. tables of holdings of the various religious orders as given in Knowles and Hadcock, *op. cit.* Kosminsky (*op. cit.,* p. 150) also credits the Hospitallers with larger holdings than the Templars in the thirteenth century.

²⁶⁰ See above, Chap. I, especially the section on "Classes of Membership," and nn. 48 and 49.

²⁶¹ *Règle,* arts. 657-86.

²⁶² *Ibid.* arts. 77-80, 99-100, 101-03, 110, 120, 125, 130, 132, 138, 169, 173, 177, 180-81.

²⁶³ Cf. *ibid.,* arts. 169-72.

²⁶⁴ Cf. letter of appeal of Terric, Grand Master of the Templars, to the West – Roger of Hoveden, *op. cit.,* RS, II, 324-25.

²⁶⁵ Charles W. Oman, *A History of the Art of War in the Middle Ages* (London, 1898), pp. 126-28, 510-14; Smail, *op. cit.,* pp. 107-09.

²⁶⁶ *Ibid.,* pp. 116-20, 199. Smail points out that the foot soldiers played a far more important part in crusading warfare than most authors have attributed to them. No doubt the Templars had some foot soldiers, too – cf. *Règle,* art. 161; Oman, *op. cit.,* p. 309 – but whether or not they actually took an active part in the fighting is not known. Each Templar knight was assigned one or two squires to stand before him and to carry his lance and to stand behind him to lead a spare horse – cf. *Règle,* arts. 51, 77, 99, 101, 110, 120, 130, 132, 138, 140, 143, 157, 180, 181.

²⁶⁷ Oman, *op. cit.,* pp. 103-04; Smail, *op. cit.,* pp. 111-12.

²⁶⁸ Smail (*op. cit., passim*) has carefully studied the tactics and strategy, the organization, and the equipment of the Crusaders during the twelfth century and has pointed out many errors and dubious interpretations of scholars who have written in this field. He has concluded (pp. 112, 201) that the Christian forces – presumably this includes the Templars – did not greatly alter their tactics and strategy in view of their actual experiences. They did, however, learn to exercise more restraint and caution in warfare; and they did introduce certain modifications in their organization and in their ways of fighting. The greatest of these changes and modifications was the creation of the Turcopole units which played a very important part in all subsequent operations and whose commander, in the case of the Templars, became one of the chief officers of the order – cf. *Règle,* arts. 169-71.

²⁶⁹ Cf. above, n. 86.

[270] Paris, *Chronica Majora*, RS, IV, 88 (1241); *CPatR*, 18 Hen. III (1234), p. 70; *ibid.*, 27 Hen. III (1243), pp. 722-23.

[271] *Règle*, arts. 190-97.

[272] *VCH: Cambridgeshire*, II, 260, Lees, p. clxxx.

[273] *VCH: Cambridgeshire*, II, 260.

Chapter Three

[1] *RLC*, 17 John (1215), I, 231b, 238, 241, 242.

[2] *CPatR*, 18-22 Hen. III (1234-38), pp. 47, 105, 161, 172, 184, 189, 230, 233; *LibR*, 14-22 Hen. III (1230-38), pp. 160, 215, 333.

[3] For some years after the disgrace of Ralph Neville, Chancellor and Keeper of the Seal (1238), King Henry III entrusted the seal, on a temporary basis, to a number of men of whom Roger the Templar was one. Cf. *Annales de Theokesberia in Annales Monastici*, ed. Henry R. Luard (RS No. 36, 5 vols.; London, 1864-69), I, 110; F. M. Powicke, *King Henry III and the Lord Edward* (2 vols.; Oxford, 1947), II, 780-83; and L. B. Dibben, "Chancellor and Keeper of the Seal under Henry III," *English Historical Review*, XXVII (1912), 42.

[4] *Chronica Majora*, RS, III, 629.

[5] *Ibid.*, V, 364-65.

[6] *Ibid.*, IV, 88. Cf. also *Calendar of Liberate Rolls preserved in the Public Record Office* (3 vols.; London, 1916-37), III, 91 [26 Hen. III (1241)] where John is instructed what to do with certain royal alms. For other instances of the use of Templars to announce royal prohibitions of tournaments, see *CPatR*, 18 Hen. III (1234), p. 70; and *ibid.*, 27 Hen. III (1243), pp. 722-23.

[7] Cf. *Calendar of Documents relating to Scotland preserved in Her Majesty's Public Record Office*, ed. Joseph Bain (vols. I-III; Edinburgh, 1881-88), I, no. 2013.

[8] Adam of Eynsham, *Magna Vita Sancti Hugonis Episcopi Lincolniensis*, ed. James F. Dimock (RS No. 37; London, 1864), pp. 358-59, 364.

[9] *CPatR*, 20 Hen, III (1236), p. 161.

[10] Cf. *RLC*, 6 John (1205), I, 27b; *CRR*, 7-9 Hen. III (1223-24), no. 2284; *ClR*, 22 Hen. III (1238), p. 55; *LibR*, 26 Hen. III (1242), p. 94; *CPatR*, 36 Hen. III (1251), p. 118; *ClR*, 36 Hen. III (1252), p. 192; *CPatR*, 47 Hen. III 1243), pp. 722-23; *CLibR*, 36-39 Hen. III (1252-55), pp. 15, 201.

[11] Cotton MS, Claud B, fol. 26 – cited by Robert W. Eyton, *Court, Household, and Itinerary of Henry II* (London, 1878), p. 68.

[12] *Ibid.*, p. 217.

[13] *PatR*, 8 Hen. III (1224), pp. 484-85; Rymer, I, 174.

[14] *PatR*, 9 Hen. III (1225), p. 558; Rymer, I, 176.

[15] Paris, *Chronica Majora*, RS, III, 335; Rymer, I, 219; *Treaty Rolls*, 19 Hen. III (1235), nos. 23, 24, 26, 89. Cf. *ibid.*, 21 Hen. III (1237), no. 48.

[16] *ClR*, 36 Hen. III (1252), pp. 108, 186-87; *CPatR*, 36 Hen. III (1252), pp. 133, 159, 161; Walter W. Shirley (ed.), *Royal and Other Historical Letters illustrative of the Reign of Henry III* (RS No. 27, 2 vols.; London, 1862-66), II, 69-72, 76-81, 83, 92, 391-92. Cf. Powicke, *op. cit.*, I, 227-30. Cf. *CLibR*, 38 Hen. III (1254), p. 173.

[17] *ClR*, 38 Hen. III (1254), p. 273; *CLibR*, 38 Hen. III (1254), p. 169. Cf. *ibid.*, 42 Hen. III (1257), p. 406.

[18] *ClR*, 38 Hen. III (1254), p. 320.

[19] *Ibid.*, 42 Hen. III (1258), p. 326; Paris, *Chronica Majora*, RS, VI, 410-16. Cf. Powicke, *op. cit.*, I, 241-48.

[20] *CPatR*, 46-49 Hen. III (1261-65), pp. 189, 275, 366, 476-77.

[21] *Ibid.*, 47 Hen. III (1263), p. 239.

[22] Roger of Wendover, *op. cit.*, RS, III, 80-83. Cf. Powicke, *op. cit.*, I, 136.

[23] Roger of Wendover, *op. cit.*, RS, III, 108.

[24] Roger of Hovedon, *op. cit.*, RS, I, 218; Ralph of Diceto, *op. cit.*, RS, I, 303; William of Newburgh, *op. cit.*, RS, I, 159.

[25] Delisle, *op. cit.*, II, 276 (no. 660).

[26] Roger of Hovedon, *op. cit.*, RS, III, 58; Benedict of Peterborough, *op. cit.*, RS, II, 129; Walter of Coventry, *Historical Collections*, ed. William Stubbs (RS No. 58, 2 vols.; London, 1872-73), I, 412.

[27] Roger of Hovedon, *op. cit.*, RS, I, 221-22; Gervase of Canterbury, *Historical Works*, ed. William Stubbs (RS No. 73, 2 vols.; London, 1879-80), I, 177, 230; Anonymous Life of Thomas Becket, No. I, *Materials for the History of Thomas Becket, Archbishop of Canterbury*, ed. James C. Robertson and J. Brigstocke Sheppard (RS No. 67, 7 vols.; London, 1879-85), IV, 35; Benedict of Peterborough, *op. cit.*, RS, I, 31-33; Delisle, *op. cit.*, I, 585-86; Roger of Wendover, *op. cit.*, RS, II, 36.

[28] Cf. *RLC*, 5 John (1204), I, 17; *LibR*, 5 John (1204), p. 81.

[29] Roger of Wendover, *op. cit.*, RS, II, 68; John de Oxenedes, *op. cit.*, RS, p. 128; Walter of Coventry, *op. cit.*, RS, II, 210; Paris, *Hist. Angl.*, RS, II, 134.

[30] *ClR*, 14 John (1213), p. 148. This sum was subsequently repaid, nine silver marks for the gold mark: *RLC*, 15 John (1213), I, 148b.

[31] Paris, *Chronica Majora*, RS, II, 589-90, 598. For a good edition of *Magna Carta*, see William S. McKechnie, *Magna Carta: A Commentary on the Great Charter of King John* (2d ed.; Glasgow, 1914).

[32] Especially arts, 1, 60, and 63; Rymer, I, 131-32; Paris, *Chronica Majora*, RS, II, 598; Continuation of William of Newburgh, *op. cit.*, RS, III, 519.

[33] Paris, *Chronica Majora*, RS, V, 544.

[34] Cf. *PatR*, 8-9 Hen. III (1224-25), pp. 484, 558; Paris, *Chronica Majora*, RS, III, 235; *ClR*, 36 Hen. III (1252), pp. 159, 161, 186-87.

[35] Rymer, I, 18.

[36] Ralph of Diceto, *op. cit.*, RS, I, 352; Roger of Wendover, *op. cit.*, RS, II, 368; Benedict of Peterborough, *op. cit.*, RS, I, 32.

[37] Roger of Hovedon, *op. cit.*, RS, II, 299; Roger of Wendover, *op. cit.*, RS, I, 134-35.

[38] Rymer, I, 47; Gervase of Canterbury, *op. cit.*, RS, I, 298; Delisle, *op. cit.*, II, 219-20 (no. 613).

[39] Cf. Roger of Hoveden, *op. cit.*, RS, III, 179. For the story of Richard on the Third Crusade, see *Itinerarium peregrinorum et Gesta regis Ricardi* in *Chronicles and Memorials of the Reign of Richard I*, ed. William Stubbs (RS No. 38, 2 vols.; London, 1864-65), Vol. I; Runciman, *op. cit.*, III, 34-75; and Grousset, *op. cit.*, III, 60-120.

[40] Roger of Wendover, *op. cit.*, RS, I, 218; Ralph of Coggeshall, *Chronicon Anglicanum*, ed. Joseph Stevenson (RS No. 66; London, 1875), p. 54.

[41] Gervase of Canterbury, *op. cit.*, RS, I, 513; Ralph of Coggeshall, *op. cit.*, RS, pp. 54-56; *Itinerarium . . . Ricardi, op. cit.*, RS, I, 441-45. Cf. also the interesting biography of Kate Morgate: *Richard the Lion Heart* (London, 1924), pp. 264-84.

[42] *Op. cit.*, RS, I, 399.

[43] Cf. Roger of Wendover, *op. cit.*, RS, II, 68, 113, 114; *RLC*, 16 John (1215), I, 196, 196b, 198, 198b, 199, 199b for John; and *ibid.*, 8-10 Hen. III (1225-26), II, 18-21, 70b, 104; *PatR*, 3-9 Hen. III (1219-25), pp. 189, 202-06, 287-88, 435-37, *et passim* for Henry.

[44] Dugdale, VII, 818; *PatR*, 15 Hen. III (1231), p. 439; *CClR*, 21 Hen. III (1237), p. 6. The £8 for chaplains at New Temple were continued by Edward I — *Issues of the Exchequer; being a Collection of Payments made out of His Majesty's Revenue from King Henry III to King Henry VI inclusive*, ed. and trans. Frederick Devon, Vol. VIII (London, 1837), 88-89 [3 Ed. I (1276)].

[45] *Flores Historiarum*, ed. Henry R. Luard (RS No. 95; 3 vols.; London, 1890), III, 28. Cf. Williamson, *op. cit.*, p. 21.

[46] *CPatR*, 36 Hen. III (1252), p. 158.

⁴⁷ *Flores Historiarum,* RS, II, 405; John of Oxenedes, *op. cit.,* RS, p. 199; Paris, *Chronica Majora,* RS, V, 478.

⁴⁸ *Ibid.,* IV, 640; VI, 142.

⁴⁹ *The Parliamentary Writs and Writs of Military Summons,* ed. Francis Palgrave (2 vols.; London, 1827-30), II, 304 [26 Ed. I (1297)].

⁵⁰ Thomas Walsingham, *op. cit.,* RS, I, 76; William Rishanger, *Chronica et Annales regnantibus Henrico Tertio et Edwardo Primo, A.D., 1259-1307,* ed. Henry T. Riley (RS No. 28; London, 1865), p. 188; Continuation of William of Newburgh, *op. cit.,* RS, III, 583; *Flores Historiarum,* RS, III, 104; *The Chronicles of London from 44 Hen. III to 17 Edw. III,* trans. Edmund Goldsmid (3 vols.; Edinburgh, 1885), I, 51-52.

⁵¹ Bain, III, nos. 508, 823; Rymer, I, 773.

⁵² *CClR,* 1 Ed. II (1307), p. 50.

⁵³ Paris, *Chronica Majora,* RS, III, 186; Roger of Wendover, *op. cit.,* RS, II, 375; *Parl. Writs,* pp. 28, 30, 47, 56, 84, 90, 112, 138, 170; *CClR,* 23-24 Ed. I (1295-96), pp. 444, 459; *ibid.,* 25-30 Ed. I (1297-1303), pp. 128, 374, 375, 408, 409, 583, 592, 598; *ibid.,* 32 Ed. I (1304), p. 225.

⁵⁴ Letters dated at New Temple: *RLC,* 16 John (1215), I, 196, 196b, 198, 198b, 199, 199b (30 letters); *ibid.,* 3 Hen. III (1219), I, 400, 400b, 401 (32 letters); *ibid.,* 9-10 Hen. III (1225-26), II, 18-21, 70b, 104 (52 letters); *ClR,* 27 Hen. III (1243), p. 91 (1 letter); *PatR,* 3-9 Hen. III (1219-25), pp. 189, 202-06, 287-88, 435-37, 480, 508-11 (35 letters); *ibid.,* 11 Hen. III (1227), p. 137 (1 letter); *CPatR,* 27 Hen. III (1243), p. 720 (1 letter); *ibid.,* 1-4 Ed. I (1272-76), pp. 1-3, 6-7, 15, 31-32, 136-37 (35 letters). Cf. also, *ibid.,* 22 Ed. I (1294), p. 102 and *Fines in the Tower of London,* pp. 496-97. Letters dated at Temple Bruer: *ClR,* 14-20 Hen. III (1230-36), pp. 283, 319; *CPatR,* 20 Hen. III (1236), p. 159; *ibid.,* 4 Ed. I (1276), pp. 137, 176; *CChanWar,* 12 Ed. I (1284), I, 18; *CPatR,* 12 Ed. I (1284), pp. 114-15; *CChanWar,* 33 Ed. I (1305), I, 245 (25 letters). Letters dated at Temple Dinsley: *ClR,* 33-35 Hen. III (1249-51), pp. 196, 426-27; *ibid.,* 36 Hen. III (1252), pp. 151, 248; *CLibR,* 35 Hen. III (1251), p. 344; *CPatR,* 36 Hen. III (1252), p. 149; *CChanWar,* 21-25 Ed. I (1293-97), I, 37, 75; *CPatR,* 22 Ed. I (1294), p. 110 (10 letters). Letters dated at Temple Cowton: *CPatR,* 28 Ed. I (1300), p. 551; *CChanWar,* 30 Ed. I (1302), I, 160-61 (3 letters).

⁵⁵ *Annales de Wintonia, op. cit.,* RS, II, 99.

⁵⁶ *Flores Historiarum,* RS, III, 28; Thomas Walsingham, *Ypodigma Neustriae,* ed. Henry T. Riley (RS No. 28; London, 1876), pp. 166-67; Rymer I, 497.

⁵⁷ *CClR,* 27 Ed. I (1299), p. 318.

⁵⁸ Cf. *Chronicon Abbatiae Ramesiensis a Saec. X usque ad an. circitur 1200,* ed. W. Dunn Macray (RS No. 83; London, 1886), pp. 400-1; *PatR,* 2-7 Hen. III (1218-23), pp. 135, 481-82; *Flores Historiarum,* RS, III, 124.

⁵⁹ Paris, *Chronica Majora,* RS, V, 524-27, 532; VI, 315; *Annales de Burton, op. cit.,* RS, I, 360; *Registrum Epistolarum Fratris Johannis Peckham, Archiepiscopi Cantuariensis,* ed. Charles T. Martin (RS No. 77, 3 vols.; London, 1882-85), I, 256-57; II, 507-09, 537, 594; Gervase of Canterbury, *op. cit.,* RS, II, 299; *CPatR,* 5 Ed. I (1277), p. 210; *ibid.,* 27 Ed: I (1299), pp. 450-51.

⁶⁰ Benedict of Peterborough, *op. cit.,* RS, II, 238; Roger of Hoveden, *op. cit.,* RS, III, 187; *ClR,* 19 Hen. III (1235), p. 55; Paris, *Chronica Majora,* RS, V, 509; *CLibR,* 39 Hen. III (1255), p. 245.

⁶¹ *Flores Historiarum,* RS, II, 269; Paris, *Chronica Majora,* RS, IV, 284, 379, 420, 561. William E. Lunt (*Financial Relations of the Papacy with England to 1327* [Cambridge, 1939], p. 581) suggests that the general collectors of papal revenue also stayed at New Temple.

⁶² *ClR,* 39 Hen. III (1255), pp. 114, 116, 117, 212.

⁶³ Paris, *Chronica Majora,* RS, III, 43, 201; IV, 136, 493. The first Earl serves as an example of those persons who joined the order just before their death — in his case in accordance with a vow taken while on a crusade in his earlier

years. Cf. Williamson, *op. cit.*, pp. 19-20 citing an old French chronicle, "L'histoire de Guillaume le Marechal."

[64] Shirley, *op. cit.*, I, 119-20.

[65] *CPatR*, 31 Hen. III (1246), p. 495.

[66] *ClR*, 34 Hen. III (1250), p. 283. For other valuables deposited in New Temple, see below.

[67] *CPatR*, 19-20 Hen. III (1234-36), pp. 81, 143; *ClR*, 52 Hen. III (1267), p. 407; *CClR*, 17-20 Ed. I (1289-91), pp. 56, 245-46.

[68] *LibR*, 17 Hen. III (1233), p. 215; *ibid.*, 26 Hen. III (1241), p. 91; *ibid.*, 32 Hen. III (1248), p. 160; *ClR*, 27 Hen. III (1243), p. 42; *ibid.*, 32-34 Hen.III (1247-50), pp. 10, 263-64; *ibid.*, 36 Hen. III (1252), p. 50.

[69] Cf. *ClR*, 42 Hen. III (1258), pp. 331-32; *ibid.*, 51 Hen. III (1267), pp. 386-88, 391-92. (These agreements covered such matters as payments of money and transfer of lands.)

[70] E.g., *PipeR*, 5 Hen. II (1158), pp. 28, 29, 32, 34, 35, 36, 38, 40 *et passim; ibid.*, 12 John (1210), pp. 18, 42, 43, 65, 69, 76, *et passim.* (Over a thousand references can be found in the Pipe Rolls.)

[71] *RLC*, 6-7 Hen. III (1221-23), I, 477, 512, 565; *LibR*, 11-23 Hen. III (1227-38), pp. 55, 104, 149, 244, 297, 347; *ibid.*, 26-28 Hen. III (1241-44), pp. 93, 160; *CLibR*, 30 Hen. III (1246), pp. 42, 48; *CClR*, 9 Ed. I (1280), p. 70. Once (*RLC*, 15 John [1213], I, 153) the same sum was granted by John.

[72] Cf. *ibid.*, 15 John (1214), I, 141; *ibid.*, 8 Hen. III (1224), I 618-43; *ClR*, 16 Hen. III (1232), p. 90; *ibid.*, 33 Hen. III (1249), p. 189.

[73] *RLC*, 15 John (1214), I, 141; *ibid.*, 9 Hen. III (1225), II, 21b; *ClR*, 19-21 Hen. III (1235-37), pp. 94, 266, 440; *ibid.*, 22-26 Hen. III (1238-42), pp. 54, 160, 190, 301, 426; *ibid.*, 27-30 Hen. III (1243-46), pp. 22, 149, 182, 192, 273, 307, 422; *CLibR*, 26-28 Hen. III (1242-44), pp. 142, 245.

[74] *RLC*, 8 Hen. III (1224), I, 618-43; *ClR*, 15 Hen. III (1231), p. 501; *ibid.*, 16-18 Hen. III (1232-34), pp. 90, 428; *ibid.*, 19-21 Hen. III (1235-37), pp. 88, 134, 135, 272, 440, 441. Except for his twenty-third and twenty-fifth years, similar entries are found for all the remaining years of Henry III's reign. Only one entry (*CClR*, 14 Ed. I [1286], p. 392) is found for Edward I. It cannot be said positively, however, that additional grants were not made by Edward I.

[75] E.g., *ClR*, 28 Hen. III (1243), p. 149; *ibid.*, 49 Hen. III (1264), p. 4.

[76] E.g., *ibid.*, 24 Hen. III (1239), p. 160.

[77] *Ibid.*, 15 Hen. III (1231), p. 510; *ibid.*, 19-20 Hen. III (1235-36), pp. 45, 227; *ibid.*, 24-29 Hen. III (1239-45), pp. 163, 229, 287, 330; *CPatR*, 19 Ed. I (1291), p. 442.

[78] *ClR*, 24 Hen. III (1239), p. 160; *LibR*, 24 Hen. III (1240), p. 443.

[79] *Ibid.*, p. 179.

[80] *Ibid.*, 22 Hen. III (1238), p. 56.

[81] *RLC*, 6 John (1205), I, 17b.

[82] *CPatR*, 27 Hen. III (1243), p. 371.

[83] Cf. comments on the inquest in Chap. II above.

[84] Clarence Perkins, "The Wealth of the Templars in England," *American Historical Review*, XV (1909), 252-63 at p. 253.

[85] *Règle*, arts. 135, 181; Lees, p. lxxxii.

[86] Cf. *ibid.*, p. lxi.

[87] We know, for example, that at Evesham (Knowles, *op. cit.*, I, 287 – citing the *Evesham Chronicle*, p. 285) that Benedictine lay brothers managed the manors of that house.

[88] For additional comments on land and personnel, see section section of Chap. II above.

[89] Lees, p. lxxi.

[90] The figures given here are taken from the extracts of several keepers' reports

published in the *Gentleman's Magazine and Historical Review* ("Original Documents relating to the Knights Templars"), III N.S. (1857), 250, 520-25.

⁹¹ J. E. T. Rogers, *A History of Agriculture and Prices in England*, Vol. I (Oxford, 1866), p. 21.

⁹² Norman S. B. Gras, *The Evolution of the Corn Market from the Twelfth to the Eighteenth Century*, "Harvard Economic Studies," Vol. XIII (Cambridge, 1915), pp. 22-24, 30.

⁹³ *Ibid.*, p. 12. Cf. also, W. H. Beveridge, "The Yield and Price of Corn in the Middle Ages," *Economic History*, I (1927), 155-67. D. L. Farmer ("Some Grain Price Movements in Thirteenth Century England," *Economic History Review*, X (1957-58) 3rd S, 207-20) adversely criticizes the methods and conclusions of Rogers, Gras, and Beveridge, and feels that Gras' price schedule is far too high; nonetheless, he definitely agrees that the general trend of grain prices in the thirteenth century was upwards and that landlords found it profitable to sell their surplus.

⁹⁴ *The Pipe Roll of the Bishopric of Winchester for the Fourth Year of the Pontificate of Peter des Roches, 1208-1209*, "Studies in Economic and Political Science," Vol. XI (London, 1913), pp. xliii-xlv. Cf. Kosminsky, *op. cit.*, pp. 324-25.

⁹⁵ *Ibid.*

⁹⁶ This involves royal permission to the Master of the Temple in Ireland to ship his grain for trading purposes where he will without payment of customs fees: *Doc. rel. to Ire.*, I, no. 1276.

⁹⁷ Cf. Lees, pp. 15, 39, 77 *et passim; Hosp. Rpt.*, pp. 144 ,145, 146, 154 *et passim.*

⁹⁸ Lees, pp. 15, 39, 77.

⁹⁹ *VCH: Bedfordshire*, III, 66; *VCH: Worcestershire*, IV, 444-45; *VCH: Leicestershire*, II, 32, 171, 173; *CPatR*, 5 Ed. II (1312), pp. 466, 467; "Original Documents relating to the Knights Templars," *op. cit.*, pp. 520-25; Perkins, "Wealth of the Templars in England," *op. cit.*, p. 256, n. 23.

¹⁰⁰ Pp. 136, 157, 168, 183, 184, 187.

¹⁰¹ R. A. Pelham, "Fourteenth-Century England," *Historical Geography of England before A.D. 1800*, ed. H. C. Darby (Cambridge, 1936), p. 240, n. 3.

¹⁰² *CChanWar*, 26 Ed. I (1298), p. 93.

¹⁰³ Lord Treasurer's Remembrancer, Enrolled Accounts, Misc. Roll 20, m. 15-17 — cited by Perkins, "Knights Templars in England," *op. cit.*, p. 255, n. 16.

¹⁰⁴ Lees, pp. 2, 72, 73.

¹⁰⁵ "Original Documents relating to the Knights Templars," *op. cit.*, pp. 520-25; *VCH: Bedfordshire*, III, 66; *VCH: Leicestershire*, II, 171.

¹⁰⁶ Hugh H. L. Bellot, *The Inner and Middle Temple* (London, 1902), p. 17

¹⁰⁷ Lees, pp. 80, 81, 131 *et passim*. Cf. *CRR*, 9-10 Hen. III (1225-26), no. 2376.

¹⁰⁸ *Ibid.*, p. 132.

¹⁰⁹ *Ibid.*, pp. 50, 127.

¹¹⁰ Eleanora Carus-Wilson, "The Woollen Industry," *Cambridge Economic History of Europe*, Vol. II: *Trade and Industry in the Middle Ages.*, ed. M. M. Postan and E. E. Rich (Cambridge, 1952), p. 409. Miss Wilson ("An Industrial Revolution of the Thirteenth Century," *Economic History Review*, XI [1941], 39-60 at p. 45) even goes so far as to say it is "conceivable" that the Templars may have introduced the fulling mill to England.

¹¹¹ E. Lipson, *An Introduction to the Economic History of England*, Vol. I: *The Middle Ages* (London, 1915); Eileen Power, *"The Wool Trade in English Medieval History* (London, 1942); W. Cunningham, *"Growth of English Industry and Commerce*, Vol. I (5th ed.; Cambridge, 1910); L. Salzman, *English Industry of the Middle Ages* (Oxford, 1923) and *English Trade in the Middle Ages* (Oxford, 1931); Carus-Wilson, "The Woollen Industry," *op. cit.*, pp. 355-428; Herbert Heaton, *The Yorkshire Woollen and Worsted Industries from the earliest Times up to the Industrial Revolution* (Oxford, 1920); and E. Lipson, *History of the Woollen and Worsted Industries* (London, 1921).

[112] Cf. Chap. II above.

[113] Nellie Nielson, "Medieval Agrarian Society in its Prime: England," *Cambridge Economic History of Europe*, Vol. I: *The Agrarian Life of the Middle Ages*, ed. J. H. Clapham and Eileen Power (Cambridge, 1941), p. 465.

[114] *CPatR*, 26 Ed. I (1298), p. 332. The stone as a unit of weight varied during the Middle Ages from 8 to 24 pounds, but was decreed by statute of Edward III (1357) to weigh 14 pounds with 26 stones making one sack — Denholm-Young, *op. cit.*, p. 57. Cf. Power, *op. cit.*, p. 23.

[115] *CPatR*, 26 Ed. I (1298), p. 332.

[116] *CChanWar*, 26 Ed. I (1298), p. 93.

[117] *CPatR*, 26 Ed. I (1298), p. 332.

[118] Cf. Coburn V. Graves, "The Economic Activities of the Cistercians in Medieval England, 1128-1307," *Analecta Sacri Ordinis Cisterciensis*, XIII (1957), fasc. 1-2, at p. 26; A. Schaube, "Die Wollsausfuhr Englands von Jahre 1273," *Vierteljahrschrift für Social- und Wirtschaftsgeschichte*, VI (1908), 39-72 and 159-85, at p. 174.

[119] Cf. Robert J. Whitwell, "English Monasteries and the Wool Trade in the Thirteenth Century," *Vierteljahrschrift für Social- und Wirtschaftsgeschichte*, II (1940), p. 17; and *CClR*, 32 Ed. I (1304), pp. 172-73 for sale to the Mozzi of Florence of wool worth 700 marks.

[120] *RLC*, 15 John (1213), I, 104, 148b, 214; *ibid.*, 8 Hen. III (1224), I, 609; *ClR*, 15 Hen. III (1231), pp. 518-19; Rymer, I, 115.

[121] Cf. *CPatR*, 55 Hen. III (1271), pp. 594-95.

[122] Carus-Wilson, "The Woolen Industry," *op. cit.*, p. 402. The tax set in 1275 was accepted by those involved in the sale and export of wool as reasonable, but there was much opposition to the very high rates of 5 and 3 marks (66s. 8d. and 40s.) set by Edward briefly in view of his great need for increased revenue during the last decade of the thirteenth century. Cf. Power, *op. cit.*, p. 78.

[123] *Ibid.*, pp. 22-23, 33. References in primary sources to the Templars as producers and sellers of wool, though few in number, are such as to suggest that the complete omission or merest mention of them by writers of secondary accounts (cf. n. 111 above) does not do them justice.

[124] Cf. *PatR*, 10-11 Hen. III (1226-27), pp. 13-14, 24, 105; *CPatR*, 26-27 Hen. III (1242), pp. 309, 330, 333; *ClR*, 14-15 Hen. III (1230-31), pp. 368, 477; *ibid.*, 26 Hen. III (1242), p. 505.

[125] *RLC*, 17 John (1215), I, 214; *PatR*, 9 Hen. III (1224), pp. 492, 517; *ibid.*, 14 Hen. III (1230), pp. 368, 370, 374; *ClR*, 14 Hen. III (1230), p. 368. Cf. *RLC*, 15 John (1213), I, 136b; *ibid.*, 8 Hen. III (1224), I, 599b; *ClR*, 14-15 Hen. III (1230-31), pp. 291, 477. Cf. Jules Piquet, *Les Templiers: étude de leurs opérations financières* (Paris, 1939), pp. 3, 30, 31 where reference to the "fleet" is made.

[126] *PatR*, 14 Hen. III (1230), p. 368; *ClR*, 15 Hen. III (1231), p. 477.

[127] Cf. *RLC*, 10 Hen. III (1226), II, 112.

[128] *PatR*, 11-12 Hen. III (1227-28), pp. 105, 197. Cf. *CPatR*, 21 Ed. I (1293), p. 20.

[129] Cf. *ibid.*, 26-27 Hen. III (1242), p. 333.

[130] *RLC*, 17 John (1215), I, 214; *ibid.*, 10-11 Hen. III (1226-27), II, 114, 115, 169; *PatR*, 9 Hen. III (1225), pp. 492, 517; *ibid.*, 10 Hen. III (1226), pp. 24, 113; *ibid.*, 14 Hen. III (1230), pp. 368, 370; *ClR*, 14-15 Hen. III (1230-31), pp. 291, 368, 477.

[131] *CPatR*, 26-27 Hen. III (1242), p. 333.

[132] *RLC*, 15-17 John (1213-16), I, 159, 229b, 238, 268b; *ibid.*, 10-11 Hen. III (1226-27), II, 114, 169; *PatR*, 9 Hen. III (1225), p. 540.

[133] *Ibid.*, 12-14 Hen. III (1228-30), pp. 197, 368; *CPatR*, 26-27 Hen. III (1242), pp. 330, 333.

154　　The Knights Templars in England

[134] *RLC*, 17 John, (1215), I, 229b, 238; *ibid.*, 9-10 Hen. III (1225-26), II, 51, 110, 112, 113, 113b, 114, 114b, 115, 117; Bain, I. no. 935.

[135] *RLC*, 17 John (1215), I, 229b, 238; *PatR*, 9 Hen. III (1225), p. 540.

[136] *Ibid.*, pp. 505, 540, 542; *ibid.*, 10 Hen. III (1226), pp. 13, 14; *RLC*, 10-11 Hen. III (1226-27), II, 94b, 160, 183.

[137] See below, Appendix D for the references in the source materials for each of these markets and fairs.

[138] Cf. Léopold Delisle, *Mémoires sur les opérations financières des Templiers*, "Académie des Inscriptions et Belles-Lettres, Mémoires," Vol. XXXIII (Paris, 1889); Piquet, *op. cit.*; Agnes Sandys, "The Financial and Administrative Importance of the London Temple in the Thirteenth Century," *Essays in Medieval History presented to Thomas Frederick Tout*, ed. A. G. Little and F. M. Powicke (Manchester, 1925), pp. 147-62; Eleanor Ferris, "The Financial Relations of the Knights Templars to the English Crown," *American Historical Review*, VIII (1902), 1-17.

[139] Cf. Thomas F. Tout, *Chapters in the Administrative History of Medieval England*, "University of Manchester Publications," No. XCCVII, Vols. I-II (Manchester, 1920), II, 74; S. B. Chrimes, *An Introduction to the Administrative History of Medieval England* (Oxford, 1952), p. 28. Even today, safekeeping (e.g., safe deposit boxes) is still an important function of banks.

[140] *Rotuli litterarum patentium in Turri Londinensi asservati*, ed. Thomas D. Hardy (London, 1835), 5-6 John (1204-05), I, 139.

[141] *PatR*, 16 Hen. III (1232), p. 490.

[142] *CPatR*, 26 Hen. III (1242), p. 281.

[143] *ClR*, 38 Hen. III (1254), p. 62.

[144] *CPatR*, 56 Hen. III (1272), p. 627; Rymer, I, 410.

[145] *Ibid.*, p. 435.

[146] *CPatR*, 17 Hen. III (1232), pp. 2, 5; *ClR*, 17 Hen. III (1233), p. 199; Bain, I, no. 1163. Cf. Paris, *Chronica Majora*, RS, III, 221, 232-33.

[147] *CPatR*, 26 Hen. III (1242), p. 270.

[148] *Ibid.*, 43 Hen. III (1259), pp. 21-22.

[149] Cf. *CClR*, 62 Hen. III (1278), p. 447.

[150] Cf. *CLibR*, 22 Hen. III (1238), pp. 326, 330; *ibid.*, 35 Hen. III (1251), pp. 326, 374.

[151] Cf. *CPatR*, 41 Hen. III (1257, pp. 587-88; *ibid.*, 4 Ed. I (1276), pp. 140-41; *ibid.*, 14 Ed. I (1286), pp. 231-32, 244.

[152] Cf. *RLC*, 9-10 Hen. III (1225), II, 40, 75, 76, 82, 84; *PatR*, 9 Hen. III (1225), pp. 534, 535, 538, 546-49; *ibid.*, 10-11 Hen. III (1226), pp. 1, 2, 8, 9, 93.

[153] Cf. *CPatR*, 54-56 Hen. III (1270-72), pp. 439, 448, 466, 487, 493, 494, 498, 508, 513, 517, 524, 538-40, 542, 547, 557, 570, 572, 578, 579, 639-40, 655-56, 682-83, 710; *CClR*, 13 Ed. I (1285), pp. 350-51.

[154] *ClR*, 22 Hen. III (1238), p. 52; *CPatR*, 22-26 Hen. III (1238-42), pp. 221, 222, 230, 275, 78; *ibid.*, 11 Ed. I (1283), p. 70; *LibR*, 22-24 Hen. III (1238-40), pp. 325-26, 330, 333, 446.

[155] *ClR*, 16 Hen. III (1232), pp. 155-56; Roger of Wendover, *op. cit.*, RS, III, 41; Paris, *Chronica Majora*, RS, III, 232; Rymer, I, 207.

[156] *Book of Fees*, I, 290, 291, 331, 1439-45; *PatR*, 9 Hen. III (1225), pp. 505, 506, 508.

[157] *ClR*, 34 Hen. III (1250), p. 321; *CPatR*, 18 Hen. III (1234), p. 75; *ibid.*, 39 Hen. III (1255), pp. 400, 401; *ibid.*, 2-3 Ed. I (1274-75), pp. 52, 83, 84, 99, 100.

[158] *ClR*, 37 Hen. III (1253), p. 448; *RLC*, 2 Hen. III (1218), I, 367.

[159] E.g., *ibid.*, 8 Hen. III (1224), I, 593, 630.

[100] *CLibR*, 32-35 Hen. III (1248-51), pp. 184, 332, 358. Cf. *ibid.*, 37 Hen. III (1252), p. 52.

[161] *CPatR*, 31 Hen. III (1247), p. 500; *ClR*, 34-35 Hen. III (1250-51), pp. 318, 500.

[162] Rymer, I, 87; *CClR*, 15 Hen. III (1231), p. 593; *CPatR*, 26 Hen. III (1242), pp. 277, 281, 282, 287.

[163] *Ibid.*, 41 Hen. III (1257), pp. 568, 605; *ibid.*, 43 Hen. III (1259), p. 30; *ibid.*, 4 Ed. I (1276), pp. 140, 147.

[164] *CClR*, 24 Hen. III (1239-40), pp. 153-54, 171-72; *CPatR*, 55-56 Hen. III (1272), pp. 657, 680-81.

[165] *RLC*, 16 John (1214), I, 175b.

[166] Bliss, I, 74-75 (Honorius III, 1220), 383 (Urban IV, 1262), 423 (Clement IV, 1266), 444 (Gregory X, 1272); *Reg. de Grég.* IX (1238), nos. 4268-72; *RLC*, 3 Hen. III (1219), I, 396b; *Select Letters of Innocenct III*, pp. 159-60 (1213); *Records of Anthony Bek, Bishop and Patriarch (1283-1311)*, ed. C. M. Fraser ("Publications of the Surtees Society," Vol. CLXII; London, 1947), no. 407 (1294). Cf. Lunt, *op. cit.*, pp. 243-45.

[167] Bliss, I, 75 (Honorius III, 1220), Rymer, I, 266-67 (Innocent IV, 1246-48); *CLibR*, 22-23 Hen. III (1237-39), pp. 295, 408; Paris, *Chronica Majora*, RS, IV, 557, 560-61, 577 (Innocent IV, 1245-46); *Reg. de Grég.* IX (1272), no. 193.

[168] Bliss, I, 75, 383, 384, 423; *Select Letters of Innocent III*, pp. 159-60.

[169] *CPatR*, 22 Hen. III (1238), p. 221.

[170] Walter of Hemingway, *op. cit.*, II, 273-74.

[171] Paris, *Chronica Majora*, RS, III, 221, 232-33; *Annales Londoniensis, op. cit.*, RS, I, 31; *Flores Historiarum*, RS, p. 291; Shirley, *op. cit.*, RS, I, 525; *CPatR* 17 Hen. III (1233), p. 2.

[172] Cf. *ibid.*, 26 Hen. III (1242), p. 270.

[173] Cf. *ClR*, 38 Hen. III (1254), p. 62. In this reference, the king orders an inventory of royal treasures made; but we are not told the results.

[174] Paris, *Chronica Majora*, RS, V, 704.

[175] *Ibid.*

[176] *Annales de Dunstaplia, op. cit.*, RS, III, 222 give the sum as £1,000; Gervase of Canterbury, *op. cit.*, RS, II, 222 gives it as £10,000. The latter figure is so large a sum of money for this period that the smaller figure is more likely to be correct. Gervase says the money was taken "de thesauro multorum magnatum terrae et mercatorium." This act so enraged Londoners that riots immediately broke out and Edward and his supporters found it necessary to flee.

[177] Cf. original papal document given by William E. Lunt, "A Papal Tenth levied in the British Isles from 1274 to 1280," *English Historical Review*, XXXII (1917), 48-89, at pp. 75-76.

[178] *Ibid.; CPatR*, 61 Hen. III (1277), pp. 326, 354.

[179] Rymer, II, 823.

[180] Walter of Hemingburg, *op. cit.*, II, 273-74. Hubert de Burgh's money was stored in strong boxes under double lock and key. Cf. above, n. 171.

[181] Cf. *CPatR*, 41 Hen. III (1257), p. 568.

[182] For a fuller discussion of the difference between these two types of deposit, see Usher, "The Origins of Banking," *op. cit.*, pp. 412-13.

[183] Piquet, *op. cit.*, pp. 46-48.

[184] *Ibid.*, p. 50.

[185] Cf. above, n. 171.

[186] Cf. Piquet, *op. cit.*, p. 48.

[187] *Ibid.*, p. 58. Cf. more general comment of Raymond A. DeRoover, "New Interpretations of the History of Banking," *Journal of World History*, II (1954), 38-76, at p. 54.

156   *The Knights Templars in England*

188 Piquet, *op. cit.*, pp. 31-32, 36-38; Delisle, *op. cit.*, p. 15.

189 *Ibid.*, p. 20; Piquet, *op. cit.*, pp. 50-51; Usher, "The Origins of Banking," *op. cit.*, p. 415; Abbott P. Usher, *The Early History of Deposit Banking in Mediterranean Europe*, "Harvard Economic Studies," Vol. LXXV (Cambridge, 1943), p. 6.

190 Cf. DeRoover, "New Interpretations of the History of Banking," *op. cit.*, p. 40, who says there was no law against doing so though some theologians disapproved; Noonan, *op. cit.*, p. 172; DeRoover, *L'evolution de la Lettre de Change*, p. 22, and *Money, Banking and Credit in Medieval Bruges*, pp. 41-42.

191 Cf. *ibid.*, p. 40; Usher, "Origins of Banking," *op. cit.*, p. 413.

192 Rymer, I, 47; *Itinerarium . . . Ricardi, op. cit.*, RS, I, 26.

193 The mark at this time was worth 13s. 4d. or two-thirds of a pound: cf. *CPatR*, 16 Hen. III (1232), pp. 514-15; Power, *op. cit.*, p. 23. Hence 20,000 marks equal £13,333.

194 *RLC*, 14-16 John (1212-15), I, 124b, 134, 136b, 141, 198b, 221b; *PatR*, 16 John (1214), p. 107.

195 *RLC*, 14-15 John (1212-14), I, 124b, 136b; Rymer, I, 108, 165, 173; *RLP*, 15 John (1214), I, 104b, 107.

196 *CPatR*, 2-4 Ed. I (1274-76), pp. 52, 83, 99, 100, 114, 140; *CCIR*, 4 Ed. I (1276), pp. 264, 410.

197 *PatR*, 9 Hen. III (1225), pp. 544-45; *ibid.*, 10 Hen. III (1226), p. 54; *CIR*, 30 Hen. III (1246), pp. 470-71.

198 *PatR*, 8 Hen. III (1224), p. 467.

199 *RLC*, 6 Hen. III (1221), I, 483.

200 *Ibid.*, 7 Hen. III (1223), I, 558.

201 *CPatR*, 31 Hen. III (1247), p. 507.

202 *LibR*, 28 Hen. III (1244), pp. 229, 238; *CPatR*, 31 Hen. III (1247), p. 497.

203 *PatR*, 8 Hen. III (1224), p. 436.

204 *Ibid.*, 11 Hen. III (1226), pp. 40-41; *LibR*, 24 Hen. III (1240), p. 452.

205 Rymer, I, 232.

206 *RLC*, 6 Hen. III (1222), I, 486b; *LibR*, 23 Hen. III (1239), p. 408; *CLibR*, 30-34 Hen. III (1246-50), pp. 115, 142, 285.

207 *PatR*, 9 Hen. III (1225), p. 325.

208 *CPatR*, 29 Hen. III (1245), pp. 449, 453; *CLibR*, 34-35 Hen. III (1250-51), pp. 310-11, 382; *CIR*, 34 Hen. III (1250), p. 32.

209 *PatR*, 8 Hen. III (1224), pp. 436, 438-39.

210 *CIR*, 19 Hen. III (1235), p. 110.

211 *Ibid.*, 29 Hen. III (1224), pp. 270, 274.

212 *PatR*, 10 Hen. III (1225), p. 534; Rymer, I, 232; *CPatR*, 22 Hen. III (1238), p. 222; *CIR*, 29 Hen. III (1245), p. 339.

213 *PatR*, 14 Hen. III (1230), p. 322; Rymer, I, 196; *LibR*, 14 Hen. III (1229), p. 160.

214 *RLC*, 5 Hen. III (1221), I, 471b; *PatR*, 6-9 Hen. III (1222-24), pp. 328, 497.

215 *CIR*, 15 Hen. III (1231), p. 544.

216 Paris, *Chronica Majora*, RS, V, 704; *CIR*, 43 Hen. III (1258), pp. 341-42, 418-19, 446-47, 471; *CPatR*, 43 Hen. III (1258-59), pp. 4, 15. Cf. Powicke, *op. cit.*, I, 384-85.

217 *CPatR*, 29 Hen. III (1245), p. 453.

218 Paris, *Chronica Majora*, RS, III, 233; Roger of Wendover, *op. cit.*, RS, III, 41; *Cal. of Doc. rel. to Scot.*, I, no. 1163; *CPatR*, 17 Hen. III (1233), p. 2

219 *RLC*, 10 Hen. III (1226), II, 214.

220 Paris, *Chronica Majora*, RS, V, 704.

221 *Annales de Dunstaplia, op. cit.*, RS, III, 222; Gervase of Canterbury, *op. cit.*, RS, II, 222.

²²² Cf. Rymer, I, 616.

²²³ *CClR*, 4 Ed. I (1278), pp. 446-47, 462; Walter of Hemingburg, *op. cit.*, II, 273; Rymer, II, 7. Cf. *The Chronicle of Walter of Guisborough previously edited as the Chronicle of Walter of Hemingford or Hemingburgh*, ed. Harry Rothwell ("Publications of the Camden Society," Vol. LXXXIX; London, 1957), p. 382.

²²⁴ Bliss, I, 117.

²²⁵ *CPatR*, 2 Hen. III (1218), p. 168; *RLC*, 4 Hen. III (1220), I, 415.

²²⁶ *ClR*, 18 Hen. III (1234), p. 556.

²²⁷ *Ibid.*, 50 Hen. III (1266), p. 239.

²²⁸ *CPatR*, 37 Hen. III (1253), p. 195.

²²⁹ *Ibid.*, 54 Hen. III (1270), p. 407.

²³⁰ *CChR*, 41 Hen. III (1256), p. 454.

²³¹ *CPatR*, 41 Hen. III (1257), p. 569.

²³² *Ibid.*, 53 Hen. III (1296), p. 358.

²³³ *Chronicles of the Mayors and Sheriffs of London*, RS, p. 117.

²³⁴ *RLC*, 10 Hen. III (1226), II, 122b.

²³⁵ *PatR*, 11 Hen. III (1227), p. 141.

²³⁶ *CPatR*, 37 Hen. III (1253), p. 174.

²³⁷ *ClR*, 41 Hen. III (1257), p. 122.

²³⁸ *CPatR*, 43 Hen. III (1259), p. 33.

²³⁹ Cf. *ClR*, 43 Hen. III (1258), pp. 341-42, 418-19; 446-47, 471; *CPatR*, 43-45 Hen. III (1258-60), pp. 4, 15, 66, 96, 126.

²⁴⁰ *ClR*, 54 Hen. III (1270), p. 258.

²⁴¹ *Ibid.*, 56 Hen. III (1271), p. 559; *CClR*, 10 Ed. I (1282), p. 184.

²⁴² *CPatR*, 43 Hen. III (1259), p. 41.

²⁴³ Paris, *Chronica Majora*, RS, VI, 220-21.

²⁴⁴ *Cal. of Doc. in France*, I, 336 (no. 1041).

²⁴⁵ *ClR*, 55 Hen. III (1271), p. 410.

²⁴⁶ *CClR*, 18 Ed. I (1290), p. 118.

²⁴⁷ E.g., *PatR*, 6 Hen. III (1221), pp. 317-18, 321-22; *ClR*, 45 Hen. III (1261), pp. 463-64; *CClR*, 28 Ed. I (1300), p. 392.

²⁴⁸ Cf. contract cited by Paris, *Chronica Majora*, RS, III, 329.

²⁴⁹ *PatR*, 16 Hen. III (1232), pp. 514-15; *CPatR*, 32 Hen. III (1247), p. 1; Rymer, I, 365; *CPatR*, 42 Hen. III (1258), pp. 629, 631; *ibid.*, 43-44 Hen. III (1259-60), pp. 16, 30, 71; *ibid.*, 50 Hen. III (1266), p. 675; *ibid.*, 52 Hen. III (1268), p. 277.

²⁵⁰ *Ibid.*, 41 Hen. III (1257), p. 562.

²⁵¹ *Historic and Municipal Documents of Ireland*, p. 168 (1266); Paris, *Chronica Majora*, RS, VI, 220-21; *Records of Anthony Bek*, no. 8 (1288).

²⁵² E.g., *CPatR*, 37 Hen. III (1253), p. 228.

²⁵³ Over forty such cases can be cited for the years from 1249 to 1272. Cf. *ClR*, 33 Hen. III (1249), p. 230; *ibid.*, 41 Hen. III (1257), p. 115; *ibid.*, 44-45 Hen. III (1260-61), pp. 161, 213, 463-64; *ibid.*, 51 Hen. III (1267), pp. 378-81, 393, 398; *ibid.*, 52 Hen. III (1268), pp. 243-45, 280-81, 501-02, 513-14, 520-22, 532, 559; *ibid.*, 53-56 Hen. III (1269-72), pp. 98, 107, 130, 139, 145, 248, 251, 266, 285-86, 474, 558, 561, 562; *CPatR*, 37 Hen. III (1253), p. 227; *ibid.*, 50 Hen. III (1266), pp. 656-57; *ibid.*, 52 Hen. III (1268), pp. 282-84; *CRR*, 4 Hen. III (1220), p. 287.

²⁵⁴ *ClR*, 52 Hen. III (1268), pp. 520-21.

²⁵⁵ *Ibid.*, 51 Hen. III (1267), p. 374.

²⁵⁶ Cf. *CPatR*, 52 Hen. III (1268), pp. 280-83.

²⁵⁷ Cf. *ibid.*

158   *The Knights Templars in England*

²⁵⁸ E.g., *CClR*, 40 Hen. III (1256), p. 442; *ibid.*, 51-52 Hen. III (1267-68), pp. 379, 381, 442, 514, 521, 522, 542, *ibid.*, 53 Hen. III (1269), p. 107; *ibid.*, 10 Ed. I (1282), p. 184; *CPatR*, 54 Hen. III (1270), p. 446.

²⁵⁹ Cf. Delisle, *op. cit.*, p. 15; DeRoover, *Money, Banking, and Credit*, p. 215.

²⁶⁰ The details of the contracts of Italian, French, and Flemish merchants which survive in large number in notarial archives, can be used for comparative purposes. Cf. Robert S. Lopez and Irving W. Raymond (eds.), *Medieval Trade in the Mediterranean World*, "Records of Civilization," No. 52 (New York, 1955); Louis Blanchard (ed.), *Documents inédits sur le commerce de Marseilles au moyen âge: contrats commerciaux du xiiiᵉ siècle* (2 vols.; Marseilles, 1884-85); Renée Doehaerd (ed.), *Les relations commerciales entre Gênes, la Belgique, et L'Outremont d'après les archives notarial génoises aux xiiiᵉ et xivᵉ siècles,* "Institut belge de Rome, Etudes d'histoire économique et sociale" (Vols. II-IV; Brussels, 1941); Federico Patetta and Mario Chiaudano (eds.), *Documenti e studi per la storia del commercio e del diritto commerciale italiano* (22 vols.; Turin, 1933-42).

²⁶¹ *RLP*, 5-7 John (1204-06), pp. 41-42, 51-52, 65; *PatR*, 5 John (1204), p. 41.

²⁶² *RLC*, 7 John (1206), I, 144; *RLP*, 7 John (1206), pp. 41b, 65.

²⁶³ *RLC*, 7 John (1215), I, 194 where the sum is ordered repaid.

²⁶⁴ *Ibid.*, 17 John (1216), I, 197; *RLP*, 17 John (1216), pp. 152-53.

²⁶⁵ *RLC*, 17 John (1216), I, 141, 177. To get the loan from the Templars of Poitou, John had to put up collateral in gold worth 2,000 marks – cf. Piquet, *op. cit.*, p. 84.

²⁶⁶ *RLC*, 16 John (1215), I, 194; *RLP*, 17 John (1216), pp. 135, 141.

²⁶⁷ *RLC*, 17 John (1216), I, 197.

²⁶⁸ Cf. *PatR*, 1-4 Hen. III (1217-20), pp. 51, 232.

²⁶⁹ *Ibid.*: 300 of the remaining 500 marks still unpaid were to be paid by Easter (1221), and the balance would have to be gotten from the revenues of Bordeaux.

²⁷⁰ *RLC*, 6 Hen. III (1221), I, 479.

²⁷¹ *Ibid.*, 8 Hen. III (1224), I, 612; *PatR*, 8 Hen. III (1224), pp. 453, 456, 497.

²⁷² *CPatR*, 10 Hen. III (1225), p. 537.

²⁷³ *Ibid.*, 18 Hen. III (1234), p. 47.

²⁷⁴ *Ibid.*, 19 Hen. III (1235), pp. 116-17; Rymer, I, 218.

²⁷⁵ *LibR*, 24 Hen. III (1239), p. 433.

²⁷⁶ *CPatR*, 27 Hen. III (1243), p. 378; *LibR*, 28 Hen. III (1244), p. 213.

²⁷⁷ *CPatR*, 31 Hen. III (1247), p. 378.

²⁷⁸ *Ibid.*, 32 Hen. III (1247), p. 2; Shirley, *op. cit.*, RS, II, 50.

²⁷⁹ *CPatR*, 32 Hen. III (1248), p. 20.

²⁸⁰ *Ibid.*, 44 Hen. III (1260), p. 114.

²⁸¹ *Ibid.*, 46-47 Hen. III (1262), p. 731.

²⁸² *Issues of the Exchequer*, III, 86.

²⁸³ Rymer, II, 514; *CPatR*, 3 Ed. I (1275), pp. 83, 114; *ibid.*, 8 Ed. I (1279), p. 353. Cf. Delisle, *op. cit.*, p. 18.

²⁸⁴ *CPatR*, 28 Ed. I (1299), p. 419. Cf. *ibid.*, 8 Ed. I (1280), p. 375.

²⁸⁵ Cf. Robert J. Whitwell, "Italian Bankers and the English Crown," *Transactions of the Royal Historical Society*, XVII NS (1903), 175-233, at pp. 173, 178, 217. It is possible, though the evidence is not conclusive, that the Templars, being conservative in the granting of loans, were not opposed to the transfer of royal borrowing to the Italian merchants – cf. Piquet, *op. cit.*, pp. 52-53, 90-92.

²⁸⁶ Shirley, *op. cit.*, RS, I, 525.

²⁸⁷ *CPatR*, 5 Ed. I (1277), p. 208.

²⁸⁸ *CClR*, 33 Ed. I (1305), p. 343.

²⁸⁹ *Ibid.*, 34 Ed. I (1306), p. 429.

²⁹⁰ *Ibid.*, p. 444.

²⁹¹ *Ibid.*, 35 Ed. I (1307), p. 535.

[292] Cf. G. LeBras, "L'usure: la doctrine écclésiastique de l'usure à l'époque classique (xiie – xve siècles), *Dictionnaire de théologie catholique*, ed. A. Vacant, E. Mangenot, and E. Amman, IX (1950), cols. 2335-72; Benjamin N. Nelson, *The Idea of Usury: from Tribal Brotherhood to Universal Otherhood*, "History of Ideas Series," No. 3 (Princeton, 1949); John M. Baldwin, *Medieval Theories of Just Price; Romanists, Canonists, and Theologians in the Twelfth and Thirteenth Centuries*, "Transactions of the American Philosophical Society," Vol. XLIX, Part 4 (Philadelphia, 1959); T. P. McLaughlin, "The Teaching of the Canonists on Usury (XII, XIII, and XIV Centuries)," *Medieval Studies*, I (1939), 81-147; II (1940), 1-22; Noonan, *op. cit.;* Edgar Salin, "Usury," *Encyclopedia of the Social Sciences*, XV (1935), 193-97; Raymond A. DeRoover, *Money, Banking, and Credit in Medieval Bruges; ibid., L'évolution de la Lettre de Change; ibid.,* "New Interpretations of the History of Banking," *op. cit.;* Ashley, *op. cit.,* I, Part I, 148-63.

[293] *CCIR*, 32 Ed. I (1204), pp. 172-73.

[294] Cf. Usher, *Early History of Banking*, p. 78; Noonan, *op. cit.,* p. 6.

[295] *Decretum, Distinctio* XLVI, *cap.* 9; XLVII, *cap.* 1-4; *Causa* XIV, *quest.* 3-6. Cf. Baldwin, *op. cit.,* pp. 32-33. The application of usury to cases of buying and selling at a profit and to all speculative transactions made for the sake of gain is not pertinent to the present discussion. Cf., however, Gratian, *Causa* XIV, *quest.* 4, *cap.* 9; Baldwin, *op. cit.,* pp. 32, 35; and McLaughlin, "Teachings of the Canonists," *op. cit.,* p. 82.

[296] Panatorius: *Usura solum in mutua cadit.* Albertus Magnus: *Usura est lucrum ex mutuo.* (Cited by DeRoover, *Money, Banking, and Credit*, p. 353.) Cf. DeRoover, *Lettre de Change*, p. 19; *ibid., Money, Banking, and Credit*, p. 54; *ibid.,* "New Interpretations," *op. cit.,* p. 42; Baldwin, *op. cit.,* pp. 32, 37; McLaughlin, "Teachings of the Canonists," *op. cit.,* p. 81, n. 1, 98-100; Noonan, *op. cit.,* pp. 80-81.

[297] *Ibid.;* McLaughlin, "Teachings of the Canonists," *op. cit.,* pp. 100, 103.

[298] *Ibid.,* p. 112.

[299] *Ibid.,* p. 143; Noonan, *op. cit.,* pp. 104-05.

[300] *Ibid.,* p. 107; McLaughlin, "Teachings of the Canonists," *op. cit.,* pp. 140-41.

[301] *Digesta*, 13:4:2:8; *Codex*, 7:47:1 – cited by Noonan, *op. cit.,* p. 106, nn. 32-33. Cf. McLaughlin, "Teachings of the Canonists," *op. cit.,* pp. 145-46; Ashley, *op. cit.,* I, Part I, 196-97, Part II, 395-405; Whitwell, "Italian Bankers and the English Crown," *op. cit.,* p. 185.

[302] Noonan, *op. cit.,* p. 106; Ashley, *op. cit.,* I, Part II, 399. Cf. Frank H. Knight, "Interest," *Encyclopedia of the Social Sciences*, VIII (1932), 131-44.

[303] Noonan, *op. cit.,* p. 110.

[304] Cf. DeRoover, *Money, Banking, and Credit*, pp. 27, 32-35, 54, 62, 126, 305; *ibid., Lettre de Change*, p. 20; *ibid.,* "New Interpretations," *op. cit.,* p. 50; Doehaerd, *op. cit.,* II, 116-18; Piquet, *op. cit.,* 52-53. Lopez and Raymond (*op. cit.,* documents no. 66-71) cite specific notarial contracts illustrating usury and interest.

[305] *Op. cit.,* p. 52.

[306] *Chronica Majora*, RS, III, 329.

[307] Noonan, *op. cit.,* p. 107; Lopez and Raymond, *op. cit.,* doc. no. 66.

[308] Cf. *PatR*, 3 Hen. III (1219), p. 203.

[309] *CPatR*, 8 Hen. III (1225), pp. 453, 456; *RLC*, 8 Hen. III (1224), I, 612.

[310] McLaughlin, "Teachings of the Canonists," *op. cit.,* pp. 113-14; DeRoover, *Money, Banking, and Credit*, p. 9.

[311] *CPatR*, 44 Hen. III (1260), p. 114.

[312] *Ibid.,* p. 71. *Donum* is the standard word found in Italian documents – cf. Lopez and Raymond, *op. cit., passim.*

[313] Rymer, I, 514. Cf. remarks of Delisle, *op. cit.,* p. 87.

[314] *CPatR*, 25 Hen. III (1241), p. 250.

[315] Shirley, *op. cit.*, RS, I, 336-37.

[316] *CPatR*, 19 Hen. III (1235), pp. 116-17.

[317] *Ibid.*, 22 Hen. III (1238), p. 222.

[318] *Ibid.*, 38 Hen. III (1254), pp. 320, 364, 367, 369; *CLibR*, 38 Hen. III (1254), pp. 159, 168, 177, 180. Cf. Piquet, *op. cit.*, p. 63.

[319] CPatR, 37-38 Hen. III (1254), p. 326. Cf. Piquet, *op. cit.*, p. 63.

[320] *CPatR*, 39 Hen. III (1255), pp. 405, 412-13.

[321] Cf. *RLC*, 8 Hen. III (1224), I, 590, 594b; *ClR*, 12 Hen. III (1228), pp. 116-17; *LibR*, 13 Hen. III (1228), p. 108.

[322] Cf. Delisle, *op. cit.*, p. 22.

[323] Cf. *ibid.*, pp. 20-24; Piquet, *op. cit.*, chap. II; DeRoover, *Money, Banking, and Credit*, p. 9; Sandys, "Financial and Administrative Importance of the London Temple," *op. cit.*, pp. 147-62; Ferris, "Financial Relations of the Knights Templars to the English Crown," *op. cit.*, p. 12; R. G. Hawtrey, "Credit," *Encyclopedia of the Social Sciences*, IV (1931), 545-50; Julius Landmann, "History of Commercial Banking to the Close of the Eighteenth Century," *ibid.*, II (1930), 423-31; M. M. Postan, "Private Financial Instruments in Medieval England, *"Vierteljahrschrift für Social- und Wirtschaftsgeschichte*, XXIII (1930), 39-90; André E. Sayous, "Le capitalisme commercial et financier dans les pays chrétiens de la Méditeranée occidentale depuis la première croisade jusqu'à la fin du moyen âge," *ibid.*, XXIX (1936), 270-95; M. M. Postan, "Credit in Medieval Trade," *Economic History Review*, I (1928), 234-61; Jacob Strieder, "Origin and Evolution of early European Capitalism," *"Journal of Economic and Business History*, II (1929), 1-19; Heaton, *op. cit.*, chap. IX. The views of Cunningham (*op. cit.*, I, 362) on the general absence of the use of credit in the Middle Ages have been shown to be incorrect.

[324] The most thorough and up-to-date discussion of these problems is to be found in DeRoover, *Money, Banking, and Credit*, and *Lettre de Change* where the ideas of earlier writers such as Adolf Schaube, André Sayous, and Levin Goldschmidt are carefully examined. Cf. also Usher, *Early History of Banking;* Doehaerd, *op. cit.*, introductory remarks to vol. II; Margaret W. Hall, "Early Bankers in Genoese Notarial Records," *Economic History Review*, VI (1935), 73-79; Robert L. Reynolds, "A Business Affair in Genoa in the Year 1200, Banking, Bookkeeping, a Broker (?), and a Lawsuit," in *Studi di storia e diritto in onore di Enrico Besta* (Milan, 1938), II, 167-81; Yves Renouard, *Les hommes d'affaires italiens du moyen âge* (Paris, 1949).

[325] *CPatR*, 39 Hen. III (1255), p. 405.

[326] *CClR*, 32 Ed. I (1304), p. 172.

[327] *RLP*, 14 John (1213), pp. 103, 141; *RLC*, 14 John (1213), I, 221b.

[328] *PatR*, 2 Hen. III (1218), p. 168; *ClR*, 4 Hen. III (1220), p. 415.

[329] *RLC*, 5 Hen. III (1221), I, 465.

[330] *Ibid.*, p. 471b.

[331] *CPatR*, 5 Hen. III (1221), p. 303.

[332] *RLC*, 10 Hen. III (1226), II, 122b.

[333] *CPatR*, 8 Hen. III (1224), p. 439; *RLC*, 8 Hen. III (1224), I, 594b.

[334] *Ibid.*, 19 Hen. III (1235), pp. 116-17; Rymer, I, 218.

[335] *ClR*, 19 Hen. III (1235), p. 110; Rymer, I, 373.

[336] *ClR*, 26 Hen. III (1242), p. 402; *CPatR*, 26 Hen. III (1242), p. 277; Delisle, *op. cit.*, pp. 13-14. Cf. Rymer, I, 616.

[337] *ClR*, 50 Hen. III (1266), p. 239.

[338] *Chronicles of the Mayors and Sheriffs of London*, RS, p. 117.

[339] Cf. DeRoover, *Lettre de Change*, introduction and chap. I; Delisle, *op. cit.*, pp. 20-24; Ferris, "Financial Relations of the Templars to the English Crown," *op. cit.*, p. 12. Usher ("Origins of Banking," *op. cit.*, p. 415), when he states, no doubt correctly, that extensive use of non-negotiable bills of exchange came only in the last half of the fourteenth century, fails to give adequate considera-

tion to the long evolution and the selective use of bills of exchange in the preceding century. Actually, G. Sayles ("A Dealer in Wardrobe Bills," *Economic History Review*, III [1931], 267-73) has shown (pp. 270-71) that Wardrobe bills were negotiated with the appearance of usualness before the mid-fourteenth century — cf. *CClR*, 20-22 Ed. III (1346-49), p. 76. Moreover, Piquet, (*op. cit.*, pp. 50-51) has pointed out that letters from clients to the Templars instructing them to pay a given sum to a named person, or his representative, considerably facilitated the mobility and transferability of funds and may be looked upon as fulfilling the economic function of a check. For fifteenth century authorizations for the drawing up of bills of exchange, see *CClR*, 7-10 Hen. IV (1409-13), pp. 439-51; *ibid.*, 1-7 Hen. VI (1422-29), pp. 477-87. Cf. also, n. 324 above.

³⁴⁰ For critical examination of these forms of exchange, see DeRoover, *Lettre de Change*, p. 24 *(cambium minutum)*, 28-32 *(instrumentum)*, 14-20, 24-26, 40-43, 54, 61 *(cambium per litteras); ibid., Money, Banking, and Credit*, pp. 49-54, 57, 61-62, and "New Interpretations," *op. cit.*, pp. 41-42, 49.

³⁴¹ *Early History of Banking*, p. 6.

³⁴² Cf. Delisle, *op. cit.*, p. 20; Piquet, *op. cit.*, p. 64.

³⁴³ William of Newburgh, *op. cit.*, RS, I, 158; Roger of Hoveden, *op. cit.*, RS, I, 218.

³⁴⁴ Rymer, I, 383.

³⁴⁵ *RLP*, 17 John (1215), p. 181; *RLC*, 6 Hen. III (1221), I, 480; *CPatR*, 4 Hen. III (1220), p. 243; Rymer, I, 137.

³⁴⁶ *RLP*, 15 John (1214), pp. 119, 121.

³⁴⁷ *CClR*, 12 Hen. III (1228), p. 72; Bain, I, nos. 1003, 1005.

³⁴⁸ *LibR*, 23 Hen. III (1239), p. 381.

³⁴⁹ *CChR*, 39 Hen. III (1255), pp. 438-39.

³⁵⁰ *ClR*, 33-35 Hen. III (1248-51), pp. 33, 41, 526; *ibid.*, 43 Hen. III (1258-59), pp. 341-42, 418-19, 446-47, 471; *CPatR*, 43 Hen. III (1258-59), pp. 4, 15, 22; *ibid.*, 44-46 Hen. III (1260-62), pp. 66, 96, 126, 218; *ClR*, 52 Hen. III (1268), p. 542; *CPatR*, 54 Hen. III (1270), p. 446.

³⁵¹ *ClR*, 44 Hen. III (1260), p. 28.

³⁵² *Cal. of Doc. in France*, RS, I, 382-83.

³⁵³ *RLP*, 16 John (1214), pp. 116b, 121b.

³⁵⁴ Rymer, I, 196, 269, 365; *RLC*, 7-8 Hen. III (1223-24), I, 544, 581, 594; II, 118, 126. Cf. Ferris, "Financial Relations of the Knights Templars to the English Crown," *op. cit.*, p. 13.

³⁵⁵ *CPatR*, 43 Hen. III (1258), pp. 3, 4, 9, 12.

³⁵⁶ *Reg. of Malmesbury Abbey*, RS, I, 428.

³⁵⁷ *LibR*, 11 Hen. III (1227), p. 19; *CPatR*, 42 Hen. III (1257-58), pp. 605, 622; Bliss, I, 117.

³⁵⁸ A detailed discussion of the material in this paragraph is to be found in Piquet, *op. cit.*, pp. 115-43, 203-11 and Delisle, *op. cit.*, pp. 73-86. Both Piquet and Delisle give extracts from the Journal.

³⁵⁹ Abbott P. Usher, "The Origins of Banking: the primitive Bank of Deposit, 1200-1600," *Economic History Review*, IV (1934), 399-428, at pp. 411-12.

³⁶⁰ Cf., Delisle, *op. cit.*, p. 2.

³⁶¹ *Munimenta Gildhallae Londoniensis: Liber Albus, Liber Custumarum, et Liber Horn*, ed. Henry T. Riley (RS No. 12, 3 vols.; London, 1859-62), II, 654.

³⁶² Benedict of Peterborough, *op. cit.*, RS, II, 31.

³⁶³ *Ibid.*, pp. 47-48; Walter of Coventry, *op. cit.*, RS, I, 360.

³⁶⁴ *LibR*, 22 Hen. III (1238), pp. 309, 333, 334; *ClR*, 22 Hen. III (1238), pp. 52, 119; *LibR*, 24 Hen. III (1240), p. 446; *CPatR*, 26 Hen. III (1242), p. 277.

³⁶⁵ *Ibid.*, 22 Hen. III (1238), p. 221.

³⁶⁶ *Ibid.*, 26 Hen. III (1242), p. 277; *ibid.*, 34 Hen. III (1250), p. 68; *ibid.*, 8-9 Ed. I (1281), pp. 212, 379.

[367] *Ibid.*, 37 Hen. III (1253), p. 312; *ibid.*, 7 Ed. I (1279), p. 298; *Cal. of Doc. rel. to Ire.*, I, no. 2157; II, nos. 238, 881, 1485.

[368] Shirley, *op. cit.*, RS, pp. 91-92 (no. 491).

[369] *CPatR*, 13 Ed. I (1285), p. 184.

[370] *Ibid.*, 22 Ed. I (1294), p. 88. Cf. Rogers Ruding, *Annals of the Coinage of Great Britain and its Dependencies*, 3rd ed. (3 vols.; London, 1840), I, 198-99. The reference here appears to be to Edward's decision to call in clipped and counterfeit coins and to issue new coins in their place.

[371] *LibR*, 22-24 Hen. III (1238-40), pp. 326-27, 452; *CPatR*, 25-26 Hen. III (1241-42), pp. 249, 278.

[372] *ClR*, 26 Hen. III (1242), p. 172; Paris, *Chronica Majora*, RS, III, 495, 543.

[373] *RLC*, 17 John (1215-16), I, 228-31, 233-34, 236-40, 252, 255.

[374] *Ibid.*, 5-10 Hen. III (1221-26), I, 471b; II, 14, 33, 44, 45, 69, 92, 94, 98, 112. Cf. *ibid.*, p. 303.

[375] *CPatR*, 22 Hen. III (1238), pp. 176, 196, 211, 214, 223, 231.

[376] Tout, *op. cit.*, I, 51, 229-32, 315-16; Chrimes, *op. cit.*, pp. 100-06; Sandys, "Financial and Administrative Importance of the London Temple in the Thirteenth Century," *op. cit.*, pp. 149-51.

[377] *Ibid.*; Chrimes, *op. cit.*, p. 137.

[378] *PatR*, 9 Hen. III (1225), pp. 505, 506, 508; *RLC*, 9 Hen. III (1225), II, 21, 26b.

[379] E.g., *ibid.*, 7 Hen. III (1222-23), I, 486b, 549.

[380] E.g., *ClR*, 26 Hen. III (1242), p. 415; *ibid.*, 35 Hen. III (1251), p. 455; *CPatR*, 26 Hen. III (1242), p. 282; *ibid.*, 34-39 Hen. III (1250-55), pp. 67, 100, 113, 398; *ibid.*, 43-44 Hen. III (1259-60), pp. 21, 22, 68; *ibid.*, 3 Ed. I (1275), p. 83.

[381] *PatR*, 10 Hen. III (1225), pp. 2, 8, 9, 10.

[382] *CPatR*, 31 Hen. III (1247), p. 497.

[383] *Ibid.*, 54-56 Hen. III (1270-71), pp. 439, 448, 466, 513.

[384] *Ibid.*, 4 Ed. I (1276), p. 141.

[385] *RLC*, 3 Hen. III (1219), I, 396b; cf. also, *ibid.*, pp. 558, 581.

[386] For Hugh of Stocton: *ClR*, 22-26 Hen. III (1237-42), pp. 46, 115, 119, 153, 171, 172, 389; *CPatR*, 18-26 Hen. III (1234-42), pp. 209, 212, 217, 218, 282, 287. For Robert of Sicklinghall: *ibid.*, 30 Hen. III (1246), p. 474; *ClR*, 34 Hen. III (1250), p. 326; Rymer, I, 380. For a list of the known treasurers of New Temple and the dates they held that office, see Appendix C.

[387] Cf. remarks regarding the Hospitallers in Benjamin Bromberg, "The Financial and Administrative Importance of the Knights Hospitallers to the English Crown," *Economic History*, IV (1940), 307-11.

[388] Delisle, *op. cit.*, pp. 41-60; Piquet, *op. cit.*, pp. 181-89, 193-224.

[389] Delisle, *op. cit.*, pp. 40-41, 58-59.

[390] *Op. cit.*, p. 182.

[391] *Ibid.*, pp. 182, 185; Delisle, *op. cit.*, pp. 60-61.

[392] Cf. Piquet, *op. cit.*, p. 184.

Chapter Four

[1] *History of the Inquisition of the Middle Ages* (3 vols.; New York, 1887), III, 238.

[2] The specific charges, which were essentially the same from country to country, will be discussed in some detail below in the section dealing with the trial in England. Some picture of the conditions at the time of the attack on the Templars can be seen in Pierre du Bois' *The Recovery of the Holy Land* (trans. Walther I. Brandt; "Records of Civilization," No. 51; New York, 1956), *passim*. DuBois himself proposed the consolidation of the military orders (pp. 8,

40, 56, 81, 200) and the confiscation of their property (pp. 40, 56, 81, 82, 201, 204, 207).

³ Cf. Lea, *op. cit.,* III, 254; Campbell, *op. cit.,* p. 238; Thomas Fuller, *Historie of the Holy Warre* (London, 1840), p. 246; Perkins, "The Trial of the Knights Templars in England," *op. cit.,* p. 432; Konrad Schottmüller, *Der Untergang des Templer-ordens* (2 vols.; Berlin, 1887), I, 63-68, 532.

⁴ For a fuller discussion, see: Heinrich Finke, *Papsttum und Untergang des Templerordens* (Münster, 1907), chaps. III-V; Schottmüller, *op. cit.,* chaps. IV-VII; Lea, *op. cit.,* III 252-98; Campbell, *op. cit.,* chaps. XIV-XVI; Prutz, *op. cit.,* chaps. VI-IX; E. Boutaric, "Clement V, Phillippe le Bel, et les Templiers," *Revue des questions historiques,* X (1871), 301-42 and XI (1872), 5-40; J. Delaville le Roulx, "La Suppression des Templiers," *ibid.,* XLVIII (1890), 29-61; and Charles V. Langlois, "Le Procès des Templiers," *Revue des deux mondes,* CIII (1891), 382-421. The documents for the trial of the Templars in France can be found in: M. Michelet (ed.), *Le Procès des Templiers* (2 vols.; Paris, 1841-51); François J. M. Raynouard (ed.), *Monumens historiques relatifs à la Condemnation des Chevaliers du Temple, et à l'Abolition de leur Ordre* (Paris, 1813); DuPuy; Georges Lizerand (ed.), *Le Dossier de l'Affaire des Templiers* (Paris, 1923).

⁵ DuPuy, no. 42. Cf. Campbell, *op. cit.,* p. 246.

⁶ DuPuy, nos. 43, 56.

⁷ *Ibid.,* nos. 50, 57.

⁸ *Ibid.,* no. 50.

⁹ Michelet (*op. cit.,* I, 90-96) cites the charges. The testimony taken at the interrogations forms the bulk of the two volumes.

¹⁰ *Ibid.,* I, 36, 37, 75, *et passim.*

¹¹ Boutaric, "Clement V, Philippe le Bel, et les Templiers," *op. cit.,* p. 336; Campbell, *op. cit.,* p. 265.

¹²Rymer, II, 16; DuPuy, no. 58.

¹³ *Ibid.,* nos. 56; 71.

¹⁴ *Ibid.,* nos. 80-83.

¹⁵ *Ibid.,* no. 93.

¹⁶ *Ibid.,* no. 91.

¹⁷ Michelet, *op. cit.,* I, 81ff.

¹⁸ DuPuy, no. 95. The 54 Templars referred to here were burned in May, 1310. In later months, 46 additional Templars, of whom only 2 recanted, were handed over to the state to be burned at Paris as heretics. Cf. John Capgrave, *The Chronicle of England,* ed. Francis C. Hingeston (RS, No. 1; London, 1858), p. 177.

¹⁹ Though official records of the council insofar as they pertain to the Templars are almost wholly lacking, considerable information on the council and Templars can be gained from the writings of contemporary chroniclers. DuPuy (nos. 111 and 113A) quotes extensively from two of these: the *Chronique* of William de Nangis and the *Histoire écclésiastique* of Abbot Fleury.

²⁰Cited by Lea, *op. cit.,* III, 321-22.

²¹ Rymer, II, 167-68; DuPuy, no. 112; *Regestum Clementis Papae V ex Vaticanis archetypis,* ed. the Monks of St. Benedict (9 vols.; Rome, 1884-92), no. 7886.

²² Few of these provincial councils ever actually met. Later (December, 1319), Pope John XXII (Dugdale, VII, 848; DuPuy, no. 137) ordered that all Templars who had abandoned the ecclesiastical life, who had married, and the like, must give up their secular activities and wives, and must be assigned no more than two to a monastery, except for the houses of the Hospitallers, which might accept more than two. Apparently, the Hospitallers had already received many Templars into their order.

²³ DuPuy (nos. 118, 119) quotes the *Chronique* of William of Nangis and *Registre des Arrêts, 1299-1318.*

²⁴ Cf. Lea, *op. cit.,* III, 329.

²⁵ DuPuy (nos. 123, 124) gives three agreements made between the Hospitallers and the French kings (1313, 1315, and 1317).

²⁶ Rymer, II, 10.

²⁷ *Ibid.*

²⁸ *Ibid.*, II, 19; DuPuy, no. 61.

²⁹ Rymer, II, 20; DuPuy, no. 61A.

³⁰ Cf. the letter of Clement to Edward (August 12, 1308) in Rymer, II, 55.

³¹ *Ibid.*, 16-17; DuPuy, no. 58.

³² On December 26, 1307, Edward wrote Clement (Rymer, II, 24; DuPuy, no. 61B) that he would carry out the pope's wishes. Cf. *CClR*, 1 Ed. II (1307), p. 49.

³³ Cf. Rymer, II, 18, 23, 24.

³⁴ *Ibid.;* DuPuy, nos. 61C-E; *CClR*, 1 Ed. II (1307), pp. 14, 48, 49. The story of the arrest of the Templars in England is narrated by many chroniclers including: *Annales Paulini*, ed. William Stubbs, *Chronicles of the reigns of Edward I and Edward II* (RS, No. 76; 2 vols.; London, 1882-83), I, 264-65; *Commendatio lamentabilis in transitu magni regis Edwardi*, ed. William Stubbs, *ibid.*, II, 32; *Annales Prioratus de Wigornia* in *Annales Monastici*, RS, IV, 560; Thomas de Burton, *Chronica monasterii de Melsa ab fondatione usque ad annum 1406*, ed. Edward A. Bond (RS, No. 43; 3 vols.; London, 1866-68), II, 248, 313; Thomas Walsingham, *Historia Anglicana*, RS, I, 120 and *Ypodigma Neustria*, RS, VII, 242; *The French Chronicle of London A.D. 1259 to A.D. 1343*, ed. Henry T. Riley (London, 1863), p. 34; and *Chronicles of London*, ed. Charles L. Kingsford (Oxford, 1905), p. 8.

³⁵ Cf. note 76 below. Campbell (*op cit.*, pp. 270, 282), without providing any evidence, speaks of "hundreds" of escaped Templars.

³⁶ Rymer, II, 18; *CClR*, 1 Ed. II (1307), pp. 14, 49.

³⁷ Cf. Rymer, II, 118, 150, 152, 173, 180, 243; *CClR*, 1 Ed. II (1307), pp. 14, 49; *ibid.*, 2 Ed. II (1308), p. 90 *et passim; ibid.*, 4 Ed. II (1310), p. 290. (There are literally scores of entries in the Close Rolls ordering the keepers of the Templar properties to make payments in support of the Templars assigned to do penance in various monasteries.) The rate of four pence per day applied to ordinary members; larger sums were authorized for chaplains (cf. *CClR*, 5 Ed. II [1312], p. 397) and for high officials (cf. *ibid.*, 6 Ed. II [1313], pp. 508, 533).

³⁸ Rymer, II, 46, 243; DuPuy, no. 62. Cf. *CClR*, 5 Ed. II (1307-13), p. 384; *ibid.*, 6 Ed. II (1313), p. 533. When William de la More died, the king ordered the same sum allowed William to be paid to Himbert Blanke, highest remaining Templar in England: *CClR*, 6 Ed. II (1313), pp. 508, 533; *ibid.*, 7 Ed. II (1313-14), pp. 6, 39.

³⁹ Rymer, II, 46; DuPuy, no. 62; *CClR*, 1 Ed. II (1308), pp. 35, 39. Cf. Williamson, *op. cit.*, p. 51.

⁴⁰ Cf. Perkins, "The Trial of the Knights Templars in England," *English Historical Review*, XXIV (1909), 432-47, at p. 433.

⁴¹ Dugdale, VII, 844-46. Cf. DuPuy, no. 70. The actual number of charges levelled by the pope against the Templars varied from 87 to 123. The bulls *Regnans in coelis* and *Faciens misericordiam* (Rymer, II, 55; DuPuy, no. 65, 66, 67, 68A), both dated August 12, 1308, recite the evils of the Templars in considerable detail. Another version of the charges can be found in the *Annales Londonienses, op. cit.*, RS, I, 179-98.

⁴² Rymer, II, 55; Dugdale, VI, 844-46. Cf. Clement's instructions to the papal inquisitor in England: *Records of Anthony Bek*, no. 128.

⁴³ Letters of safe conduct were issued for the papal representatives on September 13, 1309: Rymer, II, 88; DuPuy, no. 68C; *CPatR*, 3 Ed. II (1309), p. 190; *ibid.*, 4 Ed. II (1310), p. 289.

⁴⁴ Rymer, II, 90; *CClR*, 3 Ed. II (1309), pp. 175-77, 230. Later orders had to be issued, too: *CClR*, 3 Ed. II (1309), pp. 187, 189 (Dec. 10, 14, 1309); *ibid.*, p. 189 and Rymer, II, 100 (Dec. 14, 1309); *CClR*, 3 Ed. II (1310), p. 206 and

Rymer, II, 105 (Mar. 12, 1310); and *ibid.,* p. 125 and *CClR,* 4 Ed. II (1311), p. 295 (Jan. 4, 1311).
⁴⁵ *CClR,* 3 Ed. II (1309), pp. 175-76.
⁴⁶ Rymer, II, 88; DuPuy, nos. 68A, 68B; *CClR,* 3 Ed. II (1309), pp. 179, 230.
⁴⁷ Clement had apparently issued such a bull back in December, 1308 – cf. Du-Puy, no. 74.
⁴⁸ The manuscript sources for the trial of the English Templars are reproduced, with some exceptions, in D. Wilkins (ed.), *Concilia Magnae Britanniae et Hiberniae, A.D. 446-1718* (Vols. I-II; London, 1737), II, 329-401. The Templars in England were ordered by the crown to be transferred from the various county prisons where they had been held since their arrest in January, 1308 to three centers: the Tower of London, the Castle of York, and the Castle of Lincoln – *CClR,* 3 Ed. II (1309), pp. 175-76, 189, 230; Rymer, II, 88, 90, 91. Later (*CClR,* 4 Ed. II [1310-11], pp. 290, 291-92, 308; Rymer, II, 119) the Templars at Lincoln were ordered sent to London. The Templars at York remained there – cf. *CClR,* 3-5 Ed. II [1310-11], pp. 206, 295, 370-71. The Templars in Scotland and Ireland (*ibid.,* 3 Ed. II [1309], p. 179) were ordered imprisoned and examined at Dublin. Cf. the orders issued by the papal commission for the examination of the Templars in England and in Scotland as given in the *Records of Anthony Bek,* nos. 144-45.
⁴⁹ *Ibid.,* 334-45, gives the bulk of the testimony taken in the first phase of the examination at London. Cf. also DuPuy, no. 67B. The procedure to be followed was laid down by the provincial council which met from Oct. 8 to Nov. 24, 1309 at London: DuPuy, no. 66A. For a thorough discussion of the testimony at all of the examinations of the English Templars, see Perkins, "History of the Knights Templars in England," *op. cit.,* chap. IV. For a briefer discussion, see *ibid.,* "The Trial of the Knights Templars in England, *op. cit.,* pp. 432-47.
⁵⁰ Wilkins, II, 356-57, 383. For a discussion of this problem, see Henry C. Lea, "The Absolution Formula of the Templars," *Papers of the American Society of Church History,* V (1893), 37-58. The Templars were questioned regarding their practice of confession and absolution at each of their examinations.
⁵¹ Wilkins, II, 313-14. Cf. *Decretum,* C. 23, 8, 30; X, 5, 7, 9, *et alibi.*
⁵² *Ibid.,* 314; Rymer, II, 100; *CClR,* 3 Ed. II (1309), p. 200; *ibid.,* 4 Ed. II (1310), pp. 279, 285. Cf. remarks of Lea, *op. cit.* (especially III, 300 and throughout chap. V), on the use of torture against the Templars.
⁵³ Rymer, II, 104, 105.
⁵⁴ Wilkins, II, 349-52.
⁵⁵ Rymer, II, 104, 105; *CClR,* 3 Ed. II (1309), p. 200; *ibid.,* 4 Ed. II (1310), pp. 279, 285, 290; *CPatR,* 3 Ed. II (1310), pp. 208-09.
⁵⁶ *CClR,* 4 Ed. II (1311), pp. 308-09 (Apr. 28, 1311).
⁵⁷ Wilkins, II, 352-58.
⁵⁸ Cotton MS, Julius B, folios 80-83 – cited by Perkins, "The Trial of the Knights Templars in England," *op. cit.,* p. 437.
⁵⁹ *Reg. Clem. V,* no. 6378: ". . . *inquisitionis impedire negotium, asserebant quod contra legem seu consuetudinem patriae hoc fiebat . . ."*
⁶⁰ *Ibid.,* no. 6376.
⁶¹ Rymer, II, 115, 118. Cf. *ibid.,* 100, 119, 133, 141; *CClR,* 4 Ed. II (1310), pp. 279, 290, 308-09.
⁶² Wilkins, II, 314.
⁶³ Rymer, II, 117; *CClR,* 4 Ed. II (1310), pp. 285, 290, 292.
⁶⁴ *Ibid.,* pp. 285, 290, 291, 308; Rymer, II, 117.
⁶⁵ *Ibid.,* 133 (Apr. 28, 1311). Cf. *CClR,* 4 Ed. II (1311), p. 308.
⁶⁶ *Ibid.,* p. 290.
⁶⁷ *Ibid.,* pp. 291-92; Rymer, II, 120; DuPuy, no. 66E. The Templars were being concentrated in London.

[68] Wilkins, II, 349-52; DuPuy, no. 86B. A new list of questions had been drawn up by the examiners at London.

[69] *Reg. Clem. V*, no. 6670.

[70] Cf. Rymer, II, 88, 104. Archbishop Greenfield of York appears (Thomas Stubbs, *Lives of the Archbishops*, ed. James Raine, *Historians of the Church of York and its Archbishops* [RS, No. 71; 2 vols.; London, 1886], II, 413-14) to have been especially kind to the Templars in his diocese. A goodly amount of data on the trial and treatment of the Templars at York can be found in the *Register of William Greenfield, Lord Archbishop of York, 1306-1315*. "Publications of the Surtees Society," vols. CXLV, CLII, CLIII (London, 1931-38).

[71] Walter of Hemingburg, *Chronicon . . . de gestis regum Angliae*, ed. Hans C. Hamilton (2 vols.; London, 1848-49), II, 287-91.

[72] DuPuy, no. 106A.

[73] Wilkins (II, 358-64) gives the testimony. The three examples cited below are taken from this. Cf. also, *Annales Londonienses, op. cit.*, RS, I, 180-98.

[74] Wilkins, II, 364.

[75] *Ibid.*, 364-65; DuPuy, no. 108B.

[76] Stappelbrugge and Thoroldsby, mentioned below, were arrested in this period (*CClR*, 4 Ed. II [1310], pp. 316-17). Apparently the king's officials were so persistent that such a person as Peter Auger, a yeoman of the king's chamber, who wore a beard, found it necessary to have the king (*CPatR*, 4 Ed. II [1311], p. 330; *CChanWar*, 4 Ed. II [1311], I, 344) certify that he was not a Templar and wore a beard in fulfillment of a pilgrimage vow. In general, it would seem that few renegade Templars were found.

[77] Cf. *CClR*, 4 Ed. II (1311), pp. 308-09; *ibid.*, 5 Ed. II (1311), pp. 370-71.

[78] Wilkins, II, 383-84; DuPuy, nos. 107, 109I. Cf. *CClR*, 4 Ed. II (1311), p. 316.

[79] Wilkins, II, 384-87; DuPuy, nos. 107, 109II.

[80] *Ibid.*, nos. 107, 109III; Wilkins, II, 387-88.

[81] The public records are filled with references to the disposition of Templar lands and goods. Two valuable articles have been written on the subject: Agnes M. Leys, "The Forfeiture of the Lands of the Templars in England," *Oxford Essays in Medieval History presented to Herbert Edward Salter* (Oxford, 1934), pp. 155-63, and Perkins, "The Wealth of the Knights Templars," *op. cit.*

[82] Rymer, II, 16; DuPuy, nos. 58, 71. Cf. *ibid.*, no. 50.

[83] *Ibid.*, no. 53.

[84] See above, n. 34.

[85] Rymer, II, 59-60.

[86] *Ibid.*, 65.

[87] *Reg. Clem. V*, no. 5061. Cf. *Records of Anthony Bek*, nos. 147 and 150, which show that Edward did not respond to the papal suggestion.

[88] *CClR*, 1 Ed. II (1308), p. 221.

[89] *Ibid.*, 2 Ed. II (1309), p. 94. Cf. Rymer, II, 70. Documentary evidence of the surveys made at the order of the king are to be found in manuscript form in the Public Records Office at London. The detailed accounts submitted first by the sheriffs and then by the keepers for the period 1308-09 are to be found in the Lord Treasurer's Remembrancer, Enrolled Accounts, Miscellaneous, Rolls 18-21. This material has been gone through by Perkins and pertinent data can be gained from his article cited above.

[90] *CClR*, 2 Ed. II (1309), p. 94. Cf. Rymer, II, 70.

[91] Cf. *CClR*, 4-5 Ed. II (1310-11), pp. 290, 365, 369; *CPatR*, 3 Ed. II (1310), p. 210.

[92] Cf. *CClR*, 2 Ed. II (1309), p. 177; Rymer, II, 90, 91.

[93] *Ibid.*, 92; *CChanWar*, I, 301 (Lincolnshire), 304 (Yorkshire).

[94] *CClR*, 3 Ed. II (1309-10), pp. 184, 185; *CPatR*, 3 Ed. II (1310), p. 210; Bain, *op. cit.*, III, no. 306.

⁹⁵ The keepers were repeatedly ordered to pay certain sums out of the issues of Templar lands to the exchequer or to the king's wardrobe and were given acquittances for the sums they paid. Cf. *CCIR, 5* Ed. II (1311-12), pp. 382-83, 392, 394, 424, 438, 441, 453; *CPatR, 5* Ed. II (1312), pp. 463, 465, 467; *ibid.,* 6 Ed. II (1312-13), pp. 481, 484, 511, 523, 565, 590.

⁹⁶ *CCIR,* 6 Ed. II (1313), p. 512.

⁹⁷ *Ibid.,* 5-6 Ed. II (1312-13), pp. 419, 501; *ibid.,* 7 Ed. II (1313), pp. 7, 13; *ibid.,* 10 Ed. II (1317), p. 388.

⁹⁸ Bain, *op. cit.,* III, nos. 240, 241, 250, 253, 256, 306, 311, 315, 338, 367, 428. These grants were made in 1312-13.

⁹⁹ *CCIR,* 5-6 Ed. II (1312-13), pp. 394, 408, 467, 535; *CPatR,* 1 Ed. II (1308), p. 81.

¹⁰⁰ *CCIR,* 5-6 Ed. II (1312-13), pp. 409-10, 507; *CPatR,* 5-6 Ed. II (1312-13), pp. 461, 467, 486-87.

¹⁰¹ *CCIR,* 5-6 Ed. II (1311-12), pp. 392-93, 408, 410, 426-27; *CPatR,* 5 Ed. II (1312), pp. 466, 467, 501, 504; and *ibid.,* 1 Ed. II (1308), p. 81. This last entry is especially interesting. It contains the king's order to the justiciar in Ireland and to the treasurer at Dublin to provide for the expedition against Scotland the following items to be taken out of Templar goods: 1,000 quarters of wheat, 1,000 quarters of oats, 200 quarters of peas and beans; 300 tuns of wine, 3 tuns of honey, 200 quarters of salt, and 1,000 stockfish. It also instructs the sheriffs of thirteen counties to provide grain and livestock out of Templar goods for the same expedition.

¹⁰² *Ibid.,* 1-6 Ed. II (1308-13), pp. 57, 67, 79, 93, 100, 105, 113, 134, 135, 139, 142, 202, 206, 286, 335, 341, 391, 394, 399, 403, 460, 462, 468, 482, 488, 503, 552, 555, 573, 578; *CCIR,* 5-6 Ed. II (1312-13), pp. 423, 465, 532.

¹⁰³ *CPatR,* 4-6 Ed. II (1311-13), pp. 331, 381, 389, 390, 411, 412, 414, 415, 440, 442, 456, 457, 466, 514, 535, 569; *CChanWar,* 4 Ed. II (1311), I, 346. These grants sometimes involved the land only. At other times, they included livestock, grain, and implements as well. In at least one instance (*CPatR,* 5 Ed. II [1312], p. 456), Edward made the grant to a clerk who was to hold the land and receive the income from it until the amount owed him for his past service as Chamberlain of Scotland had been paid. One might suspect that Edward found this system especially useful for paying arrears of salary as well as for rewarding friends and vassals.

¹⁰⁴ *Ibid.,* 3-6 Ed. II (1310-13), pp. 210, 463, 551, 552, 561-62; *CCIR,* 6 Ed. II (1312), p. 480.

¹⁰⁵ *Ibid.,* 5-6 Ed. II (1312-13), pp. 365, 369, 373, 375, 376, 384, 391, 422, 468, 473, 490, 497, 504, 509, 512, 518, 521, 526; *ibid.,* 7 Ed. II (1313-14), pp. 10, 11, 12, 14, 15, 17, 19, 22, 24, 25, 26, 30, 35, 39. The sums were four pence per day for each Templar except de la More and Blanke who were authorized two shillings. The keepers were instructed to make these payments from the time of the arrest of the Templars on so long as Templar lands remained in the king's hands. The actual payments were made to the archbishops and bishops who had been responsible for assigning individual Templars to different monasteries. It is nowhere so indicated, but it would seem logical that the archbishops and bishops did transfer the money to the monasteries concerned.

¹⁰⁶ *Ibid.,* 5-7 Ed. II (1311-12), pp. 385, 388, 409-10, 413, 421, 422, 423, 429, 430, 468, 469, 470-71, 473, 476, 480, 482-83, 490-97, 507, 510, 512, 513, 516, 517, 520. For a fuller discussion of Templar corrodies, see, Chap. II above. Between 1308 and 1310, Edward had special commissioners sent out to the counties to take testimony regarding these obligations and to decide, if possible, which claims were just. The details of this survey, including the decision whether or not a claim should be paid, can be found in the "*Corrodia petita de domibus Templariorum,*" *op. cit.,* pp. 139-230. The Close Rolls, as cited here, agree with this survey.

¹⁰⁷ *CCIR,* 4-6 Ed. II (1311-12), pp. 312, 467; *ibid.,* 7 Ed. II (1313), p. 12. These authorized expenses were usually for the repair of walls, ditches, dykes, mills, and the like.

[108] *Ibid.*, 6 Ed. II (1313), p. 528.

[109] *Ibid.*, p. 508; *ibid.*, 7 Ed. II (1313), p. 17.

[110] *Ibid.*, 3-6 Ed. II (1310-13), pp. 214-15; *ibid.*, 11 Ed. II (1317), p. 502.

[111] *Ibid.*, 6 Ed. II (1313), p. 465. Cf. *ibid.*, 10 Ed. III (1336): "... all the lands which belonged to the Templars came as escheats into the hands of the late king and of other lords ..."

[112] "The Wealth of the Templars in England," *op. cit.*, pp. 252-63.

[113] *Ibid.*, pp. 257-58. Knowles and Hadcock (*op. cit.*, p. 27), without giving their evidence, state that the gross Templar revenue accruing to the crown in 1308 was £4,720.

[114] Perkins, "The Wealth of the Templars in England," *op. cit.*, p. 259.

[115] *Ibid.*, "History of the Knights Templars in England," *op. cit.*, p. 83, where the manuscript records are referred to. Cf. also, "Original Documents relating to the Knights Templars," *op. cit.*, pp. 273-80, 519-26.

[116] Cf. *CChanWar*, 6 Ed. II (1312), I, 385. Cf. Perkins, "The Wealth of the Templars in England," *op. cit.*, p. 254, n. 11.

[117] *Ibid.*, "History of the Knights Templars in England," *op. cit.*, p. 83, n. 1.

[118] *Ibid.*, p. 84, n. 6; Perkins, "The Wealth of the Templars in England," *op. cit.*, pp. 255, 257.

[119] Cf. *ibid.*, p. 255 and n. 76 above.

[120] Wilkins, II, 385.

[121] Perkins, "History of the Knights Templars in England," *op. cit.*, p. 85.

[122] *Ibid.*

[123] *Reg. Clem. V*, no. 7886; Rymer, II, 168-69; DuPuy, no. 115.

[124] What happened to New Temple, London, clearly reflects both the policy of the king and the determination of the Hospitallers to get possession of the Templar property. In December, 1312, Edward granted New Temple, along with other Templar tenements and rents in the city of London to his cousin, Aymer de Valence, in return for the latter's good service (*CChR*, 6 Ed. II [1312], p. 221). In October, 1314, it was transferred by royal order to Thomas, Earl of Lancaster (*CPatR*, 8 Ed. II [1314]) pp. 184-85), who held it until his attainder, in March, 1322, at which time it was again granted to Aymer de Valence (*CChR*, 15 Ed. II [1322], p. 441) and was held by him until his death in June, 1324 (*Annales Paulini*, *op. cit.*, RS, I, 302). Thereupon, it was granted to Hugh Despencer the Younger who held it until his execution in November, 1326 (*ibid.*, 319-20). Meanwhile, of course, New Temple was claimed by the Prior of the Hospitallers, but to no avail (Rymer, II, 174; *CClR*, 6 Ed. II [1313], p. 544), though Parliament in 1324 decided in favor of the Prior's claim (*CClR*, 17 Ed. II [1324], p. 91; *Rot. Parl.*, I, 431a). The king, however, had the Mayor of London assume possession of the property at the death of Despencer — as can be determined from royal orders to the mayor regarding the repair of the property (*CClR*, 3 Ed. III [1329], p. 580; *ibid.*, 4 Ed. III [1330], p. 102). Then, in 1332, the king let New Temple to William de Langeford (cf. *CClR*, 6 Ed. III [1332], p. 431; *ibid.*, 12 Ed. III [1338], p. 416; *CPatR*, 12 Ed. III [1338], p. 99). The Prior continued to claim the property and petitioned the king in council. An inquisition was held, the findings of which supported the Prior's claim. Ultimately, in 1337 or 1338, New Temple was handed over to the Hospitallers (*CClR*, 11 Ed. III [1337], pp. 72-73; *CPatR*, 12 Ed. III [1338], p. 99).

[125] Rymer, II, 174; *CClR*, 6 Ed. II (1313), p. 544.

[126] *Ibid.*, 7 Ed. II (1313), pp. 88, 89.

[127] Rymer, II, 236-37; *CClR*, 7 Ed. II (1313), pp. 29-30; *CPatR*, 7 Ed. II (1313), p. 52.

[128] Rymer, II, 243; *CClR*, 8 Ed. II (1314), p. 243; DuPuy, nos. 125, 126.

[129] *CPatR*, 7 Ed. II (1313), pp. 44-45.

[130] *CClR*, 8-10 Ed. II (1315-17), pp. 234, 388; *ibid.*, 12 Ed. II (1318), p. 25.

[131] *Ibid.,* 17-19 Ed. II (1324-25), pp. 126, 203. Some of the Templar records had been delivered to the king: *CClR,* 19 Ed. II (1325), p. 561; *CPatR,* 8 Ed. II (1314), p. 184.

[132] *CClR,* 18-19 Ed. II (1324-25), pp. 219, 501.

[133] *CPatR,* 8-9 Ed. II (1314-16), pp. 184-85, 214, 374, 466, 478. Cf. *CClR,* 15-16 Ed. II (1322), pp. 442, 595-96; *ibid.,* 18-19 Ed. II (1325-26), pp. 290, 391-92, 462; DuPuy, no. 122.

[134] Cf. *CClR,* 8-9 Ed. II (1314-16), pp. 184-85, 374, 466; *ibid.,* 12-15 Ed. II (1318-22), pp. 25, 438.

[135] *CPatR,* 8-9 Ed. II (1315-16), pp. 214, 374, 466; Bain, *op. cit.,* III, no. 428; *CClR,* 8-10 Ed. III (1334-35), pp. 202, 422, 638.

[136] *Reg. Clem. V,* nos. 7885, 7886; Rymer, II, 167-68.

[137] *Roman Roll,* 12 Ed. II (1319), m. 11 – cited by Perkins, "History of the Knights Templars in England," *op. cit.,* p. 197, n. 5.

[138] Register of Archbishop Reynolds, fol. 70b (Lambeth MS) – cited by Perkins, "The Wealth of the Templars in England," *op. cit.,* p. 260, n. 53.

[139] Rymer, II, 487-88.

[140] *CClR,* 17 Ed. II (1324), p. 91.

[141] *Ibid.,* p. 111.

[142] *Ibid.*

[143] *Ibid.,* p. 117.

[144] *Ibid.,* 17-18 Ed. II (1324), pp. 126, 203.

[145] *Ibid.,* 18-19 Ed. II (1325), pp. 301, 392, 437-38 *et passim; ibid.,* 1 Ed. III (1327), p. 153; *ibid.,* 6 Ed. III (1332), p. 514; *ibid.,* 7-8 Ed. III (1333-34), pp. 303-04; *CPatR,* 18 Ed. II (1325), p. 134.

[146] Cf. *ibid.,* 1-2 Ed. III (1327-28), pp. 84, 147, 152, 192, 227, 340, 354; *ibid.,* 9-10 Ed. III (1335-36), pp. 59, 60, 199, 314; *ibid.,* 20 Ed. III (1346), p. 52; *CClR,* 1-2 Ed. III (1327-28), pp. 102, 156, 286; *ibid.,* 6 Ed. III (1332), p. 444; *ibid.,* 7 Ed. III (1333), pp. 6-7. These cases frequently suggest a definite reluctance on the part of the holder to deliver the lands to the Hospitallers.

[147] *Op. cit.,* p. 217.

[148] Cf. Perkins, "The Wealth of the Templars in England," *op. cit.,* p. 262.

[149] See above, n. 113.

[150] Cf. Rymer, II, 567; *Rot. Parl.,* 3 Ric. II (1379-80), III, 78b; and *CPatR,* 3 Ric. II (1380), p. 444. The last two entries refer to a charter issued by Thomas Larcher, Prior of the Hospitallers, dated Aug. 19, 1325, granting to the king, in fee simple, the manors of Temple Hirst, Temple Newsam, Faxfleet, Denney, and Strood which were formerly Templar possessions.

[151] *CPatR,* 9 Ed. III (1335), pp. 204-05; *ibid.,* 13 Ed. III (1339), p. 304; *ibid.,* 14 Ed. III (1340), p. 39; *CClR,* 1 Ed. III (1327), pp. 13-14, 86; *ibid.,* 4 Ed. III (1330), pp 11-12, 211, 531.

[152] Cf. *CPatR,* 19 Ed. II (1325), pp. 187-88; *CClR,* 15 Ed. II (1322), p. 442; *Hosp. Rpt.,* pp. 56, 116, 143, 153, 161, 182, 184-86, 203-04, 210-11.

[153] *CClR,* 6 Ed. III (1332), pp. 496, 514; *ibid.,* 7 Ed. III (1333), p. 149.

[154] *CPatR,* 9 Ed. III (1335), p. 100.

[155] Knowles and Hadcock (*op. cit.,* pp. 235-39) include a survey of most of the Templar possessions handed over to the Hospitallers and make the rather high estimate (p. 28) that about half of the Templar property went to the king and magnates and the other half was obtained by the Hospitallers.

[156] Cf. *CClR,* 12 Ed. III (1339), p. 593; *ibid.,* 14 Ed. III (1340), pp. 470-71.

[157] Lea, *op. cit.,* III, 332-34; DuPuy, nos. 127-36.

[158] Lea, *op. cit.,* III, 329-30.

[159] Wilkins, II, 388-91.

[160] *Ibid.,* 390-93; Rymer, III, 327, 472; *Flores Historiarum,* RS, III, 334. See above, n. 37, for the authorization of payments by the king.

[161] Walsingham, *Historia Anglicana*, RS, I, 128; Wilkins, II, 400; DuPuy, nos. 106C, 109 XII. For the form of confession used at York, see Walter of Hemingburg, *op. cit.*, II, 292.

[162] DuPuy, nos. 109 IV and XII.

[163] Cf. *CClR*, 6 Ed. II (1313), p. 508.

[164] Wilkins, II, 393; *CClR*, 6 Ed. II (1313), pp. 523, 533.

[165] Bain, *op. cit.*, III, no. 103; Wilkins, II, 380; DuPuy, no. 104B. Inquisitors were sent into Scotland with guarantees of royal protection (Rymer, II, 94). Cf. also, *Records of Anthony Bek*, no. 128. There are two articles of value on the Templars in Scotland: Robert Aitken, "The Knights Templars in Scotland," *Scottish Review*, XXXII (1898), 1-36; and John Edwards, "The Templars in Scotland in the Thirteenth Century," *Scottish Historical Review*, V (1907), 13-25.

[166] DuPuy, no. 140D. Cf. *Decretum*, X, 2, 20, 14 on limiting lay testimony.

[167] Rymer, II, 94; DuPuy, no. 140C; *CPatR*, 3 Ed. II (1308), p. 192; *ibid.*, 4 Ed. II (1311), p. 267; *CClR*, 3 Ed. II (1309), p. 179; *Annals of Ireland*, in *Chartularies of St. Mary's Abbey, Dublin*, RS, II, 336; Herbert Wood, "The Knights Templars in Ireland," *Proceedings of the Royal Irish Academy*, XXVI (1907), 327-77, at pp. 348, 353-54. Wood remarks that it cannot be determined whether or not torture was used or if the report of the inquisitors was favorable or unfavorable. The papal inquisitor for England (*Records of Anthony Bek*, no. 128), in accordance with Clement's mandate ordered an inquiry in Ireland to be made.

[168] *Ibid.*, p. 354; DuPuy, no. 140C.

[169] Perkins, "The Knights Templars in the British Isles," *op. cit.*, p. 229.

[170] Most modern historians subscribe to the view that the Templars were not guilty of the charges brought against them: Lea, *op. cit.*, III, 276; Schottmüller, *op. cit.*, II, 532; Finke, *op. cit.*, p. 344; Addison, *op. cit.*, p. 408 *et passim*; Campbell, *op. cit.*, p. 349; Perkins, "History of the Knights Templars in England," *op. cit.*, p. 176; and Julius Gmelin, *Schuld oder Unschuld des Templerordens* (Stuttgart, 1893), p. 508. DuPuy (p. viii) is convinced of their guilt. Two historians, E. Boutaric ("Clement V, Philippe le Bel, et les Templiers," *op. cit.*, pp. 301-40) and J. Delaville le Roulx ("La Suppression des Templiers," *op. cit.*, pp. 29-61) are inclined toward thinking the order, and some of the members definitely, guilty. Charles V. Langlois ("Le Procès des Templiers," *op. cit.*, pp. 382-421) is inclined toward thinking the order innocent.

[171] Wilkins, II, 338: *"propter stultitiam."*

[172] Lea (*op. cit.*, III, 301-17), Schottmüller (*op. cit.*, pp. 408-57), and Prutz (*op. cit.*, pp. 208-19) give brief but informative accounts with extensive references to such materials as exist for each of the areas mentioned here.

[173] DuPuy, no. 105.

[174] See Chap. V below.

[175] DuPuy, no. 137. Cf. n. 21 above.

[176] See above, pp. 88-89.

[177] "The Knights Templars in the British Isles," *op. cit.*, p. 227.

[178] "Tres filias illas jam maritavi; primam et primaevam, scilicet Superbiam, Templariis; secundum vero, scilicet Luxuriam, nigris monachis; tertiam et ultimam, scilicet Cupiditatem, albis monachis." Gerald of Wales, *Speculum Ecclesiae*, ed. J. S. Brewer, in *Giraldi Cambrensis Opera* (RS, No. 21; 8 vols.; London, 1861-91), IV, 54 and *Itinerarium Kambriae et Descriptio Kambriae*, ed. James F. Dimock, *ibid.*, VI, 44; *Flores Historiarum*, RS, II, 116-17; Roger of Hoveden, *op. cit.*, RS, IV, 76-77.

[179] DuPuy, no. 29.

[180] Paris, *Chronica Majora*, RS, IV, 302.

[181] Inner Temple Library, Petyt MS 538, xvii, 400 — cited by Perkins, "History of the Knights Templars in England," *op. cit.*, p. 91, n. 2.

[182] *Op. cit., Lib.* xii, *cap.* 7.

[183] Paris, *Chronica Majora*, RS, II, 145; Roger of Wendover, *op. cit.*, RS, II, 195-

96. Both authors have taken William of Tyre's comment and elaborated upon it.

[184] *De nugis curialium,* tr. Frederick Tupper and Marbury B. Ogle (London, 1924), Bk. I, chap. xx.

[185] *Op. cit.,* III, 243-44.

[186] Rymer, I, 258; DuPuy, no. 32.

[187] *Ibid.,* no. 30; August Potthast (ed.), *Regesta pontificum Romanorum inde ab anno post Christum natum MCXCVIII and annum MCCCIV* (Berlin, 1875), nos. 3226, 4203, 4552.

[188] *Op. cit.,* Bk. I, chap. xxiii. Interestingly enough, in his censure of the military orders, Mapes is even more critical of the Hospitallers than of the Templars.

[189] *Op. cit.,* RS, V, 745-46.

[190] *Ibid.,* 364-65.

[191] See bull of Clement cited by Prutz, *op. cit.,* p. 276. Cf. also, other bulls of the same pope (*ibid.,* pp. 276-78) issued in the same year (1265); and Lea, *op. cit.,* III, 242.

[192] Letter no. 673, *Materials for the History of Thomas Becket,* RS, VII, 310: "Nolite ergo sperare in iniquitate, nec Templariis illis credite qui non ambulant in simplicitate, sed, regis potius quam vestram voluntatem essequi cupientes, vobis nihil aliud quam mendacia de rege ex patre mendacii afferunt ut decipiant."

[193] *Op. cit.,* RS, IV, 291.

[194] *Ibid.*

[195] *Ibid.,* p. 525.

[196] *Ibid.,* V, 148-49. (Tr. J. A. Giles, *Matthew Paris' English History from the years 1235 to 1263* [2 vols.; London, 1852-53], II, 149.)

[197] *Op. cit.,* IV, 168.

[198] *CChR,* 9 Ed. I (1280), p. 237; no. 404, "Sandford Cartulary," *op. cit.,* pp. 267-68. Cf. *Rot. Hund.,* I, 131.

[199] *CChR,* 16 Hen. III (1232), pp. 158, 267; *ClR,* 13 Hen. III (1228), p. 131; *ibid.,* 15 Hen. III (1231), p. 548; *ibid.,* 18 Hen. III (1234), p. 404; *Cal. Doc. rel. to Ire.,* II, no. 120. Cf. remarks on Templar privileges in Chap. II above where Templar exemptions are discussed in detail and where repeated pleas for maintenance of their privileges and exemptions are cited. The frequency of Templar pleas suggests not only non-compliance but envy and hostility as well.

[200] *ClR,* 15 Hen. III (1231), p. 532; *Records of Parliament holden at Westminster ...(A.D. 1305),* ed. Frederick W. Maitland (RS, No. 98; London, 1893), p. 135. Cf. *ClR,* 13 Hen. III (1228), p. 131; *ibid.,* 15 Hen. III (1231), p. 548.

[201] Cf. *Rot. Hund.,* I, 244, 255, 278, 282, 286, 291, 292, 387 (Lincolnshire); I, 106, 109, 110, 114, 115, 122 (Yorkshire); I, 210, 238, 370 and II, 59, 60, 80, 225, 570, 722 (for various other counties).

[202] *CChR,* 9 Ed. I (1280), p. 238; *Rot. Hund.* II, 228; Henry de Bracton, *De legibus et consuetudinibus Angliae,* ed. George E. Woodbine ("Yale Historical Publications," No. 3; 4 vols.; New Haven, 1915-42), IV, 280.

[203] *Cal. Doc. rel. to Ire.,* II, nos. 1447, 1448, 1493, 1495, 1539, 1647, 1811; III, nos. 20, 30, 33, 34, 57, 558, 565, 666, 778. Cf. remarks of Wood, "The Knights Templars in Ireland," *op. cit.,* p. 341.

[204] *Rot. Hund.,* I, 129 (Yorkshire).

[205] *Ibid.,* I, 117 (Yorkshire); II, 226 (Warwickshire).

[206] *Ibid.,* II, 27 (Nottinghamshire), 228 (Warwickshire).

[207] *Ibid.,* I, 401 (Grimesby, Lincolnshire).

[208] *Pipe R,* 16 Hen. II (1169-70), pp. 149-50.

[209] Cf. *Register of Malmesbury Abbey,* RS, I, 106.

[210] See above, pp. 34-39.

[211] *Op. cit.,* Lib. xii, cap. 7: "*Possessiones autem tam ultra quam citra mare adeo dicuntur immensas habere, ut jam non sit in orbe Christiano provincia, quae*

praedictis fratribus bonorum suorum portionem non contulerint; et regiis opulentis pares hodie dicantur habere copias."

[212] *Op. cit.,* RS, II, 145 copies William of Tyre almost verbatim. Also, *ibid.,* IV, 291: *"Habent insuper Templarii in Christanitate novem milia maneriorum, Hospitalarii vero novendecim, praeter emolumenta et varios proventus ex fraternitatibus et praedicationibus provenientes, et per privilegia sua accrescentes."* It would be unwise to take the figure 9,000 too literally.

[213] *Op. cit.,* p. 34: "... the defenders of Christendom loaded them with immense wealth ...;" and "... nowhere but in Jerusalem are they in poverty."

[214] Cited by Edward J. Martin, *The Trial of the Knights Templars* (London, 1928), p. 20.

[215] *Op. Cit., Lib.* XVIII, *cap.* 9. Cf. also Mapes, *op. cit.,* Bk. I, chap. xxi.

[216] *Op. cit.,* RS, IV, 291.

[217] *L'estoire de Eracles empereur et la conqueste de la terre d'outremer* [continuation of the History of William of Tyre], *Lib.* xxv, *cap.* 22-27; xxvi, 7, 9, 11, 12; xxviii, 5. Cf. Lea, *op. cit.,* III, 240; Runciman, *op. cit.,* III, 58, 66-67; Grousset, *op. cit.,* III, 47-49, 97. For details on Richard's conquest of the island, see *Itinerarium ... Ricardi,* RS, I, 177-204; William of Newburgh, *op. cit.,* RS, I, 350-54; Richard of Devizes, *De rebus gestis Ricardi Primi,* in *Chronicles of the Reigns of Stephen, Henry II, and Richard I,* ed. Richard Howlett (RS, No. 82; 4 vols.; London, 1884-89), III, 423-26; and Benedict of Peterborough, *op. cit.,* RS, II, 163-67, 172-73.

[218] Wilkins, II, 381; DuPuy, no. 140D.

[219] *Ibid.,* 140C; Wilkins, II, 381.

[220] *Quo War.,* 164, 293, 356, 684-85, 786; Shirley, *op. cit.,* RS, I, 181-83 (Letters nos. 158-59). Cf. *Rot. Parl.,* I, 49. Fines for seizure were repeatedly imposed on the Templars: cf. *CPatR,* 18-20 Ed. I (1290-92), pp. 343-44, 436, 507; *ibid.,* 21-28 Ed. I (1293-1300), pp. 26, 504, 542; *ibid.,* 31-33 Ed. I (1303-05), pp. 134, 291, 301, 322, 340.

[221] *Ibid.,* 12-20 Ed. I (1284-92), pp. 120, 243, 343, 436, 486, 507; *ibid.,* 28-29 Ed. I (1300-01), pp. 504, 592, 608.

[222] See above, p. 23.

[223] John Edwards, "The Templars in Scotland in the Thirteenth Century," *op. cit.,* pp. 18-19.

[224] *Ibid.,* p. 14.

[225] *Ibid.,* p. 21; Wilkins, II, 382; Dupuy, no. 140D.

[226] Wilkins, II, 382.

[227] *Op. cit.,* p. 39. In the same passage he commented: "By — let me not say frauds, but — pleasantries of law they evade simony ... "

[228] Dugdale, VI, 846 (arts. 77-78); Rymer, II, 55.

[229] *ClR,* 15 Hen. III (1231), p. 548; *Rot. Hund.,* I, 110; II, 65; *Reg. of Malmesbury,* RS, I, 98-99.

[230] *CPatR,* 35 Ed. I (1307), p. 548; *Rot. Hund.,* I, 200, 287, 291-92, 381, 391, 402, 405, 417; II, 29, 484, 713.

[231] Cf. Vitry, *op. cit.,* Bk. II, pp. 117-18; Tyre, *op. cit., Lib.* XII, *cap.* 7; Mapes, *op. cit.,* Bk. I, chaps. xviii, xx, xxii; Paris, *Chronica Majora,* RS, II, 144, 159, 327; III, 47, 405-06; V, 154, 158, 655; VI, 160. Generally speaking, Tyre and Paris tend to be quite unfavorable to the Templars.

[232] See above, n. 169.

[233] Many critical statements are made regarding clerics and others, especially against the Cistercians, in the *Latin Poems commonly attributed to Walter Mapes* (ed. Thomas Wright, "Camden Society Publications," No. 16 [London, 1841]); but there are no direct references to the Templars. In the *Carmina Burana* (ed. J. A. Schmeller [Stuttgart, 1847], poem no. 26, p. 30), two passing references, involving neither praise nor censure, are made to the Templars fighting in the Holy Land. Nigellus in his *Speculum Stultorum* (*Anglo-Latin Satirical Poets and Epigrammatists of the Twelfth Century,* ed. Thomas Wright

[RS, No. 59; 2 vols.; London, 1872], I, 82) has Brunellus propose to devote himself to God's service and maybe even to go to Tyre and serve under the Templars. There seems to be no criticism involved in this passage. The "Song against Monks" (*Political Poems and Songs relating to English History from the Accession of Edward III to that of Richard III*, ed. Thomas Wright [RS, No. 14; 2 vols.; London, 1859-61], I, 267) expatiates on the evils of the friars and warns them they may suffer the same fate as the Templars. The song on "The Order of Fair-Ease" (*Political Songs of England from the Reign of John to that of Edward II*, ed. Thomas Wright, "Camden Society Publications," No. 7 [London, 1839], pp. 137-48) criticizes the Hospitallers, Cistercians, Dominicans, Franciscans and others; but significantly, no specific mention is made of the Templars. Nothing can be found against the Templars in *Anecdota literaria, a Collection of Short Poems in English, Latin, and French, illustrative of the Literature and History of England in the Thirteenth Century* (ed. Thomas Wright [London, 1844]) or in Gerald R. Owst's *Literature and Pulpit in Medieval England* (Cambridge, 1933).

[234] *CClR*, 32 Ed. I (1304), p. 208.

[235] Cf. above, n. 39.

[236] Repeatedly the Templars are referred to jointly with other religious and privileged groups, especially the Hospitallers.

[237] The clerical group, of course, had had its conclusion made for it by Pope Clement V and also stood to profit, at least indirectly, from the abolition of the Templar order.

Chapter Five

[1] DuPuy, no. 40B.

[2] For information on the houses and properties of the various religious orders, see Knowles and Hadcock, *op. cit., passim,* and the appropriate volumes of the *Victoria History of the Counties of England, passim.* Cf. also, remarks in Chap. II above.

[3] Gmelin, *op. cit.,* p. 507.

[4] DuPuy, no. 134. Cf. Lea, *op. cit.,* III, 317.

[5] Addison, *op. cit.,* p. 550.

[6] *Ibid.,* p. 562.

[7] Douglas Knoop and G. P. Jones, *A Short History of Freemasonry to 1730* (Manchester, 1940).

Bibliography and Index

Bibliography

Primary Sources

Collections of Sources

Beugnot, A. and LeProvost, A. (eds.). *Recueil des Historiens des Croisades: les Historiens Occidentaux.* "Académie imperiale des Inscriptions et Belles-Lettres." 5 vols. Paris, 1884-95.

Blancard, Louis (ed.). *Documents inédits sur le commerce de Marseille au moyen age: contrats commerciaux du xiiie siècle.* 2 vols. Marseille, 1884-85.

Doehaerd, Renée (ed.). *Les relations commerciales entre Gênes, la Beligique et l'Outremont d'après les archives notariales génoises aux xiiie et xive siècles,* "Institut belge de Rome, Etudes d'histoire économique et sociale." Vols. II-IV. Brussels, 1941.

Dugdale, William. *Monasticon Anglicanum.* New edition by John Caley, Henry Ellis, and Bulkeley Bandinel. 8 vols. London, 1846.

Lopez, Robert S. and Raymond, Irving W. (eds.). *Medieval Trade in the Mediterranean World: Illustrative Documents.* "Records of Civilization," No. 52. New York, 1955.

Mansi, John D. *Sacrorum conciliorum nova et amplissima collectio.* New edition by P. Labbeus, G. Cossartius, and N. Coleti. Vol. XXI. Venice, 1767.

Migne, Jacques P. (ed.). *Patrologiae cursus completus . . . series Latina.* 221 vols. Paris, 1878-90.

Patetta, Federico and Chiandano, Mario (eds.). *Documenti e studi per la storia del commercio e del diritto commerciale italiano.* Turin, 1933.

Rymer, Thomas and Sanderson, Robert (eds.). *Foedera, conventiones, litterae et cujuscunque generis acta publica inter reges Angliae et alios quovis imperatores, reges, pontifices, principes, vel communitates.* Revised edition. Vols. I-II. London, 1816.

Wilkins, D. (eds.). *Concilia Magnae Britanniae et Hiberniae, A. D. 446-1718.* Vols. I-II, London, 1737.

Cartularies, Chronicles, Letters, etc.

Adam of Eynsham. *Magna vita santi Hugonis episcopi Lincolniensis.* Edited by James F. Dimock. Rolls Series, No. 37. London. 1864.

Adam of Murimuth. *Continuatio chronicarum.* Edited by E. Maunde Thompson. Rolls Series, No. 93. London, 1889.

The Anglo-Saxon Chronicle. Edited and translated by Charles Plummer. 2 vols. Oxford, 1892-99.

Annales Monastici. Edited by Henry R. Luard. Rolls Series, No. 36. 5 vols. London, 1864-69.

Bartholomew de Cotton. *Historia Anglicana.* Edited by Henry R. Luard. Rolls Series, No. 16. London, 1859.

Benedict of Peterborough. *Chronicle of the Reigns of Henry II and Richard I, A. D. 1169-1192.* Edited by William Stubbs. Rolls Series, No. 49, 2 vols.

Bracton, Henry de. *De legibus et consuetudinibus Angliae.* Edited by George E. Woodbine. "Yale Historical Publication," No. 3. 4 vols. New Haven, 1915-42.

Capgrave, John. *The Chronicle of England.* Edited by Francis C. Hingeston. Rolls Series, No. 1. London, 1858.

———. *De illustribus Henricis.* Edited by Francis C. Hingeston. Rolls Series, No. 7. London, 1858.

Carmina burana. Edited by J. A. Schmeller. Stuttgart, 1847.

Cartulaire général de l'ordre du Temple, 1119-1150: Receuil des chartres et des bulles relatives à l'ordre du Temple. Edited by Guignes A. M. J. d'Albon. Paris, 1913.

Chartularies of St. Mary's Abbey, Dublin: with the Register of its House at Dunbrody, and Annals of Ireland. Edited by John T. Gilbert. Rolls Series, No. 80. 2 vols. London, 1884.

Chronica monasterii sancti Albani. Edited by Henry T. Riley. Rolls Series, No. 28. 12 vols. London, 1863-76.

Chronicles and Memorials of the Reign of Richard I. Edited by William Stubbs. Rolls Series, No. 38. 2 vols. London, 1864-65.

Chronicles of London. Edited by Charles L. Kingsford. Oxford, 1905.

The Chronicles of London from 44 Hen. III to 17 Edw. III. Translated by Edmund Goldsmid. Edinburgh, 1885.

Chronicles of the Mayors and Sheriffs of London, A. D. 1188 to A. D. 1274. Translated by Henry T. Riley. London, 1863.

Chronicles of the Reigns of Edward I and Edward II. Edited by William Stubbs. Rolls Series, No. 76. 2 vols. London, 1882-83.

Chronicles of the Reigns of Stephen, Henry II, and Richard I. Edited by Richard Howlett. Rolls Series, No. 82. 4 vols. London, 1884-89.

Chronicon Abbatiae de Evesham ad annum 1418. Edited by William D. Macray. Rolls Series, No. 29. London, 1863.

Chronicon Abbatiae Rameseiensis a saec. X usque ad an. circitur 1200. Edited by W. Dunn Macray. Rolls Series, No. 83. London, 1886.

Chronicon Henrici Knighton, vel Cnitthon, monachi Leycestrensis. Edited by Joseph R. Lumby. Rolls Series, No. 92. London, 1889.

Chronicon monasterii de Abingdon. Edited by Joseph Stevenson. Rolls Series, No. 2. 2 vols. London, 1858.

Chroniques de London depuis l'an 44 Hen. III jusqu'à l'an 17 Edw. III. Edited by George J. Aungier. "Publications of the Camden Society," Vol. XXVIII. London, 1844.

Corpus Juris Canonici. Edited by Aemilius Friedberg. 2 vols. Leipzig, 1879.

Curzon, Henri de (ed.). *La Règle du Temple.* Paris, 1886.

Delaville le Roulx, J. (ed.). *Documents concernant les Templiers; extraits des archives de Malte.* Paris, 1882.

Delisle, Léopold (ed.). *Recueil des actes de Henry II, roi d'Angleterre et duc de Normandie, concernant les provinces françaises et les affaires de France.* 3 vols. Paris, 1916-27.

DuBois, Pierre. *The Recovery of the Holy Land.* Translated by Walther I. Brandt. "Records of Civilization," No. 51. New York, 1956.

DuPuy, Pierre. *Historie de l'ordre militaire des Templiers, ou Chevaliers du Temple de Jérusalem, depuis son établissement jusqu'à sa décadence et sa suppression.* Brussels, 1751.

Eracles. *L'estoire de Eracles empereur et la conqueste de la terre d'outremer.* [Continuation of the History of William of Tyre] in *Recueil des historiens des Croisades: les historiens occidentaux.* Vol. II, Paris, 1859.

Eulogium (Historiarum sive temporis): Chronicon ab orbe condito usque ad annum Domini M.CCC.LXVI. a monacho quodam Malmesburiensi exaratum. Edited by Frank S. Haydon. Rolls Series, No. 9. 3 vols. London, 1858-63.

Fitzneale, Richard. *De necessariis observatiis scaccarii dialogus qui vulge dicitur Dialogus de Scacario.* Edited and translated by Charles Johnson. London, [1950].

Fleta. Edited and translated by H. G. Richardson and G. O. Sayles. "Publications of the Selden Society," Vol. LXXII. London, 1955.

Florence of Worchester. *Chronicon ex chronicis.* Edited by Benjamin Thorpe. London, 1848-49.

Flores Historiarum. Edited by Henry R. Luard. Rolls Series, No. 95. 3 vols. London, 1890.

Foucher (Fulcher) of Chartes. *Historia Iherosalymitana gesta Francorum Iherusalem peregrinantium* in *Recueil des historiens des Croisades: les historiens occidentaux.* Vol. III. Paris, 1866.

The French Chronicle of London A. D. 1259 to A. D. 1343. Edited by Henry T. Riley. London, 1863.

Gervase of Canterbury. *Historical Works.* Edited by William Stubbs. Rolls Series, No. 73. 2 vols. London, 1879-80.

Giraldus Cambrensis. *Opera.* Edited by J. S. Brewer, James F. Dimock, and George F. Warner. Rolls Series, No. 21. Vols. IV-VIII. London, 1861-91.

Henry of Huntington. *The History of the English from A. D. 55 to A. D. 1154.* Edited by Thomas Arnold. Rolls Series, No. 74. London, 1879.

Historia et Cartularium monasterii sancti Petri Gloucestriae. Edited by William H. Hart. Rolls Series, No. 33. 3 vols. London, 1863-67.

The Historians of the Church of York and its Archbishops. Edited by James Raine. Rolls Series, No. 71. 2 vols. London, 1886.

Historic and Municipal Documents of Ireland, A.D. 1172-1320, from the Archives of the City of Dublin. Edited by J. T. Gilbert. Rolls Series, No. 53, London, 1870.

Historical Papers and Letters from the Northern Registers. Edited by James Raine. Rolls Series, No. 61. London, 1873.

Jaffé, Philipp, and Wattenbach, William (eds.). *Regesta pontificum Romanorum ab condita ecclesia ad annum post Christum natum MCXCVIII.* 2d edition. 2 vols. Leipzig, 1885-88.

Joinville, Jean Sire de. *Histoire de Saint Louis.* Edited by Natalis de Wailly. Paris, 1868.

Larking, Lambert B. (ed.). *The Knights Hospitallers in England: Being the Report of Prior Philip de Thame to the Grand Master Elyan de Villanova for A.D. 1338.* "Publications of the Camden Society," Vol. LXV. London, 1857.

Leclerq, J. "Un document sur les débuts des Templiers," *Revue d'histoire ecclésiastique,* LII (1957), 81-91.

Lees, Beatrice A. (ed.). *Records of the Templars in England in the Twelfth Century: The Inquest of 1185, with illustrative Charters and Documents.* "Records of the Social and Economic History of England and Wales," Vol. IX. London, 1935.

Lizerand, Georges (ed.). *Le Dossier de l'affaire des Templiers.* Paris, 1923.

Mapes, Walter. *De nugis curialium.* Translated by Frederick Tupper and Marbury B. Ogle. London, 1924.

Materials for the History of Thomas Becket, Archbishop of Canterbury. Edited by James C. Robertson and J. Brigstocke Sheppard. Rolls Series, No. 67. Vols. IV-VII. London, 1879-85.

Memorials of London and London Life in the Thirteenth, Fourteenth, and Fifteenth Centuries. Selected, edited, and translated by Henry T. Riley. London, 1868.

Michelet, M. (ed.). *Le Procès des Templiers.* 2 vols. Paris, 1841-51.

Munimenta Gildhallae Londoniensis: Liber Albus, Liber Custumarum, et Liber Horn. Edited by Henry T. Riley. Rolls Series, No. 12. 3 vols. London, 1859-62.

Odericus Vitalis. *Historia ecclesiastica.* Edited by Auguste le Prevost. 2 vols. Paris, 1838-40.

"Original Documents relating to the Knights Templars," *The Gentleman's Magazine and Historical Review,* III N.S. (1857), 273-80, 519-26.

Oxenedes, Johannes de. *Chronica.* Edited by Henry Ellis. Rolls Series, No. 13. London, 1859.

Paris, Matthew. *Chronica Majora.* Edited by Henry R. Luard. Rolls Series, No. 57. 7 vols. London, 1872-83.

———. *Historia Anglorum sive historia minor.* Edited by Frederic Madden. Rolls Series, No. 44. 3 vols. London, 1866-69.

Potthast, August. (ed.). *Regesta pontificum Romanorum inde ab anno post Christum natum MCXCVIII ad annum MCCCIV.* Berlin, 1874-75.

Ralph of Coggeshall. *Chronicon Anglicanum.* Edited by Joseph Stevenson. Rolls Series No. 66. London, 1875.

Ralph of Diceto. *Opera historica.* Edited by William Stubbs. Rolls Series, No. 68. 2 vols. London, 1876.

Raynouard, François J. M. (ed.). *Monumens historiques, relatifs à la condamnation des Chevaliers du Temple, et à l'abolition de leur ordre.* Paris, 1813.

Records of Anthony Bek, Bishop and Patriarch, 1283-1311. Edited by C. M. Fraser. "Publications of the Surtees Society," Vol. CLXII. London, 1947.

Regestum Clementis Papae V ex Vaticanis archetypis. Edited by the Monks of St. Benedict. 8 vols. Rome, 1884-92.

The Register of Malmesbury Abbey. Edited by J. S. Brewer. Rolls Series No. 72. London, 1879.

The Register of Richard de Kellawe, Lord Palatine and Bishop of Durham, 1311-1316. Edited by Thomas D. Hardy. Rolls Series No. 62. 2 vols. London, 1873-74.

The Register of William Greenfield, Lord Archbishop of York, 1306-1315. "Publications of the Surtees Society," Vols. CXLV, CLII, CLIII. London, 1931-38.

Les registres d'Alexandre IV: Recueil des bulles de ce pape publiées ou analysées d'après les manuscrits originaux du Vatican. Edited by C. Bourel de la Roncière, J. de Loye, and A. Coulon. 2 vols. Paris, 1902-53.

Les registres de Grégoire IX: Recueil des bulles de ce pape publiées ou analysées d'après les manuscrits originaux du Vatican. Edited by Lucien Auvray. 3 vols. Paris, 1896-1908.

Les registres d'Innocent IV publiès ou analysés d'apres les manuscrits originaux du Vatican et de la Bibliothèque nationale. Edited by Elie Berger. 3 vols. Paris, 1884-97.

Registrum epistolarum fratris Johannis Peckham, Archiepiscopi Cantuariensis. Edited by Charles T. Martin. Rolls Series, No. 77. 3 vols. London, 1882-85.

Richard, Canon of St. Trinity, London. *Itinerarium peregrinorum et gesta regis Ricardi* in *Chronicles and Memorials of the Reign of Richard I.* Edited by William Stubbs. Rolls Series, No. 38. Vol. I. London, 1864.

Rishanger, William. *Chronica et annales regnantibus Henrico Tertio et Edwardo Primo, A.D. 1259-1307.* Edited by Henry T. Riley. Rolls Series, No. 28. 2 vols. London, 1865.

Roger of Hovedon. *Chronica.* Edited by William Stubbs, Rolls Series, No. 51. 4 vols. London, 1868-71.

Roger of Wendover. *Chronica sive Flores Historiarum.* Edited by Henry G. Hewlett. Rolls Series, No. 84. 3 vols. London, 1886-89.

The Rolls and Register of Bishop Oliver Sutton, 1280-1299. Edited by Rosalind M. T. Hill. "Publications of the Lincoln Record Society," Vols. XLII-XLIII. Hereford, 1948-50.

Sancti Bernardi, Abbatis primi Claraevallensis, opera genuina. Edited by the Monks of St. Benedict. 3 vols. Paris, 1854.

"The Sanford Cartulary," *The Oxfordshire Record Society,* XIX (1937), 1-177; XXII (1940), 179-328. Edited by Agnes M. Leys.

Selected Letters of Pope Innocent III concerning England (1198-1216). Edited by C. R. Cheney and W. H. Semple. London, 1953.

Stubbs, William and Spelman, Henry (eds.). *Councils and ecclesiastical Documents relating to Great Britain and Ireland.* 3 vols. Oxford, 1869-78.

Stubbs, William (ed.). *Select Charters and other Illustrations of English Constitutional History to the Reign of Edward I.* 9th edition revised. Oxford, 1870.

Shirley, Walter W. (ed.). *Royal and other Historical Letters illustrative of the Reign of Henry III.* Rolls Series, No. 27. 2 vols. London, 1862-66.

Thomas de Burton. *Chronica monasterii de Melsa.* Edited by Edward A. Bond. Rolls Series No. 43. 3 vols. London, 1866-68.

Thomas of Elmham. *Historia monasterii S. Augustini Cantuariensis.* Edited by Charles Hardwick. Rolls Series, No. 8. London, 1858.

Vitry, Jacques de. *Histoire des Croisades.* Edited by F. P. G. Guizot. "Collection des Mémoires relatifs à l'histoire de France," Vol. XXII. Paris, 1825.

——. *The History of Jerusalem.* Translated by Aubrey Stewart. "Palestine Pilgrims' Text Society," Vol. XI, No. 2. London, 1896.

Walsingham, Thomas. *Historia Anglicana (1272-1422)* in *Chronica monasterii sancti Albani.* Edited by Henry T. Riley. Rolls Series, No. 28. Vols. I-II. London, 1863-64.

——. *Ypodigma Neustriae* in *Chronica monasterii sancti Albani.* Edited by Henry T. Riley. Rolls Series, No. 28. Vol. VII. London, 1876.

Walter of Coventry. *Historical Collections.* Edited by William Stubbs. Roll Series, No. 58, 2 vols. London, 1872-73.

Walter of Guisborough. *The Chronicle of Walter of Guiseborough previously edited as the Chronicle of Walter of Hemingford or Hemingburgh.* Edited by Harry Rothwell. "Publications of the Camden Society," Vol. LXXXIX. London, 1957.

Walter of Hemingburg. *Chronicon . . . de gestis regum Angliae.* Edited by Hans C. Hamilton. 2 vols. London, 1848-49.

William of Malmesbury. *De gestis regum Anglorum et historia novellae.* Edited by William Stubbs. Rolls Series, No. 90. 2 vols. London, 1887-89.

William of Newburgh. *Histoire rerum Anglicarum* in *Chronicles of the Reigns of Stephen, Henry II, and Richard I.* Edited by Richard Howlett. Rolls Series, No. 82. Vols. I-II. London, 1884-85.

William of Tyre. *Historia rerum in partibus transmarinis gestarum.* "Recueil des historiens des Croisades: historiens occidenteaux," Vol. I, Part I. Edited by A. Beugnot and A. LeProvost. Paris, 1844.

William [Guilelmus] of Tyre. *A History of Deeds done beyond the Sea.* Translated by Emily A. Babcock and August C. Krey. "Records of Civilization," No. 35. 2 vols. New York, 1943.

Wright, Thomas (ed.). *Anecdota literaria: a Collection of short Poems in English, Latin, and French, illustrative of the Literature and History of England in the Thirteenth Century, and more especially of the Condition and Manners of the different Classes of Society.* London, 1844.

——. *The Anglo-Latin Satirical Poets and Epigrammatists of the Twelfth Century.* Rolls Series, No. 59. 2 vols. London, 1872.

——. *The Latin Poems commonly attributed to Walter Mapes.* "Publications of the Camden Society," Vol. XVI. London, 1841.

——.. *Political Poems and Songs relating to English History from the Accession of Edward III to that of Richard III.* Rolls Series, No. 14. 2 vols. London, 1859-61..

——. *The Political Songs of England from the Reign of John to that of Edward II.* "Publications of the Camden Society," Vol. VI. London, 1839.

Public Records

Ancient Charters, royal and private, prior to A.D. 1200. Edited by John H. Round. "Publications of the Pipe Roll Society," Vol. X. London, 1888.

Calendar of Charters and Rolls preserved in the Bodleian Library. Edited by William H. Turner. Oxford, 1878.

Calendar of Entries in the Papal Registers relating to Great Britain and Ireland. Edited by William H. Bliss. Vols. I-II. London, 1893-95.

The Cartae Antiquae, Rolls 1-10. Edited by Lionel Landon. "Publications of the Pipe Roll Society," Vol. XVII N.S. London, 1939.

The Chancellor's Roll for the eighth Year of the Reign of King Richard the First, Michaelmas 1196. Edited by Doris M. Stenton. "Publications of the Pipe Roll Society," Vol. VII N.S. London, 1930.

Cole, Henry (ed.). *Documents illustrative of English History in the Thirteenth and Fourteenth Centuries, selected from the Records of the Department of Remembrancer of the Exchequer.* London, 1844.

Feet of Fines for the County of Lincoln for the Reign of King John, 1199-1216. Edited by Margaret S. Walker. "Publications of the Pipe Roll Society," Vol. XXIX N.S. London, 1954.

Feet of Fines of the Reigns of Henry II and Richard I, A.D. 1182-1199. Edited under the direction of the Council of the Pipe Roll Society. "Publications of the Pipe Roll Society," Vols. XVII, XX, XXIII-IV. London, 1894-1900.

Great Britain, Public Record Office. *The Book of Fees commonly called Testa de Nevill.* Prepared under the superintendence of the Deputy Keeper of the Records. 3 vols. London, 1920-31.

———. *Calendar of Chancery Warrants preserved in the Public Record Office, A.D. 1244-1326.* Prepared under the superintendence of the Deputy Keeper of the Records. Vol. I. London, 1927.

———. *Calendar of the Charter Rolls preserved in the Public Record Office, A.D. 1226-1326.* Prepared under the superintendence of the Deputy Keeper of the Records. 3 vols. London, 1903-09.

———. *Calendar of the Close Rolls preserved in the Public Record Office, Edward I, 1272-1307.* Prepared under the superintendence of the Deputy Keeper of the Records. 5 vols. London, 1900-08.

———. *Calendar of the Close Rolls preserved in the Public Record Office, Edward II, 1307-27.* Prepared under the superintendence of the Deputy Keeper of the Records. 4 vols. London, 1892-98.

———. *Calendar of the Close Rolls preserved in the Public Record Office, Edward III, 1327-77.* Prepared under the superintendence of the Deputy Keeper of the Records. 14 vols. London, 1896-1913.

———. *Calendar of Documents preserved in France illustrative of the History of Great Britain and Ireland.* Edited by J. Horace Round. Vol. I. London, 1899.

———. *Calendar of Documents relating to Ireland preserved in Her Majesty's Public Record Office, London, 1171-1307.* Edited by H. S. Sweetman, 5 vols. London, 1875-86.

———. *Calendar of Documents relating to Scotland preserved in Her Majesty's Public Record Office, London.* Edited by Joseph Bain. Vols. I-III. Edinburgh, 1881-88.

———. *Calendar of Fine Rolls preserved in the Public Record Office.* Edited by A. E. Bland. Vols. I-II. London, 1911-12.

———. *Calendar of Inquisitions post mortem and other analagous Documents.* Prepared under the superintendence of the Deputy Keeper of the Records. Vols. II-III. London, 1906-12.

———. *Calendar of the Liberate Rolls preserved in the Public Record Office, 1226-60.* Prepared under the superintendence of the Deputy Keeper of the Records. 4 vols. London, 1916-59.

———. *Calendar of the Patent Rolls preserved in the Public Record Office, Edward I, 1272-1307.* Prepared under the superintendence of the Deputy Keeper of the Records. 4 vols. London, 1893-1901.

———. *Calendar of the Patent Rolls preserved in the Public Record Office, Edward II, 1307-27.* Prepared under the superintendence of the Deputy Keeper of the Records. 5 vols. London, 1894-1904.

———. *Calendar of the Patent Rolls preserved in the Public Record Office, Ed-*

ward III, 1327-77. Prepared under the superintendence of the Deputy Keeper of the Records. 16 vols. London, 1891-1916.

————. *Calendar of the Patent Rolls preserved in the Public Record Office, Henry III, 1216-72.* Prepared under the superintendence of the Deputy Keeper of the Records. 6 vols. London, 1901-13.

————. *The Close Rolls of the Reign of Henry III preserved in the Public Record Office.* Prepared under the superintendence of the Deputy Keeper of the Records. 14 vols. London, 1902-38.

————. *Curia Regis Rolls of the Reigns of Richard I, John, and Henry III preserved in the Public Record Office, A.D. 1189-1230.* Edited by C. T. Fowler *et al.* 13 vols. London, 1922-59.

————. *A descriptive Catalogue of Ancient Deeds in the Public Record Office.* Prepared under the superintendence of the Deputy Keeper of the Records. 6 vols. London, 1890-1915.

————. *Issues of the Exchequer; being a Collection of Payments made out of His Majesty's Revenue from King Henry III to King Henry VI inclusive.* Edited and translated by Frederick Devon. Vol. III. London, 1837.

————. *Patent Rolls of the Reign of Henry III, A.D. 1225-32.* Prepared under the superintendence of the Deputy Keeper of the Records. London, 1903.

————. *Treaty Rolls preserved in the Public Record Office.* Printed under the superintendence of the Deputy Keeper of the Records. Vol. I: 1234-1325. Edited by Pierre Chaplais. London, 1955.

The Great Roll of the Pipe for the fifth through the thirty-fourth Years of the Reign of King Henry II (1158-1188). Edited under the direction of the Council of the Pipe Roll Society. "Publications of the Pipe Roll Society," Vols. I-II, IV-IX, XI-XIII, XVIII-XIX, XXI-XXII, XXV-XXXIV, XXXVI-XXXVIII. London, 1884-1925.

The Great Roll of the Pipe for the First Year of the Reign of King Richard the First, A.D. 1189-1190. Edited under the direction of Joseph Hunter. London, 1844.

The Great Roll of the Pipe for the Reigns of King Richard I and John and for the Fourteenth Year of the Reign of King Henry III. Edited by Doris M. Stenton *et al.* "Publications of the Pipe Roll Society," Vols. I-III, V-VI, VIII-X XII, XIV-XVI, XVIII-XX, XXII-XXIV, XXVII, XXVIII, XXX N.S. London, 1925-55.

The Great Roll of the Pipe for the second, third, and fourth Years of the Reign of King Henry the Second, 1155-1158. Edited under the direction of Joseph Hunter. London, 1844.

The Great Roll of the Pipe for the twenty-sixth Year of the Reign of King Henry III (A.D. 1241-42). New Haven, 1918.

The Memoranda Roll for the Michaelmas Term of the first Year of the Reign of King John (1199-1200). Edited by H. G. Richardson. "Publications of the Pipe Roll Society," Vol. XXI N.S. London, 1943.

The Memoranda Roll of the King's Remembrancer for Michaelmas 1230 - Trinity 1231. Edited by Chalfant Robinson. "Publications of the Pipe Roll Society," Vol. XI. Princeton, 1933.

The Parliamentary Writs and Writs of Military Summons. Edited by Francis Palgrave. Vols. I-II. London, 1827-30.

The Pipe Roll for 1292, Surrey Membrane. Edited by H. M. Mills. "Publications of the Surrey Record Society," Vol. XXI. Guilford, 1924.

The Pipe Roll of the Bishopric of Winchester for the fourth Year of the Pontificate of Peter des Roches, 1208-1209. Edited under the supervision of Hubert Hall. "Studies in Economic and Political Science," Vol. XI. London, 1903.

The Pipe Roll of 31 Henry I, Michelmas, 1130. Edited by Joseph Hunter. London, 1929.

Placita de Quo Warranto temporibus Edw. I, II & III in curia receptae scaccarij Westm. asservata. London, 1818.

184   *The Knights Templars in England*

Records of Parliament holden at Westminister on the twenty-eighth day of February, in the thirty-third Year of the Reign of King Edward the First (A. D. 1305). Edited by Frederic W. Maitland. Rolls Series, No. 98. London, 1893.

Rotuli curiae regis: Rolls and Records of the Court held before the King's Justiciars or Justices, from the sixth Year of King Richard I to the Accession of King John. Edited by Francis Palgrave. 2 vols. [London], 1835.

Rotuli de oblatis et finibus in Turri Londinensi asservati, tempore regis Johannis. Edited by Thomas D. Hardy. [London], 1835.

Rotuli hundredorum temp. Hen. III & Edw. I in Turr' Lon' et in curia receptae scaccarij Westm. asservati. Edited by W. Illingworth. 2 vols. London, 1812-18.

Rotuli litterarum clausarum in Turri Londinensi asservati. Edited by Thomas D. Hardy. 2 vols. London, 1833-44.

Rotuli litterarum patentium in Turri Londinensi asservati. Edited by Thomas D. Hardy. [London], 1835.

Rotuli Parliamentorum; ut et petitiones et placita in Parliamento tempore Edwardi R. I. Vol. I. [London], 1767.

Taxatio ecclesiastica Angliae et Walliae auctoritate P. Nicholai IV, circa A. D. 1291. [London], 1802.

Three Rolls of the King's Court in the Reign of King Richard the First, A. D. 1194-1195. Edited under the direction of the Council of the Pipe Roll Society. "Publications of the Pipe Roll Society," Vol. XIV. London, 1891.

Secondary Sources

Books

Addison, Charles G. *The Knights Templars.* American edition. New York, 1874.

Ashley, W. J. *Early History of the English Woollen Industry.* "Publications of the American Economic Association," Vol. II, No. 4. Baltimore, 1887.

———. *An Introduction to English Economic History and Theory.* Vol. I, 4th edition. London, 1923.

Baldwin, John M. *Medieval Theories of Just Price; Romanists, Canonists, and Theologians in the Twelfth and Thirteenth Centuries.* "Transactions of the American Philosophical Society," Vol. XLIX, Part 4. Philadelphia, 1959.

Bedford, William K. R. and Holbeche, Richard. *The Order of the Hospital of St. John of Jerusalem, being a History of the English Hospitallers of St. John, their Rise and Fall.* London, 1902.

Bellott, Hugh H. L. *The Inner and Middle Temple.* London, 1902.

Bretano, Robert. *York Metropolitan Jurisdiction and Papal Judges Delegate (1279-1296).* "University of California Publications in History." Vol. LVIII. Berkeley, 1959.

Bridrey, Emile. *La condition juridique des croisés et la privilège de la croix.* Paris, 1950.

The Cambridge Economic History. Vol. I: *The Agrarian Life of the Middle Ages.* Edited by J. Clapham and Eileen Power. Vol. II: *Trade and Industry in the Middle Ages.* Edited by M. Postan and E. E. Rich. Cambridge, 1941-52.

Campbell, G. A. *The Knights Templars, their Rise and Fall.* London, [1937].

Cheney, Christopher R. *From Beckett to Langton; English Church Government, 1170-1213.* Manchester, 1956.

Chrimes, S. B. *An Introduction to the Administrative History of Medieval England.* Oxford, 1952.

Cipolla, Carlo M. *Money, Prices, and Civilization in the Mediterranean World from the Fifth to the Seventeenth Centuries.* Princeton, 1956.

Coke, Sir Edward. *The Second Part of the Institutes of the Laws of England.* Vol. II. London, 1797.

Cunningham, W. *The Growth of English Industry and Commerce during the Early and Middle Ages.* 5th edition. Vol. I. Cambridge, 1910.

Darby, H. C. (ed.). *An historical Geography of England before A. D. 1800.* Cambridge, 1936.

Delisle, Léopold. *Mémoire sur les opérations financières des Templiers.* "Académie des Inscriptions et Belles Lettres, Mémoires," Vol. XXXIII. Paris, 1889.

Denholm-Young, N. *Seignorial Administration in England.* Oxford, 1937.

DeRoover, Raymond A. *L'Evolution de la lettre de change, xive-xviiie siècles.* Paris, 1953.

———. *Money, Banking, and Credit in medieval Bruges: Italian Merchant-Bankers, Lombards, and Money Changers: a Study in the Origins of Banking.* "Publications of the Medieval Academy of America," No. 51. Cambridge, 1948.

DuPuy, Pierre. *Traittez concernant l'histoire de France: sçavoir la condamnation des Templiers.* Paris, 1654.

Easson, David E. *Medieval Religious Houses, Scotland.* London, 1957.

Erdmann, Karl. *Die Entstehung des Kreuzzugsgedanken.* Stuttgart, 1935.

Eyton, Robert W. *Court, Household, and Itinerary of Henry II.* London, 1878.

Finke, Heinrich. *Papsttum und Untergang des Templerordens.* Münster, 1907.

Fuller, Thomas. *Historie of the Holy Warre.* London, 1840.

Gmelin, Julius. *Die Regel des Templerordens.* Innsbruck, 1893.

———. *Schuld oder Unschuld des Templerordens.* Stuttgart, 1893.

Gras, Norman S. B. *The Evolution of the English Corn Market from the Twelfth to the Eighteenth Century.* "Harvard Economic Studies," Vol. XIII. Cambridge, 1915.

Grousset, René. *Histoire des croisades et du royaume franc de Jérusalem.* 3 vols. Paris, 1939.

Gürtler, Nicolaus. *Historia Templariorum observationibus ecclesiasticis aucta.* Amsterdam, 1691.

Heaton, Herbert. *Economic History of Europe.* Revised edition. New York, 1948.

———. *The Yorkshire Woollen and Worsted Industries from the earliest Times up to the Industrial Revolution.* Oxford, 1920.

Heyd, Wilhelm. *Histoire du commerce du Levant au moyen-âge.* 2 vols. Leipzig, 1885-86.

Hülsen, Hans von. *Tragödie der Ritterorden; Templer, Deutsche Herren, Malteser.* München, 1948.

King, Edward J. *The Grand Priory of the Order of the Hospital of St. John of Jerusalem in England.* London, 1924.

Knoop, Douglas and Jones, G. P. *An Introduction to Freemasonry.* Manchester, 1940.

Knowles, David. *The Religious Orders in England.* Vols. I-II. Cambridge, 1950-55.

———, and Hadcock, R. Neville. *Medieval Religious Houses, England and Wales.* London, 1953.

Kosminsky, E. A. *Studies in the Agrarian History of England in the Thirteenth Century.* "Studies in Medieval History," Vol. VIII. Translated by Ruth Kisch. Oxford, 1956.

Landon, Lionel. *The Itinerary of King Richard I with Studies on certain Matters of Interest connected with his Reign.* "Publications of the Pipe Roll Society," Vol. XIII. London, 1935.

Lawton, George. *The Religious Houses of Yorkshire.* London, 1853.

Lea, Henry C. *A History of the Inquisition of the Middle Ages.* 3 vols. New York, 1888.

Lipson, E. *History of the Woollen and Worsted Industries.* London, 1921.

———. *An Introduction to the Economic History of England.* Vol. I: *The Middle Ages.* London, 1915.

Lizerand, Georges. *Clement V et Philippe IV le Bel.* Paris, 1910.

Lunt, William E. *The Financial Relations of the Papacy with England to 1327.* Vol. I of Studies in Anglo-Papal Relations during the Middle Ages. "Publications of the Medieval Academy of America," No. XXXIII. Cambridge, 1939.

———. *Papal Revenues in the Middle Ages.* 2 vols. New York, 1934.

Martin, Edward J. *The Trial of the Templars.* London, 1928.

McKechnie, William S. *Magna Carta: a Commentary on the Great Charter of King John.* 2d edition, Glasgow, 1914.

Mollat, Guillaume. *Les papes d'Avignon.* "Bibliothèque de l'enseignement de l'histoire ecclésiastique," Vol. XV. Paris, 1920.

Nelson, Benjamin N. *The Idea of Usury: from tribal Brotherhood to universal Otherhood.* "History of Ideas Series," No. 3. Princeton, 1949.

Nicolai, Christoph. *Versuch über die beschuldigingen welche dem Tempelherrenorden gemacht worden, und über dessen Geheimniss; nebst einem Anhange über das Entstehen der Freymauergesellschaft.* Berlin, 1782.

Noonan, John T. *The Scholastic Analysis of Usury.* Cambridge, Mass., 1957.

Norgate, Kate. *Richard the Lion Heart.* London, 1924.

Oman, Charles W. *A History of the Art of War in the Middle Ages.* London, 1898.

Owst, Gerald R. *Literature and Pulpit in medieval England.* Cambridge, 1933.

———. *Preaching in medieval England.* 2 vols. Cambridge, 1926.

Oxford Essays in Medieval History presented to Herbert Edward Salter. Introduction by F. M. Powicke. Oxford, 1934.

Piquet, Jules. *Les Templiers: étude de leurs opérations financières.* Paris, 1939.

Power, Eileen. *The Wool Trade in English Medieval History.* London, 1942.

Powicke, F. M. *Handbook of British Chronology.* London, 1939.

———. *King Henry III and the Lord Edward.* 2 vols. Oxford, 1947.

Prutz, Hans. *Entwicklung und Untergang des Tempelherrenordens.* Berlin, 1888.

———. *Die geistlichen Ritterorden: ihre Stellung zur kirchlichen, politischen, gesellschaftlichen, und wirtschaftlichen Entwicklung des Mittelalters.* Berlin, 1908.

Ramsey, James A. *A History of the Revenues of the Kings of England, 1066-1399.* 2 vols. Oxford, 1925.

Rastoul, Amand. *Les Templiers, 1118-1312.* 4th edition. Paris, 1908.

Raynouard, François J. M. *Les Templiers, tragédie . . . précédée d'un précis historque sur les Templiers.* Paris, 1805.

Rees, William. *A History of the Order of St. John of Jerusalem in Wales and on the Welsh Border including an Account of the Templars.* Cardiff, 1947.

Renouard, Yves. *Les hommes d'affaires italiens du moyen âge.* Paris, 1949.

Rogers, J. E. T. *A History of Agriculture and Prices in England.* Vol. I. Oxford, 1866.

Ruding, Rogers. *Annals of the Coinage of Great Britain and Its Dependencies from the earliest Period of authentic History to the Reign of Queen Victoria.* 3d ed. Vol. I. London, 1840.

Runciman, Steven. *A History of the Crusades.* 3 vols. Cambridge, 1951-54.

Salzman, L. *English Industry of the Middle Ages.* Oxford, 1910.

———. *English Trade in the Middle Ages.* Oxford, 1913.

Sayous, André E. *Les banques de dépôt, les banques de credit, et les sociétés financières.* Paris, 1901.

Schottmüller, Konrad. *Der Untergang des Templer-ordens.* Berlin, 1887.

Setton, Kenneth M. (ed.). *A History of the Crusades.* Vol. I: *The First Hundred Years.* Edited by Marshall W. Baldwin. Philadelphia, 1955.

Siedschlag, Beatrice N. *English Participation in the Crusades, 1150-1220.* Menasha, [Wis.], 1939.

Simon, André. *History of the Wine Trade in England.* 3 vols. London, 1906-09.

Simon, Edith. *The Piebald Standard: A Biography of the Knights Templars.* Boston, 1959.

Smail, Richard C. *Crusading Warfare.* Edited by M. D. Knowles. "Cambridge Studies in Medieval Life and Thought," Vol. III N. S. Cambridge, 1956.

Tanner, John. *Notitia monastica or an Account of all the Abbies, Priories, and House of Friars, heretofore in England and Wales.* London, 1744.

Throop, Palmer A. *Criticism of the Crusade: a Study of Public Opinion and Crusade Propaganda.* Amsterdam, 1940.

Tout, Thomas F. *Chapters in the Administrative History of Medieval England.* "University of Manchester Publications," No. CXXVII. Vols. I-II. Manchester, 1920.

Usher, Abbott P. *The Early History of Deposit Banking in Mediterranean Europe.* "Harvard Economic Studies," Vol. LXXV. Cambridge, 1943.

The Victoria History of the County of Bedford. Edited by H. Arthur Doubleday and William Page. "The Victoria History of the Counties of England." 3 vols. London, 1904-12.

The Victoria History of the County of Berkshire. Edited by P. A. Ditchfield and William Page. "The Victoria History of the Counties of England." 4 vols. London, 1907-24.

The Victoria History of the County of Buckingham. Edited by William Page. "The Victoria History of the Counties of England." Vols. I, III-IV. London, 1905-27.

The Victoria History of the County of Cambridge and the Isle of Ely. Edited by L. F. Salzman. "The Victoria History of the Counties of England." Vol. II. London, 1948.

The Victoria History of the County of Essex. Edited by William Page and J. Horace Round. "The Victoria History of the Counties of England." Vol. II. London, 1907.

The Victoria History of the County of Gloucester. Edited by William Page. "The Victoria History of the Counties of England." Vol. II. London, 1907.

The Victoria History of the County of Hampshire and the Isle of Wight. Edited by H. Arthur Doubleday and William Page. "The Victoria History of the Counties of England." Vols. II, III, V. London, 1903-12.

The Victoria History of the County of Hertford. Edited by William Page. "The Victoria History of the Counties of England." Vols. II-IV. London, 1908-14.

The Victoria History of the County of Huntingdon. Edited by William Page, Granville Proby and S. Inskip Ladds. "The Victoria History of the Counties of England." Vols. II-III. London, 1932-36.

The Victoria History of the County of Kent. Edited by William Page. "The Victoria History of the Counties of England." Vol. II. London, 1926.

The Victoria History of the County of Lancaster. Edited by William Farrer and J. Brownbill. "The Victoria History of the Counties of England." Vol. II. London, 1908.

The Victoria History of the County of Leicester. Edited by W. G. Hoskins. "The Victoria History of the Counties of England." Vol. II. London, 1954.

The Victoria History of the County of Lincoln. Edited by William Page. "The Victoria History of the Counties of England." Vol. II. London, 1906.

The Victoria History of the County of Northampton. Edited by R. M. Serjeantson and W. 'R. D. Adkins. "The Victoria History of the Counties of England." Vol. II. London, 1906.

The Victoria History of the County of Oxford. Edited by H. E. Salter and Mary D. Lobel. "The Victoria History of the Counties of England." Vol. II. London, 1907.

The Victoria History of the County of Somerset. Edited by William Page. "The Victoria History of the Counties of England." Vol. II. London, 1911.

The Victoria History of the County of Suffolk. Edited by William Page. "The Victoria History of the Counties of England." Vol. II. London, 1911.

The Victoria History of the County of Surrey. Edited by H. E. Malden. "The Victoria History of the Counties of England." Vols. III-IX. Westminster, 1902-12.

The Victoria History of the County of Sussex. Edited by William Page. "The Victoria History of the Counties of England." Vol. II. London, 1907.

The Victoria History of the County of Warwick. Edited by L. F. Salzmann. "The Victoria History of the Counties of England." Vols. III-VI. London, 1904-51.

The Victoria History of the County of Worcester. Edited by William Page. "The Victoria History of the Counties of England." Vols. III-IV. London, 1913-24.

The Victoria History of the County of York. Edited by William Page. "The Victoria History of the Counties of England." Vols. II-III. London, 1912-13.

The Victoria History of the County of York, North Riding. Edited by William Page. "The Victoria History of the Counties of England." Vols. I-II. London, 1914-23.

Waas, Adolf. *Geschichte der Kreuzzüge.* 2 vols. Freiburg, 1956.

Williamson, J. Bruce. *The History of the Temple, London, from the Institution of the Order of the Knights of the Temple to the Close of the Stuart Period.* London, 1924.

Woodhouse, F. C. *The military and religious Orders of the Middle Ages.* London, 1879.

Articles

Aitken, Robert. "The Knights Templars in Scotland," *Scottish Review,* XXXII (1898), 1-36.

Beveridge, W. H. "The Yield and Price of Corn in the Middle Ages," *Economic History,* I (1927), 155-67.

Boutaric, E. "Clement V, Philippe le Bel et les Templiers," *Revue des questions historiques,* X (1871), 301-42; XI (1872), 5-40.

Brett, Alfred. "The Manor of Wetherby and Lands within the Manor," *Yorkshire Archaeological Journal,* XXX (1931), 261-73.

Bromberg, Benjamin. "The Financial and Administrative Importance of the Knights Hospitallers to the English Crown," *Economic History,* IV (1940), 307-11.

Carus-Wilson, Eleanor A. "The English Cloth Industry in the late Twelfth and early Thirteenth Centuries," *Economic History Review,* XIV (1944), 32-50.

——— "An Industrial Revolution of the Thirteenth Century," *Economic History Review,* XI (1941), 39-60.

Cate, James L. "The Church and Market Reform in England during the Reign of Henry III," *Medieval and Historiographical Essays in Honor of James Westfall Thompson,* edited by James L. Cate and Eugene N. Anderson (Chicago, 1938), pp. 27-65.

Chetwynd-Stapylton, H. E. "The Templars at Templehurst," *Yorkshire Archaeological and Topographical Journal,* X (1889), 276-86, 431-43.

Delaville le Roulx, J. "La suppression des Templiers," *Revue des questions historiques,* XLVIII (1890), 29-61.

DeRoover, Raymond A. "New Interpretations of the History of Banking," *Journal of World History,* II (1954), 38-76.

Dibbon, L. B. "Chancellor and Keeper of the Seal under Henry III," *English Historical Review,* XXVII (1912), 39-51.

Edwards, John. "The Templars in Scotland in the Thirteenth Century," *Scottish Historical Review,* V (1907), 13-25.

Farmer, D. L. "Some Grain Price Movements in Thirteenth Century England," *Economic History Review,* X (1957-58), 3rd S, 207-20.

Ferris, Eleanor. "The Financial Relations of the Knights Templars to the English Crown," *"American Historical Review,"* VIII (1902), 1-17.

Flahiff, G. B. "The Use of Prohibitions by Clerics against Ecclesiastical Courts in England," *Medieval Studies*, III (1941), 101-16.

———. "The Writ of Prohibition to Court Christian in the Thirteenth Century," *Medieval Studies*, VI (1954), 261-313.

Grange, Amy. "The Fall of the Knights of the Temple," *Dublin Review*, CXVII (1895), 329-46.

Gras, Norman S. B. "Bill of Exchange," *Encyclopedia of the Social Sciences*, II (1932), 539-40.

Graves, Coburn. "The Economic Activities of the Cistercians in medieval England," *Annalecta Sacri Ordinis Cisterciensis*, XIII (1957), fascicles 1-2.

Hall, Margaret W. "Early Bankers in the Genoese Notarial Records," *Economic History Review*, VI (1935), 73-79.

Hammer-Purgstall, Joseph von. "Die Schuld der Templer," *Denkschriften der Kaiserlichen Academie der Wissenschaft, Philosophisch-historische Classe*, VI (1885), 175-210.

Hawtrey, R. G. "Credit," *Encyclopedia of the Social Sciences*, IV (1931), 545-50.

Hope, W. H. St. John. "The Round Church of the Knights Templars in Temple Bruer, Lincolnshire," *Archaeologia*, LXI (1908), 177-98.

Knight, Frank H. "Historical and Theoretical Issues in the Problem of Modern Capitalism," *Journal of Economic and Business History*, I (1928), 119-36.

———. "Interest," *Encyclopedia of the Social Sciences*, VIII (1932), 131-44.

Kosminsky, E. A. "Services and Money Rents in the Thirteenth Century," *Economic History Review*, V (1935), 24-45.

Krey, August C. "William of Tyre: the Making of an Historian in the Middle Ages," *Speculum*, XVI (1941), 149-66.

Landmann, Julius. "History of Commercial Banking to the Close of the Eighteenth Century," *Encyclopedia of the Social Sciences*, II (1930), 423-31.

Langlois, Charles V. "L'Affaire des Templiers," *Journal des Savants*, VI N.S. (1908), 417-35.

———. "Le Procès des Templiers," *Revue des deux mondes*, CIII (1891), 382-421.

Lea, Henry C. "The Absolution Formula of the Templars," *Papers of the American Society of Church History*, V (1893), 37-58.

LeBras, G. "L'usure: la doctrine ecclésiatique de l'usure a l'époque classique (xiie-xve siècle)," *Dictionnaire de Théologie Catholique*, ed. A. Vacant, E. Mangenot, and E. Amann, XV (1950), cols. 2335-72.

Lecestre, Léon. "La Règle du Temple," *Revue des questions historiques*, XL (1886), 577-83.

Leys, Agnes M. "The Forfeiture of the Lands of the Templars in England," *Oxford Essays in Medieval History presented to Herbert Edward Salter*, edited by F. M. Powicke (Oxford, 1934), pp. 155-63.

Lunt, William E. "A Papal Tenth levied in the British Isles from 1274 to 1280," *English Historical Review*, XXXII (1917), 49-89.

Martin, E. J. "The Templars in Yorkshire," *The Yorkshire Archaeological Journal*, XXIX (1930), 366-85; XXX (1931), 135-56.

McLaughlin, T. P. "The Teaching of the Canonists on Usury (XII, XIII, and XIV centuries)", *Medieval Studies*, I (1939), 81-147; II (1940), 1-22.

Minos, P. J. Oliver. "The Knights Templars' Chapel at Garway," *The Reliquary and Illustrated Archaeologist*, V. N.S. (1899), 193-98.

Perkins, Clarence. "The Knights Hospitallers in England after the Fall of the Order of the Temple," *English Historical Review*, XLV (1930), 285-89.

———. "The Knights Templars in the British Isles," *English Historical Review*, XXV (1910), 209-30.

———. "The Trial of the Knights Templars in England," *English Historical Review*, XXIV (1909), 432-47.

———. "The Wealth of the Knights Templars in England," *American Historical Review*, XV (1909), 252-63.

Postan, M. M. "Credit in Medieval Trade," *Economic History Review,* I (1928), 234-61.

———. "Private financial Instruments in Medieval England," *Vierteljahrschrift für Social- und Wirtschaftsgeschichte,* XXIII (1930), 39-90.

Reynolds, Robert L. "A Business Affair in Genoa in the Year 1200, Banking, Bookkeeping, a Broker (?), and a Lawsuit," *Studi di storia e diritto in onore di Enrico Besta,* (Milan, 1939), II, 167-81.

Salin, Edgar. "Usury," *Encyclopedia of the Social Sciences,* XV (1935), 193-97.

Sandys, Agnes. "The Financial and Administrative Importance of the London Temple in the Thirteenth Century," *Essays in Medieval History presented to Thomas Frederick Tout,* edited by A. G. Little and F. M. Powicke (Manchester, 1925), pp. 147-62.

Sayles, G. "A Dealer in Wardrobe Bills," *Economic History Review,* III (1931), 268-73.

Sayous, André E. "Le capitalisme commercial et financier dans les pays chrétiens de la Méditerranée occidentale depuis la première croisade jusqu'à la fin du moyen âge." *Vierteljahrschrift für Social- und Wirtschaftsgeschichte,* XXIX (1936), 270-95.

Schaube, A. "Die Wollausfuhr Englands vom Jahre 1273," *Vierteljahrschrift für Social- und Wirtschaftsgeschichte,* VI (1908), 39-72, 159-85.

Shannon, Albert C. "The Secrecy of Witnesses in Inquisitorial Tribunals and in Contemporary Secular Criminal Trials," *Essays in Medieval Life and Thought presented in Honor of Austin Patterson Evans,* edited by John H. Mundy et al. (New York, 1955), pp. 59-70.

Strieder, Jacob. "Origin and Evolution of early European Capitalism," *Journal of Economic and Business History,* II (1929), 1-19.

Taylor, R. V. "Ribston and the Knights Templars," *Yorkshire Archaeological and Topographical Journal,* VII (1882), 429-52; VIII (1884), 259-99; IX (1886), 71-98.

Trudon des Ormes, A. "Liste des maisons et de quelques dignitaires de l'ordre du Temple en Syrie, en Chypre, et en France d'après les pièces du procès," *Revue de l'Orient Latin,* V (1897), 389-459.

Usher, Abbott P. "The Origins of Banking: the Primitive Bank of Deposit," *Economic History Review,* IV (1934), 399-428.

Viollet, Paul M. "Les interrogatoires de Jacques de Molai, Grand Maître du Temple; conjectures," *Mémoires de l'Institut national de France, Académie des inscriptions et belles-lettres,* XXXVIII (1911), Part II, 121-36.

Whitwell, Robert J. "Italian Bankers and the English Crown," *Transactions of the Royal Historical Society,* XVII N.S. (1903), 175-233.

———. "English Monasteries and the Wool Trade in the Thirteenth Century," *Vierteljahrschrift für Social- und Wirtschaftsgeschichte,* II (1904), 1-33.

Wood, Herbert. "The Knights Templars in Ireland," *Proceedings of the Royal Irish Academy.* XXVI (1907), 327-77.

Unpublished Material

Perkins, Clarence. "The History of the Knights Templars in England." Unpublished Ph.D. dissertation, Department of History, Harvard University, 1908.

Index

The text of *The Knights Templars in England* was set by Morneau Typographers in Times Roman with chapter titles in Engraver's Old English. The book was printed by Tyler Printing Company on S. D. Warren's sixty-pound University Eggshell textstock. Arizona Trade Bindery bound the volume in Joanna parchment coral mist vellum. The dust jacket is printed on Hamilton Andorra textstock, the jacket design and drawings are by Beau Williams.